NEW DIRECTIONS

IN

KARST

PROCEEDINGS OF THE

ANGLO-FRENCH KARST SYMPOSIUM

September 1983

Edited by

K. Paterson and M.M. Sweeting

British Library Cataloguing in Publication Data

Anglo-French Karst Symposium *(1983)*
New directions in Karst : proceedings of
the Anglo-French Karst Symposium
September 1983.
1. Karst
I. Title   II. Paterson, K.   III. Sweeting, M.M.
551.4'47   GB600

ISBN 0-86094-195-7

ISBN 0 86094 195 7

Published by Geo Books
            Regency House
            34 Duke Street
            Norwich NR3 3AP
            England

Contents

List of figures

vii

List of tables

List of photographs

Preface

The Anglo-French Karst Symposium was held in England and also in Wales
in 1983 with the collaboration of the Association Françaises du
Karstologie. Professor Jean Nicod the President of A.F.K. was
unable to be present and Professor Jean Salomon represented the
A.F.K. in his place.

The theme of the Symposium was New Directions in Karst and the
intention was to demonstrate both in the paper sessions and the
field excursions the application and relevance of contemporary
methods and techniques in karst geomorphology. The papers reflected the use of many of the modern tools employed in karsts
including isotope and radiometric dating techniques, palynology
and hydro-chemical methods. They also discussed the more detailed work being done in tropical areas and the Peoples Republic
of China. Interest in the developing field of biological erosion
was highlighted by several of the studies one of which raised
the issue of a morphologically distinct 'phytokarst'. A renewed
interest in the long-term evolution of karst is seen in the
papers on palaeokarst and in the field excursion to South Wales,
where Professor Yvonne Battiau-Queney and Dr P. Wright gave
illuminating discussions.

The organizers of the Symposium are indepted to all our colleagues who helped to lead excursions and gave evening lectures
in what was a very full programme. We are also grateful to the
Department of Geography Oxford University and to Christ's and
Notre Dame College, Liverpool Institute of Higher Education who
provided support for the English side of the programme. Both
the University of Oxford and University College, Swansea gave
receptions to the participants which were much appreciated.

Dr Alan Coase had originally intended to lead the excursion into
Dan Yr Ogof cave but was unable to do so because of ill-health;
it was with regret that we learnt of his death shortly after the
Symposium.

The papers have been edited by Dr Keith Paterson and Dr Marjorie
Sweeting who gratefully acknowledge the help given in translation
by Mrs Joëlle Paterson, Professor Yvonne Battiau-Queney and
Professor Jean Salomon. We hope this series of papers will
demonstrate the continuing interest in karst landforms, the great
potential of karst process studies and the significance of the
recent investigations concerned with longer timescales.

K. Paterson
M.M. Sweeting

Alkalinity measurements in karst water studies

L. Rose and P. Vincent

SUMMARY

A rigorous but simple titrimetric method for the determination of
the alkalinity of karst waters is described. Alkalinity is here
defined as a measure of dissolved $Ca(Mg)CO_3$. Standard calcium/
magnesium estimations measure these cations from all sources.
Alkalinity does not change when CO_2 is added or removed. Spring
waters which emerge from the base of pavements at Gait Barrows
NNR are very close to Picknett/Trombe saturation. Down stream pH
rises without any change in the alkalinity of the waters. From
the alkalinity measurements we have calculated the saturation conditions of the spring waters and hence a minimum pCO_2. Variation
in pCO_2 among the spring waters is attributable to the variation
in soil/vegetation cover of the respective catchment areas.

RÉSUMÉ

Une méthode titrimètrique simple et rigoureuse est présentée pour
déterminer l'alcalinité des eaux karstiques. L'alcalinité est
définie comme la quantité dissoute de $Ca(Mg)CO_3$. Les calculs
standards de calcium/magnésium mesurent les cations qui sont
d'origines diverses. L'alcalinité ne change que lorsque l'on
ajoute ou retranche le CO_2. Les émergences qui apparaissent
au pied des affleurements calcaires de Gait Barrows NNR sont
presque saturées selon les courbes de Picknett/Trombe. Vers
l'aval le pH augmente sans aucun changement de l'alcalinité
des eaux. Grâce aux mesures de l'alcalinité on a pu calculer
l'indice de saturation des eaux d'émergence et également leur
teneur minimale en CO_2. Les variations de CO_2 des emergences
s'expliquent par les différences de sols et de couvertures
végétales des bassins versants.

INTRODUCTION

Although many European karst geomorphologists have used alkalinity as a measure of dissolved $CaCO_3$ or dissolved $Ca(Mg)CO_3$ this has not been the favoured practice of most British workers. The latter often regard alkalinity as no more than an approximation to the bicarbonate content of the water and, as a consequence it is reported only infrequently (Bray and Stenner, 1976).

In spite of views to the contrary (Mackereth *et al.*, 1978, p.52) it is not true to say that the addition or subtraction of CO_2 affects the alkalinity. Alkalinity is an easily measured conservative property of a water and changes only if $CaCO_3$ is precipitated or more rock dissolves.

Alkalinity measurements have been made at four springs draining the sloping pavements of the Gait Barrows National Nature Reserve, north-west England. Alkalinity levels not only distinguish the springs, one from another, but also allow the calculation of the pCO_2 in the soil/root zones of the various spring catchment areas; the calculated pCO_2 concentrations appear to be directly related to the observable soil and vegetation variations.

ALKALINITY: DEFINITION AND PROPERTIES

Alkalinity, as described here, is an accurate estimate of how much calcium and magnesium carbonate is dissolved and has molarity as its unit of measurement. Several properties of alkalinity are of interest to karstologists:

  i)   Alkalinity does not change in a karst water until more limestone is dissolved or carbonate precipitated.
  ii) If CO_2 is added to a water sample isolated from the rock there is no change in the alkalinity.
  iii) There is normally no fall in alkalinity as an isolated sample is allowed to evaporate away its CO_2. The proviso 'normally' is added here because if a small sample becomes highly supersaturated with calcium then the slightest seed may cause precipitation. For this reason sampling bottles should be acidified between successive use.
  iv) If, for any reason other than adding acid to the sample, the alkalinity experiences a genuine fall, then the calcium determination will exhibit the same fall; this is true even for the effects of dilution.

The above definition of alkalinity, its units and properties are not widely recognised in the English language karst literature. It is well known that as CO_2 evaporates HCO_3^- falls and it is not difficult to see why the entirely erroneous idea has built up that alkalinity will fall if CO_2 evaporates. But we must remember that alkalinity is the sum of all the titratable parts, not merely the bicarbonate, the titratable parts themselves summing to acid consumption of the original $Ca(Mg)CO_3$. There is little doubt in our minds that Hutchinson's influential monograph on limnology (Hutchinson, 1957) was a seminal work for the propagation of this confusion. In fact, Hutchinson was perfectly well aware that alkalinity does not change with the addition or subtraction of CO_2 (*op. cit.*, p.667) but in choosing mg/litre HCO_3^- as his unit of alkalinity he unfortunately chose one that does so change.

MEASUREMENT OF ALKALINITY

There are several methods for alkalinity estimation, all of them involving the titration of a karst water with a mineral acid. One very useful method which is easily adapted for field use is the simple titration of a water sample with 0.1M HCl and the indicator BDH 4.5 (Bray and Stenner, *op. cit.*). But this simple titration to a fixed endpoint has two sources of error. One source concerns a failure to deal with 'CO_2 error' which comes about because dissolved CO_2 helps the mineral acid achieve the endpoint. The other is due to a failure to correct for titration overshoot at pH 4.5.

In our modification of the basic titration method (Appendix 1.1) all 'CO_2 error' is either eliminated or allowed for. Furthermore we have eliminated the positive error, due to titration overshoot, by means of a blank. By this we mean that even in pure water some acid is needed to bring the pH down to that represented by the indicator endpoint.

From experiments we now know that if the water sample is vigorously stirred during the titration a stable endpoint will be reached when the indicator remains neutral grey for at least 90 seconds. This we call the '90 second' endpoint. Vigorous stirring helps CO_2 to escape and, at the '90 second' endpoint · the pH will be close to 4.5. However, stirring does not remove all the CO_2 and if the titration is left to stand for a further 3-4 days its pH rises asymptotically to pH 4.645. Titration back to pH 4.5 shows a titration mean of 0.045 ml of 0.1M HCl equivalent to 0.45 x 10^{-5}M 'CO_2 error'.

If pure water is allowed to equilibrate with the atmosphere, absorption of CO_2 will cause its pH to fall to 5.646 at 20°C and this small residual amount of CO_2 is equivalent to 1.13 x 10^{-6}M in 500 ml which is equivalent to 0.0113 ml of 0.1M HCl. In fact, this last type of 'CO_2 error', which cannot be removed by stirring, does not cause any difficulties in adjusting the titration for 'CO_2 error'. Of course, the titration whose pH was 4.645 at 3-4 days will not rise to pH 5.646 because the titration has overshot the endpoint due to the positive

3

error we noted earlier. This error can be measured by titrating a blank water sample, and if this commences at pH 5.646 and ends at pH 4.645 the residual 'CO_2 error' no longer enters the calculations. In fact there are two operational procedures which have identical outcomes.

These are firstly, add 0.045 ml to the '90 second' titration and deduct a blank titrated from 5.646 to 4.500 and, secondly ignore the 0.045 ml addition and operate on the '90 second' titration corrected by deducting a blank titrated from pH 5.646 to pH 4.645.

With BDH 4.5 indicator we can actually calculate adjustments rather than titrating a water blank because it has no indicator error. That is to say that the acid needed to react with the indicator in the salt form to make it partly in the red acid form has already been added by the manufacturers. We can however slightly improve on calculated adjustments by taking into account the fact that any adjustments are not entirely independent of the alkalinity itself. This is partly due to the electrolyte content and the final volume (sample plus titration) both of which increase with increasing alkalinity. These subsequent adjustments to our basic calculations are based on a series of experimental titrations using an appropriate salt solution, mostly calcium chloride, such as the karst water might contain at the end of a titration. The results of these calculations and adjustments are succinctly portrayed in a simple linear model which estimates the blank to be subtracted (B_s) as a dependent variable on the uncorrected alkalinity (A_u):

$$B_s = (1.012 + 0.0007227A) \times 10^{-5}M \qquad (1)$$

The corrected alkalinity (A_c) is thus:

$$A_c = (A_u - B_s) \times 10^{-5}M$$

ALKALINITY MEASUREMENTS AT GAIT BARROWS

Gait Barrows National Nature Reserve (NNR) has four principal springs (S1 - S4) whose waters drain the main pavement areas and woodland margins (figure 1.1). Spring S1 (SD 117697) is known locally as the Ash Tree spring and flows at all seasons. In recent years it has not been known to fail even during the prolonged summer droughts of 1976 and 1983. Spring S2 (SD 177698) usually stops flowing by early June but heavy summer thunderstorms have been known to recharge temporarily its catchment. Springs S3 (SD 157680) and S4 (SD 187675) both fail by about mid-May in an average year.

All four springs drain into Little Haweswater (figure 1.1), three by overland flow and S4 partly underground to S3. The Ash Tree spring drains via a man-made channel and S2 and S3 via ephemeral channels in the uncut hay meadow which forms the

4

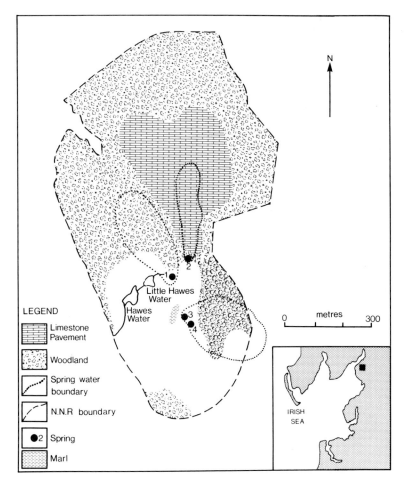

Figure 1.1   Location of Gait Barrows NNR and position of
             springs S1 - S4

southern limit of the Reserve.

Discharge measurements have not as yet been made but from
field observations the relative discharges are: S3>S1≃S2>>S4.
Of the two end-member flow systems of carbonate aquifers described by Shuster and White (1971) the springs at Gait Barrows
most resemble diffuse flow systems. None of the spring waters
discharge clastic sediments and no large conduits are known in
the area.

Table 1.1 Chemical and environmental variables at four springs in the Gait Barrows NNR

Date	Temperature (°C)*	Rainfall (mm)**	pH				Alkalinity $\times 10^{-5}$M			
			S_1	S_2	S_3	S_4	S_1	S_2	S_3	S_4
10.10.82	10.8	53.0	-	-	-	-	238.5	-	-	-
14.11.82	9.9	36.4	7.3	7.5	7.3	7.4	214.6	161.9	249.1	248.7
10.12.82	9.8	40.0	7.4	7.5	7.4	7.5	155.1	124.7	187.7	187.8
6.1.83	10.0	49.4	7.4	7.6	7.4	7.4	153.1	122.6	185.9	183.3
1.2.83	9.7	29.7	7.3	7.6	7.3	7.4	178.3	130.9	220.7	220.9
17.2.83	9.5	0.0	7.3	7.5	7.3	7.3	222.2	164.0	258.3	258.0
12.2.83	9.6	0.0	7.3	7.5	7.3	7.3	231.1	171.2	250.0	250.6
17.3.83	9.0	31.0	7.6	7.6	7.4	7.4	196.6	133.8	219.4	219.6
5.4.83	8.8	14.7	7.3	7.6	7.2	7.4	199.4	135.3	228.3	227.9
24.4.83	9.0	16.7	7.4	7.6	7.3	7.2	201.6	156.3	217.0	215.1
5.5.83	9.0	25.5	7.4	7.6	7.2	7.4	170.1	128.7	226.3	225.8
14.5.83	9.4	32.4	7.3	7.4	7.18	7.3	219.8	183.0	241.5	239.5
25.5.83	12.2	2.5	-	-	7.28	-	-	-	258.6	-
Mean:							198.4	146.6	225.8	225.2

* Water temperature at spring head

** Preceding 5 days rainfall

Table 1.1 shows the results of alkalinity measurements started in late autumn 1982 and ending in late May 1983. Each set of analyses reveals a consistent pattern. Mean alkalinities show the expected similarities of S3 and S4 which are clearly distinguishable from S2 and S1 occupying an intermediate position. These alkalinity figures appear to be related to the different catchment characteristics as also noted by Shuster and White (*op. cit.*). Detailed water tracings on this National Nature Reserve have not yet been possible but from basic field relations each catchment can be characterised as follows:

S1	vegetated pavement, thin woodland, small areas of bare pavement
S2	mainly bare pavement
S3/S4	woodland on loamy soils over limestone.

It seems most likely, therefore that the observed alkalinity levels are directly related to the soil/vegetation cover in the catchment areas.

SATURATION AT SPRING S3

On three occasions at S3 more complete analyses were undertaken. In addition to alkalinity, $[Ca + Mg]_T$ was estimated using EDTA, Solochrome Black indicator and Betz and Noll's buffer. $[Ca]_T$ was measured with EDTA at pH 12.5 using Patton and Reeder's indicator and pH by a research quality meter. The pH measurements were subsequently corrected for liquid junction potential (Picknett, 1973). $[Mg]_T$ was obtained from $[Ca + Mg]_T - [Ca]_T$ and an approximate measure of $[SO]_T$ was obtained from $[Ca + Mg]_T - [Alk]$. The results of these measurements are shown in Table 1.2.

Table 1.2 Detailed chemical measurements at Spring No.3

	Date		
	6.1.83	5.5.83	14.5.83
$[Ca + Mg]_T$ x 10^{-5}M	221.8	260.1	270.6
$[Ca]_T$ x 10^{-5}M	208.2	245.3	257.2
$[Alk]$ x 10^{-5}M	185.9	226.3	241.5
$[Mg]_T$ x 10^{-5}M	13.6	14.8	13.4
$[SO_4]_T$ x 10^{-5}M	35.9	33.8	29.1
pH (corrected)	7.40	7.22	7.18
T°C	10.2	10.0	10.4

It was of some interest to know how near to saturation S3 waters are at the exit. One general method of assessment would be to plot $[Ca]_T$, pH values on a $10°C$ Picknett-Trombe curve (Picknett, 1964).

However, this procedure is of limited validity. Such a curve is related to the system $CaCO_3/CO_2/H_2O$ in which $[Ca]_T = [Alk]$. When a Picknett-Trombe graph is used for other systems, in which $[Ca]_T > [Alk]$ it is no more valid to refer pH to $[Ca]_T$ than it is to $[Alk]$. Yet in practice, Picknett's curves used as relating $[Ca]_T$ to pH are often better approximations than when used to relate $[Alk]$ to pH. It depends on the cause of the discrepancy, whether it is mainly sulphate or magnesium. In the absence of a complete theory of the saturated pH of karst waters, the only technique for accurate work is the Stenner method (Stenner, 1969) with very accurate temperature control.

One Stenner saturation-type test was carried out on 14.5.83, using the spring itself to control the temperature. The alkalinity on the test water was $245.7 \times 10^{-5}M$ as compared with $241.5 \times 10^{-5}M$ for the spring water, indicating slight undersaturation. One possible reason for this may be that the spring exit temperatures are a little higher than the underground waters. It would require an underground water temperature of about $8°C$ to account for this slight undersaturation.

THE EFFECT OF THE MARL BED ON S3 RUNOFF

Runoff from S3 flows through a shallow grass-lined channel for some 40 m and then traverses a bed of white marl for 5 m. This marl is related to that described by Oldfield (1960) at Haweswater 0.5 km to the south-west. To examine whether the deposit is currently accumulating, water samples were taken on 6.1.82 at three positions near the Marl band (Table 1.3).

Within our measurement error ($\pm 0.3 \times 10^{-5}M$) we deduce from Table 1.3 that alkalinity remains unchanged as the spring water traverses the marl bed, and, at the time of sampling, there was no evidence of accumulation. The systematic rise in pH along the water channel is due to progressive loss of CO_2 and the rate of loss is similar to that reported by Brook and Ford (1982).

A Stenner-type saturation test was conducted on 14.5.83, 49 m from the spring exit, using the stream bed to control the temperature. Alkalinity was measured on the filtered test sample and was recorded as $225.4 \times 10^{-5}M$ as compared with the spring water of $241.3 \times 10^{-5}M$. Thus, in spite of these figures indicating supersaturation by the time the water has traversed the marl no precipitation has taken place. Why the marl fails to act as a nucleating centre for $CaCO_3$ is not understood.

Table 1.3   pH and alkalinity measurements on either side of the marl bed crossed by Spring No. 3 waters

Sampling point	Date					
	6.1.83		5.5.83		14.5.83	
	pH	Alk $\times 10^{-5}$M	pH	Alk $\times 10^{-5}$M	pH	Alk $\times 10^{-5}$M
Spring emergence	7.40	185.9	7.22	226.3	7.18	241.5
Emergence +38 m	7.68	186.0	7.47	226.6	7.48	241.3
+40 m						
+45 m	MARL BED					
Emergence +49 m	7.73	185.7	7.57	226.4	7.52	241.3

Some researchers report that small amounts of sulphate diminish the rate of calcite deposition (Bischoff and Fyfe, 1968; Akin and Lagerwerff, 1965) and it may be that the sulphates found in the S3 waters are acting in this way although the mechanism is not clear. On reflection it would have been interesting to carry out the Stenner-type test using the powdered marl instead of Analar $CaCO_2$. Brook and Ford (*op. cit.*) also discuss the problem of non-precipitation in supersaturated waters and suggest that precipitation may not occur until the SI_c index (Wigley, 1977) is greater than +0.50 and they cite a suggestion by Barnes (1965) that vegetation surfaces may be necessary for nucleation.

pCO_2 IN THE SPRING CATCHMENT AREAS

It has been established that the spring waters at Gait Barrows emerge virtually saturated and any loss of CO_2 does not change the alkalinity. We can, therefore, calculate the pCO_2 in the soil/root zones of the various catchments subject to limits set by ignorance of the saturation temperature. Before doing so, however, we propose to modify slightly the current karstological account of the solution process which has some bearing on the interpretation of pCO_2 levels.

Anaerobic solubility is said to occur when water enters a water-filled fissure having first come into equilibrium under Henry's Law with the CO_2 of the local air. The solution process thereafter involves the usage of the initial CO_2, since no more is available. Aerobic solubility is said to occur when air is constantly present during the dissolving process and, for a given pCO_2, gives rise to a very much greater solubility. For example, at 10°C, 1% CO_2 gives 2.2mM$[Ca]_T$ by the aerobic route, but only 0.4mM by the anaerobic route.

In order to accept the concept of aerobic solubility it is important to consider how much air has to be present in order to convert an anaerobic process to a fully aerobic one? The answer is, of course, an infinite quantity.

The absorption coefficient, α, for CO_2 (volume of gas at NTP absorbed by one volume of water when the partial pressure is 760 mm) is 1.194 at 10°C. This means that if an infinite amount of air is available the concentration of CO_2 in water is 1.194 the gas concentration. With a finite amount of air, such as might occur in the weathering zone under a soil cover, the aqueous concentration is less by an amount calculated as follows.

Let, $W(L)$ - be the equilibrium concentration of gas in the water, when there are L litres of air, of partial pressure P per litre of water.

and

$W(\infty)$ – is the equilibrium concentration when an infinite amount of air of partial pressure P is available.

The ratio $W(L)/W(\infty)$ will then be a measure of the effect of limiting the amount of air. $W(\infty)$ is simply $\alpha.P$, but to define $W(L)$ requires a series of calculations. Let x be the number of litres of gas (at NTP) transferred from the air to 1 litre of water. The original gas-in-air concentration is P litres and for L litres is LP. Since x litres are transferred to the water LP-x remain and, as a concentration is

$$\frac{LP - x}{L} = P - \frac{x}{L}$$

Then, by definition of the absorption conefficient

$$x = \alpha\left(P - \frac{x}{L}\right)$$

which simplifies to

$$x = \frac{\alpha PL}{L + \alpha}, \quad \text{which is } W(L)$$

$$\frac{W(L)}{W(\infty)} = \frac{\alpha PL}{L + \alpha} \cdot \frac{1}{\alpha P}$$

$$= \frac{L}{L + \alpha}$$

and for α at $10^{\circ}C$

$$= \frac{L}{L + 1.194}$$

This expression is evaluated in Table 1.4, where it is readily observed that even with ten times as much air as water in the soil zone the concentration of dissolved CO_2 is over 10% short of the assumed concentration. The data in Table 1.4 confirm the findings of many researchers who report the importance of soil moisture conditions, in addition to temperature, in determining pCO_2 levels (Brook $et\ al.$, 1983).

In order to calculate the soil pCO_2 from our alkalinity measurements we have used a fairly simple approach based on Picknett's data on the composition of waters in the system $CaCO_3/CO_2/H_2O$ (Picknett, 1976) together with some more recent additional calculations (Picknett, pers. comm.).

By interpolation, data for [ALK] against free CO_2 ([CO_2° + H_2CO_3]) have been compiled corresponding to $8^{\circ}C$ which we believe to be close to the average temperature of the deep soil zones at Gait Barrows. pCO_2 in the soil air is, therefore:

$$pCO_2(\text{soil air}) = \frac{[CO_2^{\circ} + H_2CO_3]}{k_H}$$

where k_H is the Henry Constant (k_H at $8^{\circ}C = 0.0571$).

Table 1.4   Calculated values of $W(L)/W(\infty)$ at $10^{\circ}C$

L	$W(L)/W(\infty)$
1	0.4558
2	0.6262
3	0.7153
4	0.7701
5	0.8072
10	0.8933
20	0.9437

Table 1.5 shows both the free CO_2 estimates and the calculated pCO_2 levels for the springs S1 - S3. The pCO_2 levels are clearly distinguishable. The lowest values occur in the catchment of S2 which is mostly bare pavement. The highest pCO_2 levels occur in the wooded catchment of S3.

Although the data in Table 1.5 are few they show clearly the effect of soil moisture on pCO_2. High values of pCO_2 occur on the 17.2.82 and 12.3.83 which correspond to a dry period when soil moisture levels would have fallen and $W(L)/W(\infty)$ would have increased (Table 1.1). The lowest pCO_2 levels occur on 6.1.82 which saw 49.4 mm of rain during the preceding five days. This low value must probably have been due to a lowering of $W(L)/W(\infty)$ because the temperatures were no lower than the following two sampling periods. Brook *et al.* (*op. cit.*) have discussed the complexities of modelling soil pCO_2 in terms of soil moisture and temperature. In general, it is thought that temperature is 2-5 times as important as moisture in litter respiration (Van Cleve and Sprague, 1971). It should be pointed out, however, that $W(L)/W(\infty)$, as calculated here, provides a mechanism for reduction in pCO_2 which is not the same as the effect of moisture on respiration and hence, pCO_2. Clearly both aspects are important and it is possible that $W(L)/W(\infty)$ is dominant when temperatures reduce biological activity during the winter period.

CONCLUSION

Accurate alkalinity estimations are important in karst studies. Using the method discussed in this paper there is no longer any 'CO_2 error'. Furthermore it is possible to estimate the titration overshoot by means of a blank titration. By employing the technique outlined it is only necessary to substitute uncorrected alkalinity titrations in Equation (1) to obtain a correction figure. This is an obvious advantage if the titration procedure is carried out in the field.

12

Table 1.5   Estimated soil pCO_2 levels in the catchments of Springs 1-3

Date	Free $CO_2 \times 10^{-5}M$			Minimum $pCO_2 \times 10^{-2}$		
	S_1	S_2	S_3	S_1	S_2	S_3
10.10.82	68.0	-	-	1.19	-	-
14.11.82	48.8	22.2	78.1	0.85	0.39	1.36
10.12.82	19.1	10.0	33.6	0.35	0.18	0.59
6.1.82	18.6	9.8	32.4	0.33	0.18	0.57
1.2.82	29.1	11.7	54.0	0.51	0.21	0.95
17.2.83	55.1	22.7	86.9	0.97	0.40	1.52
12.3.83	62.3	26.0	78.9	1.09	0.46	1.38
17.3.83	37.8	12.7	52.7	0.66	0.22	0.92
5.4.83	39.4	13.1	60.0	0.69	0.23	1.05
24.4.83	40.5	19.5	50.2	0.71	0.34	0.88
5.5.83	25.8	11.0	57.9	0.45	0.19	1.01
14.5.83	53.2	31.1	70.6	0.93	0.55	1.24
25.5.83	-	-	87.1	-	-	1.53

Simple alkalinity measurements allow the direct calculation of soil pCO_2 in the karst water catchment zones and this method may be adopted by those researchers who do not have access to computer programs such as WATSPEC (Wigley, *op. cit.*). At Gait Barrows pCO_2 levels are associated with the types of soil/vegetation cover on the pavements and temporal variations seem essentially associated with soil moisture and its influence on the ratio $W(L)/W(\infty)$.

APPENDIX 1

In the main, the pre-war method has been retained but with several modifications: the acid titrant is 0.1M HCl instead of 0.1N H_2SO_4; the indicator is BDH 4.5 (BDH Company, Poole, Dorset) instead of Methyl Orange; there is a systematic control of end-point timing; the blank is calculated and not measured.

Apparatus

> 50 ml 'A' quality burette and stand
> 1 litre beaker, Pyrex
> Polythene stirring rod, or rubber-tipped
> glass rod
> 0.1M HCl
> 1 ml graduated pipette
> BDH 4.5 indicator
> 500 ml 'A' quality volumetric flask.

Procedure

Adjust water temperature to at least $17^{\circ}C$ and preferably to $22^{\circ}C$. 500 ml of karst water are placed in the beaker together with 0.6 ml BDH 4.5 indicator. Commence stirring vigorously and begin the titration. When blue is replaced by grey or pink stop additions but continue stirring. When faint blue returns, restart titrations adding by 2 drop quantities. When it takes a few seconds to return to blue, slow to 1 drop additions. The time taken to drift back to blue increases and when it takes more than 20 secs, slow down to half drop additions. The end-point is now near. Continue with half drop additions to make it grey. When the time for return to a blue tinge reaches more than 90 secs, the '90 second' end-point is reached. Multiply the titration by 10 to yield the uncorrected alkalinity A_u in units $M \times 10^{-5}$. Substitute A_u into

$$B_s = 1.012 + 0.0007227 \ A_u$$

to find the blank correction, B_s. Subtract B_s from A_u to find A_c the corrected alkalinity in units $M \times 10^{-5}$.

REFERENCES

Akin, G.W. and Lagerwerff, J.V. 1965. Calcium carbonate equilibria in solutions open to the air. II. Enhanced solubility $CaCO_3$ in the presence of Mg^{2+} and SO_4^{2-}. *Geochim et Cosmochim Acta,* **29**, 353-360.

Barnes, I. 1965. Geochemistry of Birch Creek, Inyo County, California; a travertine depositing creek in an arid climate. *Geochim et Cosmochim Acta*, **29**, 85-112.

Bischoff, J.L. and Fyfe, W.S. 1968. Catalysis inhibition and the calcite-aragonite problem. I. The aragonite-calcite transformation. *Amer. Journ. Sci.*, **266**, 65-79.

Bray, L.G. and Stenner, R.D. 1976. Practical techniques. In: *The Science of Speleology,* (eds) Ford, T.D. and Cullingford, C., (Academic Press), Ch.7.

Brook, G.A. and Ford, D.C. 1982. Hydrologic and geologic control of carbonate water chemistry in the subarctic Nahanni karst, Canada. *Earth Surface Processes and Landforms*, **7**, 1-16.

Brook, G.A., Folkoff, M.E. and Box, E.O. 1983. A world model of soil carbon dioxide. *Earth Surface Processes and Landforms*, **8**, 79-88.

Hutchinson, G.E. 1957. *Treatise on Limnology*. (Wiley).

Mackereth, F.J.F., Heron, J. and Talling, J.F. 1978. Water Analysis. *Freshwater Biological Assoc. Publ.*, No. 36.

Oldfield, F. 1960. Late Quaternary changes in climate, vegetation and sea-level in lowland Lonsdale. *Trans. Inst. Brit. Geogr.*, **28**, 99-117.

Picknett, R.G. 1964. A study of calcite solutions at 10°C. *Trans. Cave Res. Grp. GB*, **7**, 41-62.

Picknett, R.G. 1973. Saturated calcite solutions from 10° to 40°C: a theoretical study evaluating the solubility product and other constants. *Trans. Cave Res. Grp. GB*, **15**, 67-80.

Shuster, E.T. and White, W.B. 1971. Seasonal fluctuations in the chemistry of limestone springs: a possible means for characterising carbonate aquifers. *Journ. Hydrol.*, **14**, 93-128.

Stenner, R.D. 1969. The measurement of the aggressiveness of water towards calcium carbonate. *Trans. Cave Res. Grp. GB*, **11**, 175-200.

Wigley, T.M.L. 1977. WATSPEC: A computer program for determining the equilibrium speciation of aqueous solutions. *Brit. Geomorph. Res. Grp. Tech. Bull.*, **20**.

Van Cleve, K. and Sprague, D. 1971. Respiration rates in the forest floor of birch and aspen stands in interior Alaska. *Arctic and Alpine Res.*, **3**, 17-26.

2

Controls on the composition of authigenic percolation water in the Burren, Ireland

P.L. Smart, H. Friederich and S.T. Trudgill

SUMMARY

Samples of authigenic percolation water were collected from
diffuse seepages and cave drips throughout the karst area of the
Burren, Co. Clare, Ireland. They were sub-divided into six
classes, based on the soil and vegetation cover overlying the
limestone, comprising Bare Pavements, Vegetated Pavements, Thin
Mineral Soils, Calcareous Drift, Shale Drift and in situ Shale
Cover. Three processes were identified as controlling the concentration of the major ions present in the samples: evaporative
concentration of rainfall; cation exchange in the soil; and
weathering of the limestone and shale bedrock. Chloride and
sulphate concentrations were controlled largely by the first of
these processes, although oxidation of pyrites present in the
shales gave significant non-carbonate hardness from sulphuric
acid. Sodium, potassium and magnesium concentrations were
affected by cation exchange in the soil, but fertiliser applications increased the concentrations at Calcareous Drift sites.
Calcium concentrations in most waters were controlled by the
PCO_2 of the overlying soil, which was highest for the thick,
continuous agricultural soils, and lowest for the discontinuous
gryke soils of the Bare Pavements. Ground air was important in
reducing short-term temporal changes in PCO_2, and ensuring open-
system solution of the limestone.

RÉSUMÉ

Les échantillons des eaux d'infiltration authigènes ont été prélevés dans les grottes et les étroitures de la région de Burren, Comté de Clare, en Irlande. Les résultats ont été répartis en six groupes en fonction de la nature du sol et de la végétation qui couvrent le calcaire. Les groupes sont: les affleurements calcaires sans couverture superficielle (Bare Pavements); les affleurements avec couverture végétale (Vegetated Pavements); les sols minéraux peu épais (Thin Mineral Soils); les dépôts d'origine glaciaire contenant du calcaire (Calcareous Drift); les dépôts glaciaires marneux (Shale Drift); la couverture marneuse en place (*in situ* Shale Cover). Trois processus sont responsables des concentrations ioniques dominantes dans les échantillons: l'évaporation sur la concentration de la pluie; l'échange des cations dans le sol, et la dissolution des roches calcaires et marneuses. La concentration de chlorure et de sulphate est controlée essentiellement par le premier processus bien que l'oxydation des pyrites, qui sont présentes dans les marnes, ait donné une teneur non carbonatée importante liée à l'acide sulfurique. Le sodium, le potassium et le magnésium ont été affectés par l'échange de cations dans le sol tandis que les apports d'engrais ont augmenté les concentrations dans les secteurs à 'Calcareous Drift'. La teneur en calcium de la plupart des eaux est liée à la PCO_2 des sols. Les PCO_2 les plus élevées sont celles des sols épais; les plus faibles ont été enregistrées dans les sols des tables de lapiés, éparpillés dans les affleurements calcaires. L'air souterrain joue un rôle important. Il amortit les variations de PCO_2 dans le temps et assure par sa diffusion continuelle un système ouvert de dissolution au sein des calcaires.

INTRODUCTION

Previous work on the chemistry of waters in karst areas has emphasised the contrasts in calcium concentrations which occur between different geochemical environments, such as stream sinks and cave drips. This has allowed general models of the evolution of water hardness to be prepared, such as that of Smith and Nicholson (1964) for north-west Co. Clare. Subsequent to this work, statistical differentiation of the waters described in these models was accomplished (Drake and Harmon, 1973), and more complete chemical analysis permitted the use of pCO_2 and saturation with respect to calcite as the primary variables controlling evolution of carbonate waters (Thraillkill, 1976). Attention has also been directed to other ions present in karst waters (Christopher and Wilcock, 1981). However, most spatial studies have emphasised the balance between conduit and diffuse flow (Shuster and White, 1971) or concentrated (swallet) versus percolation recharge (Newson, 1971) in explaining differences in the chemistry of karst springs. In contrast, Ford (1971) and later Lauritzen (1981) have shown elevated pCO_2 and calcium concentrations for waters below the tree line in Alpine areas. Similar studies of the effects of different soil cover and vegetation on the spatial variation of karst water chemistry are, however, rare in the literature.

In this study, the effects of different soil and vegetation covers on the carbonate and non-carbonate chemistry of karst waters from The Burren (Co. Clare, Ireland) are investigated, with samples drawn from a single geochemical environment, diffuse authigenic percolation.

THE STUDY AREA

The Burren is a distinctive karst upland region some 450 km² in extent, on the north-west coast of Co. Clare, Ireland. Mean annual rainfall in the area is between 1200 and 1500 mm. February to June are the dryest months, with 80 to 100 mm per month, compared with about 150 mm per month for the remainder of the year. Mean annual temperature is 10°C, varying from 5.5°C in winter to 15°C in summer. In the north and west of the Burren, a summit surface at about 300 m rises steeply from the coast, and is dissected by deep north-south valleys. This is bounded to the east by the Gort lowlands, an area of low relief less than 30 m in elevation. To the south, the upland passes into a lower lying area 100 to 150 m in elevation, and limestone is no longer exposed at the surface.

The karst is developed in well-bedded massive grey biomicrite to biosparite limestones of the Visean Carboniferous Limestone Series (Douglas, 1909). Textural and purity differences in the limestones do occur, but have not been described in detail. Shale Horizons are rare, but lenticular and banded cherts up to 15 cm thick are common. The base of the succession is not seen but at least 450 m of limestones are known below the mid-Carboniferous unconformity which truncates the sequence. The Clare Shales overlie this unconformity with no angular discordance, and comprise a 40 m sequence of impervious black pyritiferous shales, sandy near the top (Hodson, 1953). The base of the succession is often phosphate rich, and calcareous concretions and beds are also found. The shales are capped by massive flaggy, micaceous sandstones of the Gronagort Sandstone Group. The complete succession dips gently to the south and south-west at between 1 and 2°, although in the south-east gentle folding on north-east/south-west trending axes can be observed. The shales therefore overlie the limestones to the south of the Burren, and form caps protected by the massive sandstones on three isolated hills in the south-west of the Burren (Figure 2.1). These caps provide catchments for numerous small streams, which sink into extensive stream-cave systems on reaching the limestones. Isolated caves are also known in the east of the

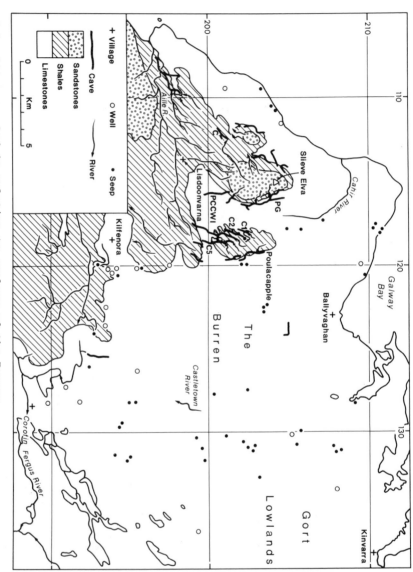

Figure 2.1 Sites sampled in relation to geology of the Burren. Key to cave sites – C: Coolagh River Cave; C1: Callaun 1; C2: Callaun 2; C5: Callaun 5; PCCW1: Pollcaherecloggaun West 1; PG: Poulnagollum.

area, where surface water is common only during the winter in
seasonally flooded depressions (turloughs). There are, however,
many small seepages of percolation water in this area, which are
often used for watering cattle.

The Burren was extensively glaciated from the north-east,
and only the summit of Slieve Elva appears to have remained ice
free during the last glaciation (Finch, 1965). Glacial action
has given rise to extensive areas of bare limestone pavement,
and steep terraced hillsides (Williams, 1966). Drift is however
found plastered onto some of the north-eastern slopes and infilling depressions and lower-lying ground in the lee of the
uplands. The drift is predominantly derived from the limestone
and comprises 60-90% limestone clasts set in a quartz sand and
clay matrix (Farrington, 1965). South of Poulacapple and Slieve
Elva, however, a black boulder clay derived from the Clare Shales
is found. This varies in composition from wholly clay or
comminuted shale, to a matrix of this material with limestone
and subordinate sandstone clasts.

METHODS AND SAMPLING

Samples of authigenic diffuse percolation water were collected
throughout the Burren from caves, surface seepages and wells in
July 1977 (see Figure 2.1 for sites). The chemistry of well
waters was not found to differ significantly from surface seepages when tested statistically for samples drawn from the
Calcareous Drift class (see below), the only class with significant numbers of well samples. The samples were collected over
a six-day period after two weeks without significant rainfall
and therefore represent summer baseflow. No change in the
chemistry of three continuously monitored sites occurred during
the main sample period, but two further limited rounds were
collected after significant rainfall. These samples were excluded from the main analysis. Temperature and pH were determined in the field, while calcium and alkalinity were measured
by titration with 0.125M EDTA and 0.01M HCl respectively to
± 1 mg.l^{-1}(calcium) and ± 3 mg.l^{-1}(alkalinity). Samples were then
decanted into small polythene bottles, acidified with concen-
trated HNO_3 and returned to Bristol for determination of sodium
(± 0.2 mg.l^{-1})and potassium (± 0.05 mg.l^{-1}) by flame emission,
magnesium (± 0.2 mg.l^{-1})by atomic absorption, and chloride (± 1.0
mg.l^{-1}) by mercurimetric titration. For some samples sulphate was
analysed turbidimetrically with barium chloride. Saturation with
respect to calcite and the negative log of carbon dioxide partial
pressure ($pPCO_2$) were then calculated for the samples using
Watspec (Wigley, 1977). Due to failure of 2 pH meters, pH measurements were not available for all samples. However, for those
where saturation was calculated, a total of 64 analyses, the
waters were on average at equilibrium with respect to calcite
($\bar{x} = 0.04$, SE ± 0.05) and showed no systematic variation of
saturation with $pPCO_2$ (Figure 2.2). Picknett's (1973) data for
saturated calcite solutions could therefore be used to calculate

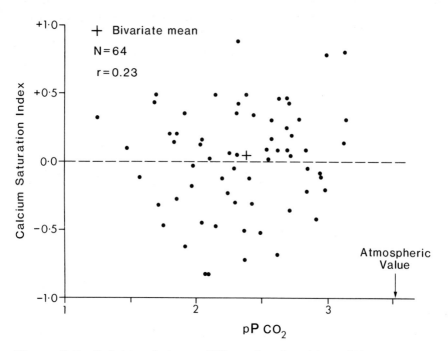

Figure 2.2   Relation between PCO_2 and saturation with respect
to calcite for analyses with pH measurements

an equilibrium $pPCO_2$ for the remaining samples, or calcium concentrations could be used directly to infer PCO_2.

Each sample site was ascribed to one of six different classes,
based on the soil and vegetation cover in the catchment area.
These were predominantly up-dip of the point of emergence for
surface seepages and in the immediate vicinity for wells.   In
the case of cave drips, it was assumed that flow was predominantly
vertical in the unsaturated zone with little dispersion, and the
drips therefore reflected the overlying terrain.   Sites marginal
between two categories were rejected, a particular problem with
samples drawn from the cave Cullaun 5, which runs along the
margin of the shale cap.   The six soil and vegetation categories
recognised are as follows:

i) *Bare Pavements* No mineral or organic soil is present over the
majority of the surface.   A limited specialised shade-loving
flora with *Teucrium scorodonia* and *Epipactis atrorubens* as
prominent members is, however, developed on accumulations of
material washed into the grykes (Dickinson *et al.*, 1964).
Quadrat measurements at three sites give an average vegetation-
soil cover of only 10 ± 11% (n = 95).   Some lichens are present
on the bare pavement surface.

ii) *Vegetated Pavements*   A thin organic mat directly overlies the limestone on parts of the clints, and supports a denser species rich vegetation cover, characterised by *Dryas octopetala,* common calcicoles such as *Thymus drucei* and large calcicolous mosses, including *Breutelia chrysocoma, Hylocomium brevirostre* and *Neckera crispa.*   Saxicolous bryophytes are found on exposed rock.   Clayey soils are frequently found in the fissures. Quadrat measurements at five sites indicate a mean cover of 23 ± 24% (n = 149).

iii) *Thin Mineral Soils*   This grouping comprises a complex of different vegetation types which have in common a thin (10-15 cm) mineral soil largely derived from drift, which almost completely covers the limestone.   The species rich limestone grasslands of the *Antennaria dicia* - *Hieracium pilosella* nodum of Ivimey-Cook and Proctor (1966) comprise the most common vegetation association of this class, but these interdigitate with the *Dryas octopetala* - *Hypericum pulchrum* nodum more characteristic of the Vegetated Pavements.   Also included in this class is the *Corylus avellana* - *Oxalis acetosella* association (hazel scrub) with its dense moss cover, which occurs in sheltered areas on drift derived soils throughout the region.

iv) *Calcareous Drift* Where a substantial thickness of limestone derived drift is present (sometimes up to 10 m), deeper, well-drained mineral soils occur.   These have been extensively modified by agriculture, and vegetation ranges from the limestone grassland described above to agricultural *Centaureo* - *Cynosuretum* grassland.   The bedrock surface underlying calcareous till shows little modification, with well preserved glacial striations and little development of solutional fissures (Trudgill, 1972).

v) *Shaley Drift*   As discussed above, drift derived dominantly from the shales is frequently clayey and impermeable, giving rise to water-logged gley mineral soils, particularly common south-west of Poulacapple.   This hosts a characteristic rushy meadow association, the *Juncus acutiflorus* - *Senecio aquaticus* nodum of Ivimey-Cook and Proctor (1966).

vi) *Shale Cover*   In places caves developed in the top of the limestones pass under *in situ* Clare Shales.   These passages are generally dry but in places cave seepages do occur and are often associated with ochreous iron-rich calcite deposits such as the 'Bloody Guts' in Cullaun 2.   The vegetation cover developed on the wet clayey gley soils is similar to that of the Shaley Drift. Thick peats are, however, also found, and on Poulacapple some areas have recently been drained and afforested with spruce.

The first three classes correspond approximately to the extremely rocky, very rocky and rocky phases of the Burren Series of Finch (1971).   The Shaley Drift and Shale Cover are largely overlain by the Kilrush and Abbeyfeale Series, while Calcareous Drift encompasses a wide range of soils, but is dominantly the Kilcolgan and Kinvara Series (Finch, 1971).

The data grouped into the six site classes were then examined
for individual ions and ionic ratios using the non-parametric
Mann Whitney U-Test (Siegel, 1967) to determine if significant
differences in concentration occurred (at the 95% confidence
level). Where no differences were observed between two classes,
these were merged to form a larger group, and this was then
tested against the remaining classes or groups until statistically
distinct groups remained. These analyses formed the basis for
identification of four processes which control authigenic percolation water chemistry in the Burren. These are discussed in
turn below.

ATMOSPHERIC SOLUTE SOURCES

Only one analysis of rainfall was made during this study but
this was comparable with ten analyses from Rosscahill (170380),
just north of Galway Bay, published by Gorham (1957), and collected throughout the year. The chemistry of rainfall in these
coastal areas with onshore prevailing winds is dominated by inland transport of salt spray aerosols. Sodium and chloride are
therefore the major ions (Table 2.1). A terrestrial dust component is also present, which is particularly significant in the
case of calcium, as would be expected in a limestone area. In
fact, the major source of chloride in the terrestrial portion of
the geochemical cycle is rainwater, little being present in most
bedrock and only a small amount arising from non-natural sources
such as road salt applications. One or two wells adjacent to
roads in the East Burren appear to be outliers from the general
distribution of chloride values in the area, and are possibly
contaminated by road runoff. Three coastal sites also show
abnormally high chloride levels (up to 174 mg.l^{-1}), suggesting
admixture of sea-water. At the remaining sites, chloride
serves as a tracer of atmospheric solute sources, and can be
used to estimate the extent of weathering as a source of solutes
in groundwater.

When the average composition of rainfall is compared with
that of authigenic percolation waters sampled in this study
(Table 2.1), it can be seen that in every case much higher concentrations are found in the latter. This increase in concentration is due to three important processes: evaporative concentration of rainfall, bedrock weathering, and solution of carbon
dioxide in the soil. The latter controls alkalinity and is a
major source of acidity during weathering reactions, as demonstrated by the 36-fold increase in calcium concentrations due to
solution of limestone by carbonic acid. Both chloride and sulphate show a similar concentration increase, with sodium a little
higher, but potassium has a very much lower enhancement, probably
because it is taken up into biotic material (see for instance
Likens et al., 1967). The concentration factor for rainfall will
be overestimated where dry deposition, which may comprise 0 to
50% of the total meteorological flux, is not included (Juang and
Johnson, 1967). It is not, however, clear whether the results

Table 2.1 Comparison of the chemical composition of rainfall
           and authigenic percolation water, concentrations
           in mg.l^{-1}

	Ca	Mg	Na	K	Alkalinity	Cl		SO4	
Rainfall*									
X	1.9	0.5	3.1	0.5	6.2	4.3		3.0	
SD	1.2	0.3	1.6	0.8	4.7	2.0		2.0	
n	11	11	11	11	11	11		11	
% Sea spray	5	6.2	77	17	<1	(100)		20	
Authigenic Percolation						Cl		SO4	
						Others	Shales	Others	Shales
X	69	3.1	9.6	0.7	194	11.6	15.2	8.5	11.0
SD	39	2.1	3.6	0.4	97	3.7	4.5	3.3	6.6
n	104	50	72	81	104	44	22	33	21
Ratio of Authigenic Percolation: Rainfall									
	36	6.2	3.1	1.4	31	2.7	3.5	2.8	3.7

* 10 analyses from Rosscahill (Gorham, 1957) plus 1 this study

reported by Gorham (1957) are of bulk precipitation. Using long-
term rainfall (P) and evaporation (E) data for the summer months
(April to September), the evaporative concentration factor (ECF)
can be calculated, assuming no soil drainage or dry deposition,
using:

$$ECF = \frac{P}{P-E}$$

     This gives a best long-term estimate for ECF of 3.1 ± 0.5,
which compares well with the specific values calculated for the
1977 percolation samples, particularly as the assumption of no
soil drainage will tend to overestimate ECF. The data indicate
that weathering is important in controlling the concentrations
not only of calcium, but also of magnesium and possibly sodium.

     Sulphate and chloride analyses for the Shale Cover and Shale
Drift classes are presented separately, as they are significantly
different from those of all other sites. This may indicate a
greater ECF on these deeper soils, a suggestion supported by the
occurrence of several high values at Calcareous Drift sites,
these soils being of comparable depth. Unfortunately, after
elimination of sites contaminated by seawater, there are insufficient samples to adequately determine the chloride level of
this class. In the case of sulphate, oxidation of iron pyrites
during weathering of the shales appears to be the most probable

explanation. This would then imply that the ECF for these soil types was not significantly higher. The increased chloride levels are therefore most probably due to leaching of connate chlorides from these marine shale deposits. Shale derived samples are excluded from the further analysis of chloride concentrations presented below.

It is generally observed that chloride concentrations in rainfall decline inland as the marine dominance of rainwater chemistry gives way to terrestrial sources of solutes, primarily dust particles (Hutton and Leslie, 1958; Junge and Werby, 1958). The rate of this decline, however, varies with the local topography, macro-climate and synoptic situation. Constant chloride concentrations are observed from 30 km to in excess of 250 km from the coast. Examination of the chloride data for the Burren, suggested a greater marine influence (higher chloride concentration) in the south near Kilfenora, than in the north at an equivalent straight-line distance from the coast in Galway Bay. This is due to the prevailing west-southwesterly winds in the area, particularly the stronger winds which accompany rain-bearing depressions from the Atlantic (Irish National Committee of Geography, 1979). This enhanced maritime influence in the Kilfenora area is accentuated by the topographic effects of the high ground backing the Cliffs of Mohr, and further to the south the large indentation of Liscannor Bay. Distance inland was therefore measured parallel to the prevailing west-southwesterly winds for each sampling site, and a regression of chloride concentrations with distance computed (Figure 2.3). This shows a significant inverse linear trend in chloride concentrations inland, as expected, with a gradient of approximately 1 mg.l^{-1} per 3 km. There is, however, a considerable scatter in the relationship, and adjacent drips in caves may often have very different chloride concentrations. This limits the utility of the relationships as a means of predicting the catchment areas of karst springs in the area, the probable catchments being conveniently sub-parallel to the coast. Higher chlorides may also be found in springs distant from the coast which receive contributions of shale waters.

The concentrations of sodium, sulphate and chloride in non-shale areas of the Burren are thus controlled primarily by the concentrations in rainfall, and the degree of evaporative concentration in the soil. In the case of other solutes, and for chloride and sulphate in shale derived waters, weathering processes are more significant, and will be discussed further below.

SOLUTION OF LIMESTONE BY CARBONIC ACID

It is widely recognised that in most karst areas carbonic acid, predominantly from the solution of biogenic carbon dioxide produced in the soil, is the major cause of limestone dissolution (Adams and Swinerton, 1937; Smith and Mead, 1962; Thrailkill, 1976). This is also the case for the Burren, as demonstrated in

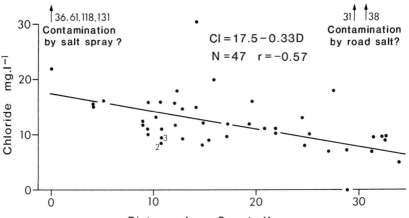

Figure 2.3   Relation between chloride concentration and
distance in the direction of the prevailing wind
from the coast for non-shale sites

Figure 2.4, which shows that the ratio of calcium to alkalinity
for 176 water samples does not differ significantly from the
1:1 ratio (expressed in mequiv. l^{-1}) expected from theory.   Thus,
it would be expected that the wide range of soil cover types
investigated in this study would result in significant differences in the PCO_2 of authigenic percolation waters, as reflected
in the calcium concentrations.

The mean calcium concentration for Vegetated and Bare Pavements samples are very similar (50 and 48 mg.l^{-1} respectively),
and the distribution (Figure 2.5) are not significantly different.
Thus the presence of a thin organic mat at the surface does not
affect the PCO_2 of the percolation waters, at least during baseflow.   In a limited sample, however, direct measurements of
carbon dioxide concentrations in organic mats on the Vegetated
Pavements during water sampling, indicated high PCO_2 (mean $pPCO_2$
1.57, n = 5), compared to 2.52 ± 0.21 (n = 19) for the $pPCO_2$ of
percolation water.   There must therefore be limited contact between infiltrating water and this atmosphere, a suggestion supported by the low calcium concentrations observed both in this
study and by Williams (1966) for water standing in contact with
the organic mat.   In fact, as little or no long-term storage of
water occurs in the organic litter, it is effectively decoupled
from the evolving percolation water in the unsaturated zone.

The material plugging grykes is frequently clayey and organic
rich, maintaining a PCO_2 in excess of the atmospheric value.
More comprehensive soil PCO_2 measurements made with gas detector
tubes in 1978 gave a $pPCO_2$ of 2.74 ± 0.12 (n = 36) for gryke
soils, comparable but rather lower than the equilibrium $pPCO_2$

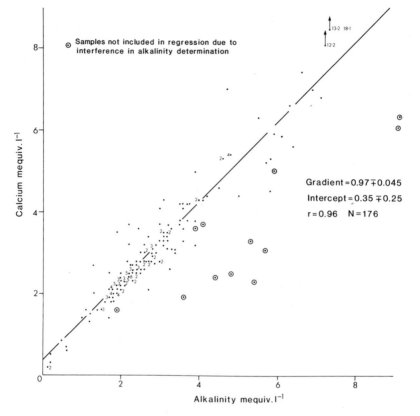

Figure 2.4   Relation between calcium concentration and alkalinity

derived from the calcium data of 2.58 ± 0.19 (n = 34).   As values
for the organic mat soils yielded much lower PCO_2 values in 1978
than in the limited 1977 sample, it is probable that the dryer
conditions depressed the 1978 values, and it is, therefore, the
gryke soils which are important in controlling the pCO_2 of authigenic percolation water in the Pavement group.   Whilst a greater
supply of organic debris must occur in Vegetated compared to
Bare Pavements, the lack of difference in calcium concentrations
for waters from these classes suggests that at depth CO_2 production is essentially similar, as the mineral infill, derived in
all cases from glacial drift, can be considered homogeneous.
Much of the additional litter supply in Vegetated Pavements must
therefore be decomposed without incorporation into the mineral
soil.

No significant difference was found between calcium concentrations in samples derived from beneath *in situ* Shale Cover or
Shale Drift.   These classes were therefore merged to produce a

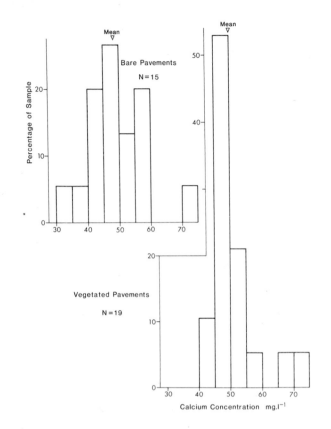

Figure 2.5 Calcium concentrations of authigenic percolation
water sampled beneath Bare and Vegetated Pavements

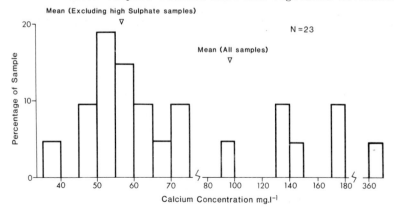

Figure 2.6 Calcium concentrations in authigenic percolation
waters from the Combined Shales group

new group of Combined shales sites. The histogram of this group (Figure 2.6), however, showed a markedly skewed distribution, with a peak at 50-55 mg.l^{-1} and a scatter of sites with much higher concentrations. The latter can be distinguished by their high sulphate concentrations, and are dealt with below. When the Combined Shales groups excluding these others was tested against the Thin Mineral Soil class, no significant difference in calcium concentrations was indicated (Shales $\bar{x}$ = 56 ± 9, n = 15, Thin Mineral Soils $\bar{x}$ = 62 ± 10, n = 25). This three class group is therefore characterised by the presence of a mineral soil. Differences in the depth and permeability of this soil cover do not appear to be reflected in the PCO$_2$ of percolation waters, a somewhat surprising finding. The explanation could be in the fortuitous balance between the CO$_2$ production and gas permeability of the two soil types. High PCO$_2$ can result from either a high production of CO$_2$ in a well ventilated soil, or a much lower production in a low permeability soil, where a steeper gas concentration gradient is required for diffusive loss of CO$_2$ into the atmosphere (Miotke, 1974). Higher biological productivity would be expected in the rich limestone grasslands of the Thin Mineral Soils, giving rise to both greater root respiration and more rapid recycling of organic matter, compared to the poorer, wetter clay soils. However, whilst the poor texture and structure of these soils adversely affect production, they also significantly reduce gas permeability, permitting the development of a higher CO$_2$ concentration to production ratio than in the Thin Mineral Soils. Alternatively, the upper horizons of the Shale Soils, which are more similar in texture, composition and chemistry to the Thin Mineral Soils than the clayey B and C horizons, may dominate recharge of water. Samples from the top 10-15 cm of both soil types show very similar chemistries when leached with distilled water (Table 2.2), with the exception of pH. This similarity is also shown by the natural waters sampled, which are not, however, well modelled by the distilled water leachate. Furthermore, the PCO$_2$ of soil gas from the A horizons of both Thin Mineral and Shale Soils do not differ significantly ($\bar{x}$ pPCO$_2$ = 2.03 ± 0.73, n = 35 and 2.10 ± 0.42, n = 49 respectively, sampled 1978). In the Shale Soils recharge would occur predominantly from lateral throughflow in the upper soil horizons giving seepage into sinkholes, limestone cliffs and structural voids in the subsoil, caused by suffosion. Such recharge would be spatially and volumetrically limited, compared to that through the Thin Mineral Soils, a contrast which is readily observed in caves passing beneath the two cover types. This suggestion, however, implies a closed system evolution for shale derived percolation water, which would result in a much lower calcium concentration for the same initial soil PCO$_2$. This problem is discussed further below.

As Figure 2.7 shows the calcium concentration of the Mineral Soil samples was significantly higher than that of the combined Pavements samples ($\bar{x}$ = 58 ± 13 and 49 ± 8.0 mg.l^{-1}), but lower than those derived from sites overlain by Calcareous Drift ($\bar{x}$ = 84 ± 21 mg.l^{-1}). The deepest and most productive calcareous soils are included in this category (Finch, 1971), giving a

Table 2.2 Comparison of the chemistry of distilled water
          leachate (of top 10-15 cm of soil) and authigenic
          percolation waters for Thin Mineral Soil and
          Combined Shale Soils

Authigenic percolation water

	Thin Mineral Soils			Combined Shales		
	X̄	SD	N	X̄	SD	N
Ca	56	9.0	25	62	10	16
Mg	4.3	4.1	14	3.1	2.1	14
Na	8.8	1.9	13	11.3	2.9	11
K	0.6	0.4	13	0.7	0.4	11
SO4	7.6	3.0	12	10.0	5.1	11
Cl	10	2.6	14	13	6.1	14
Alkalinity	188	46	24	179	42	16
pH	7.6	0.3	8	7.9	0.2	11

Distilled Water Leachate

	Thin Mineral Soils		Combined Shales	
	X̄	SD	X̄	SD
Ca	9.6	4.0	5.1	2.1
Mg	3.4	4.0	5.1	2.1
Na	0.9	0.2	1.2	1.3
K	0.20	0.19	0.28	0.17
SO4	4.6	2.2	4.9	1.7
pH	4.8	0.2	4.2	0.2

n = 16	n = 15

higher PCO_2 in recharge water than in the other categories
($pPCO_2$ Pavements 2.58 ± 0.19; Mineral Soils 2.38 ± 0.26; Calcareous Drift 2.0 ± 0.26).   The PCO_2 of soil gas at the base of
these deeper profiles could not be measured with the equipment
available.   No direct confirmation of this finding can therefore
be made.

    Open system solution, with continuous contact between gas,
liquid and solid phases, will certainly occur in the Calcareous
Drift class, where limestone fragments are common in the B and
C horizons, giving a high soil pH (Figure 2.8).   In fact, the
observed lack of solutional modification of bedrock surfaces
below calcareous drift suggests that the bulk of carbonate solu-

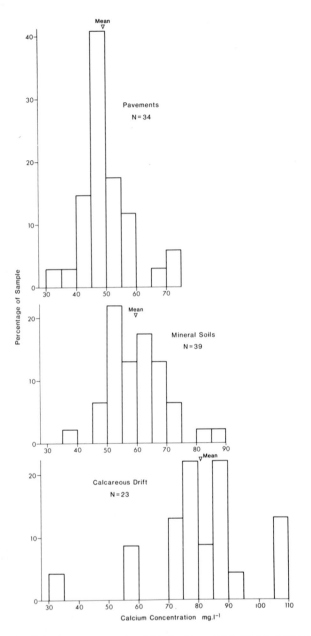

Figure 2.7   Calcium concentrations in authigenic percolation
waters from the Pavement, Mineral Soils and
Calcareous Drift Groups

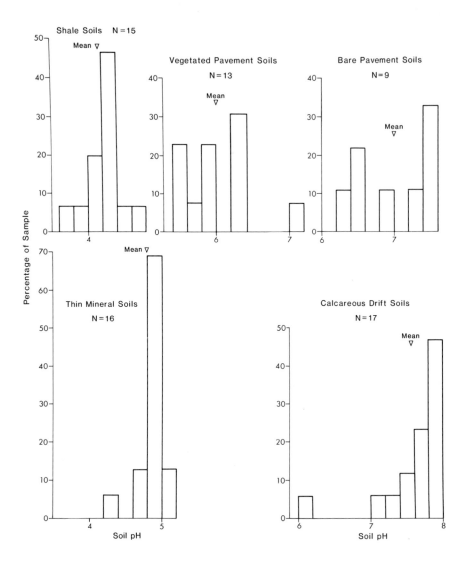

Figure 2.8   pH of soil samples from top 10-15 cm
using the sticky point method

tion is completed before the waters enter the bedrock. The pH of gryke soils, represented by the data from Bare Pavements, also suggests open system evolution is possible, although it is difficult to envisage sufficient storage in these limited soils to maintain the observed base flow. In contrast, the Thin Mineral Soils have little or no limestone present, concentrating limestone solution at the soil/bedrock interface (Trudgill, 1973). Thus it is possible that after equilibrating with the soil atmosphere, the water passes into the bedrock to evolve under closed system conditions. This, however, appears unlikely as the required $pPCO_2$ of 1.5 would be rather high for such shallow permeable soils. Thus open system evolution is probable, as found by Pitman (1978) for chalk groundwaters.

For the Pavements, where significant unsaturated zone storage in bedrock fissures must occur, and for the Thin Mineral Soils, open system evolution indicates the presence of ground air within the unsaturated zone, as suggested by Atkinson (1977) for the Mendip Hills. Further work in the same area by Friederich (1981) has however shown that the PCO_2 of this ground air need not be higher than that of the soil air, as originally proposed by Atkinson (1977). Furthermore, the significant differences in PCO_2 of waters beneath different surface covers found in this study, and in that of Friederich and Smart (1982), suggest that the composition of ground air varies spatially with soil cover. This could be due to differences in the amounts of organic material entering the unsaturated zone beneath the different soils, but it is more simply explained in terms of diffusive exchange between the soil and ground air. Production of CO_2 in the unsaturated zone is limited, compared to that in the soil, by the small amounts of organic input (Friederich et $al.$, 1982). Thus under steady state conditions, a ground air PCO_2 only slightly higher than that of soil air will provide a sufficient gradient for loss of CO_2. Production in the unsaturated zone is also more constant than in the soil due to the more stable isothermal environment. Thus sudden increases in soil CO_2 production (associated with warming of the soil for instance) could reverse the normal upward gradient, and give rise to a downward flux of CO_2 into the unsaturated zone. This effect can in fact be seen in the seasonal data from the 10 m deep soil profile monitored by Reardon et $al.$, (1979). Conversely, enhanced upward diffusion will occur when the soil CO_2 falls. The ground air therefore provides a substantial gas reservoir, buffering changes in soil CO_2. This explains why calcium concentrations observed in 1977 during this study are closely mirrored in repeat samples collected in the summer of 1978 (Figure 2.9), and in the summer values reported by Smith and Nicholson (1964), despite the differing conditions. Further work is needed to determine the relative importance of ground air, and lateral dispersion and storage of waters as described by Friederich and Smart (1981), in smoothing temporal and spatial variations in recharge chemistry.

In fact, the ground air underlying the Shale and Shale Drift cover may be dominated by the PCO_2 of the Thin Mineral Soils, which generally surround these areas. This would then explain

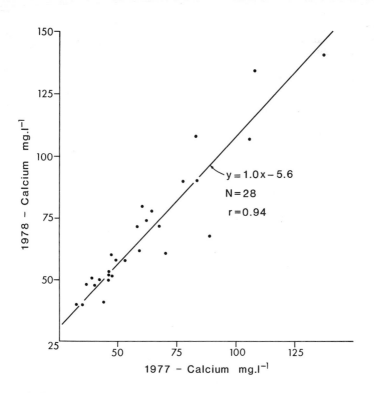

Figure 2.9   Comparison of calcium concentrations for selected
sample sites in July 1977 and 1978

the observed similarity between the PCO_2 of Combined Shale and
Thin Mineral Soil derived waters.   The saturated impermeable
clay C horizons of the shale soils may isolate the overlying
soil atmosphere from the ground air, whose concentration is then
controlled by lateral diffusion from neighbouring Thin Mineral
Soils.   Thus whilst the A horizon throughflow dominated recharge
mechanism described above is probably correct, the carbonate
chemistry of these shale waters is controlled predominantly by
the ground air, which is not directly related to the overlying
soil and vegetation cover.

As expected, the data suggest that the thicker, more continuous and productive soils had the highest PCO_2, which gave
greater concentrations of calcium in solution.   However, the open
system evolution observed at Pavement sites with little soil
water storage, and Thin Mineral Soils leached of calcium carbonate, indicates the importance of ground air in controlling the
chemical evolution of authigenic percolation water.   The PCO_2
of ground air must be controlled primarily by diffusive exchange
with the soil atmosphere, because soil cover/calcium concentration

relations would not be expected if this were not the case, and ground air was either uniform in composition or affected by other factors.

WEATHERING OF THE CLARE SHALES

Whilst the major part of the calcium dissolved in the sampled waters can be ascribed to solution by carbonic acid, the positive calcium intercept of 0.35 mequiv. 1^{-1} on the plot of calcium versus alkalinity (Figure 2.4), suggests the presence of significant non-carbonate hardness. However, because the best-estimate gradient is not equal to 1, the intercept may be over-estimated. The non-carbonate hardness data was therefore sub-divided into the six soil classes. On analysis, only three significantly different groups were obtained (Figure 2.10): Bare Pavements ($\bar{x}$ = 0.15 ± 0.19 mequiv. 1^{-1}, n = 20); Combined Shales ($\bar{x}$ = 1.14 ± 2.23, n = 32); and the remaining classes ($\bar{x}$ = 0.23 ± 0.21, n = 100). Shale samples with high non-carbonate hardness are characterised by both high calcium and high sulphate concentrations, due to solution of limestone by sulphuric acid derived from oxidation of iron pyrites in the Clare Shales.

$$FeS_2 + 3.75O_2 + 3.5H_2O \rightleftharpoons Fe(OH)_3 + 4H^+ + 2SO_4^{2-}$$
$$4H^+ + 2CaCO_3 \rightleftharpoons 2Ca^{2+} + 2H_2CO_3$$

Some sites in fact show the stoichimetric ratios predicted from these equations. A well at Noughaval, for instance, gave concentrations in mmoles. 1^{-1} of 7.8 calcium, 7.8 sulphate and 7.2 bicarbonate, with 0.65 mmoles. 1^{-1} of dissolved iron. The most geochemically interesting sites were in caves passing beneath the shale cap, where seepage passing through *in situ* shales was clearly indicated by precipitation of intermixed iron hydroxide and calcite in spongy gelatinous formations, such as the aptly named Bloody Guts in Cullaun 2. In such cases, the PCO_2 of the water was elevated by the release of carbonic acid from the sulphuric acid dissolution. Degassing of this additional dissolved CO_2 could occur if a lower PCO_2 atmosphere was present in the fissures, as was observed in the cave passages, giving eventual super-saturation.

The majority (60%) of Shale sites did not, however, have high non-carbonate hardness (Figure 2.10), supporting the earlier suggestion that these waters do not come into contact with un-weathered shale material in the soil C horizons and bedrock, but flow laterally in the more weathered upper horizons of the soils. Samples collected from three wells in Calcareous Drift near Kilferora had moderately high non-carbonate hardness. Inspection of the geology map suggests that these may well be underlain by shale bedrock, or at least receive waters from the shales to the south. In these cases, pyrites oxidation accounted for some 8-10% of the dissolved calcium.

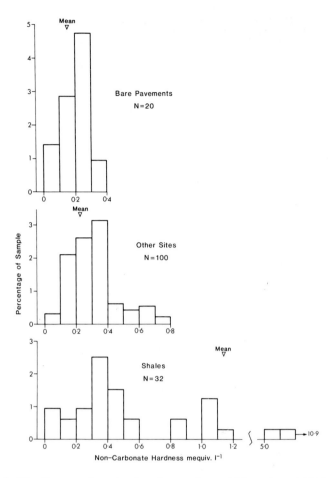

Figure 2.10   Non-carbonate hardness in authigenic percolation
waters for Bare Pavement, Combined Shales, and all
other classes. (7 negative values are omitted
from plots but included in calculated means)

Weathering of the Clare Shales, which are the major non-carbonate formation in the Burren, is not limited to oxidation of iron pyrites, but also results in release of sodium, potassium and particularly magnesium. The concentrations of these ions are, however, only higher in those sites with high sulphate, other shale derived samples having similar concentrations to the other classes (Table 2.3). It is clear from this association that weathering of pyrites and silicate minerals occurs simultaneously in the unweathered shales. Unfortunately, no chemical or mineralogical analyses of the Clare Shales are available, although a single analysis of the basal phosphorite horizons has

Table 2.3   Comparison of concentrations of sodium, potassium and magnesium in authigenic percolation water from the 6 classes and rainfall (Combined Shales have been separated into sites with and without high sulphate from oxidation of pyrites). Concentrations in mg.l^{-1} : ± 1 standard deviation

Class	Sodium	Potassium	Magnesium	N
Rainfall	3.1 ± 1.6	0.5 ± 0.8	0.5 ± 0.3	11
Bare Pavements	7.2 ± 1.5	0.59 ± 0.17	1.5 ± 0.3	11
Vegetated Pavements	8.6 ± 2.1	0.58 ± 0.18	2.3 ± 1.0	12
Thin Mineral Soils	9.0 ± 1.7	0.61 ± 0.36	4.3 ± 4.1	13
Calcareous Drift	10.4 ± 3.6	2.5 ± 2.2	3.8 ± 2.3	9
Shales with Pyrites Oxidation	17.6 ± 8.8	0.98 ± 0.39	11.8 ± 10.5	10
Other Shales	10.7 ± 2.8	0.48 ± 0.28	2.7 ± 1.0	11

been published by Oakley (1942), in which only 0.2-0.3% each of sodium, potassium and magnesium oxides are present. In waters containing significant weathering products from the shales, approximately half the sodium and potassium are derived from this source. For magnesium the figure is higher at between three and four times the non-shale contribution. It is readily demonstrated that this magnesium is derived from the shales and not from enhanced solution of the bedrock, because the molar ratio of calcium to magnesium (Ca/Mg) is less for these waters than for all others sampled (Shales with high sulphate $\bar{x}$ = 8.8 ± 4.5, n = 11; all other sites $\bar{x}$ = 15.6 ± 4.7, n = 40). Atkinson and Smith (1976) suggest that the ratio of calcium to magnesium in limestone waters gives a direct indication of the bedrock ratio. However, in the Burren, a much greater proportion of magnesium than calcium is derived from rainfall, which has Ca/Mg of 2.9 ± 2.2 (n = 11). Assuming the calcium and magnesium become concentrated to the same extent as sulphate and chloride during evaporation from the soil solution, on average for non-shale waters about half the magnesium present is derived from limestone solution. A better estimate of Ca/Mg in the Carboniferous Limestone of the Burren would therefore be 23 ± 13. This is in good agreement with a Ca/Mg of 27 for three limestone samples from Poulacapple (High, 1970) but a more representative series of bedrock analyses is clearly needed.

Where percolation water comes in contact with unweathered shales, significant release of sodium, potassium, magnesium and sulphuric acid occurs. The latter, from the oxidation of iron pyrites, provides the major source of non-alkaline hardness in the area. For non-shale derived waters, approximately half the magnesium in solution is derived from solution of limestone.

CATION EXCHANGE PROCESSES

It has been suggested that the ratio of potassium to sodium may give an indication of the residence time of karst waters (Christopher, 1975). Potassium has a smaller hydrated ionic radius than sodium, and can be shown experimentally to be adsorbed with a selectivity coefficient of about 5 compared to sodium. This is somewhat higher than expected simply from the difference in radius of the hydrated ions, because potassium may also penetrate the hexagonal 'holes' between oxygen atoms in the tetrahedral layers of clay minerals, particularly important in the case of illite. The major problem with application of this theory is that most groundwater systems do not have a single simple source of sodium and potassium, but receive variable contributions from several sources. Thus in Derbyshire, more recent work by Christopher and Wilcock (1981) has demonstrated that weathering of shales and larvas is also important in controlling potassium to sodium ratios, although deep circulation groundwaters do show potassium concentration. Other workers in karst areas have described additions of potassium and/or sodium from surface application of fertilisers and animal wastes (Manley and Taylor, 1978), and bat guano and shale interbeds in the limestone (Crowther, 1981). Similarly in Co. Clare, the release of sodium and potassium from the Clare Shales limits the application of the theory, the ratio being controlled primarily by the relative amounts of sodium and potassium bearing minerals in the shales, and their susceptibility to weathering.

However, based on an analysis of the chloride and sulphate concentrations, it was suggested above that the only significant input of sodium and potassium in the non-shale classes was from rainfall. This conforms well with the single common input with subsequent adsorption required by theory. The molar ratio of potassium to sodium (K/Na hereafter) for Rainfall, Bare and Vegetated Pavements, Thin Mineral Soil and Calcareous Drift sites are presented in Figure 2.11. These form statistically separate classes with the exception of the Bare and Vegetated Pavements, which form an independent group when combined. It is evident that the ratio for 60% of Calcareous Drift samples is in excess of the mean for Rainfall, which is strongly biased by two high outlier values. Whilst the mean sodium value is slightly higher for Calcareous Drift samples (excluding those coastal sites affected by salt spray) than for other non-shale sites (Table 2.3), the potassium concentration is approximately four times higher. The majority of Calcareous Drift soils are extensively developed as grassland for grazing and fodder, being the best agricultural land in the Burren (Finch, 1971). They therefore receive applications of both organic manure and fertilisers, such as Kaynitro (potassium nitrate). In addition to these direct sources, replacement of potassium on exchange sites by preferentially adsorbed ammonium from the ammonium nitrate fertilisers widely used on grasslands may occur. The composition

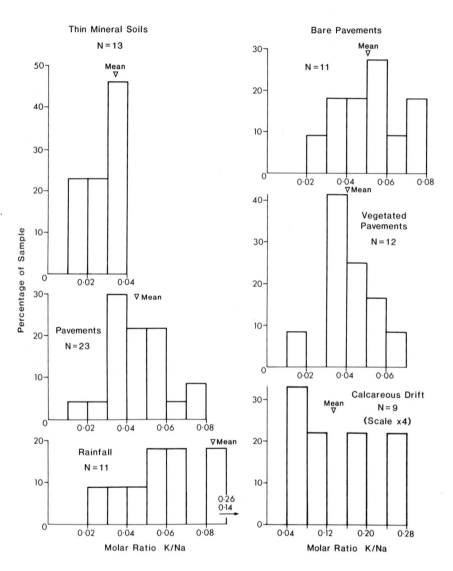

Figure 2.11   Molar ratio of potassium to sodium in 5 classes and rainfall

of distilled water leachates (Table 2.4) confirms the greater
abundance of potassium in Calcareous Drift soils, the mean concentration being over twice that found for Thin Mineral Soils,
while sodium and magnesium are present in similar amounts.

For the remaining classes, there is a decrease in K/Na from
high values in rainfall, through intermediate values at Pavement
sites, to low values for Thin Mineral Soil-derived waters. This
conforms well with theory, the residence time and therefore
potential for adsorption in the Thin Mineral Soils being considerably greater than on Pavements, where storage is limited
to the clayey gryke soils and water thus enters the bedrock more
rapidly. Furthermore, whilst not statistically different, there
appears to be greater adsorption of potassium on the Vegetated
than Bare Pavements. It is unlikely, however, that there would
be a significant difference in residence time due to the presence
of the vegetation cover, the micro-topography being identical for
both site types as they have a common origin (Williams, 1966).
The greater adsorption is thus more readily explained by the
additional exchange capacity of the humus rich organic mat.
This is supported by laboratory distilled water leaching of the
organic rendzina soils from Vegetated Pavements, gryke soils
from Bare Pavements and Thin Mineral Soils (Table 2.4). For
the cations sodium, potassium and magnesium, the exchange capacity was highest on the wholly organic soils, and lowest on the

Table 2.4   Composition of distilled water leachate from gryke
soils (Bare Pavements), rendzinas (Vegetated Pavements), Thin Mineral Soils and Calcareous Drift
Soils.   Units are $mg.g^{-1}$ dry soil

Soil	Sodium		Potassium		Calcium		Magnesium	
	$\bar{x}$	SD	$\bar{x}$	SD	$\bar{x}$	SD	$\bar{x}$	SD
Rendzina Soils n = 13	5.3	3.8	3.0	2.1	27	7	20	14
Gryke Soils n = 9	1.5	0.8	1.0	0.5	26	6	6.7	5.0
Thin Mineral Soils n = 16	0.9	0.2	0.20	0.19	9.6	4.0	3.4	4.0
Calcareous Drift Soils n = 15	0.9	0.7	0.45	0.45	17	8	3.6	3.9

predominantly mineral soils. The figures for calcium are affected by the presence of limestone fragments in the gryke soils (compare with pH data Figure 2.8). These results also indicate that the significant difference in K/Na between the Pavements and Thin Mineral Soils cannot be explained in terms of a greater cation exchange capacity for the latter, but must be due to the more prolonged contact of water and soil.

When the concentrations of sodium and potassium are examined for Pavement and Thin Mineral Soils, it is clear that there is no significant difference in potassium concentrations between these classes as expected (Table 2.3). The observed differences in K/Na are therefore due to increasing sodium concentrations with greater residence. The mean values quoted are rather affected by extreme values in the limited, non-normal samples, but this can be demonstrated by use of non-parametric tests. In particular, there is a consistent difference between Bare Pavements and the other two classes for sodium, magnesium and non-alkaline hardness. This pattern is best explained by evaporative concentration of rainwater in the soil cover, as is the significantly higher potassium concentration observed in authigenic percolation compared to rainwater. Gryke soils, which cover less than 10% of the pavement surface area, can retain a smaller proportion of the summer rainfall in their limited storage than the continuous Thin Mineral Soils, resulting in a greater proportion of unconcentrated recharge in the former case, and a lower sodium concentration. A parallel variation in chloride concentrations would provide confirmation of this mechanism. However, the known spatial organisation of chloride concentrations, in combination with the non-random distribution of sample sites of particular classes, would give rise to biased estimates of representative chloride concentrations.

Because potassium has greater preferential adsorption than either sodium or magnesium, any evaporative increase in the potassium concentration of the soil solution is balanced by uptake onto soil cation exchange sites, with release of less preferentially bound cations. Because calcium is both present in high concentrations in the soil solution, and preferentially adsorbed compared to magnesium, this exchange process results in release of magnesium into solution. Clearly this uptake of potassium and release of magnesium cannot occur indefinitely because of the increasing concentration of adsorbed potassium on the finite exchange sites. During the summer months, uptake of potassium by growing plants will occur, with subsequent release following litter decomposition giving rise to peaks in concentration following rainfall in late summer and autumn (see, for instance, Walling and Foster, 1975). This is confirmed by the data of Miserez (1970) for springs and boreholes in the Jura karst. These show a sudden fall in potassium concentrations at the start of the growing season in April, and higher figures during the autumn and winter. Furthermore, during the winter when the concentration of soil water will fall following extensive recharge, release of potassium from exchange sites will maintain the concentrations in solution. In fact, rough calculations indicate that the total summer supply of potassium in rainfall is relatively small compared to the exchange capacity of the Thin Mineral Soils, based on data in Finch (1971). The degree of exchange proposed is thus quite feasible.

More work is clearly needed to understand these complex exchange processes, including more detailed spatial and temporal monitoring. The results presented do, however, suggest that it is exchange and concentration processes occurring in the soil which control the concentrations of sodium, potassium and magnesium in the Burren. Therefore, differences in bedrock residence time are not significant for the authigenic percolation sampled.

CONCLUSIONS

In this work, by widening the range of analyses conducted compared to many previous studies of the chemical evolution of karst waters, it has been possible to describe in considerable detail three major processes controlling the composition of authigenic percolation in the Burren. These are evaporative concentration of atmospheric inputs, exchange processes in the soil, and bedrock weathering. In all of these, the nature of the soil and vegetation overlying the limestone has been demonstrated to be of considerable importance.

For non-shale waters, sulphate and chloride concentrations are controlled by the inputs in rainfall, which in the case of chloride can be shown to decrease inland in the direction of the prevailing winds. Rainfall inputs become concentrated by evaporation in the soil, but this process gives rise to higher concentrations for thick soils, which can store a greater proportion of the rainfall inputs than thin or discontinuous soils. During concentration, exchange processes are important, being controlled both by the residence time of soil water (greater in thicker soils), and by cation exchange capacity, which is higher for the more organic soils. These exchange processes are particularly significant in controlling the concentrations of sodium, potassium and magnesium in non-shale derived waters. On average, however, about half the magnesium in solution is derived from solution of the limestone bedrock. In the case of Calcareous Drift soils, which are widely used for agriculture, significant amounts of potassium are derived from fertiliser applications. In areas overlain by Shale Drift or *in situ* Shales, the majority of waters enter the limestone by lateral throughflow in the upper soil horizons, giving a composition similar to that of the Thin Mineral Soils which directly overlie the limestone. About one-third, however, come into direct contact with shales, weathering of which liberates magnesium, sodium, potassium and sulphuric acid. The latter, derived from oxidation of pyrites, gives significant non-carbonate hardness after contact with the limestones.

In all authigenic percolation waters sampled, calcium and bicarbonate were the major ions present, as would be expected. The deeper soils had a higher PCO_2 than shallow soils, giving greater calcium concentrations in solution at equilibrium. The presence of an organic mat on pavement surfaces did not affect calcium concentrations because infiltrating water had little contact with this material, and it did not maintain a high PCO_2. All waters appeared to evolve under open-system conditions in the presence of a co-existing ground air atmosphere. This appeared to be important in reducing small scale spatial and temporal variations in the PCO_2 of authigenic percolation. The PCO_2 of shale waters may also be controlled by lateral diffusion of ground air under the impermeable clay cover from the surrounding thin mineral soils.

Acknowledgements

Our interest in the Burren was greatly stimulated by Professor E.K. Tratman, whose company is now sorely missed. Professor Tratman, Chris Pepper, Bob Crabtree, Pete Walker, Jill Ulmanis and Gunners Ulmanis all assisted in field sampling. Financial and technical support from the Universities of Bristol and Sheffield, including drafting of the diagrams by Simon Godden, is gratefully acknowledged. During the research, Dr. Hans Friederich was supported by a grant from Phillips van der Willigenfonds, Eindhoven, Netherlands.

REFERENCES

Adams, A.C. and Swinnerton, A.C. 1937. The solubility of limestone. *Trans. Amer. Geophys. Union,* **18**, 504-508.

Atkinson, T.C. 1977. Carbon dioxide in the atmosphere of the unsaturated zone: an important control of groundwater hardness in limestones. *Journ. Hydrol.,* **35**, 111-123.

Atkinson, T.C. and Smith, D.I. 1976. The erosion of limestones. In: *The Science of Speleology,* (eds) Ford, T.D. and Cullingford, C.H.D., (Academic Press, London), 151-177.

Christopher, N. 1975. The use of saturation index and potassium to sodium ratio as indicators of speleological potential with special reference to Derbyshire. *Trans. Brit. Cave Res. Assoc.,* **2**, 29-34.

Christopher, N. and Wilcock, J.D. 1981. Geochemical controls on the composition of limestone groundwaters with special reference to Derbyshire. *Trans. Brit. Cave Res. Assoc.,* **8**, 135-158.

Crowther, J. 1981. Small-scale spatial variations in the chemistry of diffuse-flow seepages in Gua Anak Takun, West Malaysia. *Trans. Brit. Cave Res. Assoc.,* **8**, 168-177.

Dickinson, C.M., Pearson, M.C. and Webb, D.A. 1964. Some micro-habitats of the Burren, their micro-environments and vegetation. *Proc. Roy. Irish Acad.*, **63B**, 291-302.

Douglas, J.A. 1909. The Carboniferous Limestone of Co. Clare. *Quart. Journ. Geol. Soc. Lond.*, **65**, 538-586.

Drake, J.J. and Harmon, R.S. 1973. Hydrochemical environments of carbonate terrains. *Water Resour. Res.*, **9**, 949-957.

Farrington, A. 1965. The last glaciation in the Burren, Co. Clare. *Proc. Roy. Irish Acad.*, **64**, 33-39.

Finch, T.F. 1965. Slieve Elva, Co. Clare - a Nunatak. *Irish Nat. Journ.*, **15**, 133-136.

Finch, T.F. 1971. Soils of Co. Clare. *Soil Survey of Ireland Bull.*, **23**, p. 246.

Ford, D.C. 1971. Characteristics of limestone solution in the Southern Rocky Mountains and Selkirk Mountains, Alberta and British Columbia. *Can. Journ. Earth Sci.*, **8**, 585-609.

Friederich, H. 1981. *The hydrochemistry of recharge in the unsaturated zone, with special reference to the Carboniferous Limestone aquifer of the Mendip Hills,* (Unpub. Doctoral thesis, University of Bristol).

Friederich, H. and Smart, P.L. 1981. Dye tracer studies of the unsaturated zone recharge of the Carboniferous Limestone aquifer of the Mendip Hills, England. *Proc. 8th Int. Cong. Speleol.*, I, 283-286.

Friederich, H. and Smart, P.L. 1982. The classification of autogenic percolation waters in karst aquifers: a study in GB Cave, Mendip Hills, England. *Proc. Univ. Bristol Spelaeol. Soc.*, **16**, 143-159.

Friederich, H., Smart, P.L. and Hobbs, R.P. 1982. The micro-flora of limestone percolation water and its implications for limestone springs. *Trans. Brit. Cave Res. Assoc.*, **9**, 15-26.

Gorham, E. 1957. The chemical composition of rain from Rosscahil in County Galway. *Irish Nat. Journ.*, **7**, 122-126.

Halliwell, R.A. 1980. Karst waters of the Ingleborough area, North Yorkshire. *Proc. Univ. Bristol Spelaeol. Soc.*, **15**, 183-205.

High, C. 1970. *Aspects of the solutional erosion of limestone with a special consideration of lithological factors,* (Unpub. Doctoral thesis, University of Bristol).

Hodson, F. 1953. The beds above the Carboniferous Limestone in north-west County Clare, Eire. *Quart. Journ. Geol. Soc. Lond.*, **109**, 259-283.

Hutton, J.T. and Leslie, T.I. 1958. Accession of non-nitrogenous ions in rainwater to soils in Victoria. *Aust. Journ. Ag. Res.*, **9**, 492-507.

Irish National Committee for Geography, 1979. *Atlas of Ireland.* (Royal Irish Academy, Dublin).

Ivimey-Cook, R.B. and Proctor, M.C.F. 1966. The plant communities of the Burren, Co. Clare. *Proc. Roy. Irish Acad.,* **64B**, 211-302.

Juang, F.H. and Johnson, N.M. 1967. Cycling of chlorine through a forested watershed in New England. *Journ. Geophys. Res.,* **72**, 5641-5647.

Junge, C.E. and Werby, R.T. 1958. The concentration of chloride, sodium, potassium, calcium and sulphate in rainwater over the United States. *Journ. Met.,* **15**, 417-425.

Lauritzen, S. 1981. A study of some karst waters in Norway. *Norsk Geogr. Tidsskr.,* **35**, 1-19.

Likens, G.E., Borman, F.H., Johnson, N.M. and Pierce, R.A. 1967. The calcium, magnesium, potassium and sodium budgets for a small forested ecosystem. *Ecol.,* **48**, 772-785.

Manley, D.B. and Taylor, G.S. 1978. Some practical considerations in the use of K/Na ratios in speleological reconnaissance. *Trans. Brit. Cave Res. Assoc.,* **5**, 17-21.

Miotke, F.D. 1974. Carbon dioxide and the soil atmosphere. *Karst u Hohlenkunde Ser.,* **A9**, 1-49.

Miserez, J.J. 1970. Correlations Na/K dans les eaux karstiques du Jura-Applications aux diagrammes d'equilibre des systeme Na_2O-resp. K_2O-CO_2-H_2O et Na_2O-resp. K_2O-Al_2O_3-SiO_2-H_2O. *Zeit. Deutsch. Geol. Ges. Sonderh. Hydrogeol. Hydrogeochem.* **5**, 161-181.

Newson, M.D. 1971. A model of limestone erosion in the British Isles. *Trans. Inst. Brit. Geog.,* **54**, 55-70.

Oakley, K.P. 1942. British phosphates. Part IV: Occurrences of phosphate in Pre-Cretaceous rocks. *Geol. Surv. GB Wartime Pamphlet,* **8**, 1-25.

Picknett, R.G. 1973. Saturated calcite solutions from 10 to 43°C a theoretical study evaluating the solubility product and other constants. *Trans. Cave Res. Grp. GB,* **15**, 67-80.

Pitman, J.I. 1978. Carbonate chemistry of groundwater from chalk Givendale, East Yorkshire. *Geochim. Cosmochim. Acta,* **42**, 1885-1897.

Reardon, E.J., Allison, G.B. and Fritz, P. 1979. Seasonal, chemical and isotopic variations of soil CO_2 at Trout Creek, Ontario. *Journ. Hydrol.,* **43**, 355-371.

Shuster, E.T. and White, W.B. 1971. Seasonal fluctuations in the chemistry of limestone springs; a possible means for characterising carbonate aquifers. *Journ. Hydrol.,* **14**, 93-128.

Smith, D.I. and Mead, D.G. 1962. The solution of limestone. *Proc. Univ. Bristol Spelaeol. Soc.,* **9**, 188-211.

Smith D.I. and Nicholson, F.H. 1964. A study of limestone solution in North-west Co. Clare, Eire. *Proc. Univ. Bristol Spelaeol. Soc.,* 10, 119-138.

Thrailkill, J. 1976. Carbonate equilibria in Karst waters. In: *Karst Hydrology and Water Resources,* Yeujeuich V. (ed), Water Resources Publications, Fort Collins, 34.1-34.27.

Trudgill, S.T. 1972. The influence of drifts and soils on limestone weathering in N.W. Clare, Ireland. *Proc. Univ. Bristol Spelaeol. Soc.,* 13, 113-118.

Trudgill, S.T. 1973. Limestone erosion under soil. *Proc. 6th Int. Cong. Speleol.,* II, 409-422, (Academia, Prague).

Walling, D.E. and Foster, I.D.L. 1975. Variations in the natural chemical concentration of river water during flood flows, and the lag effect: some further comments. *Journ. Hydrol.,* 26, 237-244.

Wigley, T.M.L. 1977. WATSPEC: A computer program for determining the equilibrium speciation of aqueous solutions. *Brit. Geomorph. Res. Grp. Tech. Bull.,* 20, p. 48.

Williams, P.W. 1966. Limestone pavements with special reference to Western Ireland. *Trans. Inst. Brit. Geog.,* 40, 155-172.

Additional reference:

Siegel, S. 1967. *Nonparametric Statistics,* McGraw Hill, York, 312pp.

3

L'Evolution saissonière de la teneur en CO_2 de l'air de deux grottes Belges: Ste-Anne et Brialmont, Tilff

M. Gewelt and C. Ek

RÉSUMÉ

Les variations de la pCO_2 ont été mesurées dans deux grottes belges durant 13 mois consécutifs. Le maximum très net en été-automne et le minimum hivernal sont attribués au rythme du métabolisme de la biomasse. Des décalages progressifs entre les pics observés à diverses profondeurs sous terre et le pic du maximum de l'activité biologique suggèrent l'existence d'un flux de CO_2 venant du sol. Dans la grotte de Brialmont, qui a deux entrées opposées, les teneurs sont plus basses que dans la grotte Ste-Anne. Les teneurs des fissures sont dans l'ensemble plus fortes que celles des galeries : les fissures représentent la voie d'accès du CO_2 du sol dans les grottes. Le ruisseau souterrain (à la grotte Ste-Anne) est une autre source d'apport de CO_2 à l'air de la cavité. Des contaminations anthropiques ont été décelées et mesurées; les précautions prises pour éviter des erreurs dues à cette cause lors de nos analyses sont décrites. Les nouveaux résultats présentés ici sont comparés aux teneurs en CO_2 observées par divers auteurs dans neuf autres grottes de Belgique et dans des cavités de huit autres pays.

SUMMARY

pCO_2 variations have been measured in two Belgian caves during
13 consecutive months. The clear maximum in summer-autumn and
the minimum during winter are correlated with biological activity.
The delays between CO_2 peaks at different depths and the peak of
maximum plant growth suggest CO_2 fluxes coming from the soil air.
In the Brialmont cave which has two entrances at opposite ends
CO_2 contents are lower than in the Ste-Anne cave. CO_2 contents
in the joints and fissures are commonly higher than those in the
galleries. These fissures are thus the pathways by which soil
CO_2 passes into the cave. The underground river (in the Ste-
Anne cave) is another source of CO_2 for the cave atmosphere.
Human contamination has been identified and measured. The pre-
cautions taken during our measurements to avoid contamination
are discussed. The results are compared with the CO_2 contents
observed by researchers in nine other Belgian caves and also in
caves of eight other countries.

INTRODUCTION

Le 'moteur' de la dissolution du calcaire est, le plus souvent,
le dioxyde de carbone (H. Roques, 1959). C'est dire son importance dans les phénomènes karstiques. Son étude présente
d'autre part un grand intérêt biologique : le CO_2 provient en
très grande partie du métabolisme de la biomasse et, en retour,
la teneur en dioxyde de carbone de l'air a des répercussions
biologiques. Du fait de l'importance et de la complexité des
échanges entre phase gazeuse et phase liquide, l'étude de la
répartition du CO_2 de l'air dans les karsts et de ses modifications présente donc un intérêt évident.

Les premières mesures de CO_2 en grotte datent d'il y a bien
longtemps (voir par ex. M. Forel, 1865). Mais c'est à une quinzaine d'années seulement que remonte la systématisation des
analyses dans ce milieu (C. Ek *et al.*, 1968; F.-D. Miotke, 1974;
T.C. Atkinson, 1975; J.M. James, 1977; P. Renault, 1979), et
c'est tout récemment que les mesures ont pris une grande extension (C. Ek, 1981; C. Ek *et al.*, 1981; A. Klimchuck *et al.*, 1981;
W.C. Lewis, 1981; P. Renault, 1982).

Le présent travail est basé sur 237 mesures faites en 1982
et 1983 dans la grotte Ste-Anne et la Grotte de Brialmont à
Tilff (Belgique).

Les deux grottes se présentent comme des superpositions de
galeries subhorizontales plus ou moins longues (la plus longue
a environ 620 m), étagées au flanc d'un versant de vallée.

Les mesures ont été faites mensuellement en une série de lieux précis; en outre, les recherches ont fourni une connaissance générale de l'évolution des teneurs en CO_2 avec la distance à l'entrée et une idée précise des effets contaminants de la présence humaine. Enfin, on a comparé les nouvelles mesures aux quelque 350 analyses déjà publiées sur des grottes belges et à une centaine de mesures inédites.

LES GROTTES ETUDIEES

Situation et site

La grotte Ste-Anne et la grotte de Brialmont sont toutes deux situées à Tilff (Belgique), à une dizaine de kilomètres au sud de Liège. Elles s'ouvrent dans la vallée de l'Ourthe, affluent de la Meuse, sur le versant de rive droite de la vallée (Figure 1). L'Ourthe coule à cet endroit à l'altitude de septante-cinq mètres environ, mais les terrasses fluviales quaternaires de sa vallée s'observent jusqu'à plus de deux cents mètres d'altitude sur les versants. Les grottes étudiées sont des étagements de longs couloirs subhorizontaux situés entre ces deux limites altitudinales.

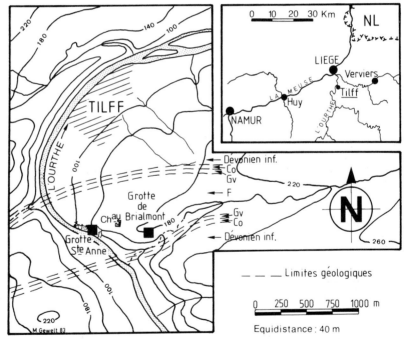

Figure 3.1   Localisation des grottes Ste-Anne et Brialmont, Tilff, (d'après C. Ek, 1962, légèrement modifié)

Développement et morphologie

i) *La grotte Ste-Anne* La grotte Ste-Anne est constituée de quatre étages superposés dont l'inférieur débouche dans l'Ourthe même, et dont celui qui le surmonte immédiatement s'ouvre dans une carrière de calcaire frasnien abandonnée. Le développement total de la grotte est de l'ordre de 1200 m, sa dénivelée d'environ 35 m (Figure 2). On trouvera dans *l'Inventaire spéléologique de la Belgique,* édité par la Société spéléologique de Wallonie (1982), une bibliographie très fournie sur la grotte et divers renseignements. La grotte a été, au point de vue de la morphologie, étudiée en particulier par E. van den Broeck, E. Martel et E. Rahir (1910) puis par C. Ek (1961 et 1962).

Les étages de la grotte représentent les cours successifs d'un ruisseau souterrain affluent de l'Ourthe qui a suivi l'encaissement de la rivière épigée au cours du Quaternaire. L'étage conservé sur sa plus grande longueur (parfois dit l'étage moyen ou la galerie principale), vers l'altitude de 90 m, est long de quelque 620 m. Les étages sont reliés par des fissures subverticales, parfois étroites, parfois notablement élargies, et, par endroits, par des passages obliques (Figure 2).

La grotte présente peu de salles notables : la morphologie dominante est celle de longs couloirs creusés par l'eau courante, avec la présence de formes dues à des circulations en conduite forcée et d'autres formes liées à l'action d'une rivière souterraine.

ii) *La grotte de Brialmont* Constituant la partie supérieure du réseau de Ste-Anne, la grotte de Brialmont a un développement de quelque 150 m. Elle comporte essentiellement deux galeries horizontales superposées. L'entrée naturelle est vers 176 m, au-dessus de ces étages; une autre entrée, artificielle, s'ouvre dans le versant vers 168 m, au niveau de l'étage supérieur.

Le plancher de la galerie supérieure s'étant effondré sur une vingtaine de mètres de longueur dans la galerie inférieure, les deux conduits se réunissent là en une salle de quelque 10 m de haut (Figure 3).

Un puits s'ouvre à l'étage inférieur, menant vers des galeries étroites situées plus bas. Cependant, la jonction de la grotte de Brialmont avec celle de Ste-Anne, sous-jacente, n'a pas encore été réalisée.

La grotte de Brialmont, qui est située vers le haut du versant de la vallée de l'Ourthe, représente donc apparemment les vestiges de deux galeries qui se sont formées bien antérieurement à celles de la grotte Ste-Anne en tant que conduits d'un affluent souterrain de l'Ourthe. La seule entrée naturelle de la grotte de Brialmont représente un ancien ponor (Figure 3). Les galeries ont été obstruées à leurs extrémités par d'abondants concrétionnements et on ne peut retrouver le prolongement des conduits: en particulier, les anciennes exsurgences ne sont pas connues.

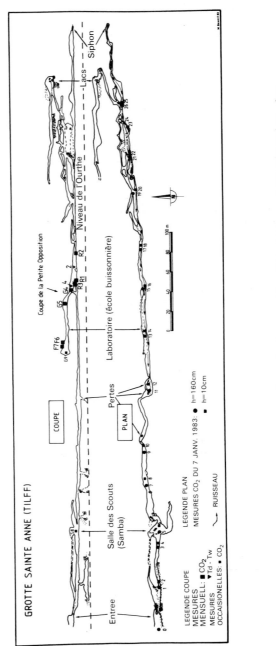

Figure 3.2 Coupe longitudinale et plan de la grotte Ste-Anne. Localisation des mesures CO_2 et Td – Tw. D'après un levé de l'Equipe Spéléo. Tilffoise (J. Silberstein et R. Warginaire, 1972); modifications partielles d'après C. Ek (1961)

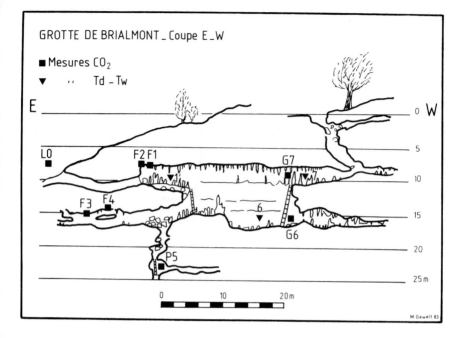

Figure 3.3   Coupe longitudinale de la grotte de Brialmont.
Localisation des mesures CO_2 et Td -Tw.   D'après
un levé de E. Naveau, S.S.D., 1971 (dans R.
Delbrouck, s.d.)

METHODES DE MESURES

Les mesures de la teneur en CO_2 de l'air ont toutes été effectuées au moyen d'un détecteur de gaz GASTEC constitué d'une
pompe manuelle à piston qui aspire 100 ± 5 ml d'air à travers un
tube de verre contenant un indicateur coloré.   La teneur en CO_2
est lue directement en ppm (par volume) sur le tube réactif :
elle correspond à la longueur de la zone ayant viré de couleur.
Les tubes réactifs 2 LL (*extra low range*) permettent de mesurer
des teneurs de 300 à 5000 ppm.   Pour les teneurs plus élevées,
de 2500 à 30 000 ppm, on utilise les tubes 2 L (*low range*).
Dans le modèle 2 LL, le CO_2 réagit avec l'hydrazine: $CO_2 + N_2H_4$
$\rightarrow N_2.NH.COOH$,   ce qui décolore l'indicateur rédox en violet.
Dans le modèle 2 L, le CO_2 neutralise de l'hydroxide de potassium: $CO_2 + KOH \rightarrow K_2CO_3 + H_2O$, réaction décolorant un indicateur
pH de l'orange au jaune.

La précision minimale garantie par le constructeur est de
± 25% mais l'étalonnage de l'appareil montre une meilleure précision effective et une reproductibilité des mesures à 10% près
(C. Ek *et al.*, 1981).

Par rapport au dosage du CO_2 effectué par électrolyse d'une
solution de NaCl ayant absorbé le CO_2 d'un échantillon d'air
(H. Koepf, 1952; F. Hilger, 1963; F. Delecour, 1965; C. Ek
et al., 1968 et F. Delecour *et al.*, 1968), la pompe Gastec offre
un avantage tant au niveau du poids de l'appareillage (moins de
0.5 kg contre plus de 10 kg) qu'au niveau de la rapidité de la
mesure (2 ou 3 minutes suivant le modèle de tube réactif utilisé,
contre plus de 20 minutes pour le dispositif par électrolyse).
Si la précision de l'ancien appareil de dosage du CO_2 est
meilleure - ± 0.1 mg CO_2/l soit environ ± 60 ppm (C. Ek, 1981)
- le détecteur à pompe nous paraît nettement mieux adapté à une
utilisation souterraine. Signalons d'ailleurs qu'en France
(P. Renault, 1982) et en Allemagne (F.D. Miotke, 1974), les
mesures de la teneur en CO_2 de l'air des grottes sont principalement effectuées avec des pompes à soufflet Dräger qui sont
basées sur le même principe de coloration de tubes indicateurs.

Des précautions particulières ont été prises pour mesurer
la teneur en CO_2 de l'air dans les fissures. Un système absor-
bant le CO_2 exhalé par l'opérateur a systématiquement été
utilisé (Figure 4). Le système se compose d'une enceinte en
plexiglas munie de deux soupapes de grand diamètre dont l'une
est reliée avec l'extérieur (pour l'inspiration), l'autre conduisant l'air expiré dans un réservoir en acier inoxydable
rempli de chaux sodée. Un embout buccal (type plongée) est
relié à l'enceinte en plexiglas tandis qu'un pince-nez oblige
l'opérateur à respirer par la bouche, à travers le système
absorbeur. L'embout buccal est nettement plus confortable que
le masque couvrant nez et bouche que nous utilisions auparavant.
L'utilité de l'absorbeur de CO_2 lors de mesures dans les endroits
confinés est certaine et sera mise en évidence plus loin. Dans
une même optique, les moyens d'éclairage par combustion sont
systématiquement écartés au profit de l'éclairage électrique.

Les mesures de température et d'humidité relative ont été
effectuées avec un psychromètre. Un abaque permet de déterminer
l'humidité relative (en %) en fonction des températures lues sur
le thermomètre sec (Td) et sur le thermomètre mouillé (Tw). La
précision de lecture sur les températures est de ± 0.1°C et
l'erreur sur l'humidité relative est de ± 2 à 3%.

Les treize séries de mesures mensuelles ont été effectuées
de janvier 1982 à janvier 1983. Les mesures ont toujours été
faites le matin dans la grotte de Brialmont et l'après-midi dans
la grotte Ste-Anne.

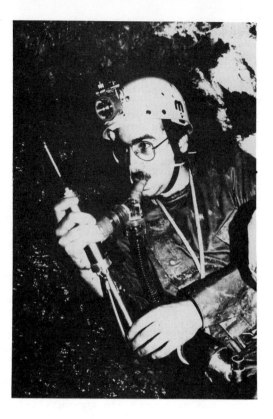

Figure 3.4   Mesure de la teneur de l'air en CO_2 en milieu
confiné: le CO_2 respiratoire est absorbé sur
de la chaux sodée contenue dans le réservoir
visible à l'avant-plan. L'opérateur manipule
la pompe à piston munie à son extrémité du tube
indicateur (détecteur) (Photo C. Ek).

RESULTATS

Les variations mensuelles de la teneur en CO_2 de l'air des
deux grottes

i) *La grotte Ste-Anne* Les résultats des mesures mensuelles sont
consignés dans le tableau 1. La localisation des points
(Figures 2 et 7) montre que les mesures ont été effectuées à
plus de 300 m de l'entrée de la grotte.

56

Tableau 3.1 Mesures mensuelles de la teneur en CO_2, de la température et de l'humidité relative de l'air de la grotte Ste-Anne (1982-1983)

n° pts	Date	29/01 1982	04/03 1982	26/03 1982	30/04 1982	28/05 1982	02/07 1982	22/07 1982	02/09 1982	30/09 1982	29/10 1982	26/11 1982	30/12 1982	28/0 198
0	(1)	-	-	-	400	-	-	-	-	-	-	-	-	-
	(2)	6,1	9,0	17,4	8,8	-	-	19,0	18,0	-	10,6	8,0	4,2	-
	(3)	90	59	45,5	93,5	-	-	58	71	-	79	73	69	-
R1	(1)	2800	3400	3600	3500	4400[+]	8000	5200[+]	6000	7000	4500	3500	3000	3200
R2	(1)	2900	3500	3800	3900	4900[+]	5000	5000[+]	6000	8000	4800	3700	3000	3600
	(2)	8,2	8,7	-	9,0	9,3	10,0	9,8	9,9	10,1	10,0	9,4	9,1	9,2
	(3)	100	100	-	-	100	99,5	98,5	100	99,5	100	100	100	100
R3	(1)	2900	3100	3500	3300	4200[+]	5500	5200[+]	6500	7000	4500	3400	3000	-
G4	(1)	2800	3400	3400	3800	4800[+] 4000	5200	5500[+]	6500	8000	4600	3500	2900	3200
	(2)	9,4	9,4	9,2	9,4	9,4	9,7	10,0	9,8	10,1	10,0	9,6	9,6	9,4
	(3)	100	99	99	-	99	99	100	99	98	100	100	99	100
G5	(1)	2900	3500	3200	3500	4200[+]	5000	5500[+]	6500	7500	4500	3800	2900	3000
F6	(1)	3200[+]	3900	3800 5000[+]	4000	5100[+]	5300	6000[+]	7000	9000	5200	4100	3000	3500
F7	(1)	3500[+]	1900	3800	4000	5000[+]	5500	6000[+]	6500	9000	4800	4100	3000	3300
S8	(1)								2400					
G9	(1)									9000				

Localisation des points : voir figures 2 et 7.

(1) = teneur de l'air en dioxyde de carbone (ppm CO_2 vol).
(2) = température de l'air (°C).
(3) = humidité relative (%)

[+] Contamination anthropique pouvant affecter les mesures: visiteurs vus dans la grotte.
[++] "   "   "   "   "   : masque absobeur CO_2 défectueux.
Contamination anthropique mesurée avant et après le passage de visiteurs
[+++] (ou après quelques expirations dans les fissures).
R = Rivière; G = Galerie; F = Fissure; S = Salle

Tableau 3.2 Mesures mensuelles de la teneur en CO_2, de
la température et de l'humidité relative
de l'air de la grotte de Brialmont (1982-83)

n° pts		21/01 1982	29/01 1982	04/03 1982	26/03 1982	30/04 1982	28/05 1982	25/06 1982	02/07 1982	22/07 1982	29/08 1982	30/09 1982	29/10 1982	26/11 1982	30/12 1982	28/01 1983
0	(1)	-	-	350	-	350	350	300	300	350	350	350	350	300	300	300
	(2)	-	5,0	7,2	9,2	6,0	13,4	18,2	21,3	13,6	15,0	13,4	8,4	5,8	-1,6	8,5
	(3)	-	97,5	76	68,5	95	78	72,5	65	91,5	78	100	98	88	-	83
1'	(2)	-	4,2	5,7	5,1	5,6	8,2	9,6	9,7	10,6	10,6	10,6	8,4	6,2	3,7	7,1
	(3)	-	97	97	100	94,5	97,5	97	99	97	99	100	95	95	91	96
F1	(1)	1450$^+$	1500^{++}	500	600	700	600	400	400	1000	400	500	400	350	300	400
F2	(1)	-	1100^{++}	400	700	1100	800	1200^{++}	1700	1000	450	500	400	400	400	300
F3	(1)	-	-	1000	500	800	800	-	2700	3000	2800	2000	400	350	400	400
F4	(1)	1000	1200^{++}	1200	600	900	1100	-	2900	3200	2600	2100	500	1500	600	500
	(1)	1900^{+++}														
P5	(1)	1000	500	400	500	500	500	2000$^+$	2000	2800	2400	7000	9000	600	400	550
G6	(1)	450	500	400	500	450	600	1900$^+$	2000	2900	1900	2000	350	500	300	300
	(2)	-	4,4	4,9	4,8	5,8	6,7	7,2	7,5	7,6	7,9	8,2	8,0	7,4	3,6	6,0
	(3)	-	96,5	100	98,5	97,5	100	97,5	99	98	100	100	100	93	94	100
G7	(1)	500	550	600	600	500	600	500	500	1000	400	500	350	300	300	300
	(2)	-	5,4	6,3	6,1	6,2	8,3	9,7	10,4	10,1	10,4	10,6	9,1	7,4	5,0	6,8
	(3)	-	97	94	92,5	100	99	99	96,5	99,5	100	100	96	95	91	99
G8	(1)											2000				

Localisation des points : voir figure 3.

(1) = teneur de l'air en dioxyde de carbone (ppm CO_2 vol).
(2) = température de l'air ($^\circ$C).
(3) = humidité relative (%).
$^+$ Contamination anthropique pouvant affecter les mesures : visiteurs vus dans la grotte.
$^{++}$ "   "   "   "   "   : masque absorbeur CO_2 défectueux.
$^{+++}$ Contamination anthropique mesurée avant et après le passage de visiteurs
(ou après quelques expirations dans les fissures).

F = Fissure; P = Puit; G = Galerie

Trois secteurs ont été distingués dans l'identification des points de mesures :

La rivière souterraine: R1 = mesure à 15 cm au-dessus du niveau de l'eau; R2 = même type de localisation mais 30 m en amont; R3 = mesure à 10 cm de la voûte surplombant la rivière, 3 m en aval de R1.

la galerie : G4 et G5.

les fissures : F6 et F7.

En outre, deux mesures ponctuelles ont été effectuées à la salle Samba (S 8) et à l'extrémité du Laboratoire (G9).

Au niveau de la rivière, les teneurs extrêmes varient de 2800 ppm en janvier 82 à 8000 ppm en septembre. Dans la galerie, les valeurs minimales et maximales sont identiques, alors que dans les fissures nous avons mesuré de 1900 ppm début mars à 9000 ppm fin septembre.

ii) *La grotte de Brialmont* Le tableau 2 reprend les mesures mensuelles effectuées dans cette petite grotte munie de deux entrées.

Les teneurs en CO_2 de l'air du bois de feuillus dans lequel se trouvent les entrées de la grotte sont toujours comprises entre 300 et 350 ppm (point L0). On retrouve donc bien ici la teneur en CO_2 habituelle de l'atmosphère. Au sein de la grotte, trois secteurs de mesures ont également été distingués :

les fissures : F1, F2, F3, F4.

le puits : P5.

la galerie inférieure (G6) et la galerie supérieure (G7).

Les teneurs extrêmes mesurées dans les fissures sont 300 et 3200 ppm; dans le puits, elles sont 400 et 9000 ppm. Dans les galeries, les valeurs varient entre 300 et 2900 ppm.

iii) *Les variations mensuelles dans les galeries* Comme le montre très bien la Figure 5, les deux grottes sont nettement différenciées sur le plan des teneurs en CO_2. Les teneurs en CO_2 mesurées à Brialmont sont toujours inférieures à celles trouvées à Ste-Anne. Dans cette dernière, l'évolution mensuelle montre un minimum en hiver, plus particulièrement en décembre et janvier. Les teneurs de l'air en CO_2 dans les galeries et au-dessus de la rivière évoluent parallèlement et elles restent toujours proches les unes des autres. La seule exception est la mesure R1 du 2 juillet (8000 ppm) qui ne cadre pas avec les mesures faites en amont (R2 : 5000 ppm) et au même endroit à 140 cm au-dessus de l'eau (R3 : 5500 ppm) et qui doit donc être considérée avec circonspection, d'autant plus qu'une contamination anthropique semble peu plausible, la mesure R1 ayant été effectuée en premier lieu.

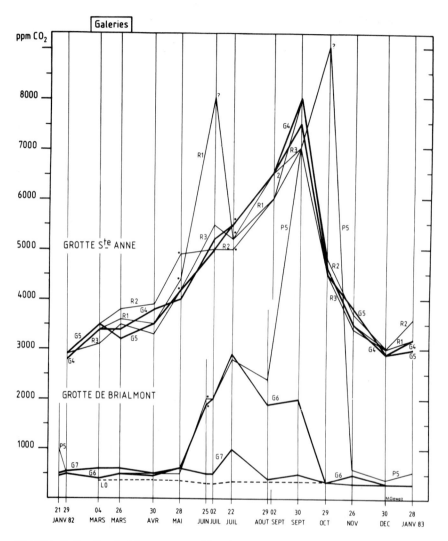

Figure 3.5   Evolution mensuelle de la teneur en CO_2 des
             galeries dans les grottes Ste-Anne et Brialmont

Le maximum dans les galeries et au-dessus de la rivière à la grotte Ste-Anne s'observe fin septembre, alors qu'à Brialmont il apparaît dans les galeries le 22 juillet, soit deux mois auparavant. Dans cette grotte, contrairement à Ste-Anne, il n'existe pas de minimum défini en hiver, la teneur étant toujours faible, sauf durant la période comprise entre juin et fin septembre.

60

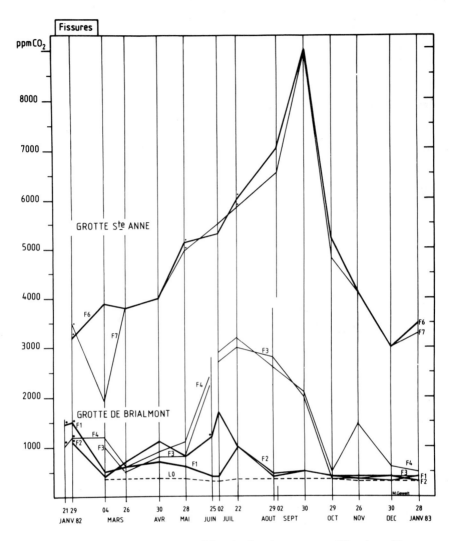

Figure 3.6   Evolution mensuelle de la teneur en CO_2 des fissures dans les grottes Ste-Anne et Brialmont

iv) *Les variations mensuelles dans les fissures*   Ici aussi, les deux grottes restent très bien différenciées (Figure 6). Les fissures de la grotte Ste-Anne contiennent toujours plus de CO_2 que celles de la grotte de Brialmont. Mais, dans les deux grottes, les fissures présentent les mêmes variations annuelles que les galeries.

A Ste-Anne, le maximum ($\simeq$ 9000 ppm) est enregistré le 30 septembre et le minimum s'observe en décembre-janvier. Les deux fissures sont voisines et leurs teneurs sont presque toujours identiques (Figure 7).

Dans les fissures de la grotte de Brialmont, les teneurs sont plus irrégulières et un premier maximum apparaît d'abord dans les fissures (F1 - F2) proches du sol, fin juin - début juillet. Le second maximum est décalé vers juillet-août. Ici aussi, on s'aperçoit que la grotte de Brialmont enregistre un maximum de teneur en CO_2 avant la grotte Ste-Anne située environ 70 m plus bas. Il semble donc qu'un flux de CO_2 provenant du sol superficiel se propage vers la profondeur.

Evolution longitudinale de la teneur de l'air en CO_2 dans la grotte Ste-Anne

Une série de 27 mesures échelonnées par paires tout au long de la grotte Ste-Anne a été effectuée le 7 janvier 1983. Au sein de chaque paire de mesure, la première est toujours effectuée au niveau du sol (h = 10 cm) et la deuxième mesure, distante de 5 à 6 m de la première, est faite à hauteur d'homme (h = 160 cm), sauf lorsque la hauteur de la galerie ne le permet pas. La hauteur totale des salles ou des galeries à l'endroit de la mesure à également été évaluée. Les résultats, consignés dans le tableau 3, montrent une évolution vers des teneurs en CO_2 croissantes en s'enfonçant plus profondément dans la grotte. Les teneurs en CO_2 passent de 300 à 3200 ppm entre l'entrée et le point de mesure le plus éloigné de celle-ci, à 520 mètres à l'intérieur de la cavité. La localisation des mesures (Plan de la Figure 1) montre que les 10 premières mesures sont effectuées dans la partie sèche de la grotte, tandis que les points 11 à 26 sont situés dans la partie de la grotte où coule le ruisseau souterrain.

DISCUSSION

L'évolution saisonnière

L'examen des résultats mensuels fait clairement apparaître un décalage dans le temps des maxima de la teneur en CO_2. Ces décalages sont en relation directe avec la distance entre le sol et le point de mesure dans la grotte. Si on se rappelle que les deux grottes sont étagées (Figure 5 et 6), on a la situation suivante:

> Maximum en juin-juillet pour les fissures proches de la surface à Brialmont (F1 et F2).
>
> Maximum en juillet-août dans les fissures de l'étage inférieur de la grotte de Brialmont (F3 et F4).
>
> Maximum fin septembre dans les fissures de la grotte Ste-Anne, près de 70 m plus bas dans le massif calcaire.

Tableau 3.3 Variation de la teneur en CO_2 de l'air
de la grotte Ste-Anne en fonction de la distance
par rapport à l'entrée, le 07/01/1983

N° des points	X (m)	Y (ppm CO_2)	h (cm)	H (cm)
0	0	300	160	∞
1	29	1000	160	170
2	34	700	10	170
3	63	800	160	260
4	69	800	10	250
5	84	800	160	400
6	90	800	10	400
7	120	900	160	300
8	125	900	10	30
9	165	1300	160	180
10	173	1500	10	180
11	227	2300	160	180
12	235	2300	10	180
13	289	2300	100	110
14	295	2500	10	80
15	334	2400	100	110
16	340	2700	10	800
17	373	2800	160	400
18	379	2900	10	70
19	432	3100	160	400
20	437	2800	10	400
21	475	2900	70	80
22	482	2900	10	200
23	504	2800	160	1200
24	510	3000	10	1200
25	522	3000	80	1200
26	520	3200	10	1200

X = distance par rapport à l'entrée de la grotte (en mètres).
Y = teneur de l'air en CO_2 (ppm CO_2 vol).
h = hauteur au-dessus du plancher à laquelle est effectuée la mesure.
H = hauteur totale de la salle ou de la galerie à l'endroit de la mesure.

Le même décalage des pics de la teneur en CO_2 se manifeste aussi dans les mesures effectuées dans les galeries:

Maximum en juillet à Brialmont (G6 - G7).

Maximum en septembre dans les galeries et au-dessus du ruisseau souterrain de la grotte Ste-Anne.

Ces décalages successifs dans l'apparition des teneurs maximales en CO_2 semblent suggérer l'existence d'un flux de CO_2 se déplaçant par diffusion et par gravité depuis le haut (c'est-à-dire la zone de production du CO_2 constituée par le sol) vers le bas. L'examen de la Figure 3 montre en coupe la localisation des points de mesure à Brialmont et permet de suivre verticalement le flux du haut (F1 - F2) vers le bas (F3 - F4); le raccord peut être effectué avec les fissures F6 et F7 de Ste-Anne situées beaucoup plus bas (Figure 7).

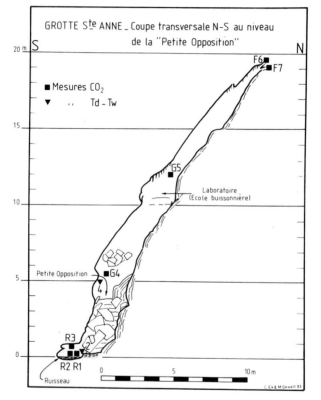

Figure 3.7 Coupe transversale dans la grotte Ste-Anne, au niveau de la 'Petite Opposition'. Localisation des mesures mensuelles (CO_2 et Td - Tw). Levé par C. Ek

La relation entre l'évolution des teneurs en CO_2 et la source de CO_2 (le sol) est nette au niveau des variations annuelles qui paraissent bien refléter le rythme saisonnier de la biomasse, avec son minimum d'activité en hiver. Le pic du maximum de l'activité des végétaux doit très probablement être situé vers la fin mai-début juin, alors que le premier maximum de la teneur en CO_2 est enregistré début juillet dans les fissures proches de la surface (Fl - F2). Le flux de CO_2 descend ensuite progressivement au sein du massif calcaire, ce qui explique les décalages des maxima mis en évidence plus haut. Des décalages semblables viennent d'être également trouvés par H. Haas *et al.*, (1983) dans des sols épais surmontant du lignite dans le Dakota du Nord. Des mesures effectuées à près de 3 mètres de profondeur ont montré des variations en corrélation avec les fluctuations annuelles de la croissance des plantes et un décalage de deux mois entre le pic de la croissance des végétaux en juin et le pic du CO_2 dans le sol à 2.7 m de profondeur en août.

Si les décalages que nous avons observés sont du même ordre de grandeur, mais à plus forte profondeur, il faut probablement en chercher la cause dans une épaisseur de sol moindre et une fissuration du massif importante qui favorise la diffusion et la propagation du CO_2 par gravité.

Relation entre la teneur en CO_2, la température et l'humidité

La Figure 8 montre l'évolution saisonnière de deux paramètres climatiques importants : la température et l'humidité relative.

Dans la grotte Ste-Anne, l'humidité relative varie très peu et elle est toujours comprise entre 98 et 100%, cette dernière valeur étant la plus fréquente. Cette situation assez banale en grotte s'explique par le confinement de la zone de la grotte étudiée et par la présence du ruisseau souterrain (Figure 7). Les eaux de percolation contribuent aussi à la saturation de l'atmosphère.

Dans la grotte de Brialmont, l'humidité relative est toujours assez élevée, mais elle varie plus (91 à 100%) en raison de la ventilation de la grotte provoquée par les deux entrées. En général, en hiver l'air de la partie inférieure (6) de la grotte est plus humide que celui de la partie supérieure (7). Au printemps et en été la situation inverse est observée sans que les différences soient très fortes (quelques % d'humidité relative).

La température dans la grotte Ste-Anne (points 2 et 4, Figure 8) est presque constante durant toute l'année. Elle est en moyenne de 9.6 ± 0.3°C au point 4 ('petite opposition'), alors qu'au niveau de la rivière elle est en moyenne légèrement inférieure et varie un peu plus : 9.4 ± 0.6°C.

Dans la grotte de Brialmont, les températures de l'étage supérieur (1 et 7, Figure 8) sont plus élevées que celles de

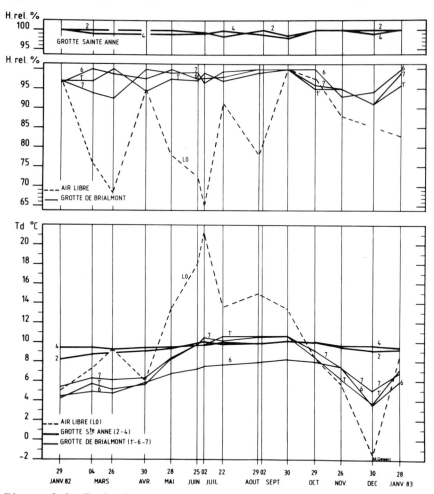

Figure 3.8   Evolution mensuelle de la température (Td) et de
l'humidité relative (H. rel.) de l'air dans les
grottes Ste-Anne et Brialmont

l'étage inférieur. En particulier, le point 7, situé presque
sur une même verticale quelques mètres au-dessus du point 6
(Figure 3), a durant toute l'année une température plus élevée.
Il existe donc une inversion de température permanente, le
point 6 (galerie inférieure) ayant toujours une température plus
basse par accumulation de l'air froid plus dense. Cette situation d'inversion thermique est plus marquée en été (plus de
2.5°C de différence) qu'en hiver. Cette situation micro-
climatique influence bien évidemment les teneurs en CO_2. Ainsi,

66

le point G6 dans la galerie inférieure a toujours montré une teneur en CO_2 supérieure à son homologue G7 dans la galerie supérieure. Cette situation est particulièrement nette durant la période des maxima estivaux de teneur en CO_2 où la stratification du CO_2 par gravité est encore accentuée par la stratification thermique. L'inversion de température bloque en quelque sorte le CO_2 et l'air plus froid dans l'étage inférieur. Le comportement thermique de la grotte influence donc la répartition du CO_2 de l'air. La mesure au milieu de la grande échelle, effectuée le 30 septembre (G8, tableau 2) permet de préciser l'importance de la stratification. Cette mesure a donné 2000 ppm CO_2, comme celle effectuée plus bas en G6. Au point situé dans la galerie supérieure (G7), nous avons mesuré 500 ppm. Ceci tend à démontrer que la couche d'air riche en CO_2 n'est pas uniquement localisée au ras du sol, mais qu'elle est présente sur près de la moitié de la hauteur de la grotte; les deux galeries sont en effet en communication, le plancher qui les séparait à l'origine étant partiellement effondré (voir figure 3).

L'évolution longitudinale

Les données du tableau 3 concernant l'évolution longitudinale de la teneur en CO_2 dans la grotte Ste-Anne (mesures du 07/01/83) ont été reportées sur la Figure 9. L'augmentation des teneurs en CO_2 en fonction de la distance par rapport à l'entrée de la grotte est clairement mise en évidence sur cette figure. La droite de régression n°3 calculée sur l'ensemble des mesures ($y = 5.27 x + 563.27$) et le très bon coefficient de corrélation ($R = 0.96$) montrent bien l'existence d'une corrélation linéaire positive entre la teneur en CO_2 et la distance depuis l'entrée de la grotte. Dans un premier temps, on peut attribuer cette corrélation à l'augmentation du confinement et donc à la diminution de la ventilation vers la partie distale de la grotte. Cependant, l'examen de la Figure 9 permet de distinguer deux groupes de mesures séparés par un seuil d'environ 800 ppm. La première série de mesures (0 - 10) est proche de l'entrée et correspond à la partie sèche de la grotte; cette zone d'entrée s'étend sur environ les 160 premiers mètres de la grotte. Le gradient est d'abord assez faible (de 300 à 900 ppm) puis il augmente (les teneurs atteignent 1300 à 1500 ppm aux points 9 et 10 à 160 m de l'entrée). La droite de régression n°1 calculée avec les valeurs de ce premier groupe de mesures est $y = 4.69 x + 484.70$ ($r = 0.83$). Le second groupe de mesures (11 a 26) est séparé du premier par un seuil d'environ 800 ppm. La régression linéaire effectuée sur les mesures du second groupe fournit une droite d'équation $y = 2.58 x + 1717.65$ et un coefficient de corrélation $r = 0.89$. Le seuil observé coïncide avec la disparition du ruisseau souterrain dans l'étage inférieur (voir plan de la grotte Ste-Anne, Figure 2). Dès le point de mesure 11, on remonte le cours du ruisseau, la mesure étant toujours effectuée dans le réseau actif (point 11 à 26). Nous pensons pouvoir expliquer les teneurs en CO_2 plus fortes et surtout le décalage entre réseau sec et réseau actif par le dégagement de CO_2 dans l'eau. Celui-ci est maximum à l'amont (point 26 : 3200 ppm)

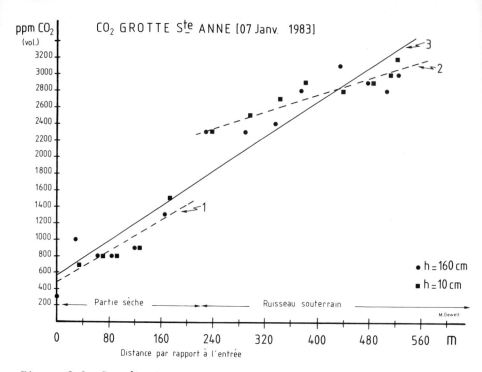

CO₂ GROTTE Ste ANNE [07 Janv. 1983]

Figure 3.9   Corrélation entre la teneur en CO_2 et la distance
par rapport à l'entrée de la grotte Ste-Anne.
Droite de régression et coefficients de corrélation.
1 : y = 4.7 x + 484.70; r = 0.83. 2 : y = 2.6 x +
1719.65; r = 0.89.   3 : y = 5.3 x + 563.27;
r = 0.96. h = hauteur des prélèvements d'air par
rapport au sol

puis il se ralentit progressivement le long du parcours du
ruisseau, en fonction de la loi de Nernst sur les vitesses de
réactions.   Ceci avait déjà été observé par C. Ek *et al.*, (1968)
sur 5 mesures effectuées au-dessus de la rivière souterraine de
la grotte de Remouchamps.   Le ruisseau souterrain joue donc un
rôle de fournisseur de CO_2 à l'atmosphère de la grotte, complémentairement au CO_2 fournit par les fissures.   Ce dernier provient d'une part de l'activité biologique dans le sol (avec le
rythme saisonnier mis en évidence plus haut) et également de la
transformation bactérienne et microbienne (oxydation) de la
matière organique présente dans les fissures et les joints du
sous-sol.   Cette distinction entre air du sol (soil air) et air
du sous-sol (ground air) en tant que sources distinctes de CO_2
a été discutée par T.C. Atkinson (1977) et étudiée dans le karst
des Mendip Hills.

La série de mesures du 7 janvier 83 a été effectuée près du sol et à hauteur d'homme afin de rechercher la présence éventuelle d'une stratification de l'air. Dans environ la moitié des cas, les teneurs en CO_2 étaient égales à 10 cm du sol et à 160 cm. L'autre moitié des mesures montre des teneurs en CO_2 légèrement plus fortes près du sol et surtout près de la rivière (voir Figure 9). Dans ce dernier cas, la cause est probablement la proximité de la source de CO_2 (l'eau) plutôt qu'une stratification de l'air comme celle précédemment décrite à Brialmont. L'air est en effet brassé par le courant d'eau qui circule en général à une vitesse de plusieurs dm par seconde et comporte en certains endroits des petits rapides.

Les contaminations anthropiques

Les tableaux 1 et 2 indiquent par un ou plusieurs astérisques les mesures pouvant être trop élevées par suite d'une contamination par du CO_2 d'origine anthropique:

+   des visiteurs ont été rencontrés dans la grotte le jour de la mesure;

++   le masque absorbeur est tombé en panne. Cet incident ne s'est produit que lorsqu'on utilisait des soupapes de petit diamètre;

+++   des contaminations anthropiques ont été mesurées : deux mesures ont pu être effectuées soit avant et après le passage de visiteurs, soit à titre expérimental, en respirant à proximité des fissures, après avoir fait une première mesure avec le masque absorbeur (voir Figure 4).

Il faut également souligner que dans les Figures 5 et 6, ces différentes sources d'erreur n'ont été reprises qu'avec un seul astérisque.

Pour tenter d'apprécier l'influence des visiteurs sur les teneurs en CO_2 mesurées et également pour vérifier l'utilité du dispositif absorbeur de CO_2, un certain nombre de vérifications ont été effectuées. Ceci paraissait indispensable, notamment lorsque l'on sait que la concentration en CO_2 de l'air expiré par les êtres humains est d'environ 40 000 ppm (F.D. Miotke, 1974).

Dans la grotte Ste-Anne (le 26/03/82), la fissure F6 mesurée avec le masque absorbeur avait une teneur de 3800 ppm. La même fissure après 5 minutes de respiration à environ 1 mètre du site de mesure avait une teneur de 5000 ppm, soit 1.3 fois plus.

Dans la grotte de Brialmont (le 21/01/82), mesure rapide de la fissure, sans masque, en évitant de respirer : 1000 ppm. La même mesure répétée après 6 expirations : 1900 ppm, soit une augmentation de 1.9 fois.

Au Trou Joney, à Comblain-au-Pont, cinq mesures ont été effectuées avec, puis sans masque absorbeur de CO_2. Les trois premièrs couples de mesures, faits dans un couloir d'environ 1 m^2 de section, ont montré que sans absorbeur la teneur de l'air en CO_2 était presque doublée, passant de 1.18, 1.66 et 1.72 mg CO_2/l respectivement à 2.34, 3.12 et 2.88 mg/l; l'augmentation moyenne de la teneur est donc de 1.8 fois. A l'extrémité distale de la grotte, dans la salle terminale, les teneurs sont passées de 2.03 et 2.32 mg/l à 5.96 et 6.46 mg/l lorsque l'opérateur a travaillé sans masque. Ceci représente une augmentation moyenne de la teneur de 2.9 fois:près du triple (mesures du 12/07/1969, C. Ek, inédit).

A la Grotte de Rochefort, au milieu de la vaste salle du Val d'Enfer, la teneur de l'air en CO_2, initialement de 2.30 mg/l ($\simeq$ 1260 ppm) est passée, après cinq heures de présence de trois opérateurs à 3.31 mg/l ($\simeq$ 1800 ppm), ce qui représente 1.4 fois la teneur initiale (mesures du 13/09/1969, C. Ek, inédit).

A la grotte Ste-Anne, le 28/05/82, on mesure dans la galerie (G4) 4000 ppm. Après le passage de 18 personnes (avec deux lampes à carbure), 20 minutes après, la teneur de l'air en CO_2 est passée à 4800 ppm, soit une augmentation de 1.2 fois.

A la grotte (touristique) de Remouchamps, B. Mérenne-Schoumaker (1975) a observé, en compagnie de C. Ek, que le passage d'un groupe d'une vingtaine de touristes provoque en moyenne, dans les couloirs étroits, une augmentation instantanée de l'ordre de 0.25 mg CO_2/l ($\simeq$ 140 ppm), ce qui représente une hausse directe de 6% de la teneur en CO_2 initiale. La variation quotidienne due au passage des touristes en saison est beaucoup plus importante, de l'ordre de 1.5 mg/l ($\simeq$ 820 ppm), soit une augmentation de près de 30%.

On a donc montré ici que l'influence du CO_2 d'origine anthropique est non négligeable dans les mesures de la teneur de l'air en CO_2. L'augmentation de la teneur initiale varie en général de 20 à 90% mais peut parfois atteindre près du triple de la teneur en CO_2 initiale dans les endroits très confinés. Les facteurs qui entrent en ligne de compte sont nombreux et on peut par exemple citer : la configuration de la grotte (confinement et ventilation); le nombre de personnes présentes; la fréquence des visites et leur durée.

Les exemples de contamination anthropique mesurée présentés ci-dessus nous conduisent à affirmer la nécessité d'effectuer les mesures de teneur en CO_2 de l'air avec un dispositif absorbeur de CO_2, en tous les cas dans les endroits très confinés et dans les fissures. Si cette précaution n'est pas prise, les résultats obtenus fournissent des valeurs beaucoup trop élevées (20 à 90% d'augmentation et davantage).

D'autre part, la présence d'un groupe de visiteurs influence également les teneurs, principalement dans les galeries peu spacieuses. Ce type de contamination pouvant difficilement être évité, il conviendrait probablement de retrancher aux mesures effectuées en période de forte fréquentation spéléologique une sorte de bruit de fond. Celui-ci est assez difficile à évaluer, d'autant plus que la teneur en CO_2 de l'air, augmentée par le CO_2 anthropique, ne redescend pas rapidement à sa valeur antérieure (C. Ek *et al.*, 1981).

Les pics significatifs devraient sans doute être moins élevés si aucune contamination ne se produisait. C'est principalement durant la période estivale que nous avons rencontré le plus de visiteurs. Le pic du CO_2 anthropique s'ajoute donc au pic du CO_2 lié au rythme de la végétation (avec les retards que nous avons décrits). Pour nous affranchir de cette composante humaine dans nos mesures, nous prévoyons d'installer un compteur de personnes électronique à l'entrée des grottes étudiées.

Remarquons enfin que les fortes teneurs observées en été dans les galeries de la grotte Ste-Anne dépassent les normes admises par l'American Conference of Governmental Industrial Hygienists (A.C.G.I.H., 1981, cité par la firme Gastec). Ces normes, utiles pour le spéléologue, sont les suivantes:

Valeur limite moyenne en fonction de la durée;
5000 ppm CO_2 pendant 7-8 heures.

Valeur limite en cas de courte exposition;
15 000 ppm pendant 15 minutes.

Il importe de rappeler que le CO_2 n'est pas un gaz toxique, c'est plutôt la déficience en oxygène qui peut être nocive. Les fortes teneurs mesurées à Ste-Anne ne sont pas dangereuses pour autant que la durée d'exposition n'excède pas quelques heures.

Comparaison avec d'autres grottes belges

Diverses grottes belges ont déjà été l'objet d'analyses du CO_2 atmosphérique; la Grotte de Comblain-au-Pont, celle de Rochefort, celle de Floreffe (C. Ek *et al.*, 1968), celle de Remouchamps (F. Delecour *et al.*, 1968; B. Mérenne-Schoumaker, 1975), la Grotte Lyell (à Engis), la Grotte du Père Noël (à Wavreille), la Grotte de Hohière, la Grotte Ste-Anne (à Tilff) et celle de Han (F. Delhez, 1972), et le Trou Joney à Comblain-au-Pont (C. Ek, 1979). Environ 350 mesures sont citées dans les cinq publications reprises ci-dessus, sans compter des mesures encore inédites faites par l'un de nous (C. Ek) au Trou Joney, à la Grotte de Rochefort et à la Grotte Lyell.

Les valeurs absolues sont, dans toutes les grottes belges déjà étudiées, systématiquement supérieures à celle de l'atmosphère libre, mais jamais supérieures aux valeurs maximales de 9000 ppm observées à Ste-Anne.

Les variations saisonnières avaient déjà été mises en évidence au Trou Joney (C. Ek, 1979), mais avec beaucoup moins de finesse quant à l'évolution des teneurs. A la Grotte de Remouchamps, une différence avait aussi été notée entre l'été et l'hiver (B. Mérenne-Schoumaker, 1975, Figure 5), mais sans qu'il fût possible, dans cette cavité touristique, de distinguer l'influence des visiteurs du rythme saisonnier naturel.

Les variations spatiales peuvent être envisagées à deux points de vue principaux, suivant que l'on considère les variations dans une direction verticale ou le long d'un parcours horizontal.

Les variations verticales, liées à la profondeur ou à la distance au sol végétal, avaient été mises en évidence à la Grotte de Rochefort et à l'Abîme de Comblain-au-Pont (C. Ek *et al.*, 1968; F. Delecour *et al.*, 1968). L'existence d'un gradient conforme à la densité, mais aussi au confinement, avait été mise en évidence à Comblain. La fourniture de CO_2 par les fissures et sa descente progressive dans la grotte par diffusion avait été établie à Rochefort et à Floreffe (C. Ek *et al.*, 1968). Ceci a été confirmé en 1969 par des mesures (inédites) de C. Ek à Rochefort, puis par F. Delhez (1972), dans diverses cavités belges; celui-ci a montré aussi la teneur parfois forte au ras du sol dans des fissures de dessication de l'argile où certaines araignées tissent leur toile.

Enfin, les variations le long d'un parcours subhorizontal ont été mises en évidence dans plusieurs grottes également. A Remouchamps (C. Ek *et al.*, 1968), elles ont été attribuées au fait qu'un cours d'eau souterrain riche en CO_2 dissous diffusait ce CO_2 dans l'air de la grotte (cinq mesures prises à 20 cm au-dessus de l'eau et réparties sur un parcours souterrain de plus de 600 m). B. Mérenne-Schoumaker (1975) a observé un semblable gradient, dans la même grotte, le long des galeries (sèches) de l'étage supérieur. Elle n'en donne pas d'interprétation mais dans l'ensemble le phénomène semble lié au plus grand confinement des parties distales de la grotte, où le CO_2 fourni par les fissures d'une part et par le cours d'eau souterrain d'autre part s'évacue moins facilement.

Comparaison avec des grottes d'autres pays

Aux 42 mesures inédites et aux quelque 350 mesures déjà publiées pour la Belgique, le présent travail en ajoute 237. Les 629 mesures ainsi effectuées vont de 300 à 7000 ppm de CO_2 dans les salles et galeries et atteignent 9000 dans certaines fissures. En Angleterre, T.C. Atkinson (1977) note des valeurs comparables; sur 33 mesures à G.B. Cave, la moyenne s'établit à 4100 ppm dans les galeries, et dans les fissures à 8200 ppm, avec des maxima de 16 000 dans les fissures.

Des chiffres beaucoup plus faibles ont été trouvés dans des régions froides (en Pologne, au Canada et en Suède) mais aussi dans certaines grottes de pays tempérés (France, Kentucky, Italie).

Dans les Carpathes polonaises, on a trouvé à la fonte des neiges dans quatre grottes des valeurs allant de 200 à 1100 ppm, et un maximum de 2000 ppm dans une fissure (40 mesures, C. Ek *et al.*, 1969).

Au Québec, les salles et galeries donnent des valeurs allant de 400 à 1100 ppm. Les fissures atteignent une teneur de 2800 ppm en été (200 mesures); C. Ek, 1981; C. Ek *et al.*, 1981).

En Laponie suédoise, les valeurs mesurées en juillet 1982 vont de 200 à 850 ppm, cette dernière dans une fissure (36 mesures, C. Ek, inédit).

Dans les Pyrénées françaises, la grotte de Moulis présente des valeurs allant de 200 à 4400 ppm (P. Renault, 1982).

Au Kentucky, les teneurs observées dans les salles et galeries vont de 400 à 800 ppm en été, de 400 à 600 en hiver. Les fissures peuvent atteindre 1300 ppm (F.-D. Miotke, 1974).

En Italie du Nord, une grotte des Alpes ligures montre en septembre des teneurs de 400 à 800 ppm. Un maximum de 1500 est observé dans une fissure (24 mesures, M. Gewelt et C. Ek, 1983).

Quelques auteurs, par contre, rapportent des teneurs beaucoup plus élevées qu'en Belgique. Des pressions partielles de CO_2 importantes ont été relevées dans certaines grottes de France, d'Iowa et d'Ukraine.

En France, des mesures allant de 200 à 66 000 ppm, et fréquemment supérieures à 5000 ppm, sont citées par P. Renault (1982).

En Iowa, le dioxyde de carbone d'une grotte située sous des cultures a une concentration de 5000 à 25 000 ppm. Ces fortes teneurs sont attribuées à l'abondance de matières organiques dans la grotte même (W.C. Lewis, 1981).

En Ukraine, des valeurs de 500 à 40 000 ppm sont notées dans une grotte, et sont également mises en relation avec de la matière organique et la production et l'oxydation de méthane (A.B. Klimchuck *et al.*, 1981).

CONCLUSIONS

Les mesures de la teneur en CO_2 de l'air dans les grottes Ste-Anne et Brialmont ont révélé des teneurs comprises entre 300 et 7000 ppm dans les galeries, mais pouvant atteindre 9000 ppm dans les fissures. L'évolution saisonnière de ces teneurs montre que le CO_2 diffuse progressivement du sol vers la profondeur du massif. La teneur observée à quelques mètres sous le sol passe par un maximum en mai-juin, maximum qui se propage en plusieurs mois vers le bas des cavités karstiques.

Des mesures faites tout au long de la grotte Ste-Anne ont montré une très bonne corrélation linéaire positive entre la teneur de l'air en CO_2 et la distance à l'entrée. De plus, ces données ont confirmé le rôle joué par l'eau du ruisseau souterrain comme fournisseur de dioxyde de carbone à l'atmosphère de la grotte, complémentairement au CO_2 du sol.

Des contaminations par du gaz carbonique anthropique ont été mises en évidence, et nous avons montré la nécessité, en particulier dans les endroits confinés, de prendre des précautions spéciales pour éviter que la seule présence de l'observateur fausse la mesure. L'usage d'un absorbeur de CO_2 pour éliminer le dioxyde de carbone expiré s'est révélé indispensable, par exemple, dans les mesures faites dans les fissures.

Les autres grottes de Belgique auxquelles nous avons pu comparer les grottes étudiées montrent les mêmes phénomènes, mais qui n'avaient jamais encore été mis en évidence avec autant de certitude. Dans d'autres pays, les teneurs observées sont fréquemment plus basses, en particulier dans les régions froides. Dans diverses grottes françaises et dans certaines cavités de l'Iowa et d'Ukraine, les teneurs sont au contraire parfois nettement plus élevées. Dans les deux dernières régions citées, les teneurs très fortes sont attribuées à des activités organiques particulièrement intenses.

Remerciements

Nous remercions le F.N.R.S. dont des crédits de recherche accordés au Professeur A. Pissart et à C. Ek ont contribué a financer nos campagnes d'analyses.

Nous exprimons aussi notre gratitude au Professeur A. Pissart dont les avis ont toujours constitué un encouragement dans notre travail.

Les prélèvements ont été effectués avec le concours de Mme N. Lousberg, technicienne-chimiste à notre Laboratoire. Les mesures ici présentées doivent beaucoup à son zèle et à son endurance.

REFERENCES

Atkinson, T.C. 1975. Carbon dioxide in the atmosphere of the unsaturated zone : an important control of groundwater hardness in limestones. *12th I.A.H. Congress,* Alabama, Abstract, 498.

Atkinson, T.C. 1977. Carbon dioxide in the atmosphere of the unsaturated zone: an important control of groundwater hardness in limestones. *J. of Hydrology,* **35**, 111-123.

Delbrouck, R. *Atlas des grottes de Belgique.* tome **4**, (Setek, Namur.)

Delecour, F. 1965. Détermination des activités biologiques par la méthode de Koepf. Standardisation et essai de la technique du dosage du CO_2. *Note de recherche n°2, Centre d'Ecopédologie forestière,* Gembloux.

Delecour, F., Ek, C. et Weissen, F. 1968. An electrolytic field device for the titration of CO_2 in air. *Nat. Speleol. Soc. Bull.,* **30**, 131-136.

Delhez, F. 1972. La teneur en CO_2 dans les biotopes des divers arthropodes troglobies terrestres de la faune belge. *L'Electron,* 1, 39-49.

Ek, C. 1961. Conduits souterrains en relation avec les terrasses fluviales. *Ann. Soc. Géol. Belg.,* **84**, 313-340.

Ek, C. 1962. La genèse d'une cavité polycyclique. La grotte Ste-Anne à Tilff. *Rassegna Speleologica Italiana,* **14**, 1-11.

Ek, C., Delecour, F. et Weissen, F. 1968. Teneur en CO_2 de l'air de quelques grottes belges. *Ann. Spéléol.,* **23**, 243-257.

Ek, C., Gilewska, S., Kaszowski, L., Kobylecki, A., Oleksynowa, K. et Oleksynówna, B. 1969. Some analyses of the CO_2 content of the air in five Polish caves. *Zeit. für Geomorph.,* **13**, 267-286.

Ek, C. 1979. Variations saisonnières des teneurs en CO_2 d'une grotte belge: le Trou Joney à Comblain-au-Pont. *Ann. Soc. Géol. Belg.,* **102**, 71-75.

Ek, C. 1981. Mesures de CO_2 dans l'air des grottes: comparaison Québec-Belgique. *Eighth Internat. Congress of Speleology,* U.S.A., **2**, 672-673.

Ek, C., Caron, D. et Roberge, J. 1981. La forte teneur en gaz carbonique de l'air d'une cavité du Québec: la grotte de Saint-Léonard, île de Montréal. *Naturaliste can.,* **108**, 57-63.

Forel, M. 1865. Visite à la Grotte des Fées. *Bull. Soc. vaudoise Sc. nat.* Lausanne, **8**, 247.

Gewelt, M. et Ek, C. 1983. Le CO_2 de l'air d'une grotte des Alpes ligures: la Caverna delle Fate. Premières mesures. *Bull. Soc. Géogr. Liège,* 19, 107–117.

Haas, H., Fisher, D.W., Thorstenson, D.C. et Weeks, E.P. 1983. $^{13}CO_2$ and $^{14}CO_2$ measurements on soil atmosphere. *Radiocarbon,* 25(2), 301–314.

Hilger, F. 1963. Activité respiratoire des sols équatoriaux. Application de la méthode respirométrique *in situ. Bull. Inst. Agron. Stat. Rech.,* Gembloux, 31, 154–182.

James, J.M. 1977. Carbon dioxide in cave atmosphere. *Trans. Brit. Cave Res. Assoc.,* 4, 417–429.

Klimchuck, A.B., Yablokovna, N.L. et Olshtynsky, S.P. 1981. The regularities in the formation of gas composition of air in the large karst caves of Podolia and Bukovina. *Eighth Internat. Congress of Speleology,* U.S.A., 1, 21–23.

Koepf, H. 1952. Laufende Messung der Bodenatmung im Freiland. *Land. Forsch.,* 4, 186–194.

Lewis, W.C. 1981. Carbon dioxide in Coldwater cave. *Eighth Internat. Congress of Speleology,* U.S.A., 1, 91–92.

Mérenne-Schoumaker, B. 1975. Aspects de l'influence des touristes sur les microclimats de la grotte de Remouchamps. *Ann. Spéléol.,* 30(2), 273–285.

Miotke, F.D. 1974. Carbon dioxide and the soil atmosphere. *Abh. Karst- u. Höhlenkunde,* Reihe A, 9, 1–49.

Renault, P. 1979. Mesures périodiques de la pCO_2 dans des grottes françaises. *Actes Symp. int. Erosion karstique,* U.I.S., Aix-en-Provence, 17–33.

Renault, P. 1982. CO_2 atmosphérique karstique et spéléomorphologie. Intérêt pour les spéléologues. *Revue belge de Géographie,* 106, 121–130.

Roques, H. 1959. Sur la répartition du CO_2 dans les karsts. *Ann. Spéléol.,* 14, 9–22.

Silberstein, J. et Warginaire, R. 1972. Fiche et topographie de la grotte Ste-Anne. *Spéléo - Flash,* 58, 28–29.

Société Spéléologique de Wallonie 1982. *Inventaire spéléologique de la Belgique,* (S.S.W. édit., Liège), 521p.

Van den Broeck, E., Martel, E. et Rahir, E. 1910. *Les cavernes et les rivières souterraines de la Belgique.* 2 tomes, Bruxelles, 1592p.

4

Chemical weathering of the
East Yorkshire chalk

J.I. Pitman

SUMMARY

The chalk groundwater aquifer of East Yorkshire exhibits three
major hydrogeochemical zones characterised by distinctive water
chemical compositions. Zone 1 is coincident with the unconfined aquifer, with an area of 822 km². Here, Ca^{2+} concentrations average 93 mg.l^{-1}, HCO_3^- 235 mg.l^{-1}, and all samples are
saturated with calcite at mean log pCO_2 of -2.02. Recharge
waters (rain) contribute most of the 12.3 mg.l^{-1} of SO_4^{2-}, and
are acid (pH 4.83 ± 1.55). Measured soil log pCO_2 are predic-
table from the equation -2.50 + 0.044T for arable soils.
Shallow groundwaters are predominantly open to soil CO_2, have
higher Ca^{2+} (~126 mg.l^{-1}) and HCO_3^- levels (211 mg.l^{-1}) and are
saturated with calcite (log SIc -0.02) at an average log pCO_2
of -2.08; deeper scarpfoot springs (Ca^{2+} 88 mg.l; HCO_3^-
133 mg.l^{-1}) probably evolve under closed CO_2 conditions (log pCO_2
-2.40), and are undersaturated with calcite (log SIc -0.27).
Zone 2 is the 3-5km wide semi-confined artesian flow area
on the chalk dip slope. Groundwater composition changes rapidly
within this zone (Ca^{2+} increases to 120 mg.l^{-1}, HCO_3^- to 212-317
mg.l^{-1}, with a mean log pCO_2 of -1.81) associated with oxidation-
reduction reactions and ion exchange of Na^+, K^+ for Ca^{2+}. This
is a zone of very active solutional activity.
In zone 3, the fully confined aquifer, equilibrium with
calcite is maintained by a combination of cation exchange of Ca^{2+}
for $2(Na^+ + K^+)$ and calcite deposition, so that dissolved Ca^{2+}
decreases to 70 mg.l^{-1}. Carbonate ion activity is increased by
increased pH and HCO_3 (to 7.34 and 370 mg.l^{-1} respectively) as a
result of reduction of SO_4^{2-} and NO_3^-. Log pCO_2 is kept at -1.81
by these processes.
After correction for atmospheric inputs average Ca^{2+} fluxes
from Givendale are 315 kg.ha.$^{-1}$yr^{-1} equivalent to a surface lowering
rate of about 39mm in 1000 years. Chemical mass balance calculations suggest that low magnesium calcite is preferentially dissolved, with some secondary calcite precipitation.

RÉSUMÉ

Les nappes souterraines de la craie, dans le Yorkshire oriental, appartiennent à trois zones hydrogéochimiques principales, différenciées par la composition chimique de leur eau.

La zone 1 coincidant avec la nappe libre, s'étend sur 822 km². Les eaux y contiennent en moyenne 93 mg/l de Ca^{++} et 235 mg/l de HCO_3. Tous les échantillons sont saturés en calcite avec un log pCO_2 de -2.02 en moyenne. Les eaux de recharge (précipitations) sont la source principale des 12.3 mg/l de SO_4. Elles sont acides (pH 4.83 ± 1.55). Les log pCO_2 des sols peuvent être prédit par l'équation -2.50 + 0.044T, valable pour les sols cultivés. Les nappes peu profondes qui sont en communication avec le CO_2 des sols ont des teneurs plus élevées en Ca^{++} (~126 mg/l) et en HCO_3 (211 mg/l). Elles sont saturées en calcite (log SIc -0.02) avec un log pCO_2 moyen de -2.08. Des sources de pied d'escarpement, provenant d'eaux plus profondes (88 mg/l de Ca et 133 mg/l de HCO_3) ont probablement évolué à l'état confiné pour le CO_2 (log pCO_2 -2.40) et sont sous-saturées en calcite (log SIc -0.27).

La zone 2 est une nappe artésienne semi-captive, large de 3 à 5 km, sur le revers structural de la craie. La composition de l'eau varie rapidement dans cette zone (le Ca^{++} atteint 120 mg/l, HCO_3 atteint 212-317 mg/l, avec un log pCO_2 moyen de -1.81), qui est associée à des réactions d'oxydation et de réduction et à des échanges d'ions Na^+, K^+ contre Ca^{++}. Les processus de dissolution sont très actifs dans cette zone.

La zone 3 correspond à la nappe complètement captive. Elle est dominée par la précipitation de la calcite (70 mg/l de Ca^{++}), la reduction du NO_3 et du SO_4^{++}, avec un log pCO_2 stable à -1.87, associées à l'échange de cations Na^+ contre Ca^{++}. Les solutions ont une teneur en calcite équilibrée, grâce à ces réactions. Après corrections, pour tenir compte des apports atmosphériques, la quantité moyenne de Ca^{++} provenant de Givendale est de 315 kg/ha/an, correspondant à un abaissement moyen de la surface topographique de 39mm/millénaire. Le calcul des bilans chimiques suggère une dissolution préférentielle de la calcite associée à un faible taux de magnésium, et une faible précipitation secondaire de calcite.

INTRODUCTION

The chemical composition of groundwater in the East Yorkshire Chalk shows a systematic change as groundwater moves from the recharge areas downdip eastwards and southward towards Holderness Spring waters draining the escarpment differ in their chemistry from those draining from the dip slope.

The objective of this paper is threefold. Firstly it describes the chemical variation observed throughout the aquifer. Secondly, the major chemical processes that control this variation are identified and, thirdly, the geomorphological significance of those processes to the karstification of the Chalk is assessed.

W. Back and B. Hanshaw (1971) neatly summarised the chronological sequence of events as follows:

> 'In the functioning of a carbonate aquifer,
> rainfall infiltrates through the soil zone,
> becomes charged with carbon dioxide, moves
> to the water table, dissolves soluble
> minerals of the aquifer, increases in che-
> mical concentration, and continues to move
> into deeper parts of the aquifer, eventually
> discharging into the sea'

The Yorkshire Wolds is a gently dipping limestone aquifer, dominated by fissure flow in the saturated zone, and by intergranular flow in the unsaturated zone. The outcrop area of unconfined Chalk is 822 km^2, and is typical of the 17 200 km^2 of the English Cretaceous Chalk outcrop.

Despite the fact that the outcrop area of the English Chalk is greater than either the Jurassic or Carboniferous limestones, few studies have been made of the groundwater geochemistry, or of the rate of solute removal.

Perrin (1964) gave estimates of the rate of solutional lowering based on the analyses of leachates from lysimeters at Fleam Dyke near Cambridge, of 16.7mm per 1000 years. Atkinson (1957) estimated the rate of surface lowering from archaeological evidence, as being 127mm per 1000 years. However, neither of these investigators described the processes operating in terms of the solutional geochemistry of calcite.

Previous geomorphological investigations in East Yorkshire have largely concentrated on Quaternary features (De Boer, 1944; De Boer, *et al.*, 1958; Penny, 1974; Catt, *et al.*, 1974), valley form (Cole, 1879, 1887; Mortimer, 1885) and morphometric analysis (Lewin, 1969). Imeson (1970) investigated the solute chemistry of a small stream and spring system at Drewton Beck, whilst Douglas (1968) described the relationship between the Ca^{2+} concentration and discharge of the River Hull at Hempholme Lock.

There are few studies of the groundwater chemistry of chalk, apart from those of Casey, (1969) and Casey and Newton, (1973), who described the chemistry of chalk springs and rivers in Hampshire and Dorset, and the British Geological Survey (Edmunds *et al.*, 1973; Bath and Edmunds, 1981). Pitman (1976, 1978a) described in detail the groundwater geochemistry of a small outlier of chalk at Givendale, East Yorkshire, and showed that simple carbonate geochemical models could be used to predict the chemical composition of chalk groundwaters, and hence the rate of solute transfer for a given water flux through the system.

LOCATION AND GEOLOGY

The Yorkshire Wolds forms an arcuate shaped outcrop of Upper Cretaceous Chalk, terminated on its western and northern flanks by steep escarpments overlooking the Vales of York and Pickering respectively (Figure 1). Maximum elevations occur behind the escarpments, and are 241m four kilometres north of Givendale (Figure 1). The regional dip is to the south and east, and reflects the structural control of a synclinal basin, the axis of which trends NNW to SSE. The backslope cuts across successively younger Chalk zone (Wright and Wright, 1942; Neale, 1974) until it dips beneath the glacial tills of pre-Ipswichian, and Devensian age (Kent, 1980), which form the undulating lowlands of Holderness. The western edge of the Ipswichian till is marked by a raised beach and cliff line cut into the chalk at +1.5m O.D. (Catt and Penny, 1966).

Lithology and Stratigraphy

The total thickness of the Yorkshire Chalk exceeds 420m, and consists of four distinctive lithostratigraphical units (Wood and Smith, 1978; Kent, 1980). In ascending order these are the Ferriby, Welton, Burnham and Flamborough Chalk Formations.

The Ferriby Chalk corresponds to the Lower Chalk of S. England, and consists of 18 to 36m of flintless, marly, soft chalk, relatively high in insoluble residue (Jeans, 1968; Pitman, 1978). The Welton Chalk forms 150m of massively bedded flinty chalk, with well developed fissures. This is succeeded by the flinty, thinly bedded Burnham Chalk (130 to 150m thick), and the flintless, well bedded Flamborough Formation.

Physical properties of the Chalk

Chalks are fine grained micrites, characterised by calcitic particles in the size ranges 0.5μm to 4μm, and 10μm to 100μm (Hancock, 1975). The finer fraction are coccoliths (Mimran, 1978) within a protective framework of larger polygonal intergrown calcite crystals (Figure 2).

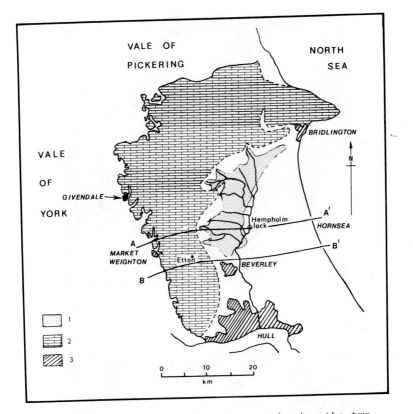

Figure 4.1　The Yorkshire Chalk outcrop, showing the two sampling areas at Givendale, and along the E-W transect AA'-BB'. 1 = artesian aquifer zone, 2 = Upper Cretaceous Chalk, and 3 = major urban areas

Yorkshire chalks have densities in the range 2.00 to 2.56 g.cm^{-3} (Mimram, 1978; Clayton, 1983), corresponding to porosities of 8 to 25 per cent. Measurements by Bird (1976) on borehole samples from the Welton and Burnham Chalks ranged from 14 to 25 per cent, with outcrop samples in the range 20 to 26 per cent. Outcrop samples from the upper part of the Burnham Chalk, and the Flamborough Chalk ranged between 26 and 38 per cent porosity.

The small void size associated with these small porosities results in the massive chalk having very low permeabilities, generally in the order of 0.0002m^{-1} day (Foster and Milton, 1974, 1976). Other physical properties of chalk have been reviewed by Scholle (1977), Hancock (1975), and Pitman (1984). It should be noted that the Yorkshire Chalks differ from the more southerly outcrops in having a much higher density and lower porosity.

Figure 4.2   SEM of chalk from East Yorkshire, showing abundant,
well preserved coccoliths within a matrix of
secondary calcite crystals (x4000)

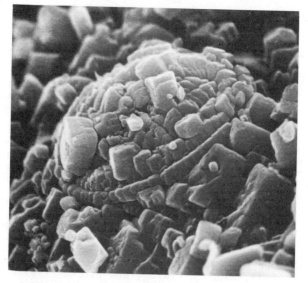

Figure 4.3   Characteristic coccolithic remains, overgrown by a
matrix of large blocky euhedral secondary calcite
crystals (x6000, SEM)

Chemical properties

Chalks are usually pure calcite or low magnesium calcitic limestone. Table 1 gives the results of chemical analyses of some Yorkshire chalk samples from the Ferriby and Welton Chalks (Pitman, 1978c), which confirm the high purity of these chalks, and their low Mg^{2+} contents. Other chalks from England show a similar degree of purity, with the $CaCO_3$ content generally exceeding 97 per cent. Mimran (1978) attributes the low porosity and high density of Yorkshire chalk to postdepositional lithification by two mechanisms: precipitation of secondary calcite, and recrystallisation. However, Scholle (1977) attributes the lithification to pressure solution. Figures 2 and 3 show well developed rhombohedral calcitic crystals, suggesting that calcite precipitation has been, or is, active within the aquifer.

Mineralogy

Calcite and low magnesium calcite, with the mole per cent of Mg^{2+} not exceeding 5 percent, are the dominant minerals in the aquifer, constituting over 98 per cent of the aquifer material. The insoluble residue of the chalks are dominated by clays, particularly smectites, illite and apatite; quartz; and trace amounts of feldspar, limonite, pyrites, hornblend, rutile and zircon (Jeans, 1968; Pitman, 1978c). All of these minerals will influence the final water composition to some degree, although it is reasonable to assume that only the most abundant and fast reacting minerals, such as calcite, will dominate the water chemistry (Garrels, 1976). Clay minerals, particularly those concentrated by pressure solution to form stylolites, or in the not infrequent marl bands can be expected to participate in cation exchange reactions, particularly in the confined, more saline aquifer where Na^+ dominates the chemistry.

HYDROGEOLOGY

The Yorkshire Chalk is an important regional aquifer, with a large, as yet untapped potential for water supply to the Humberside region (Foster and Milton, 1976). Springs at Driffield, and wells and bores in the confined aquifer are used to supply water to agriculture, industry and the local community (Figure 4). Over extraction of groundwater around Hull has resulted in the intrusion of saline water from the River Humber (Foster, et al., 1976).

Average rainfall over the Wolds varies from over 800mm over the higher ground to less than 700mm around Beverly. With an average evaporation rate of about 480mm per year, effective recharge of the aquifer averages 300mm, usually between November and March. Mean annual temperatures are 8.5°C.

Table 4.1 Chemical analyses of chalks from Givendale, East Yorkshire. Samples 1, 2, 3 and 4 are from the Ferriby (L. Chalk) Formation. Samples 5-9 are from the Welton and Burnham Formation

Total chemical composition of Chalk, in per cent

	1	2	3	4	5	6	7	8	9	$\bar{x}$	sd
SiO_2	3.04	1.31	0.85	0.82	1.35	0.94	0.90	1.85	1.70	1.42	±0.72
Al_2O_3	0.99	0.17	0.11	0.34	0.16	0.18	0.23	0.58	0.21	0.33	±0.28
Fe_2O_3	0.50	0.14	0.11	0.17	0.09	0.13	0.18	0.36	0.14	0.20	±0.14
TiO_2	0.03	0.02	0.01	0.01	0.01	0.01	0.02	0.02	0.01	0.02	±0.007
MgO	1.82	0.85	0.52	1.17	1.02	0.02	1.56	1.06	1.16	1.03	±0.53
CaO	50.82	53.86	54.88	53.85	53.90	55.21	53.80	53.24	53.23	53.67	±1.24
Na_2O	0.15	0.14	0.11	0.13	0.14	0.11	0.10	0.11	0.14	0.13	±0.02
K_2O	0.21	0.11	0.07	0.08	0.07	0.08	0.07	0.14	0.06	0.10	±0.05
Cl	0.12	0.16	0.06	0.10	0.22	0.41	0.06	0.13	0.36	0.18	±0.13
CO_2	42.30	42.67	42.94	43.02	42.89	42.94	43.14	42.32	42.82	42.78	±0.30
Insoluble residue	4.46	1.67	1.07	1.07	1.61	1.18	1.21	2.61	2.00	0.88	±1.09
	99.98	99.43	99.65	99.69	99.85	100.03	100.06	99.81	99.83		

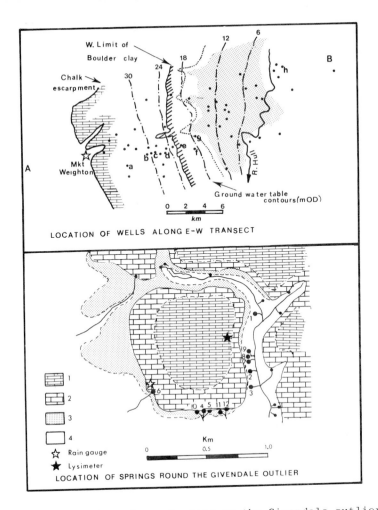

Figure 4.4   Location of sample site on the Givendale outlier, and of wells and bores (dots) on the E-W transect between Market Weighton and Hornsea. 1 = Ferriby Chalk Formation; 2 = Welton and Burnham Chalk Formation; 3 = Flamborough Chalk Formation

The chalk aquifer is conviently subdivided into three hydrogeological units (Figure 5):

i)   The unconfined aquifer of the chalk Wolds

ii) The artesian flow zone and semi-confined aquifer of Holderness,

iii) The fully confined aquifer of Holderness.

85

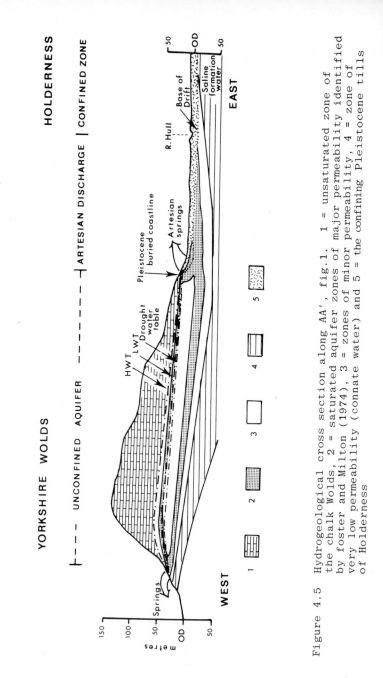

Figure 4.5   Hydrogeological cross section along AA', fig.1.   1 = unsaturated zone of the chalk Wolds, 2 = saturated aquifer zones of major permeability identified by foster and Milton (1974), 3 = zones of minor permeability, 4 = zone of very low permeability (connate water) and 5 = the confining Pleistocene tills of Holderness

The unconfined chalk aquifer

This aquifer has recently been intensivily investigated by the Institute of Geological Sciences (I.G.S.) as part of their investigations into nitrate pollution of the chalk groundwater (Foster and Crease, 1974; Lawrence *et al.*, 1983), saline water intrusion (Foster *et al.*, 1976) and large scale development of groundwater storage. The result of these investigations is that more is now probably known about the Yorkshire Chalk aquifer than comparable limestone aquifers elsewhere.

Detailed groundwater investigations around Etton have shown that the aquifer approximates to a layered, moderate trans-missivity (T ~1000m day^{-1}), low specific yield (< 0.005) water table system, dominated by fissure flow. Major zones of fissure flow are associated with the water table elevations at their highest (during winter), and lowest (summer), and with a second layer, at about -20m O.D., 5 to 7m thick (Figure 5). This lower zone has T values of ~1200m day^{-1}. These fissured zones parallel the water table, and have a gradient of about 1:80. Pumping tests at Etton show that the aquifer is isotropic. Foster (1974) has also shown that the layered hydraulic structure of the aquifer is reflected by the relationship between groundwater recession of springwater flow, and water table elevations.

The best explanation of groundwater flow in the saturated zone (Foster and Milton, 1974) is by fissures with an average density of 10 per metre, with openings between 0.5 to 1.0mm. Actual velocities measured at Etton varied between 13 to 50m day^{-1}, but were thought to reach 200m day^{-1} under natural hydraulic gradients. Little flow was detected in the aquifer below -30m O.D.

Flow through the unsaturated zone, as determined by tritium profiles, approximate to plug flow conditions through the inter-granular pore space at velocities of 0.88 to 1.4m per year (Foster *et al.*, 1982; Lawrence *et al.*, 1983).

Natural groundwater discharge occurs as springs along the foot of the chalk escarpment, along a line coincident with the buried cliff line in Holderness, and as artesian springs. The largest springs are at Driffield, with winter discharges over 1m sec^{-1}.

The confined chalk aquifer

Data on flow in the confined aquifer is meagre, although several large public pumped wells occur in this zone north of Beverly. Tritium analysis of groundwater from this zone by Foster and Crease (1974) gave pre-bomb levels. Flow rate is therefore thought to be very low.

Between the buried cliff line and the River Hull north of Beverly, the aquifer is semi-confined, with extensive artesian

flow occurring over an area of 170 km² (Figures 1 and 4).
Springs and 'kelds' are a common feature of this area.

The groundwater samples described in this study were col-
lected from springs draining a small chalk outlier at Givendale
(Pitman, 1976; 1978a), and from wells and boreholes along an
East-West transect of the Wolds between Market Weighton and
Hornsea (Figure 4).

SOILS AND LANDUSE

Soils developed over the chalk are rendzinas (rendolls). They
are very shallow (<30cm deep), have A/C horizons, and overlay
frost shattered chalk. They are generally calcareous, with A
horizon Ca^{2+} contents >35 per cent. Cation exchange capacities
average 24 meq.100 g⁻¹. About 90 per cent of the Wolds is culti-
vated, the major crops being barley, wheat, root crops and grass.
Fertilizer inputs average 120kg.ha⁻¹.year⁻¹NO_3^-.

SAMPLING PROCEDURES

Details of the rainfall, soil lysimeters and spring water sampling procedure are given in Pitman (1978a). Groundwater samples
from the unconfined aquifer were collected by a battery operated
stainless steel 850ml well sampler lowered to the appropriate
depth by cable. Temperature, conductivity, pH, dissolved oxygen
and HCO_3^- were determined at the well head. Field filtered
samples (0.45μm) were acidified and analysed for cations in the
laboratory, whilst anions were determined for unacidified samples. Waters from the confined zone were sampled at the pump
head, after the pump had been running for 30 minutes, using the
same procedures above. Soil gases were collected and measured
at the Givendale site.

DATA ANALYSES

There were three stages to the data analysis: firstly, computation of chemical equilibria; secondly, statistical and graphical analysis; thirdly, calculation of the mass transfer, using
the program BALANCE (Parkhurst et al., 1982), between selected
sample points in the aquifer.

Ion activities were calculated on all samples with an ion
balance better than 5 percent, after allowing for the effect of
ion pairing and complex formation (Pitman, 1978a). Corrected
free ion activities (α_i) were then computed from:

$$\alpha_i = \gamma_i m_i \qquad (1)$$

where m_i is the molality of the ith ion, and γ_i the activity coefficient calculated from the extended form of the Debye-Huckle expression. Sample pCO_2 was then calculated from the expression:

$$pCO_2 = \left[\frac{\alpha\ H^+ \alpha\ HCO_3^-}{B.K_1} \right] \tag{2}$$

where H^+ is the field measured H^+, and HCO_3^- the field mesured bicarbonate concentration. The reader is referred to Plummer and Busenberg (1982) for the values of the constants used in the calculations (B, K_1, K_2, Kc).

The saturation index of any mineral is defined by:

$$SIc = \left[\frac{\alpha Ca^{2+}.\ \alpha CO_3^{2-}}{Kc} \right] = \left[\frac{I.A.P}{Kc} \right] \tag{3}$$

where SIc is the saturation for calcite, IAP the ion activity for the mineral, and Kc the equilibrium constant of the reaction, after allowing for the effects of the ion pairs $CaHCO_3^+$ and $CaCO_3^\circ$ (Plummer and Busenberg, 1982). If the value of log SIc > 0, the sample is supersaturated, if log SIc = 0, the sample is at equilibrium with the mineral, and if log SIc < 0, the mineral will dissolve. Generally the errors in determination of field pH and HCO_3^- induce an error of ±0.1 log units of SIc. The values of disassociation constants used were determined from the least squares expressions of Busenberg and Plummer (1982) for K_1, K_2, Kc, B, $KCaCO_3^\circ$, $KCaHCO_3^+$, from Jacobsen and Langmuir (1974, a, b) for $KMgHCO_3^+$, and Truesdell and Jones (1974) for $KCaOH^+$, $KMgOH^+$, $KNaHCO_3^\circ$, $KNaSO_4^-$, $KKCl^\circ$ $KKSO_4^-$ and $KCaSO_4^\circ$.

RESULTS

The chemical composition of selected groundwaters along the East-West transect is shown in Figure 6. Table 2 summarises the data collected and previously analysed by Pitman (1978a).

The data indicate that the chalk aquifer can be subdivided into three distinctive hydrogeochemical units, corresponding to the unconfined, semi-confined and fully confined aquifers previously described. In the sections that follow, the changing chemistry of the water will be traced from its precipitation origin, through the aquifer, to the points of natural discharge.

Chemistry of recharge water

Ion concentrations in rainfall in low (Table 2), although the amounts of the ions Cl^- and Na^+, due to their seawater origin, would be expected to increase towards the east of the outcrop. Solute loads deposited on the chalk are given in Table 3 and are in good agreement with other United Kingdom data (Pitman, 1976; Barrett, *et al.*, 1984). Thus whilst the inputs

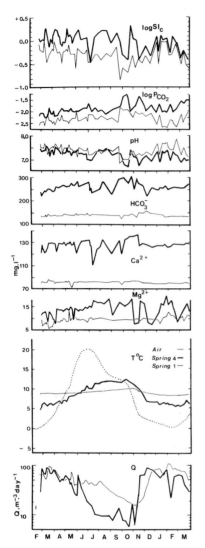

Figure 4.6 Seasonal variation of chemical properties for two springs at Givendale, showing the characteristic differences that occur between dip (Spring 4) and scarp springs (Spring 1)

of Ca^{2+} and Mg^{2+} are low, the input of the anions SO_4^{2-}, NO_3^- and Cl^- are moderately high, and reflect the wet and dry deposition of atmospheric pollutants (Barrett, *et al.*, 1984). The significance of these inputs and their associated protons is threefold. Firstly, evaporation naturally increases the concentrations by the ratio (P/P-E), where P is the precipitation and E the evaporation. Secondly, the ionic strength is increased, resulting in a reduction in the value of the activity coefficient, reducing the ion activity. Thirdly, the anions, particularly SO_4^{2-} form

90

Table 4.2 Means of the chemical analyses of rain, soil leachate and springs from the dip (2, 3, 4, 5, 6, 11, 12) and scarp (1, 7, 8, 9) locations at Givendale

	Ca^{2+}	Mg^{2+}	Na^+	K^+	HCO_3^-	NO_3^-	SO_4^{2-}	pH	log pCO_2	log SIc	$T^\circ C$	N
Precipitation												
X	0.8	0.2	2.6	0.7	4.4	3.8	12.3	4.83	-	-		48
SD	1.2	0.2	4.0	1.3	11.4	2.6	9.3	1.55	-	-		
Arable Lysimeter												
X	94.9	7.4	4.7	3.7	116.1	69.1	22.7	7.44	-2.41	-0.24	5.51	19
SD	53.5	6.4	1.9	2.7	12.7	43.4	16.1	0.23	0.65	0.46	6.41	
Bare Earth Lysimeter												
X	60.8	4.1	4.3	1.6	135.2	31.3	22.3	7.57	-2.65	-0.32	5.51	13
SD	17.3	2.0	2.2	1.1	47.5	49.8	15.2	0.24	0.42	0.24	6.41	
Natural Grassland Lysimeter												
X	51.3	5.7	9.7	4.2	134.9	8.5	23.2	7.52	-2.61	-0.32	5.51	13
SD	6.3	1.9	4.6	1.7	20.7	8.3	10.7	0.34	0.26	0.36	6.41	
Dip slope springs (2,3,4,5,6,10,11,12)												
X	125.7	6.1	8.5	2.5	211.4	56.2	89.2	7.29	-2.08	-0.09	8.51	394
SD	14.2				39.2			0.24	0.28	0.23	1.91	
Scarp slope springs (1,7,8,9)												
X	87.6	5.5	8.7	1.2	132.8	44.1	70.9	7.43	-2.40	-0.27	8.68	205
SD	6.7				12.2			0.19	0.21	0.20	0.38	

X is the mean, SD the sample standard deviation, and N the sample size

ion pairs with the cations, particularly Ca^{2+}. This also reduces the free ion concentrations in solution, and thus increases the solution of calcite (Pitman, 1976 and in preparation).

Soil water chemistry

Table 3 shows the soil solute balance for the arable, grass and bare earth lysimeters at Givendale. All profiles loose Ca^{2+} and Mg^{2+}, whereas K^+ and Na^+ are retained, probably by cation exchange reactions with soil clays. The rate at which Ca^{2+} and Mg^{2+} are mobilised from the soil is a function of the soil gas composition. Pitman (1978a) showed that for these soils, soil carbon dioxide was positively correlated with the soil temperature, by the following regressions:

$$\text{Arable site} \quad \log pCO_2 = -2.50 + 0.044T$$

$$\text{Grass site} \quad \log pCO_2 = -3.12 + 0.042T$$

where T is the soil temperature in degrees centigrade.

Table 4.3   Flux of ions, after correcting for rain and fertilizer inputs from the arable lysimeter ($kg.ha^{-1}.yr^{-1}$)

Soil Solute Balance, Kg $ha^{-1}yr^{-1}$
(arable lysimeter)

	Ca^{2+}	Mg^{2+}	Na^+	K^+	Cl^-	SO_4^{2-}	NO_3^-
Inputs							
(i) Precipitation	4.1	1.2	16.8	2.9	40.2	79.1	29.8
(ii) Fertilizers	14.4	-	-	17.6	-	-	528
Outputs							
(iii) Soil Leachate	318	30.4	15.2	17.5	56.5	93.2	247
(iv) Net Soil Loss (iii-(ii+i))	299	29.2	-1.6	-3.0	16.3	14.1	-310
(v) Crop Removal*	11.2	4.5	2.5	42.3	3.5	21.6	248
TOTAL removed from soil (iv+v) **	310	33.7	-0.9	39.7	19.8	35.7	-63

* by 4.5 tonnes Barley, 4.2 tonnes Wheat, and 31.4 tonnes potatoes.

** Negative sign implies accumulation in soil.

Soil water leachates had calculated log pCO_2 values that when correlated with the 100mm soil temperature, corresponded to that above, and it was concluded that the soil solution evolves under open system conditions with respect to CO_2. Generally the soil leachates were undersaturated with calcite (Table 2).

The above regressions are similar to those of Drake and Wigley (1975), with a temperature coefficient close to their open system case. Recent measurements by Dever *et al.*, (1983) show summer pCO_2 values similar to those measured at Givendale. From the data at Givendale, the range of soil pCO_2 that can be expected are:

Season	Temperature	Arable	Grass
Summer	22°C	−1.55 +0.22	−2.50 +0.05
Winter	0°C	−2.50 +0.10	−3.12 +0.18

Spring water chemistry

Figure 7 shows the seasonal variation in the spring water chemistry of two typical springs draining the Givendale outlier. The difference in the chemical composition is marked, is invariant with discharge, and constant throughout the year. Similar differences are exhibited between springs draining the escarpment, and those draining the dip slope. Generally, the springs with the higher concentration of Ca^{2+} are associated with the dip slope, whilst those with the lower values occur beneath steep escarpments.

The complete data set from Givendale was subjected to a stepwise linear discriminant function, using the SPSS statistical package. With springs 1 and 6 as training sets, 90.6 per cent of the 599 samples were correctly classified by Ca^{2+} ion alone, 96.8 per cent by Ca^{2+} and pH together, and 91 per cent by log SIc and log pCO_2 together (Pitman, 1978a).

The only other variables thought to affect spring water chemistry are temperature and discharge. The relationship between discharge and concentration over an annual cycle may be expected to be obscured by other seasonal variables, particularly temperature, and the effect this has on biological activity. The variation of Ca^{2+} with discharge for typical dip and scarp springs is shown in Figure 8. Generally, the relationship is not good, and Ca^{2+} appears to be invariant with changing discharge.

Shuster and White (1972) made a conceptual sub-division of carbonate aquifers into diffuse flow and conduit flow systems, each having characteristic hydrological features, and differentiated by their chemical response to recharge events (Jacobsen and Langmuir, 1974a). The small variations in chemistry shown by the chalk springs here are typical of the diffuse flow systems.

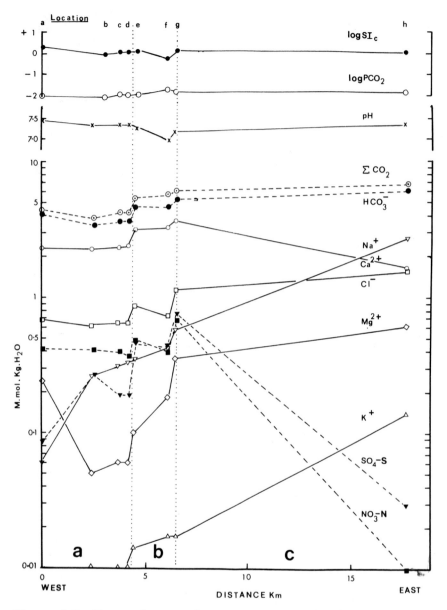

Figure 4.7   Change in groundwater chemistry along the unconfined
(A), confined (C) and semi-confined/artesian aquifer
zone (B).   a = Arras; b = Etton Wold House; c = Etton
2; d = Etton 4E; e = Etton Rectory; f = Woodhouse
Farm; g = Bygott; h = Connygarth: see Fig 2 for
locations

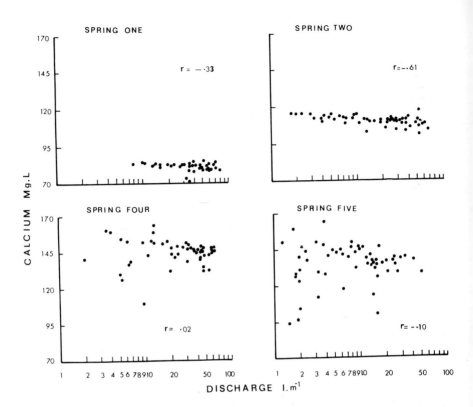

Figure 4.8 Relationship between spring water discharge and Ca^{2+} concentrations, for dip (Springs 2,4,5), and scarp (Spring 1) locations. Dip springs always show a greater variation when compared to scarp springs

Multiple regression analysis of the percent SIc versus log discharge, log pCO_2 and water temperature (Table 4) show that when the effects of temperature and pCO_2 are allowed for, the effect of discharge becomes minor. Interestingly, temperature variation for dip springs is more significant than for the scarp springs. It may be concluded, therefore, that the single most important control on the amount of Ca^{2+} is pCO_2 and that discharge alone cannot explain the differences between the spring types.

Unconfined aquifer waters

The statistics for the 22 well water samples collected in October are given in Table 5. The most significant feature of the data is the remarkable constancy of the chemical composition, for both measured and calculated parameters, with log SIc within

Table 4.4   Regression analysis of carbonate chemistry parameters and temperature against discharge for Givendale springs

Multiple Regressions for %SIcip

Spring	No	Regression	equations			R^2
2	i) ii)	y= -3.716	+ 0.113T .42	+ 0.036Q .04	-1.64LpCO$_2$ -.85	0.86
3	i) ii)	y= -4.15	+ 0.108T .65	+ 0.050Q .08	-1.99LpCO$_2$ -.87	0.88
4	i) ii)	y= -2.96	+ 0.085T .48	+ 0.256Q .27	-1.58LpCO$_2$ -.86	0.87
5	i) ii)	y= -1.64	+ 0.025T .12	+ 0.258Q .18	-1.78LpCO$_2$ -.76	0.77
6	i) ii)	y= -1.455	+-0.056T -.21	+ 0.009Q .01	-1.39LpCO$_2$ -.86	0.87
. . . .
1	i) ii)	y= -1.537	+ 0.012T .07	+ 0.049Q .10	-0.814LpCO$_2$ -.86	0.89
8	i) ii)	y= -2.196	+ 0.266T .21	+ 0.021Q .02	-0.221LpCO$_2$ -.21	0.41
9	i) ii)	y= -2.036	+ 0.113T .21	+ 0.033Q .10	-0.636LpCO$_2$ -.64	0.64
12	i) ii)	y= -2.051	+ 0.347T -.11..	+ 0.256Q -.03	-0.317LpCO$_2$ -.05	0.18
11	i) ii)	y= -3.284	+ 0.143T .29	+ 0.152Q .15	-1.606LpCO$_2$ -.58	0.71

Notes   T = temperature, ^{o}C; Q = Log Discharge, $l.ha^{-1}.min^{-1}$
LpCO$_2$ = log pCO$_2$.
The second row below the regression equation gives the partial correlation coefficients.
The sample size for 1 to 8 is 60(d.f. =56).

±0.1 of saturation, and log pCO_2 almost constant at -2.02. Monthly samples collected from Etton by the Yorkshire Water Authority show that seasonal variations of Ca^{2+} and HCO_3^- and pH are within the range observed in Table 5. The almost constant values of HCO_3^- and pH must result from dissolution or precipitation of carbonate minerals, assuming that reactions of dissolved CO_2 with silicate minerals is insignificant. Evidence for this is the low silica and aluminum concentration measured in these groundwater (not reported here) of 4.0 $mg.l^{-1}$ and 0.05 $mg.l^{-1}$ respectively. Calculated saturation indices for the minerals quartz, gibbsite, montmorillonite and illite are all positive, indicative of precipitation; only chalcedony and albite are dissolving.

Table 4.5   Means and standard deviations of 22 well samples from the unconfined chalk aquifer, collected October 27-29, 1977, in $mg.l^{-1}$

Mean composition of 22 Unconfined chalk aquifer samples, October 1977, mg.1

	Ca^{2+}	Mg^{2+}	Na^+	K^+	HCO_3^-	$(NO_3^- - N)$	$(SO_4^{2-} - S)$	pH	log pCO_2	log SIc	$T°C$
X̄	92.9	1.3	6.1	.58	234.5	5.2	21.9	7.31	-2.02	-0.02	11.3
SD	5.7	.3	1.2	.04	17.8	0.8	5.4	0.08	0.09	0.08	0.63
CV%	6.2	19.9	18.9	100	7.6	15.4	24.9	1.03	4.47	424	5.6

Depth profiles from Etton 4E borehole in both October and March were obtained; data for the March, high water table position, are shown in Figure 9. The major zones of fissure development are shown shaded. Whilst mixing within the well makes it difficult to eliminate the effects of mixing, which does not obviously occur in the undisturbed aquifer, slight stratification of the water chemistry is apparent. In particular, the lower zone of fissure development has a slightly lower Ca^{2+} concentration, although all the samples have similar log pCO_2 and log SIc values. Profiles obtained at Etton 3E, 244m WSW of 4E are almost identical to that observed at 4E. Pumping tests have shown that between 70 to 90 per cent of the pumped water came from the lower fissure zone (Foster and Milton, 1974). Seasonal variations of the water table average 20m at Etton, which is average for the southern Wolds area.

Artesian flow zone

Artesian springs, locally known as 'kelds' occur along a zone some 192 km^2 in extent, and up to 5 km eastward from the buried cliff line. Because they represent natural groundwater discharge, their chemical properties will indicate the extent to which solution is active in the semi-confined aquifer.

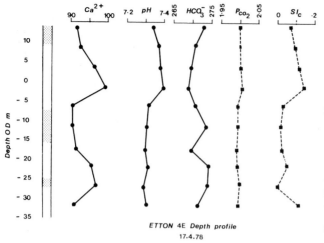

Figure 4.9
Depth profile of groundwater obtained at Etton 4E borehole. The stratification shown here is typical. Shaded zones are the areas of maximum fissure development

Table 6 gives the data for 17 samples from this area, collected from overflowing stand pipes, bores and springs. Considerable variation exists in the carbonate chemistry parameters, with several samples being undersaturated with calcite. Very high log pCO_2 values are encountered in this zone.

Table 4.6   Chemical composition of artesian and semi-confined borehole samples, mg.l^{-1}

Range of chemical composition of samples from the artesian and semi-confined aquifer, in mg.l

	Ca^{2+}	Mg^{2+}	Na^+	K^+	HCO_3^-	(NO_3^--N)	$(SO_4^{2-}-S)$	pH	log pCO_2	log SIc	T°C
Max	120.0	8.0	10.3	3.9	316.9	6.7	35.5	7.48	-1.42	-0.30	13.6
Min	85.0	.9	5.6	0.2	212.8	0.1	4.5	6.82	-2.12	+0.29	10.4
X	97.8	3.4	7.4	1.4	278.3	3.8	11.3	7.17	-1.81	-0.06	11.6
SD	11.5	1.5	2.5	0.9	32.9	1.9	9.1	0.17	0.19	0.13	0.9

Confined Aquifer

Changes in groundwater chemistry of samples from the onset of semi-confined to fully confined conditions are shown in Figure 6. Most samples are close to saturation with calcite, with several marked changes in the chemistry apparent. Firstly, the amount of Ca^{2+} steadily decreases along the flow path, after an initial rise in the first 3 km of semi-confining conditions. Dissolved oxygen, nitrate and sulphate progressively disappear along the flow path, whilst alkalinity, total carbon and sodium steadily increase. This sequence is typical of that predicted by theory (Champ *et al.*, 1979), and described in other English limestone aquifers (Edmunds, 1973; Ineson and Downing, 1963).

These changes are indicative of the onset of two processes within the aquifer. Firstly, the onset of oxidation-reduction reactions and, secondly, the occurrence of Ca^{2+} ion exchange for Na$^+$.

DEVELOPMENT AND TESTING OF REACTION MODELS

In order to predict the location and the rate of chemical mass transfer through the aquifer, and hence the observed distribution of dissolved ion concentration, reaction models are required that explain the ion distribution. The ions of interest are Ca^{2+}, Mg^{2+}, HCO_3^-, and H^+, along with the calculated values of total carbon, pCO_2 and SIc.

Any successful model or models must be able to explain:

i) Why the escarpment and dip slope springs differ in their chemistry

ii) Why the unconfined aquifer has such a uniform chemistry

iii) What solutional processes caused the zones of enhanced permeability to develop

iv) The increase of Ca^{2+}, pCO_2 and HCO_3^- in the semi-confined aquifer

v) The decrease of Ca^{2+}, increase of Na^+, HCO_3^- and total carbon in the confined zone.

Chemical evolution of spring water

The solution of calcite is given by,

$$CaCO_3 + CO_2 + H_2O = Ca^{2+} + 2HCO_3^- \qquad (4)$$

the equilibrium constant of this reaction being,

$$K_1 K_c B \ / K_2 \qquad (5)$$

as determined from the addition of the following reactions,

$$CaCO_3 = Ca^{2+} + CO_3^{2-} \qquad K_c \qquad (6)$$

$$CO_2 + H_2O = H_2CO_3^o \qquad B \qquad (7)$$

$$H_2CO_3 = H^+ + HCO_3^- \qquad K_1 \qquad (8)$$

$$HCO_3^- = H^+ + CO_3^{2-} \qquad K_2 \qquad (9)$$

Given that electrical neutrality requires that $2Ca^{2+} = HCO_3^-$,

$$\left[\frac{\alpha Ca^{2+} . \alpha HCO^-}{pCO_2}\right] = \left[\frac{4 \ \alpha Me^{2+}}{pCO_2}\right] = \left[\frac{K_1 K_c B}{K_2}\right] \qquad (10)$$

where the α is the ion activity,

$$\alpha Ca^{2+} = 0.63 \left[\left(\frac{K_1 K_c B}{K_2}\right)^{1/3}\right] . pCO_2^{1/3} \qquad (11)$$

In so far as the last first term of the RHS of (11) is solely a function of temperature, (f(T)), theory predicts that,

$$\alpha Ca^{2+} \quad = \quad f(T).pCO_2^{\,1/3}$$
(12)

The pCO_2 of all of the spring waters has a minimum in March and a maximum in Autumn. Dip springs have pCO_2 values which exceed -1.50, whereas scarp springs seldom exceed -1.80. Winter values of both springs average -2.40 to -2.70. Major differences are best examined in terms of the mode of carbonated evolution, with CO_2 being the major variable (Hendy, 1971; Langmuir, 1971; Pitman, 1978a).

Three modes of evolution are possible:

A. Open system evolution

$$mHCO_3^- \quad = \quad (K_1 BpCO_2)/(10^{-pH}. \ HCO_3^-)$$
(13)

B. Closed system evolution

$$mHCO_3^- \quad = \quad Constant/(2.10^{-pH} + K_1)$$
(14)

C. Equilibrium conditions

$$mHCO_3^- \quad = \quad 0.5(pH-log(2K_c/K_2)+log(Ca^{2+} + HCO_3^-)$$
(15)

Using the regressions found for the soil gas composition under arable, and HCO_3^- and pH as the master variables, Figure 10 was constructed. This shows all three evolution paths, assuming that the pCO_2 regression is realistic.

It can be concluded that scarp springs evolve under essentially closed conditions, option B above, whilst dip springs appear to be at least partially open to CO_2, option A above (Pitman, 1978a). It was postulated that the difference between open and closed system paths was related to the thickness of the unsaturated zone, and with groundwater temperature, as it is primely controlled by the penetration of the annual thermal heat flux (Pitman, 1984), which penetrates to a depth of at least 20m.

Groundwaters from the unconfined aquifer (Figure 11) evolve along saturation conditions, moving up and down the calcite saturation line in response to changing pCO_2 and temperature.

Groundwaters in the confined aquifer also follow type C conditions, modified by cation exchange and/or calcite precipitation. The scatter of points below the saturation line are the artesian samples, which are generally undersaturated with calcite as a result of the extra carbon dioxide input by either soil gas or by oxidation-reduction reactions.

These simple models, however, fail to tell us very much about the location of solutional activity in the aquifer. For the confined aquifer, several sets of reactions can be shown to predict where in the aquifer changes will take place.

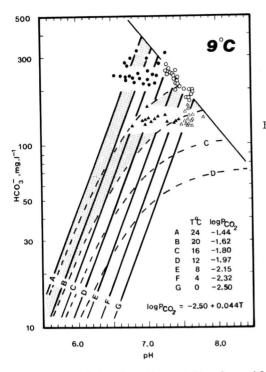

Figure 4.10 Plot of open (solid), closed (dashed) and equilibrium (solid diagonal) evolution curves of CO_2 evolution in terms of HCO_3 and pH. Dots spring 4 samples (dip type), triangles scarp (spring 1). Closed symbols are October samples; open, March samples. The regression equation is that determined from soil gas analyses on arable soils

T°C	$\log P_{CO_2}$
A 24	-1.44
B 20	-1.62
C 16	-1.80
D 12	-1.97
E 8	-2.15
F 4	-2.32
G 0	-2.50

$\log P_{CO_2} = -2.50 + 0.044T$

Chemical models for the confined aquifer

In the typical closed system aquifer, groundwaters originally containing dissolved oxidised species, such as oxygen, NO_3^-, $SO4^{2-}$ and CO_2 and excess dissolved organic carbon (DOC), (usually a simple carbohydrate, CH_2O) which acts as a reducing agent, under oxidation/reduction reactions:

a. Oxygen consumption, using CH_2O as DOC source

$$CH_2O + O_2 = CO_2 + H_2O \qquad (16)$$

b. Denitrification

$$CH_2O + 0.8NO_3^- + 0.8H^+ = CO_2 + 0.4N_2 + 1.4H_2O \qquad (17)$$

c. Iron reduction

$$CH_2O + 0.8H^+ + 4Fe(OH)_3 = 4Fe^{3+} + 11H_2O + CO_2 \qquad (18)$$

d. Sulphate reduction

$$2CH_2O + SO_4^{2-} = 2HCO_3^- + H_2S \qquad (19)$$

101

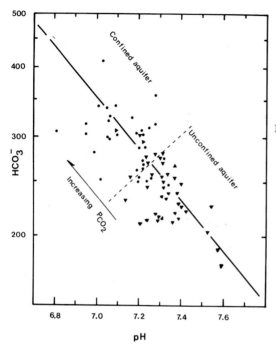

Figure 4.11 Distribution of unconfined well samples (triangles) and semi and fully confined bore and keld samples (dots) about the calcite saturation line (solid diagonal) for $9\,^\circ C$

In the confined aquifer, Fe^{3+} increases downdip, and H_2S is present in the bore samples. These reactions also predict that the total carbon increases, as does alkalinity. As the groundwaters are generally saturated with calcite, any increase in HCO_3^- is balanced by removal of calcite either by precipitation or by cation exchange for sodium and potassium:

$$\text{Mineral}|\,2Mex|^+ + Ca^{2+} = \text{Mineral}|\,Cax|^{2+} + 2Me^+ \qquad (20)$$

where Mex and Cax are the exchangeable cations. Between Bygot and High Esk, the $mmol.kgH_2O$ loss of Ca^{2+} (2.0 $mmol.kgH_2O$) is roughly balanced by the gain of Na^{2+} (2.3 $mmol.kgH_2O$) (see Figure 6).

In the first 2-3km of the semi-confined aquifer, HCO_3^- increases without any reduction of NO_3^- or SO_4^{2-}; indeed, these ion actually increase in this zone. Therefore the extra CO_2 must come from reaction (a) above, or by the influx of soil CO_2. Determination of DOC and ^{13}C would help resolve this point (Pitman, in preparation).

Determining chemical mass transfer in the aquifer

L.N. Plummer and W. Back (1980) have shown that if the changes in water composition between any two points in a groundwater system flow path can be determined, and are only due to *in situ* chemical reactions, then the net chemical change can be quantified by mass balance relations.

The mass balance method consists of balancing a net reaction of the form,

Initial solution composition + 'Reactant phase' =

Final solution composition + 'Product phase'

The 'reactant phase' and the 'product phase' are constituents that *enter or leave the aqueous phase* during chemical reaction. (Plummer *et al.*, 1983).

If the chemical composition of the final and initial waters is known, the geochemical reactions defined, and the solid phases present identified, a mass balance can be described between the reactants and products, using N equations, one for each constituent, of the form,

$$\text{where} \quad \sum_{j=1}^{\phi} \alpha_j \beta_{c,j} = \Delta M_c \Big|_{c\,=\,1,n} \tag{21}$$

ϕ is the total number of minerals and gases,

n the number of constituents necessary to define the composition of the chosen minerals and gases,

α_j the stoichiometric coefficient of the jth mineral or gas, mol.kg.H_2O, positive for reactant, negative for products.

$\beta_{c,j}$ the stoichiometric coefficients of the cth constituents in the jth mineral or gas (not H^+ or O)

ΔM_c is the change in moles.kg.H_2O of the cth component in the aqueous phase along the reaction path (final solution minus initial solution).

In this paper the program BALANCE (Parkhurst *et al.*, 1982) was used to determine the reaction coefficients. Plummer *et al.*, (1983) have described the difficulties associated with this method, as well as indicating its power to answer questions on plausible phases and reaction rates.

The most plausible phases present in the Yorkshire Chalk are as follows:

i) Calcite, $CaCO_3$

ii) Low magnesium calcite, $(Ca(1-x)Mgx)CO_3$, where x is the mole percent of Mg^{2+}, either 0.02 or 0.05

iii) CO_2 gas (soil)

iv) CO_2 gas (from CH_2O)

v) Pyrites.

vi) Ion exchange of $2(Na^+ + K^+)$ for $(Ca^{2+} + Mg^{2+})$

The amount of mass transfer was calculated for the following parts of the aquifer:

i) Rain to dip springs, scarp springs and Arras groundwater.

ii) Between Arras and Etton.

iii) Between Etton and Bygott nurseries (semi-confined aquifer)

iv) Between Bygott and Connygarth Farm.

For a system in which only calcite and CO_2 are present as phases, the following mass transfers (in mmoles per kg H_2O) take place between the wells or bore specified (Figure 12a). These results are of a preliminary nature, and require complete and rigorous testing before confidence can be placed on them (Pitman, in preparation).

From these reactions describing mass transfers, it is evident that the relative rates of calcite dissolution per kg H_2O are roughly in the order; vadose zone semi confined aquifer unconfined aquifer, with calcite precipitation being a feature of the fully confined aquifer. Ion exchange transfers become increasingly important in the confined aquifer; ion exchange plus precipitation serve to keep the groundwaters at calcite saturation throughout this part of the aquifer.

If consideration is given to the flux of water through the groundwater system, then the smaller hydrological cross section associated with the seasonal movement of the water table in the semi confined zone, which is the major area of natural groundwater discharge for the whole aquifer (Figure 5), imply that actual rates of solutional activity are probably highest in that zone of the aquifer. The driving force here is the reduction of the CO_2 donor, probably CH_2O.

Mimram (1978) has produced convincing evidence that the Yorkshire chalks have undergone moderate cementation by secondary calcite, high in strontium. Figures 2 and 3 illustrate the presence of secondary calcite within the chalk matrix and pore space. With calcium as the only carbonate phase present, secondary cementation is unlikely. However, if, in addition to calcite, a low magnesium calcite is introduced into the mass transfer calculations -the low magnesium calcite is probably a 5 mole percent Mg^{2+} carbonate/95 mole percent Ca^{2+} carbonate (Mimram, 1978; Pitman, 1978c)- then the following picture emerges.

The reactions are the same as before with low magnesium calcite added to the phases (Figure 12b). It should be noted that the experimental data for the solubility of low $CaMgCO_3$ is uncertain (see the review by MacKenzie *et al.*, 1983), but field sedimentological evidence attest to the disappearance of low $CaMgCO_3$ during freshwater diagensis, and its replacement with calcite (Bathhurst, 1976).

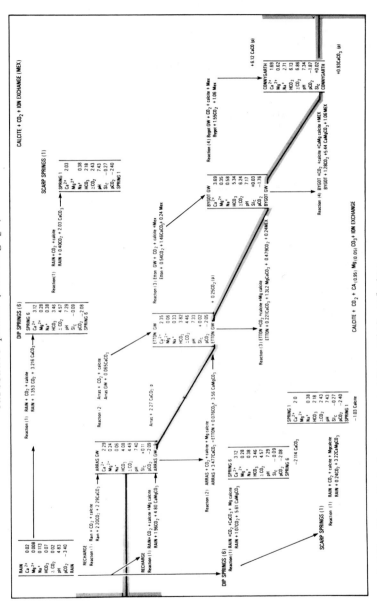

Figure 4.12a Calculated mass transfer between selected points in the East Yorkshire Chalk, with calcite as the only carbonate phase (mmol.kgH₂0)

Figure 4.12b Calculated mass transfer, with calcite and 5%mole Mg calcite as phases. (mmol.kgH₂0)

The advantage of adding $CaMgCO_3$ to the phases is that not only does it explain the observations of Mimram (1978), but it also predicts that calcite will precipitate in the vadose zone, as has been recently demonstrated by Dever *et al.*, (1983). Additionally, smaller amounts of CO_2 are required, and the Mg^{2+} contents are accounted for. However, further work is required before confidence can be placed on these observations.

Rates of weathering from the Givendale Data

Rates of weathering have been determined from the flux of ions through the small outlier, after correcting the total groundwater flux for changes in groundwater storage in the census period March to March. Whilst the seasonal rate of ion flux is highly variable, the total fluxes (Table 7) averaged over the whole catchment give a Ca solute rate of 315.5 $kg.ha^{-1}.year^{-1}$. If the scarp and dip springs are treated separately, then the flux is 315 $kg.ha^{-1}.year^{-1}$ from the arable soils, and 198 $kg.ha^{-1}.year^{-1}$ for the fallow soils. Rates of denudation are given in Table 8. If these rates are compared to the lysimeter data, then the probable origin of the dissolved calcium is as follows:

Landuse	Arable	Grass
soil lysimeter	80.3%	72.6%
Vadose/phreatic		
solution	19.7%	27.2%

Comparison with other estimated rates of denudation

Equation (11) can be used to estimate directly the rate of calcite dissolution as a function of temperature (Pitman, 1976). Substituting the values of B, K_1, K_2, and Kc, as given by the temperature functions of Plummer and Busenberg (1982), Table 9 was constructed. Denudation rates calculated from this equation, assuming a chalk bulk density of 2.00 $g.cm^{-3}$, are in reasonable agreement with the measured rates of solutional lowering at Givendale.

Finally, it needs to be stressed that the traditional black box approach to solution studies has major limitations, particularly in so far as it is not possible to find out the details of chemical mass transfer within the aquifer. Only by tracing the detailed evolution of carbonate groundwaters by direct sampling of the saturated aquifer waters can our understanding be improved. The mass balance approach offers a method whereby this information can be acquired.

Table 4.7 Total ion flux (kg.ha⁻¹.yr⁻¹) at Givendale, before and after correcting for the contribution of groundwater storage change to the total water flux, and for rain and fertilizer ion inputs

Ion removal, kg.ha⁻¹.annum⁻¹

Spring	1	2	3	4	5	6	7	8	9	11	12	Mean	S.D.
Ca^{2+}	462.2	327.3	352.6	556.0	509.4	411.7	189.1	281.3	263.0	366.0	399.7	315.5	79.4
	224.1	325.4	327.5	424.8	431.9	362.3		257.4	243.5	363.0	321.4		
Mg^{2+}	16.64	15.5	11.34	29.2	16.5	24.9	10.1	19.1	21.7	14.8	18.6	16.5	3.92
	13.93	15.4	10.5	22.7	13.9	21.8		17.5	20.2	14.6	14.9		
Na^{+}	26.5	23.5	18.8	37.1	24.4	37.2	15.3	28.1	28.9	24.2	24.7	23.3	5.0
	22.1	23.4	17.5	28.4	20.7	32.7		25.7	26.7	24.1	19.9		
K^{+}	2.44	2.86	3.00	9.20	2.38	25.6	6.40	2.80	3.01	3.31	3.48	3.46*	1.75
	2.10	2.85	2.78	6.99	2.02	22.6		2.56	2.79	3.29	2.80		
Cl^{-}	66.5	51.6	55.1	92.2	80.2	83.2	60.4	68.8	68.1	75.7	77.1		
	56.9	51.4	51.2	69.5	67.9	73.2		62.9	63.1	73.4	62.1		
NO_3^{-}	79.3	111.0	185.1	137.1	292.1	213.1	72.4	168.3	181.3	157.9	229.5	147.0	54.1
	67.8	116.0	171.3	105.4	247.7	187.5		153.9	168.2	157.8	184.4		
Area, hectres**	5.74	3.44	1.46	3.86	1.57	26.93	1.47	6.62	0.61	3.7	10.28		65.

*   This mean ignores the figure for spring six.

** To obtain the original load, multiply the load, kg.ha⁻¹.annum⁻¹ by the area in hectres.

The lower figure refers to the net ion removal, after subtraction of storage load.

Table 4.8 Rates of denudation estimated for Givendale under different landuse types

Net rate of ion removal, $kg.ha^{-1}.annum^{-1}$.

	Arable	Bare earth	Grass
Ca^{+2}	314.58	198.00	172.23
Mg^{+2}	29.25	8.91	24.25
Na^{+}	-4.42(-1.64)	-3.04(-0.26)	-3.20(-0.42)
K^{+}	14.6	4.94	9.87
SO_4^{-2}	14.14	15.27	4.76
NO_3^{-}	217.55	89.45	-3.59
Cl^{-}	16.51	3.18	-2.01

Rate of Chemical Weathering

	Arable	Bare earth	Grass
$cm.annum^{-1}$	0.0039	0.0025	0.0021
$annum.cm^{-1}$	254	405	465

Table 4.9 Theoretical rates of denudation estimated solely as a function of the fundamental constants of calcite equilibria, and the arable regression of temperature versus soil pCO_2, from the expression

$$\alpha Ca = 0.63 \left[((B.K_1.K_c)/K_2)^{1/3} \right].pCO_2^{1/3}$$

It should be noted that this result is an approximation, as ion molalities are assumed to equal ion activities (Pitman, 1976 gives an exact solution, corrected for sample ionic strength and ion pairs)

Temperature, C	log f(T)	log pCO_2	Ca, $mg.l^{-1}$	mm.k yr^{-1}*
0	-2.0061	-2.50	58.01	21.7
5	-2.0369	-2.28	63.98	23.9
10	-2.0693	-2.06	70.29	26.3
15	-2.1043	-1.84	76.79	28.7
20	-2.1356	-1.62	84.59	31.6

* This assumes a chalk BD of 2.0g.cm, with a measured (P-E) of 300mm per year (Pitman, 1976)

CONCLUSIONS

Systematic changes in the dissolved concentration of Ca^{2+}, Mg^{2+}, Na^+, HCO_3^- and the derived parameters log pCO_2 and log SIc occur along the hydrological flow path of groundwater in the East Yorkshire Chalk. Three major zones, coincident with the major hydrological subdivision of the aquifer can be identified.

In the unconfined zone, water chemistry is dominated by dissolution/precipitation reactions, involving CO_2 and calcite, producing a groundwater dominated by Ca^{2+}, Mg^{2+} and HCO_3^-. Recharge water is low in dissolved cations, but inputs most of the groundwater SO_4^{2-} and Cl^-; most NO_3^- comes from fertilizers. These ions serve to increase the Ca^{2+} concentrations over that predicted by the pCO_2, as a result of their effects on ionic strength, ion-pairing and solute charge balance. Output from the soil profile contributes 80% of the dissolved Ca^{2+} and Mg^{2+}, after reacting under open system conditions with soil CO_2. This effect is further manifest in the difference in spring water composition draining the unconfined aquifer, with shallow parts of the aquifer being partially or wholly open to soil CO_2. Groundwater from this aquifer zone is saturated with calcite.

The movement of groundwater from unconfined conditions to semi-confined conditions along the chalk dipslope results in major changes in the dissolved concentrations of Ca^{2+}, Mg^{2+}, Na^+, K^+ and HCO_3^-. These changes are best explained by a combination of oxidation-reduction reactions, calcite dissolution, and ion exchange with aquifer clay minerals. The addition of CO_2 in the first 3km of this zone results in marked dissolution of calcite in this zone.

In the third, fully confined aquifer zone, ion exchange, and the precipitation of calcite coupled with the reduction of SO_4^{2-} and NO_3^- best explain the water chemistry observed, and demonstrate the control of calcite equilbria on the Ca^{2+} concentrations.

Overall rates of surface lowering are in reasonable agreement with rates estimated by a theoretical calcite solubility equation.

Chemical mass balance calculations can be used to predict the loci and amount of calcite dissolution and precipitation within the aquifer, with estimates of rates determined from the water flux through the system.

REFERENCES

Atkinson, R.J. 1957. Worms and weathering. *Antiquity,* **31**, 218-233.

Back, W. and Hanshaw, H.H. 1971. Rates of physical and chemical processes in a carbonate aquifer. In: *Non equilibrium systems in natural water chemistry,* Advances in Chemistry, No. 106, 77-93, Amer. Chem. Soc., (Reinhold, NY).

Barrett, C.F., Atkins, D.H.F., Cape, J.N., Fowler, D., Irwin, J.G., Kallend, A.S. Martin, A., Pitman, J.I., Scriven, R.A. and Tuck, A.F. 1984. *Acid deposition in the United Kingdom,* UKRGAR, (Warren Spring Laboratory, Stevenage), 72pp.

Bath, A.H. and Edmunds, W.M. 1981. Identification of connate water in interstitial solutions of chalk sediment. *Geochim. et Cosmochim. Act.,* **45**, 1449-61.

Bathurst, R.G.C. 1976. *Carbonate sediments and their diagenesis.* Dev. Sedimentology, **12**, 2nd (Elsevier, Amsterdam), 658pp.

Bird, M.J. 1976. Core analysis results from the East Yorkshire Chalk. IGS Rept. 76/3, (HMSO, Lond.), 58-62.

Casey, H. 1969. The chemical composition of some S. English chalk streams and its relation to discharge. *Assoc. River Authorities Yr. Bk.,* 100-113.

Casey, H. and Newton, P.V.R. 1973. The chemical composition and flow of the River Frome and its tributaries. *Freshwater Biology,* **3**, 317-333.

Catt, J.A. and Penny, L.F. 1966. The Pleistocene deposits of Holderness, East Yorkshire. *Proc. Yorks. Geol. Soc.,* **35**, 375-420.

Catt, J.A., Weir, A.J. and Madgett, P.A. 1974. The loess of Eastern Yorkshire and Lincolnshire. *Proc. Yorks. Geol. Soc.,* **40**, 23-39.

Champ, D.R., Culens, J. and Jackson, R.E. 1979. Oxidation-reduction sequences in groundwater flow systems. *Can. J. Earth Sci.,* **16**, 12-23.

Clayton, C.R.I. 1983. The influence of diagenesis on some index properties of chalk in England. *Geotechnique,* **33**, 225-241.

Cole, E.M. 1879. On the origin and formation of the Wolds of Yorkshire. *Proc. Yorks. Geol. Soc.,* **7**, 128-140.

Cole, E.M. 1887. Note on dry valleys of the Chalk. *Proc. Yorks. Geol. Soc.,* **9**, 333-336.

De Boer, G. 1944. A system of glacier lakes in the Yorkshire Wolds. *Proc. York. Geol. Soc.,* **25**, 223-233.

De Boer, G., Neale, J.W. and Penny, L.F. 1958. A guide to the geology of the area between Market Weighton and the Humber. *Proc. Yorks. Geol. Soc.,* **31**, 157-209.

Dever, L., Durand, R., Fontes, J.Ch. and Vacher, P. 1983.
Etude pedogénetique et isotopique des neoformations de
calcite dans un sol sur craie. *Geochim. et Cosmochim. Acta.*,
47, 2079-2090.

Douglas, I. 1968. Some factors in the denudation of limestone
terrains. *Zeit. fur Geomorphologie,* **NF.12**, 214-253.

Drake, J.J. and Wigley, T.M.L. 1975. The effect of climate on
the chemistry of carbonate groundwater. *Water Res. Res.*,
11(6), 959-962.

Edmunds, W.M. 1973. Trace element variations across an oxidation-
reduction barrier in a limestone aquifer. *Proc. Symp.*
Hydeo-geochemistry and Biogeochemistry, Tokyo, 1972,
(ed. E. Ingerson), Clarke, Washington, DC, 500-526.

Edmunds, W.M., Loverlock, P.E.R. and Gray, D.A. 1973. Interstitial water chemistry and aquifer properties in the Upper
and Middle Chalk of Berkshire. *J. Hydrol.*, **19**, 21-31.

Foster, S.S.D. 1974. Groundwater storage-riverflow relations
in a chalk catchment. *J. Hydrol.*, **23**, 299-311.

Foster, S.S.D. and Crease, R.E. 1974. Nitrate pollution of
chalk groundwater in East Yorkshire-a hydrological appraisal.
J. Inst. Water Engrs., **28**, 178-194.

Foster, S.S.D. and Crease, R.E. 1974. Hydraulic behaviour of
the Chalk aquifer in the Yorkshire Wolds. *Proc. Inst. Civil*
Engrs., Pt.2, **59**, 181-188.

Foster, S.S.D., Cripps, A.C. and Smith-Carington, A. 1982.
Nitrate leaching to groundwater. *Phil. Trans. R. Soc. Lond.*,
296, 477-489.

Foster, S.S.D. and Milton, V.A. 1974. The permeability and
storage of an unconfined chalk aquifer. *Hydrol. Sci. Bull.*,
18, 485-500.

Foster, S.S.D. and Milton, V.A. 1976. *Hydrological basis for*
large scale development of groundwater storage capacity
in the East Yorkshire Chalk. IGS Rept. 76/3, (HMSO, Lond.),
71pp.

Foster, S.S.D., Parry E.L. and Chilton, J. 1976. *Groundwater*
resource development and saline water intrusion in the
Chalk aquifer of North Humberside. IGS Rept. 76/4, (HMSO,
Lond.), 34pp.

Garrels, R.M. 1976. A survey of low temperature water-mineral
relations. *Interpret. Environ. Isot. Hydrochem. Data*
Groundwater Hydrology, Proc. Advis. Grp. Meeting, 1975,
65-84.

Hancock, J.M. 1975. The petrology of the chalk. *Proc. Geol.*
Assoc., **86**, 499-535.

Hendy, C.H. 1971. The isotropic chemistry of speleotherms-I.
Geochim. et Cosmochim. Act., **35**, 801-824.

Imeson, A.C. 1970. *Erosion in three East Yorkshire catchments and variation in dissolved, suspended and bed loads.* Unpublished Ph.D. thesis, Univ. Hull.

Ineson, J. and Downing, R.A. 1963. Changes in the chemistry of groundwaters in the chalk passing beneath argillaceous strata. *Bull. Geol. Surv. Gt. Brit.,* **20**, 176-192.

Jacobson, R.L. and Languir, D. 1974a. Controls on the quality variation of some carbonate spring waters. *J. Hydrology,* **23**, 247-265.

Jacobson, R.L. and Languir, D. 1974b. Dissociation constants of calcite and $CaHCO_3^+$ from 0-50°C. *Geochim. et Cosmochim. Acta,* **38**, 301-318.

Jeans, C.V. 1968. The origin of the montmorillonite of the European Chalk with special reference to the Lower Chalk of England. *Clay Minerals,* **7**, 311-330.

Kent, P.E. 1980. *Eastern England from the Tees to the Wash.* 2nd edition, IGS, NERC, (HMSO, London) 155pp.

Langmuir, D. 1971. The geochemistry of some carbonate groundwaters in central Pennsylvania. *Geochim. et Cosmochim. Acta,* **35**, 1023-1045.

Lawrence, T., Foster, S.S.D. and Izzard, W. 1983. Nitrate pollution in East Yorkshire revisited. *J. Inst. Water. Engrs. Sci.,* **38**, 408-420.

Lewin, J. 1969. *The Yorkshire Wolds: a study in geomorphology.* Occasional papers in Geography, No. 11, Univ. Hull, 85pp.

MacKenzie, F.T., Bischoff, W.D., Bishop, F.C., Loijens, M., Schoonmaker, J. and Wollast, R. 1983. Magnesium calcites: low temperature occurrence, solubility, and solid solution behaviour. In: *Carbonates: Mineralogy and Chemistry, Rev. Mineralogy,* ed. R.J. Reeder, 11, Amer. Min. Soc., 97-144.

Mimram, Y. 1978. The induration of the Yorkshire and Irish Chalks. *Sed. Geol.,* **20**, 141-164.

Mortimer, J.R. 1885. The origin of the chalk dales of Yorkshire. *Proc. York Geol. Soc.,* **9**, 29-42.

Neale, J.W. 1974. Cretaceous. In: *The Geology and Mineral Resources of Yorkshire,* eds. D.H. Rayner and J.G. Hemingway, York. Geol. Soc., Leeds, 405pp.

Parkhurst, D.L., Plummer, L.N. and Thorstenson, D.C. 1982. BALANCE: a computer program for calculating mass transfer from geochemical reactions in groundwater. *U.S. Geological Survey, Water Resources Invest. 82-14,* 33pp, NTIS Tech. Rept. PB82-255902, Springfield, V.A. 22161.

Penny, L.F. 1974. Quaternary. In: *ibid,* eds D.H. Rayner and J.G. Hemingway.

Perrin, F. 1964. The use of drainage water analysis in soil studies. In: *Experimental Pedology,* eds E.G. Hallsworth and C.V. Crawford, 73-96.

Pitman, J.I. 1976. *The geochemistry of some waters draining the Chalk of East Yorkshire, and their geomorphological significance*. Unpublished Ph.D., Univ. Hull.

Pitman, J.I. 1978a. Carbonate chemistry of groundwater from Chalk, Givendale, East Yorkshire. *Geochim. Cosmochim. Acta,* 42, 1885-1897.

Pitman, J.I. 1978b. Carbonate chemistry of groundwater from tropical Tower karst, S. Thailand. *Water Re. Res.,* 14(3), 961-967.

Pitman, J.I. 1978c. Chemistry and mineralogy of some Lower and Middle Chalks from Givendale, East Yorkshire. *Clay Minerals,* 13, 93-100.

Pitman, J.I. 1984. Thermal diffusivity of Upper Chalk from Hampshire, England. *Engineering Geology,* 20, 207-218.

Pitman, J.I. 1984. Hydrogeochemistry of the East Yorkshire Chalk. In preparation.

Plummer, L.N. and Back W. 1980. The mass balance approach: its application to interpreting the chemical evolution of hydrologic systems. *Amer. J. Sci.,* 280, 130-142.

Plummer, L.N. and Busenberg, E. 1982. The solubilities of calcite, aragonite and vaterite in CO_2-H_2O solutions between 0-90°C and an evaluation of the aqueous model for the system $CaCO_3$-CO_2-H_2O. *Geochim. Cosmochim. Acta,* 46, 1011-1040.

Plummer, L.N., Parkhurst, D.L. and Thorstenson, D.C. 1983. Development of reaction models for groundwater systems. *Geochim. Cosmochim. Acta,* 47, 665-86.

Reardon, E.J. and Langmuir, D.L. 1974. Thermodynamic properties of the ion pairs $MgHCO_3{}^+$ and $CaCO_3{}^o$ from 10-50°C. *Amer. J. Sci.,* 274, 599-612.

Scholle, P.A. 1977. Chalk Diagensis and its relation to petroleum exploration: Oil from chalks, a modern miracle? *Amer. Ass. Petr. Geol. Bull.,* 61, 982-1009.

Truesdell, A.H. and Jones, B.F. 1974. WATEQ: a computer program for calculating chemical equilibria of natural water. *J. Res. U.S. Geol. Surv.,* 2, 233-48.

Wood, C.J. and Smith, E.G. 1978. Lithostratigraphical classification of the Chalk of North Humberside and Lincolnshire. *Proc. Yorks. Geol. Soc.,* 42, 263-87.

Wright, C.W. and Wright, E.V. 1942. The Chalk of the Yorkshire Wolds. *Proc. Geol. Ass.,* 53, 112-127.

Additional reference:

Shuster, T.E. and White, W.B. 1972. Source areas and climatic effects in carbonate groundwaters determined by saturation indices and carbon dioxide pressures. *Water Resources Research,* 8(4), 1067-1073.

5

'Phytokarst', blue-green algae and limestone weathering

H.A. Viles and T. Spencer

SUMMARY

A micro-organic layer, dominated by blue-green algae or lichens, is found on most carbonate substrates and appears to influence limestone weathering. With advances in taxonomy and microscopy, the nature of this layer can now be more accurately defined. Studies on Aldabra Atoll, Indian Ocean and Grand Cayman Island, Caribbean Sea, have shown that algal colonization rates are rapid in subtidal and intertidal environments. However, colonization rates are much slower on subaerial surfaces and it is unlikely that 'phytokarst' landscapes are solely the product of blue-green algae.

RÉSUMÉ

Sur la plupart des roches calcaires on trouve une couche micro-organique composée principalement d'algues bleues-vertes et de lichens. Elle semble influencer les processus d'altération de ces roches. Grâce aux progrès de la taxonomie et de la micro-scopie la nature de cette couche peut être définie maintenant de façon plus précise. Les études menées sur l'atoll d'Aldabra dans l'Océan Indien et à l'île de Grand Cayman aux Caraibes ont montré que la vitesse de colonisation des algues est rapide dans les zones supralittorales et médiolittorales. Toutefois les vitesses de colonisation sont plus lentes sur les surfaces subaériennes et il est improbable que les paysages dits de 'phytokarst' soient uniquement le résultat des algues bleues-vertes.

INTRODUCTION

One of the major problems continuing to face karst geomorphology is to explain how solution and other weathering processes acting upon limestones become translated into overall surface lowering, erosion rates and ultimately, karst landforms. Limestone weathering has often been equated with limestone solubility and thus, at its simplest, seen to be a function of carbon dioxide concentration and temperature. Even on apparently simple sub-aerial surfaces, however, the solution of limestone does not conform to that expected and must be influenced by additional factors. The position is even more marked in littoral environments where recent studies have shown the importance to limestone weathering of a whole suite of chemical, physical and biological processes (Schneider, 1976; Trudgill, 1976; Torunski, 1979).

One of the confounding influences on limestone weathering is that provided by the presence of organisms. This influence varies greatly with the type of organism involved and Bull and Laverty (1982) provide a good review of the range of possible biological action. To date, studies of biological influences upon limestone weathering have been fragmentary and have tended to concentrate upon the explanation of unusual landforms which may be directly correlated with biological activity. By comparison, the general presence of a cover of micro-organisms on so-called 'bare' limestone surfaces and the direct and indirect influence of this layer on limestone weathering processes and landform development has not yet been adequately investigated.

In this paper we attempt to assess this more general 'biological component of weathering'. Specifically, our arguments are structured around the following questions:

(a)   What is the distribution and nature of the surface microflora on carbonate substrates and how can it be adequately identified?

(b)   in what way, and how quickly, do micro-organisms colonize littoral surfaces in the tropics and how does this process influence limestone weathering and erosion?

(c)   what is meant by 'phytokarst'? Does this term hold implications for the evolution of large-scale karst landforms?

116

DISTRIBUTION OF MICRO-ORGANISMS

Observations of the presence of micro-organisms on calcareous substrates throughout the world are fragmentary. Nevertheless, Table 5.1 shows that a surface microflora covers outcrops of limestone (and other calcareous substrates such as corals, shells and calcareous sands) in terrestrial, littoral and marine environments and in polar, temperate and tropical regions.

The major constituents of the surface microflora are eukaryotic algae (green algae, red algae and other types possessing a nucleus in their cells), prokaryotic algae (blue-green algae, which lack a true nucleus), fungi, lichens and bacteria. No detailed studies have been made of the different global distributions of these organisms. Most are widespread, but factors such as competition and micro-environmental control will condition the type of organism found in any one area. However, it may be significant that blue-green algae are the dominant constituent of the terrestrial microflora of tropical Aldabra Atoll (Whitton, 1971), whereas lichens seem to make up the bulk of the surface flora in many temperate areas (e.g. Klappa, 1979).

In all these localities, the micro-organic layer is often clearly visible, giving the rock surface a characteristic colour which differs from that of the internal rock structure. Its thickness ranges from a few microns to several millimetres. In terrestrial environments on Aldabra Atoll for example, the characteristically black surface layer, found on most unshaded rock surfaces, usually has a thickness of 0.5 to 2.0 mm (Viles, unpublished data). Little is known about the extent of surface cover provided by micro-organisms, but this paper shows that it often reaches 100 per cent. The controls on thickness and extent have not yet been elucidated, but it is likely that environmental factors, the nature of the substrate and grazing pressure from larger organisms all play contributing roles.

Within the general surface community several distinct niches can be recognized. The epilithic niche is occupied by organisms dwelling purely on the surface, the endolithic niche by organisms actively boring into the substrate and subsequently inhabiting their boreholes, and the chasmolithic cavities (Golubic *et al.*, 1981). Organisms associated with these various niches may play active or passive roles, or both, in the weathering of limestone. Firstly, the epilithic 'mat' found in many areas creates its own micro-environment. Secondly, it has long been shown (Duncan, 1877; Duerden, 1902; Nadson, 1927) that the endolithic types form a network of boreholes. This both directly weakens the host substrate and indirectly encourages surface removal by grazing activity and abrasion. The presence of an endolithic component, composed of many communities of micro-organisms, means that in effect the surface layer extends down into the substrate, usually to several hundred microns, but sometimes deeper where particular

Table 5.1 Observations of surface micro-organisms on calcareous substrates

Location	Environment and Substrate	Organisms present	Author(s) and date
Poland, Yugoslavia, Switzerland, Czechoslovakia	Terrestrial, Limestone	Bacteria, Fungi	Smyk and Drzal (1964)
Malham, Yorkshire, U.K.	Limestone pavement	Lichens	Jones (1965)
Jerusalem – Dead Sea, Israel	Terrestrial, Limestone	Lichens, Blue-green algae	Danin et al. (1982)
Negev desert, Israel	Desert Limestone	'Biological solution fronts' of Lichens, Blue-green algae, Fungi	Krumbein (1979)
Ceylon	Terrestrial, various	Blue-green algae	Fritsch (1907)
Java	Terrestrial, Limestone	Blue-green algae	Koster (1939)
Aldabra Atoll, Indian Ocean	Terrestrial, Limestone	Blue-green algae	Whitton and Donaldson (1971)
West Malaysia	Terrestrial, Limestone	Lichens	Crowther (1979)
Caribbean	Terrestrial, Limestone	Lichens, Algae	Pfeffer (1981)
Cayman Islands, Caribbean	Terrestrial, Limestone	Blue-green algae	Folk et al. (1973)
Antarctica	Dry valleys	Blue-green algae	Friedmann and Ocampo (1976)
France	Caves	Blue-green algae	Bourelly and Dupuy (1973)
New South Wales, Australia	Caves	Green algae, Blue-green algae, fungi and bacteria	Cox and Marchant (1977)
Gunong Mulu, Sarawak	Caves	Algae	Bull and Laverty (1982)
Malham, Yorkshire, U.K.	Fluvial, Tufa	Blue-green algae	Pentecost (1978)
Mallorca	Littoral, Limestone	Algae	Kelletat (1980)
Mallorca, Ibiza, S.E. Spain	Littoral, Limestone, Calcrete	Lichens	Klappa (1979)
Spain, Sorrento	Littoral, Limestone	Blue-green algae	Golubic (1972)

Cont...

Location	Environment	Organisms	Reference
Marseilles, France	Littoral, Limestone	Blue-green algae, Green algae	Le Campion-Alsumard (1970)
Yugoslavia	Littoral, Limestone	Blue-green algae, Green algae, Fungi	Schneider (1976); Torunski (1979)
Gulf of Aqaba, Israel	Beachrock	Red algae, Green algae, Blue-green algae, Bacteria	Krumbein (1979)
Aldabra Atoll, Indian Ocean	Littoral, Limestone	Blue-green algae	Whitton and Potts (1980); Potts and Whitton (1980)
Raroia, Tuamotu Archipelago	Littoral, Reef sediments	Blue-green algae	Newhouse (1954)
Onotoa, Gilbert Islands	Littoral, Reef sediments	Algae	Moul (1953)
Perth, West Australia	Littoral, Limestone	Blue-green algae	Hodgkin (1964)
Heron Island, Great Barrier Reef	Beachrock	Algae, esp. Blue-green algae	Davies and Kinsey (1973)
Bahamas	Intertidal, Limestone	Blue-green algae	Purdy and Kornicker (1958)
Cayman Islands	Beachrock	Green algae	Jones and Goodbody (1982)
Arlington Reef, Great Barrier Reef	Reef sediments	Green algae, Red algae, Fungi	Rooney and Perkins (1972)
Bermuda	Reefs	Green algae	Schroeder (1972)
Bahamas	Oolitic ridge	Blue-green algae	Harris et al. (1977)
Connemara, W. Ireland	Shelf, Skeletal sands	Algae	Gunatilika (1976)
Strait of Juan de Fuca, British Columbia	Subtidal, Shells	Green algae, Red algae, Fungi	Henderson and Styan (1982)
S.E. United States	Continental margin, Sediments	Green algae, Fungi	Edwards and Perkins (1974)
Puerto Rico	Shelf, Sediments	Blue-green algae, Green algae, Fungi	Budd and Perkins (1980)
St. Croix, Virgin Islands	Subtidal shelf, Calcite and Shells	Blue-green algae, Green algae, Fungi	Perkins and Tsentas (1976)
Discovery Bay, Jamaica	Subtidal, Calcite	Green algae	Kobluk and Risk (1977)

organisms are not dependent upon light as a source of energy. Furthermore, the presence of a chasmolithic layer may increase the potential for substrate modification to a depth of 5.0 mm.

TAXONOMY AND METHODOLOGY

Unfortunately, there are problems in trying to refine the general comments above into more quantitative assessments of the geo-morphological significance of micro-organisms. These difficulties concern the recognition of individual organisms and the niches which they inhabit.

The very small size of most micro-organisms, often only 1-10 microns in diameter, creates obvious problems of recognition. These have been partly overcome by the advent of high-powered microscopy, but the basic taxonomy of many organisms is still uncertain. This is, firstly, because the lack of knowledge of organism structure and function makes taxonomic grouping difficult and, secondly, because morphological variation occurs with changing environmental conditions in many micro-organisms. Thus the blue-green alga *Entophysalis deusta* is seen by some workers as having a wide range of forms, whereas other researchers reserve this species name for organisms having only a narrow range of characteristics (Le Campion-Alsumard, 1970). The green algae have also suffered from problems of identification; Lukas (1979), for example, has pointed out that Kobluk and Risk (1977) wrongly identified the genus *Phaeophilia* as *Ostreobium*. Similarly, fungi and bacteria are notoriously hard to identify and their taxonomy is even less well developed than that of the algae. Clearly, comparative studies have been hindered by the lack of agreement on identification. Recently, however, methods have been developed by botanists to ensure greater comparability. In particular, the work of Golubic (1969), expanded by Whitton and co-workers (Potts and Whitton, 1980) has helped to establish more rigorous guidelines for the identification of blue-green algal species. Their work is based upon the classic taxonomic schemes of Geitler (1932) and Desikachary (1959), adding carefully established size criteria to aid identification in controversial cases. The studies of Aldabran blue-green algae (Donaldson and Whitton, 1977; Potts and Whitton, 1980; Whitton and Potts, 1980) have all been carried out using these guidelines and the data computer-coded and stored, providing a valuable data bank and example of method for other workers.

The assessment of which niche type an organism inhabits is also very difficult, as in most cases substrates are often opaque and heterogeneous and many micro-organisms are capable of coating their outer surfaces with calcium carbonate. Light microscope techniques generally cannot provide information on the growth position of the organism, unless the substrate is transparent, for example calcite, or can be rendered transparent by mounting in liquid of an appropriate optical density. A partial way around this problem is to use Donaldson's method, devised for the terrestrial blue-green algae of Aldabra Atoll (personal communication). His procedure compares the algal flora derived from simple surface scrapes with that obtained by dissolving the upper layers of calcium carbonate with HCl or EDTA (Van Reine and Den Hoek, 1966) in an attempt to differentiate between epilithic and other types. Unfortunately, however, it is not clear from Donaldson's procedure whether the 'released algae' occupied endolithic niches, chasmolithic niches or were just buried beneath a layer of precipitated carbonate. To study the flora *in situ,* techniques associated with scanning electron microscopy are required. Golubic and his co-workers (1970) have developed combined casting and embedding techniques which allow the direct observation of the relationship between organism and substrate. This method involves the replacement of the host rock and/or the organisms present with an epoxy resin, followed by examination under the scanning electron microscope. Excellent photographs of patterns of endolithic boring obtained with this method are shown by Le Campion-Alsumard (1979a, 1979b); she has also illustrated how quantitative assessment of borehole density and substrate penetration can be made using this technique. A similar method involves the replacement of calcite with fluorite (Glover, 1978). Whatever the embedding technique, the subsequent scanning electron microscope observations of *in situ* organisms must be combined with rigorous taxonomic identification from the resin casts. This means that the complete Golubic procedure is complicated, time-consuming and beyond the scope of most geomorphologists. Fortunately, it is possible to work from more simply prepared material, with scanning electron microscopy being performed on samples where the organisms have been removed by a peroxide agent or preserved in their growth positions using freeze-hydration techniques. These findings can then be compared with the floral composition identified by light and scanning electron microscopy to obtain some notion of the nature and habit of the surface-dwelling organisms. The use of these techniques, allied with standard microscopic counting techniques to establish the quantitative importance of different forms, gives about as complete a description of the surface flora as is possible at the present time.

COLONIZATION OF LITTORAL LIMESTONES BY MICRO-ORGANISMS

Nips, notches and littoral karren are particularly well developed on limestone coasts in the tropics and subtropics. Such landforms also support a conspicuous colour zonation from the subtidal zone to the supratidal region (e.g. Florida: Ginsburg, 1953; Bahamas: Newell, Imbrie, Purdy and Thurber, 1959; Grand Cayman: Rigby and Roberts, 1976; Curacao: Föcke, 1978a; Aldabra Atoll: Potts and Whitton, 1980, Whitton and Potts, 1980; Figure 3). These broadly similar patterns are due to the presence of micro-organisms and especially to the dominance of the blue-green algae. Colouration is only partly due to the presence or absence of particular species of algae (Schneider, 1976) as shoreline position both directly affects the intensity of pigmentation and indirectly influences colour zoning through the type of niche occupied. Thus the supratidal and upper intertidal is characterized by epiliths and shallow-boring endoliths, whilst the lower intertidal is dominated by the deeper boring species (Le Campion-Alsumard, 1970; Golubic et al., 1975).

Recent experimentation on limestone coasts, designed to evaluate a range of possible weathering styles and erosive agents, has suggested that solution is by no means the dominant process of coastal recession and that abrasion may be locally important (Trudgill, 1976). Furthermore, biological action may be particularly destructive and, at least on coasts with a low tidal range, may be the dominant process of cliff retreat on high energy coasts (e.g. Yugoslavia: Schneider, 1976; Torunski, 1979; Curaçao: Föcke, 1978b; Grand Cayman: Spencer, unpublished data). Biological processes involve boring, grazing and encrusting strategies. The micro-organic layer plays a fundamental role in this suite of processes by weakening the rock surface through boring, by providing a food source for herbivores and by placing an organic layer between the rock and its immediate environment. The combination of the relative ineffectiveness of simple solution processes, a rich surface flora and high rates of colonization make littoral limestones useful sites for the study of micro-organic influences on rock weathering. Studies carried out by the present authors aimed to assess the colonization process in littoral and terrestrial environments on Aldabra Atoll, Indian Ocean and Grand Cayman Island, Caribbean Sea. The substrate studied on Aldabra was relatively unconsolidated beachrock; on Grand Cayman colonization was observed on tablets of Pleistocene and Tertiary limestone.

ALGAL COLONIZATION ON BEACHROCK: ALDABRA ATOLL, INDIAN OCEAN

Recently cemented beach sand, or beachrock, is a common intertidal deposit on atoll shores. Whilst it is generally believed that the cement is the product of mineral precipitation from groundwater or sea-water, it is possible that micro-organisms may also be involved in beachrock genesis (Bathurst, 1976; Hopley, 1982). Although it has been argued (Davies and Kinsey, 1973) that the algal mat only traps carbonate particles and does not actually participate in rock formation, Krumbein's (1979) model suggests that, at a later stage, reducing conditions may become established in the lower zone of the mat, decay of algae may occur and carbonate precipitation may take place. Similarly, Berner (1971) has argued for precipitation in anaerobic environments produced by bacterial processes. In spite of these studies, however, the exact role of micro-organisms in beachrock formation has still to be elucidated.

Aldabra Atoll ($9°24'S, 46°20'E$) is a slightly elevated coral reef north of Madagascar. Four main islands, with a land area of 155 km^2, surround a large central lagoon (Stoddart et al.,

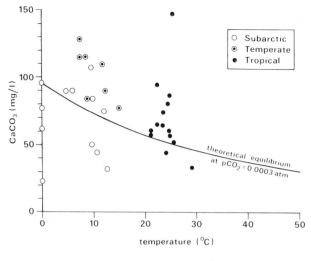

after Atkinson and Smith, 1976
and Crowther, 1979

Figure 5.1   Variation in calcite solubility with temperature
(after Atkinson and Smith, 1976 and Crowther, 1979)

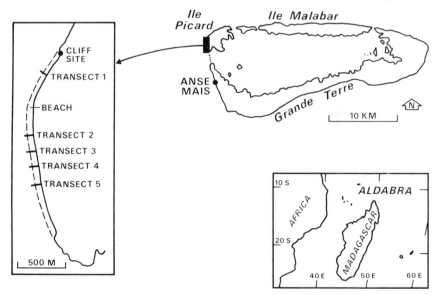

Figure 5.2   Location of beachrock site, Aldabra Atoll

1971). The mean annual precipitation is 1089 mm (1968-1982; D.R. Stoddart, personal communication).

The area of beachrock studies on the atoll was on Ile Picard on the more sheltered western oceanic coast (Figure 5.2). Observations were made over a four month, dry season period (June-September 1982). The beachrock outcrop is 1.5 km long, up to 35m wide and dips 10-15° in a seaward direction. It is composed of sand and coral debris with a mineralogy of aragonite and high magnesium calcite (Trudgill, 1981) and a variable hardness and morphology. Colour and morphological zonation is variable along the beachrock but three basic divisions can be recognized (Figure 5.3). These are, from beach crest to reef flat:

(a)   An upper zone, dissected into pools and ridges and coloured blue-grey or brown-grey.

(b)   An intermediate zone of generally low and flat morphology, often with large, shallow, seaward-pointing runnels and covered with a light and variably-coloured, spongy crust of sand and algae.

(c)   A lower zone of variable morphology and relief, often with ridge-and-pool development and grading into a debris zone where the reef flat begins.

This zonation is comparable to that described by Davies and Kinsey (1973) for Heron Island, Great Barrier Reef.

Few observations of colonization rates have been made previously. Whitton and Potts (1980) noted that on upper zone strata of the Ile Picard outcrop, freshly exposed after storms, colonization by blue-green algae proceeded at such a rate as to make this beachrock indistinguishable from surrounding areas after a period of five weeks. However, the characteristic green chasmolithic layer had not appeared by this time. It is not clear whether these observations were made under wet or dry season conditions. Previous studies of colonization rates in littoral and sublittoral environments have used experimentally-introduced substrates of calcite crystals (Le Campion-Alsumard, 1975; Golubic, 1969; Kobluk and Risk, 1977), sometimes in combination with shell material (Perkins and Tsentas, 1976; May and Perkins, 1979). These methods, however, were found to be unsuitable for the beachrock environment on Aldabra because of the high (2.79m) tidal range (Pugh, 1979) and the presence of large volumes of beach sand. Some calcite crystals attached to perspex plates (following the method of Le Campion-Alsumard, 1979c) were used, but the rates of crystal loss were high and the results equivocal. Furthermore, there is no reason why colonization rates on artificial substrates should be the same as those on limestone strata. It was decided, therefore, to study the colonization process on natural surfaces by clearing the surface layer (the micro-organic layer and the upper few millimetres of beachrock) from 10 x 10 cm squares of *in situ* rock. Seventeen sites were cleared on the five beachrock transects (Figure 5.3) and two sites were located in the notch zone

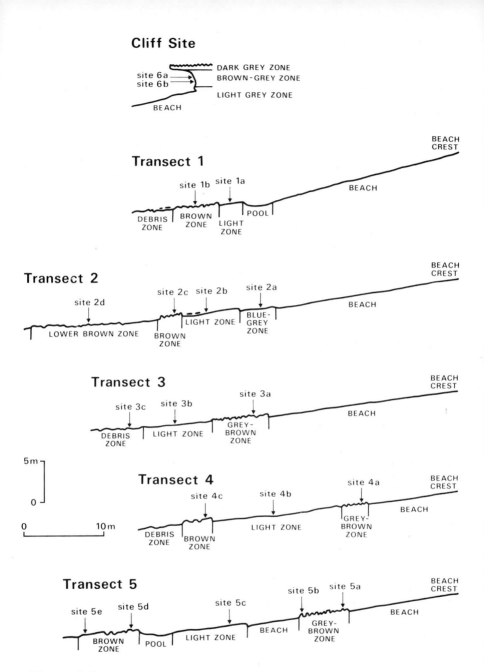

Figure 5.3   Beachrock profiles and study sites, Aldabra Atoll

125

of a cliff in the Aldabra Limestone facies (Braithwaite *et al.*, 1973). On clearance, the colour of the fresh surface was compared with that of the surrounding beachrock using a standard Colour Chart. This process was repeated when the sites were re-surveyed one week, one month, two months and four months after the initial clearance. At each visit surface scrapes of small amounts of the square were sampled for micro-organisms. The results of this exercise are presented in Table 5.2, representing the analysis of over two hundred microscope slides. The floral observations were not made to species level but have been grouped into characteristic types. Given the state of the taxonomy of the blue-green algae, this would seem realistic. Table 5.2 does not record the total abundance of micro-organisms present, although it should be clear that a site with a well developed, spongy crust has a more dense flora than a site with only sparse colouration. Also, the relative abundance of particular types of organism is not noted as, in most cases, there was no clearly dominant species. Although there was variability in the rates of colonization observed, some basic trends can be identified.

In general, surface colonization commenced between one week and one month after clearance and most sites were almost indistinguishable from their surroundings after four months, being identifiable only because of the absence of the larger surface organisms, such as barnacles (*Tetrachthamalus oblitteratus*; Taylor, 1971). By comparison, beachrock cementation commenced less than a week after site clearance and preceded widespread colonization. Some micro-organisms were present in an initial grain binding role but they were not numerous enough to identify.

In particular, sites in the low and intermediate beachrock zones showed high rates of colonization, with all sites being indistinguishable from the neighbouring beachrock after four months and most after two months. Colonization at these sites was associated with the development of both a spongy surface crust of micro-organisms and sand and, at the four month stage, a green chasmolithic/endolithic layer. Sites on the upper beachrock zone exhibited the slowest rates of colonization, with often no sign of overgrowths after one month and with most sites still being distinguishable from the surrounding rock after four months. In this zone no spongy crust develops and the surface flora establishes itself purely on the bare rock surface. The two cliff notch sites showed comparable colonization rates to those of the beachrock. Colonization began between one week and one month after clearance and the squares were difficult to identify after the four month monitoring period.

These results, however, indicate slower colonization rates than those previously observed for the same location by Whitton and Potts (1980) and several sites did not follow the general trend for simple, cumulative colonization over the four month study period. Four sites were affected by the large scale detachment and removal of beachrock blocks and two sites were obscured by moving sand after clearance. Finally, grazing activity may have modified the beachrock flora; the migratory, herbivorous

Table 5.2 Observations of micro-organic cover, Ile Picard, Aldabra Atoll, June–September 1982

STATUS OF SITE AFTER CLEARANCE INTERVAL

SITE No.	1 WEEK	1 MONTH	2 MONTHS	4 MONTHS
1a		Beginnings of spongy crust Not enough material to identify	Spongy crust well developed ● □ ▲	
1b		Beginnings of spongy crust ● □ ▲	Spongy crust well developed ● □ ▲ ○	
2a		Slight crust developed ● △ ▲ *	Hardish crust developed ● □ △ ■ ▲ *	Sites obscured by
2b		Spongy crust well developed ●	Indistinguishable from surrounding rocks	large-scale
2c		Little surface colouration Not enough material to identify	Some surface colouration ● □ △ ■ ▲ *	erosion
2d		Some surface colouration *	Some surface colouration ● □ △ ▲ *	Well developed surface cover ● □ △ ■ ○ ⊙ ▲ *
3a		No obvious colonisation	Colouration around edges of site ● ■ ▲ *	Site obscured by sand
3b		Some surface colouration *	Well developed spongy crust ● ■ *	Indistinguishable from surrounding rocks
3c	Surface cemented	Some spongy crust development *	Well developed spongy crust ● ■ ▲	Indistinguishable from surrounding rocks
4a	No obvious colonisation	No obvious colonisation	Some sparse colouration ●	Some colouration ● □ △ ■ ○ ▲
4b		Site covered by sand	Site covered by sand	Site covered by sand
4c		Beginnings of spongy crust ● *	Spongy crust well developed ● □ △ ⊙	Spongy crust well developed ● △ ■ ○ ⊙ ▲ *
5a		No obvious colonisation	No obvious colonisation	Some colouration ● △ ■ ⊙ ▲
5b		No obvious colonisation	Some sparse colouration Not enough material to identify	Much colouration ● △ ○ *
5c		Spongy crust developing Not enough material to identify	Indistinguishable from surrounding rocks	Indistinguishable from surrounding rocks
5d		Spongy crust developing ⊙ ▲ *	Spongy crust well developed ● □ ■ ▲ *	Spongy crust well developed ● △ ■ ○ ▲ *
5e		Spongy crust developing ● ⊙ ▲ *	Spongy crust well developed ● □ ⊙	Spongy crust well developed △ ○ *
6a		Sparse colouration Not enough material to identify	Some colouration ○ ▲ *	Indistinguishable from surrounding rocks
6b		Sparse colouration Not enough material to identify	Some colouration △ ■ ○ *	Almost indistinguishable ● ○ ⊙ ▲ *

KEY:
- ● = unicellular blue-green algae
- □ = Small (<5μ width) blue-green algal filaments
- △ = 'Calothrix type' blue-green algal filaments
- ■ = 'Lyngbya type' blue-green algal filaments
- ○ = *Mastigocoleus testarum* (blue-green alga)
- ⊙ = 'Hyella type' blue-green algae
- ▲ = Fungi
- * = Eukaryotic algae

gastropods *Nerita* and *Littorina* have been described (Taylor, 1971) from the Ile Picard site. The rapidity of colonization and breakdown on littoral surfaces contrasts markedly with the behaviour of supralittoral sites. It appears that colonization proceeds much more slowly away from the littoral zone. For Aldabra, the beachrock results can be compared with cliff-top colonization at Anse Mais, north west Grande Terre (Figure 5.2). These sites were located on a transect stretching 100m inland from the cliff edge. After three months most sites were only sparsely colonized by micro-organisms, no site had more than half the cleared square colonized and all the growths were thin. Chasmolithic and endolithic niche development was negligible. These findings are reinforced in the following section which investigates inter-environmental differences in colonization rates from the Caribbean.

ALGAL COLONIZATION ON LIMESTONES: GRAND CAYMAN ISLAND, CARIBBEAN

Grand Cayman (81°W, $19^{\circ}20$'N) is a small (197 km^2) coralline island in the western Caribbean. The mean annual precipitation, at 1495 mm (1926-1965; Hsu *et al.*, 1972), is similar to that of Aldabra Atoll. The eastern interior of the island is composed of the low, dolomitic Bluff Limestone of Oligocene-Miocene age. This is surrounded by the Pleistocene Ironshore Formation, comprising a series of reef and reef- and lagoon-associated facies (Brunt *et al.*, 1973). Clusters of weight loss tablets (Trudgill, 1975), made to a 1.5 x 1.5 x 0.5 cm design from Ironshore Formation limestones, were deployed on Grand Cayman between 1977 and 1979 in order to evaluate the controls of lithology and environment upon limestone erosion rates. In particular, in the subtidal and intertidal zones, suites of tablets were enclosed in envelopes of differing mesh size and in small wire cages to establish the relative importance of abrasion, bioerosion, solution and other processes, following the approach of Trudgill (1975, 1976). The results of these experiments were then compared to the behaviour of similar tablets emplaced on the coastal platform, an environment subject only to sea spray at its outer margin. Tablets on the coastal platform were subjected to three periods of exposure between March/April 1977 and November/December 1978 of which only the last monitoring period is discussed here; the littoral tablets were part of a shorter series of experiments which ran from September 1978 to December 1978/January 1979.

It was expected that the littoral tablets would simply lose weight when immersed in seawater. However, it soon became apparent that micro-organism colonization was taking place on the enclosing mesh bags and on the tablets themselves. Quantitative estimates of the percentage of encrusting organisms on tablet surfaces were made after the standard tablet recovery, treatment and re-weighing procedure (Trudgill, 1975). Tablet topography was observed under reflected light with a binocular

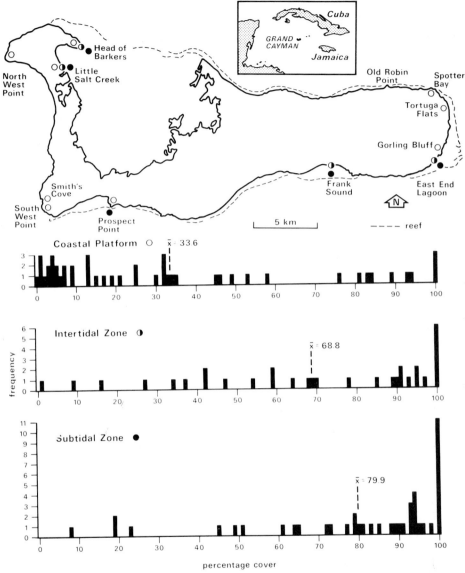

Figure 5.4 Limestone tablet colonization by environment, Grand Cayman Island, West Indies

microscope, giving a stereoscopic image of the surface at a magnification of x 40. Sampling location on each tablet was fixed by reference to a random numbers table and percentage cover of micro-organisms then estimated using a 10 x 10 grid from an eyepiece-mounted graticule. The range of cover values was very high in all environments which may reflect the varying micro-

Table 5.3   Colonization by environment, Grand Cayman Island, West Indies

A. Cover characteristics on limestone tablets
B. Tablet exposure times

A

	Environment	No. of tablets	Mean percentage cover	S.D. (%)	Range (%)
1	Coastal Platform	48	33.6	32.7	0 - 100
2	Intertidal Zone	32	68.8	29.6	1 - 100
3	Subtidal Zone	44	79.9	24.7	8 - 100

$x_1 - x_2$: $t = -4.83$ (degrees of freedom = 78); Significant at $p = 0.001$

$x_1 - x_3$: $t = -7.52$ (degrees of freedom = 90); Significant at $p = 0.001$

$x_2 - x_3$: $t = -1.75$ (degrees of freedom = 74); Not significant.

B

	Environment	No. of tablets	Mean length of exposure (days)	S.D. (days)	Range (days)
1	Coastal Platform	48	129.4 (512.9)[1]	7.2 (16.0)	121 - 146 (485) - (536)
2	Intertidal Zone	32	111.3	18.4	88 - 133
3	Subtidal Zone	44	106.5	16.6	88 - 133

$x_1 - x_2$: $t = +6.07$ (degrees of freedom = 78); Significant at $p = 0.001$

$x_1 - x_3$: $t = +8.61$ (degrees of freedom = 90); Significant at $p = 0.001$

$x_2 - x_3$: $t = +1.17$ (degrees of freedom = 74); Not significant.

NOTES: [1] Figures in parentheses refer to total length of time tablets ever exposed; calculations based only on last period of exposure.

morphology of the tablets, colonization being slower on smoother tablets. Nevertheless, micro-organism cover was significantly greater on tablets from both subtidal and intertidal sites than on coastal platform sites (Figure 5.4, Table 5.3). These differences are unlikely to be due to variations in tablet exposure time (Table 5.3). There is no statistical difference in the length of exposure for the intertidal and subtidal tablets and the coastal platform tablets which had the longest exposure also showed the lowest mean level of colonization. The degree of colonization on the littoral tablets made them difficult to distinguish from natural surfaces and confirmed the findings that algae occupy supplied substrates rapidly, often with 8-9 days of initial exposure (e.g. Marseille: Le Campion-Alsumard, 1975; Virgin Islands: Perkins and Tsentas, 1976; Jamaica: Kobluk and Risk, 1977). The Grand Cayman results compare well with the figures of 90 per cent coverage after 90 days (Le Campion-Alsumard, 1975) and 76.7 per cent after 95 days (Kobluk and Risk, 1977) on chips of Iceland Spar calcite, although it has been suggested that infestation rates are higher on natural shell materials (Perkins and Tsentas, 1976). By contrast, the lower levels of coverage on supra-littoral tablets made for much easier recognition in the field (Figure 5.5). This point can be further illustrated by the colonization rates experienced by a site on Tertiary Bluff Limestone at Old Robin Point, North Coast. The subtidal and intertidal tablets exhibited a coverage of 46.9 ± 32.0 per cent after 102 days, compared with only 0.5 ± 0.7 per cent coverage after 140 ± 6 days on the Bluff coastal platforms. These results parallel the findings from Anse Mais, Aldabra and clearly show that the littoral-supralittoral boundary marks a major break in the speed of micro-organic colonization and microfloral development.

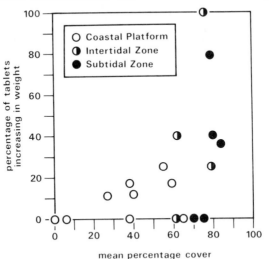

Figure 5.5   Tablet behaviour with environment and percentage
micro-organic cover, Grand Cayman Island, West Indies

131

BLUE-GREEN ALGAE AND 'PHYTOKARST'

The evidence for algal colonization on subaerial limestone surfaces leads ultimately to the question of whether a distinctive
'phytokarst' landscape exists. In discussing 'phytokarst', this
paper follows Folk et al.'s (1973) definition that it is 'a
landform produced by rock solution in which boring plant filaments are the main agent of destruction, and the major morphological features are determined by the peculiar nature of this
mode of attack'. This definition contrasts with the rather
broader use of the term by Bull and Laverty (1982). Their field
of enquiry covers, in effect, the wider range of 'biokarst'.
This paper considers their category named 'destructive
(erosional)' but ignores their classes 'physical (tectonic)'
and 'constructive (depositional)'.

Whilst the beachrock colonization studies suggest that
blue-green algae may aid initial diagenesis, there is no doubt
that boring activity in relatively unconsolidated carbonate
sediments leads, locally, to the collapse of the rock fabric.
This process has been reported from the Mediterranean (Fremy,
1945) and extensively from the tropics and subtropics (Jamaica:
Duerden, 1902; Florida: Swinchatt, 1965; Bahamas: Purdy and
Kornicker, 1958; Gulf of Botabano, Cuba: Bathurst, 1966;
Persian Gulf: Taylor and Illing, 1969). In heterogeneous sediments, algae are often involved in the *post mortem* invasion of
shells and skeletal fragments (Perkins and Halsey, 1971;
Schroeder, 1972). Empty boreholes are apt to be filled with
micritic carbonate. Repeated boring and subsequent infill leads
to the gradual, centripetal replacement of the original carbonate grains. The details of this process, known as micritization,
were first set by Bathurst (1966) using material from Bimini
lagoon, Bahamas. Subsequent studies have confirmed and extended
Bathurst's findings, although it is still not clear whether
algal metabolism influences micrite deposition or whether passive
precipitation merely fills vacant algal bores (Margolis and Rex,
1971; Scherer, 1975; Gunatilika, 1976; Lukas, 1979).

The question arises, however, as to the effectiveness of
algal activity when confronted by lithified limestone. Recently
this debate has centred upon the work of Robert Folk and his
co-workers at Hell, West Bay, Grand Cayman. This site consists
of a small, presumably fault-bounded, block of the Bluff Limestone, forming an inland - not coastal (Bull and Laverty, 1982)
- rocky swamp. The limestone is dissected into blocks and pinnacles, with a local relief in places in excess of 1.5m, separated by shallow, brackish pools (for illustrations see Folk *et
al.*, 1973, Figures 5.3 & 5.4) and Rigby and Roberts, 1976, Figure
5.5). The highly fretted and pitted relief supports a conspicuous
algal cover, thought to consist of the species *Gloeocapsa alpina*
(Folk *et al.*, 1973) which often gives the limestone a black
colour. Folk *et al.*'s (1973) paper is, therefore, important in

calling attention to this kind of landscape in general and to the spectacular Hell site in particular.

Under the scanning electron microscope, the algal filaments at the Hell site appear to be extending into the dolomitic limestone by selectively attacking the calcite crystals. From this evidence and from field observations, Folk *et al.* claim to identify an algal karst which can be distinguished from 'ordinary rain-produced karst' (1973, Figure 10). Furthermore, noting the connection between large-scale tower karst and cockpit karst and luxuriant vegetation in the tropics, they conclude (Folk *et al.*, 1973, p 2358) that 'perhaps there is a link between the vigour of boring algae and the occurrence of this most spectacular type of landform. It would indeed be interesting if such humble and inconspicuous creatures as boring algae were responsible for some of the world's most curious landforms...' There are, however, dangers in trying to identify phytokarst as a morphologically distinct karst and, more importantly, in extrapolating observations made at a microscopic level to large-scale karst landforms.

That micro-topography and algal growth can be related is well illustrated by the 'light-directed' karst (Bull and Laverty, 1982) from cave entrances in the Gunong Mulu National Park, Sarawak. However, under normal subaerial conditions algal-covered surfaces often show signs of both rain fluting and the 'intricate, spongy dissection' and 'random orientation' which are thought to be diagnostic of phytokarst. Thus Folk *et al's* (1973) two distinct morphological subsets are not always easy to isolate. Furthermore, we agree with Bull and Laverty (1982) when they state that '... there is an association between the algal filaments and the limestone removal: whether the algae can be demonstrated to be preferentially colonizing the hollows (and hence, concentrating erosional phases) rather than the flanks of phytokarst cones or rods, remains unresolved'. For Bull and Laverty (1982), therefore, the discovery, by scanning electron microscopy, of blue-green algae on the flanks of hollows qualifies their argument for the destructive role of algae. Similarly, Lukas (1979), in viewing Folk *et al.'s* (1973) photographs, suggests that the algae may be etching their way into the rock surface rather than actively boring into it. These arguments represent modifications of the original 'phytokarst' idea but Mustoe (1982), in discussing 'honeycomb weathering' in general, has taken an opposite view and argued that algae are protective, putting an organic skin between precipitation and/or wave action and the underlying limestone. Mustoe's (1982) investigations have revealed that the chlorophyll content of rock samples from the walls of honeycombed surfaces appears to be significantly greater than that of the back-wall depressions, thereby promoting hollow deepening rather than coalescence. At this stage his simple experiments do not allow causal links to be established between algal biomass and micro-topography but they do at least suggest that further experimentation should be carried out in this direction.

The above discussion casts some doubt on the nature of the relationship between micro-topography and endolithic algae. Given these difficulties it is perhaps premature to extrapolate any findings to the meso- or macro-scale. Furthermore, it is not necessarily correct to infer that landscapes at these higher scales are simply the aggregate result of processes operating at the micro-scale. This point can be illustrated by a further reference to the Bluff Limestone of Grand Cayman. The major control of the island's surface topography on this lithology is jointing. Rigby and Roberts (1976) state that the 'island appears to be a single massive block, intensely jointed but otherwise relatively unbroken' and illustrate their argument by constructing joint rose diagrams for eight localities around Grand Cayman (Rigby and Roberts, 1976, Figure 30). On coastal cliffs, there are often sharp changes of level where cliff-edge blocks have been quarried along joint lines and bedding planes. Inland, joint lines are often picked out by lines of sub-parallel pinnacles. At Great Pedro Point, Grand Cayman, thin, sheet-like pinnacles, up to a metre above the general limestone surface, form lines intersecting at larger, pyramidal pinnacles (Spencer, unpublished data). A similar argument for joint-controlled topo-graphy can be applied to Folk *et al's* (1973) Hell site. Dominant joint trends, with NW-SE and WSW-ENE orientations have been des-cribed for this locality (Rigby and Roberts, 1976, Figure 30) and it appears that the major blocks at Hell are defined by joint trends and intersections. Blue-green algae are undeniably assoc-iated with the limestones at Hell but they do not determine the larger scale pattern of the karst. For a more complete descrip-tion of the site, two complementary explanations are required, joints (meso-scale) and algae (micro-scale). It seems unlikely that any limestone landscape could be described as solely phyto-karstic.

CONCLUSIONS

Several points need to be made in evaluating the potential impor-tance of micro-organisms to limestone weathering.

Clearly such organisms are widespread both in broad global terms and in the sense that they cover a range of terrestrial and marine environments. Furthermore, colonization rates are rapid. The evidence from Aldabra, for example, with the initi-ation of colonization one week to one month after clearance and the establishment of a full epilithic, endolithic and chasmo-lithic flora after four months shows that surfaces are only fleetingly truly bare and that solutional processes, for example, will normally be mediated by a complete cover of organisms. The presence of an endolithic/chasmolithic layer after four months indicates that active alteration of the substrate occurs rapidly on beachrock. Thus surfaces made bare by large-scale rock frac-ture, sand removal or grazing activity will be speedily colonized and weakened, thereby facilitating a further round of destruction. The Grand Cayman studies show that such processes are not confined to relatively unconsolidated substrates but also characterize lithified limestones and, to a lesser extent, non-marine environments. However, it is difficult to unambiguously define a distinctive terrestrial 'phytokarst' landform.

Coastal retreat, biological processes and the presence of blue-green algae appear closely related. Thus, for example, the high grazing pressure of the lower intertidal is reflected in the prevalence of endolithic algae in this zone (Schneider, 1976). The balance between algal penetration and erosion is, however, a fine one. Deep boring is advantageous to grazers as it effectively extends the food source into the substrate. However, if grazing is too successful, then there must be a hiatus whilst algal re-colonization takes place (Golubic *et al.*, 1975). This re-invasion may be complex and the new community may not repeat taxonomically the structure of the community which originally occupied the substrate as in Les Calanques, Marseilles (Le Campion-Alsumard, 1970). Pioneer species often produce unstable epilithic communities and only over time do slow-growing but more resilient endolithic communities develop. It is perhaps not surprising, therefore, that whilst Caribbean limestone tablets in subaerial environments generally show more weight gains with increasing extent of colonization, marine tablets, with 60 to 80 per cent micro-organic cover, exhibit a range of behaviour from solely weight losses to only weight gains (Figure 5.5) a fact reflected in the correlation between the percentage of tablets increasing in weight and the mean percentage cover (r_s = 0.45; t = 2.35; significant at p = 0.05). At most sites, therefore, some tablets showed weight gains and some weight losses, altering calculations of surface lowering based on weight losses alone by between 29 and 63 per cent (Spencer, unpublished data). It is hoped that the methodology suggested in this paper might now be used in controlled experimental designs to further decipher the inter-relationships between substrate type and environment, algal colonization, impact of larger organisms and limestone morphology.

Acknowledgements

Fieldwork support on Aldabra Atoll (H.A.V.) and Grand Cayman (T.S.) was provided by the Natural Environment Research Council. H.A.V. would like to thank Harry Charles and Alan Donaldson for their help; T.S. is grateful to Dr. M.E.C. Giglioli and the Cayman Islands Government for the provision of facilities and transport.

REFERENCES

Bathurst, R.G.C. 1966. Boring algae, micrite envelopes and lithification of molluscan biosparites. *Geol. J.*, 5, 15-32.

Bathurst, R.G.C. 1976. *Carbonate Sediments and their Diagenesis,* 2nd ed., (Elsevier, Amsterdam), 658pp.

Berner, R.A. 1971. Bacterial processes affecting the precipitation of calcium carbonate in sediments. In: *Carbonate Cements,* ed. Bricker, O.R., (J. Hopkins Press, Baltimore), 247-251.

Bourrelly, P. and Dupuy, P. 1973. Quelques stations françaises de *Geitleria calcarea* Cyanophycée cavernicole. *Schweiz. Z. Hydrol.*, 35, 136-140.

Braithwaite, C.J.R., Taylor, J.D. and Kennedy, W.J. 1973. The evolution of an atoll: the depositional and erosional history of Aldabra. *Phil. Trans. Roy. Soc. Lond.*, 266B, 307-340.

Brunt, M.A., Giglioli, M.E.C., Mather, J.D., Piper, D.J.W. and Richards, H.G. 1973. The Pleistocene rocks of the Cayman Islands. *Geol. Mag.*, 110, 209-221.

Budd, D.A. and Perkins, R.D. 1980. Bathymetric zonation and palaeological significance of microborings in Puerto Rican shelf and slope sediments. *J. Sedim. Petrol.*, 50, 881-894.

Bull, P.A. and Laverty, M. 1982. Observations on phytokarst. *Z. Geomorph. N.F.*, 26, 437-457.

Cox, G. and Marchant, H. 1977. Photosynthesis in the deep twilight zone: Microorganisms with extreme structural adaptations to low light. *Proc. 7th Int. Speleol. Cong.*, Sheffield, 31-33.

Crowther, J. 1979. Limestone solution on exposed rock outcrops in West Malaysia. In: *Geographical Approaches to Fluvial Processes,* ed. Pitty, A.F., (Geo Abstracts, Norwich) 31-50.

Danin, A., Gerson, R., Marton, K. and Garty, J. 1982. Patterns of limestone and dolomite weathering by lichens and blue-green algae and their palaeoclimatic significance. *Palaeo. Palaeo. Palaeo.*, 37, 221-233.

Davies, P.J. and Kinsey, D.W. 1973. Organic and inorganic factors in recent beachrock formation, Heron Island, Great Barrier Reef. *J. Sedim. Petrol.*, 43, 59-81.

Desikachary, T.V. 1959. *Cyanophyta,* Indian Council Agric. Res., New Delhi.

Donaldson, A. and Whitton, B.A. 1977. Algal flora of freshwater pools on Aldabra. *Atoll Res. Bull.*, 215, 1-26.

Duerden, J.E. 1902. Boring algae as agents in the disintegration of corals. *Bull. Amer. Mus. Nat. Hist.*, 16, 323-332.

Duncan, P.M. 1877. On some thallophytes parasitic within recent Madreporia. *Proc. Roy. Soc. Lond.*, **25**, 238-257.

Edwards, B.D. and Perkins, R.D. 1974. Distribution of micro-borings within continental margin sediments of the S.E. United States. *J. Sedim. Petrol.*, 44, 1122-1135.

Föcke, J.W. 1978a. Limestone cliff morphology and organism distribution on Curaçao (Netherlands Antilles). *Leid. Geol. Meded.*, **51**, 131-150.

Föcke, J.W. 1978b. Limestone cliff morphology on Curaçao (Netherlands Antilles) with special attention to the origin of notches and vermetid/coralline algal surf beaches ('cornices', 'trottoirs'). *Z. Geomorph. N.F.*, **22**, 329-349.

Folk, R.L., Roberts, H.H. and Moore, C.H. 1973. Black phyto-karst from Hell, Cayman Islands, British West Indies. *Bull. Geol. Soc. Amer.*, **84**, 2351-2360.

Fremy, P. 1945. Contribution à la physiologie des thallophytes marines perforant et cariant les roches calcaires et les coquilles. *Ann. Inst. Océanog.*, **22**, 107-144.

Friedmann, I. and Ocampo, R. 1976. Endolithic blue-green algae in the dry valleys: Primary producers in the Antarctic desert ecosystem. *Science*, (N.Y.), 193, 1247-1249.

Fritsch, F.E. 1907. The role of algal growth in the colonization of new ground and in the determination of scenery. *Geogr. J.*, 30, 531-547.

Geitler, L. 1932. Cyanophyceae. In: *Rabenhorst's Kryptogamen Flora*, 14, (Akademische Verlag, Leipzig).

Ginsburg, R.N. 1953. Intertidal erosion on the Florida Keys. *Bull. Mar. Sci. Gulf Carib.*, 3, 55-69.

Glover, E.D. 1978. Organic remains seen in oolites after con-version to fluorite. *J. Sedim. Petrol.*, 48, 795-798.

Golubic, S. 1969. Distribution, taxonomy and boring patterns of marine endolithic algae. *Amer. Zool.*, 9, 747-751.

Golubic, S. 1972. Scanning electron microscopy of Recent boring Cyanophyta and its possible palaeontological application. In: *Taxonomy and biology of blue-green algae*, ed. Desikachary, T.V., (Symp. Univ. Madras, Bangalore Press, Bangalore), 167-170.

Golubic, S., Brent, G. and Le Campion, T. 1970. Scanning elec-tron microscopy of endolithic algae and fungi using a multi-purpose casting-embedding technique. *Lethaia*, 3, 203-209.

Golubic, S., Perkins, R.D. and Lukas, K.J. 1975. Boring micro-organisms and microborings in carbonate substrates. In: *The Study of Trace Fossils*, ed. Frey, R.W. (Springer Verlag, Berlin), 229-259.

Golubic, S., Friedmann, I. and Schneider, J. 1981. The litho-biontic ecological niche, with special reference to micro-organisms. *J. Sedim. Petrol.*, 51, 475-479.

Gunatilika, A. 1976. Thallophyte boring and micritization within skeletal sands from Connemara, W. Ireland. *J. Sedim. Petrol.*, **46**, 548-554.

Harris, P.M., Lukas, K.J. and Halley, R.B. 1977. Comparison of endolith floras from Holocene-Pleistocene (Bahamas-Florida) ooids (Abstr.) *Bull. Amer. Assoc. Petrol. Geol.*, **61**, 793-794.

Henderson, C.M. and Styan, W.B. 1982. Description and ecology of Recent endolithic biota from the Gulf Islands and banks in the Strait of Juan de Fuca, British Columbia. *Canad. J. Earth Sci.*, **19**, 1382-1394.

Hodgkin, E.P. 1964. Rate of erosion of intertidal limestone. *Z. Geomorph. N.F.*, **8**, 385-392.

Hopley, D. 1982. *The Geomorphology of the Great Barrier Reef.* (Wiley Interscience, New York), 453pp.

Hsu, S.-A., Giglioli, M.E.C., Reiter, P. and Davies, J. 1972. Heat and water balance studies on Grand Cayman. *Carib. J. Sci.*, **12**, 9-22.

Jones, B. and Goodbody, Q.H. 1982. The geological significance of endolithic algae in glass. *Canad. J. Earth Sci.*, **19**, 671-678.

Jones, R.J. 1965. Aspects of the biological weathering of limestone pavement. *Proc. Geol. Assoc.*, **76**, 421-433.

Kelletat, D. 1980. Formenschatz und Prozeogefüge des 'Biokarstes' an der Küste von Nordost Mallorca (Cala Guya). *Berliner Geogr. Stud. Bd.*, **7**, 99-113.

Klappa, C.F. 1979. Lichen stromatolites: Criterion for subaerial exposure and a mechanism for the formation of laminar calcretes (caliche). *J. Sedim. Petrol.*, **49**, 387-400.

Kobluk, D.R. and Risk, M.J. 1977. Rate and nature of infestation of a carbonate substratum by boring algae. *J. Exp. Mar. Biol. Ecol.*, **27**, 107-115.

Koster, J.T. 1939. Notes on Javanese calcicole cyanophyceae. *Blumea*, **3**, 243-247.

Krumbein, W.E. 1979. Photolithotrophic and chemoorganotrophic activity of bacteria and algae as related to beachrock formation and degradation (Gulf of Aqaba, Sinai). *Geomicrobiol. J.*, **1**, 139-203.

Le Campion-Alsumard, T. 1970. Cyanophycées marines endolithes colonisant les surfaces rocheuses denudées: etages supralittoral et mediolittoral de la région de Marseille. *Schweiz. Z. Hydrol.*, **32**, 552-558.

Le Campion-Alsumard, T. 1975. Etude expérimentale de la colonisation d'éclats de calcite par les cyanophycées endolithes marines. *Cah. Biol. Mar.*, **16**, 177-185.

Le Campion-Alsumard, T. 1979a. Les Cyanophycées endolithes marines Systèmatique, ultrastructure, écologie et biodestruction. *Oceanol. Acta*, **2(2)**, 143-156.

Le Campion-Alsumard, T. 1979b. Le biokarst marin: Rôle des organisms perforantes. *Act. Symp. Int. Eros. Karst U.I.S.,* 133-140.

Le Campion-Alsumard, T. 1979c. Quelques méthodes d'étude des algues endolithes et de leurs galeries. *Rapp. Comm. Int. Mer. Medit.,* 25/26, 295-302.

Lukas, K.J. 1979. The effects of marine microphytes on carbonate substrata. *Scan. Electron. Micr.,* II, 447-456.

Margolis S. and Rex, R.W. 1971. Endolithic algae and micrite envelope formation in Bahamian oolites as revealed by scanning electron microscopy. *Bull. Geol. Soc. Amer.,* 82, 843-852.

May, J.A. and Perkins, R.D. 1979. Endolithic infestation of carbonate substrates below the sediment-water interface. *J. Sedim. Petrol.,* 49, 357-378.

Moul, E.T. 1953. Algae of Onotoa, Gilbert Islands. *Phycol. News Bull.,* 6, 19-20.

Mustoe, G.E. 1982. The origin of honeycomb weathering. *Bull. Geol. Soc. Amer.,* 93, 108-115.

Nadson, G. 1927. Les algues perforantes, leur distribution et leur rôle dans le nature. *C.R. Hebd. Séanc. Acad. Sci. Paris,* 184, 1015-1017.

Newell, N.D., Imbrie, J., Purdy, E.G. and Thurber, D.L. 1959. Organism communities and bottom facies, Great Bahama Bank. *Bull. Amer. Mus. Nat. Hist.,* 117, 177-228.

Newhouse, J. 1954. Floristics and plant ecology of Raroia Atoll, Tuamotus. Pt. 2: Ecological and floristical notes on the myxophyta of Raroia. *Atoll Res. Bull.,* 33, 42-54.

Pentecost, A. 1978. Blue-green algae and freshwater carbonate deposits. *Proc. Roy. Soc. Lond.,* 200B, 43-61.

Perkins, R.D. and Halsey, S.D. 1971. Geological significance of micro-boring fungi and algae in Carolina shelf sediments. *J. Sedim. Petrol.,* 41, 843-853.

Perkins, R.D. and Tsentas, C.I. 1976. Microbial infestation of carbonate substrates planted on the St. Croix shelf, West Indies. *Bull. Geol. Soc. Amer.,* 87, 1615-1628.

Pfeffer, K.-H. 1981. Solution et precipitation calcaire. Observations pendant un voyage d'exploration dans les Caraibes. *Actes du Coll. A.G.F. Formations carbonates externes tufs et travertimes,* 129-136.

Potts, M. and Whitton, B.A. 1980. Vegetation of the intertidal zone of the lagoon of Aldabra, with particular reference to the photosynthetic prokaryotic communities. *Proc. Roy. Soc. Lond.,* 208B, 13-55.

Pugh, D.T. 1979. Sea levels at Aldabra Atoll, Mombasa and Mahé, western equatorial Indian Ocean, related to tides, meteorology and ocean circulation. *Deep-Sea Res.,* 26, 237-258.

Purdy, E.G. and Kornicker, L.S. 1958. Algal disintegration of Bahamian limestone coasts. *J. Geol.*, **66**, 97-99.

Rigby, J.K. and Roberts, H.H. 1976. Geology, reefs and marine communities of Grand Cayman Island, British West Indies. *Geol. Stud. Brigham Young Univ.*, **4**, 1-95.

Rooney, W.I. and Perkins, R.D. 1972. Distribution and geological significance of microboring organisms within sediments of the Arlington Reef complex, Australia. *Bull. Geol. Soc. Amer.*, **83**, 1139-1150.

Scherer, M. 1975. Cementation and replacement of Pleistocene corals from the Bahamas and Florida: diagenetic influence of nonmarine environments. *Neues Jahrb. Geol. Pal. Abh.*, **149**, 259-285.

Schneider, J. 1976. Biological and inorganic factors in the destruction of limestome coasts. *Contr. Sedimentol.*, **6**, 112pp.

Schroeder, J.H. 1972. Calcified filaments of an endolithic alga in recent Bermuda reefs. *Neues Jahrb. Geol. Pal. Mh.*, **1**, 16-33.

Smyk, B. and Drzal, M. 1964. Research on the influence of micro-organisms on the development of karst phenomena. *Geogr. Polon.* **2**, 57-60.

Stoddart, D.R., Taylor, J.D., Fosberg, F.R. and Farrow, G.E. 1971. Geomorphology of Aldabra Atoll. *Phil. Trans. Roy. Soc. Lond.*, **260B**, 31-65.

Swinchatt, J.P. 1965. Significance of constituent composition, texture and skeletal breakdown in some Recent carbonate sediments. *J. Sedim. Petrol.*, **35**, 71-90.

Taylor, J.C.M. and Illing, L.V. 1969. Holocene intertidal calcium carbonate sedimentation, Qatar, Persian Gulf. *Sedimentology,* **12**, 69-107.

Taylor, J.D. 1971. Intertidal zonation at Aldabra Atoll. *Phil. Trans. Roy. Soc. Lond.*, **260B**, 173-213.

Torunski, H. 1979. Biological erosion and its significance for the morphogenesis of limestone coasts and for nearshore sediments (N. Adriatic) *Senckenbergiana Marit.*, **11**, 193-265.

Trudgill, S.T. 1975. Measurement of erosional weight loss tablets. *Tech. Bull. Brit. Geomorph. Res. Grp.*, **17**, 13-19.

Trudgill, S.T. 1976. The marine erosion of limestones on Aldabra Atoll, Indian Ocean. *Z. Geomorph. Suppl. Bd.*, **26**, 201-210.

Trudgill, S.T. 1981. Geochemistry and mineralogy of carbonate rock samples from Aldabra Atoll, Indian Ocean. *Atoll Res. Bull.*, **255**, 11-22.

Van Reine, W.F.P. and Van Den Hoek, C. 1966. Isolation of living algae growing in the shells of molluscs and barnacles with E.D.T.A. *Blumea,* **14**, 331-332.

Whitton, B.A. 1971. Terrestrial and freshwater blue-green algae of Aldabra. *Phil. Trans. Roy. Soc. Lond.*, **260B**, 249-255.

Whitton, B.A. and Potts, M. 1980. Blue-green algae (Cyano-bacteria) of the oceanic coast of Aldabra. *Atoll Res. Bull.*, **238**, 1-8.

6

Soils associated with Carboniferous Limestone in England and Wales

D.M. Carroll

SUMMARY

Carboniferous Limestone is the only rock of England and Wales which shows marked karstic features. Its solution provides little residual material, but it can be covered by various drift deposits in which soils develop. Calcareous soils are rare, and clay translocation is commonly observed. In areas unaffected by glaciation older clay-enriched horizons can be preserved. Soil patterns in the main limestone occurrences are described.

RÉSUMÉ

Les calcaires carbonifères sont les seules roches en Angleterre et au Pays de Galles qui montrent des phénomènes karstiques prononcés. La dissolution de ces roches fournit très peu de dépôts résiduels mais elles peuvent être recouvertes de dépôts d'origine glaciaire qui permettent le développement de sols. Les sols calcaires sont rares et l'on observe souvent la migration des argiles. Dans les régions qui n'ont pas été touchées par les glaciations des horizons enrichis en argile peuvent être conservés. La distribution des sols dans les principales régions karstiques est décrite.

INTRODUCTION

The best examples of karst formation in England and Wales are associated with the Viséan or Carboniferous Limestone Series of the Lower Carboniferous (Figure 1). These are thick, hard and massive rocks with extensive outcrops in North Yorkshire, the Peak District and the Mendips. In other regions limestone may form only a small part of the sequence or be replaced by non-marine facies and much is also hidden by deep drift deposits.

Numerous studies have shown that the very pure limestone contributes little to soil formation and that even shallow soil profiles are largely formed in drift, which could be a till or an aeolian silt. Recent mapping by the Soil Survey for a National Soil Map has provided much information on the distribution and nature of soils over Carboniferous Limestone and related drift deposits. These soils vary in depth, organic matter content, colour, particle-size, base status, degree of clay translocation and moisture regime. The soil patterns occurring in different localities reflect the extent of karstic features, relief, climate glacial history and land use.

PARENT MATERIALS

Carboniferous Limestone is very pure and contains little insoluble material (less than five per cent and often only one or two per cent). Solution is slow and only a few centimetres of soil would be formed by post-glacial weathering; Sweeting (1972) has estimated the rate of denudation in north-west Yorkshire at only 50 mm per 1000 years, but Piggott (1962) concluded that the residue from limestone weathering can often constitute a large part of the superficial deposits, implying the solution of an enormous amount of rock and the lapse of a very long period of undisturbed accumulation. The permeable limestone is resistant to denudation and, where there has been no glacial action, this favours the preservation of paleosols. Many soils over limestone, however, are shallow, stony and rocky and the formation of deeper soils requires a drift cover, whether till or a wind-blown deposit.

The concentration of soil particles in the coarse silt (20-60μm) fraction has suggested to workers in several areas that the common occurrence of silty soils over limestone is not exclusively due to the limestone residue but to the presence of aeolian dust, intimately mixed with the residue through almost the full profile depth by vigorous cryoturbation under periglacial conditions close to an ice-front. Piggott's (1962) studies in the Peak District showed that silty soils over limestone largely consisted of detrital quartz grains that are absent in the limestone residue; the soil had a much richer assemblage

142

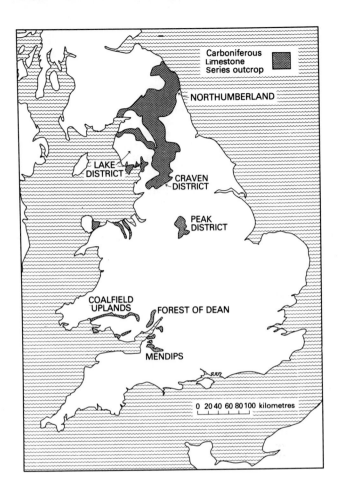

Figure 6.1   Outcrop of Carboniferous Limestone Series in
England and Wales

of heavy minerals than the residue and also included micaceous
clay minerals not contained in the limestone. Bryan (1970)
later postulated a less extensive distribution of aeolian silt,
largely confined to summit plateaux because of erosion and redistribution, and the greater part of soils over limestone
formed from the limestone residue. Findlay (1965) found coarse
silt predominant in both soil and limestone residue in the Mendips. His microscopic analysis, however, showed that little
soil was derived from the underlying limestone as the soil had
less quartz euhedra, but more feldspar than the residue and also
heavy minerals were scarce or absent in the residue. Crampton's

(1961) mineralogical studies in South Wales produced similar results; he believed the source of the aeolian material to be coastal shore sands. Bullock (1971), working at Malham, North Yorkshire, suggested that about a third of the soil's sand and silt fraction came from the insoluble residue and the remainder from the adjacent Millstone Grit rocks.

In many places the limestone outcrop is covered by a thick mentle of till. Even silty drift has occasional pebbles of sandstone, quartzite and other erratics where small patches of till have been incorporated by cryoturbation. Layering of profiles is often found, however, and a profile might consist of stoneless silty clay loam overlying shaly clay loam over calcareous clay on massive limestone. Work by Smithson (1953) and also by Jenkins and Smith (quoted by Thompson 1978) has demonstrated that most of even a thin drift over limestone is of glacial origin. The till is often quite local and tends to reflect the surrounding solid geology. In North Yorkshire it consists of abundant sandstone and shale fragments in a medium to fine greyish matrix while in Cumbria much of the very stony till consists of Lower Palaeozoic sedimentary and igneous rocks. Over much of Wales, the soils incorporate material from a former extension of a reddish brown boulder clay derived from Triassic sediments of the Irish Sea basin. Smithson (1953) found similar mineral assemblages in this drift to those in soils over limestone. Soil redness can have other causes, however. Contamination from Old Red Sandstone rocks in Pembroke imparts a red colour to soils. George (1978) attributes a reddish colour to a high content of iron in some parent limestones of Northumberland. The limestone itself can be reddened by its metasomatic replacement by iron-rich waters from overlying red Triassic sandstones, since removed by erosion (Hall and Folland 1970). A characteristic feature of shallow tills over limestone are swallow holes, which are best seen when the till is less than about three metres deep; local surface drainage systems develop where it is deeper. Clayton (1966) notes that the incidence of swallow holes in the Malham area increases where the till is up to a depth of 1.8-2.4 metres, and then declines where the till is deeper.

TYPES OF SOIL

The sequence from bare rock to a well developed soil on limestone pavements (Table 1) through colonization by lichens, mosses and grasses has been well summarized by Bullock (1971) and Barratt (1973).

The shallowest soils are on steep slopes or over limestone pavements scoured by glacial action and not subsequently covered by deep drift, although they can be contaminated by it. Both humose and non-humose profiles occur, the humose varieties being more common in higher, wetter and colder areas and on north-facing slopes. Organic matter is easily incorporated into the

Table 6.1   Classification of soils associated with Carboniferous
            Limestone

| Soil groups (Avery 1980) | Approximate equivalents | |
	Great Groups Soil Survey Staff (1975)	Map Units F.A.O. (1974)
Rankers	Udorthents; haplumbrepts	Rankers; regosols
Rendzinas	Rendolls	Rendzinas
Brown calcareous earths)	Eutrochrepts	Calcic Cambisols
Brown earths)		Eutric Cambisols
Argillic brown earths)	Hapludalfs	Orthic Luvisols
Paleo-argillic brown earths)		Chromic Luvisols
Stagnopodzols	Placaquods; placaquepts	Placic Podzols
Stagnogley soils	Haplaquepts	Eutric Gleysols
Stagnohumic gley soils	Humaquepts	Humic Gleysols
Raw peat soils	Borohemists	Dystric Histosols

mineral soil and a fine granular stucture developed, the peds
being intimately bound by a mat of fibrous roots. The most common are rankers with a non-calcareous fine earth fraction and
only moderate base status because of strong leaching. Calcareous
rendzinas often occur on steep slopes where the soil's base content can be renewed by down-slope wash; they are usually associated with much bare rock and scree and a calcicole vegetation
dominated by blue Sesleria (*Sesleria albicans*).

Deeper brown calcareous earths with a well developed B
horizon are uncommon in strongly leaching environments. They
are generally confined to very fragmented superficial deposits
derived from limestone such as very stony tills, glaciofluvial
gravels or river terrace deposits, but they have been recorded
over limestone bedrock in Gloucestershire (Colborne 1981). Non-
calcareous brown earths cover much of the limestone outcrop and
the associated drift deposits. They vary greatly in depth and
acidity. Increasing thickness of drift causes progressive decalcification of the soil by preventing roots from reaching
limestone and thus there is little or no recycling of bases to
retard leaching. The least decalcified carry grassland dominated
by *Agrostis tenuis* and *Festuca ovina*, whereas, when the depth to
limestone exceeds about 50cm, this is replaced by calcifuge
vegetation dominated by mat grass (*Nardus stricta*). These soils
are loamy or silty throughout and their origin is often complex.
Short-range variation, reflecting irregular relief of the underlying limestone bedrock, is common.

There is often a clayey horizon above the limestone in some localities, usually those at low altitudes and subject to seasonal droughtiness. This is a characteristic of argillic brown earths; these develop when an underlying clayey limestone residue combines with clayey particles suspended in the soil solution and migrates down the profile to the depth at which the high pH generated by limestone solution acts as a barrier. The increase of clay with depth is not always detectable by particle-size analysis, even when micromorphological examination shows clear evidence of clay movement. In areas unaffected by the last glaciation there are paleo-argillic brown earths with clay-enriched horizons and properties attributable to long-continued weathering in pre-Devensian interglacial or earlier periods. They have strongly oriented clay skins on ped faces or filling pores, and reddish colours that are not due to inheritance from haematite-rich rock. Their profiles can be truncated, or buried by subsequent deposition and cryoturbated. These soils persist on plateaux as dissected remnants of older ground surfaces beyond the limits of the Devensian ice-sheets.

Stagnopodzols with evidence of anaerobic conditions such as a wet peaty topsoil and often a thin ironpan, are characteristic of upland soils in thin drift over limestone where some calcifuge semi-natural vegetation remains. Most are in silty stoneless drift but they also occur in till, especially about swallow holes or other places where drainage is locally improved. Other kinds of podzolic soil are rarely found. Stagnogley and stagnohumic gley soils are more common in deep drift. They have stony loamy or clayey relatively impermeable subsurface horizons and often a peaty or humose topsoil. Raw peat soils, also over deep drift, are extremely acid and consist mainly of the moderately humified (semi-fibrous) remains of *Eriophorum* and *Sphagnum* species. Exceptionally, a shallow peat soil can be found immediately above limestone.

SOIL DISTRIBUTION

Northern England

Much of the outcrop of the Carboniferous Limestone Series in north-east England is covered by thick till and individual limestone beds are thin, the sequence consisting mostly of shale and sandstone. Limestones occur at the surface as small plateaux or bench-like features and the associated soils are shallow brown earths or rankers. Limestone outcrops are more extensive in the north-west around Morecombe Bay and on the flanks of the Lake District, generally as isolated hills with pavements and aeolian silty deposits. The presence of occasional erratics within these deposits led Furness and King (1972) to suggest that aeolian silt was probably deposited at the end of one glaciation, and redistribution and incorporation of erratics was effected by a later, more localized ice-sheet. Brown earths are common over limestone, the aeolian deposits and associated very stony reddish

146

till. Further inland, limestone only occurs as knoll-like features protruding through a thick cover of till. High altitude
and rainfall are factors favouring the development of wet soils
in slowly permeable till, and the underlying porous limestone
has little discernible effect on profile formation. The best
example of a karstic landscape in northern England is the Craven
District of north-west Yorkshire where there are limestone pavements, steep-sided scree-covered valleys and a wide range of
soil types (Figure 2). In this strongly leaching environment
soils are strongly decalcified and there is little clay translocation within the profile compared with more southerly areas.
Dolines partly filled by till have gleyed or podzolic soils.
Little evidence of pre-Devensian deposits remains in northern
England because of glacial action, although Sweeting (1972) describes red soil associated with smoothed limestone slopes beneath
glacial or periglacial screes, which may represent an earlier,
warmer period of karst development.

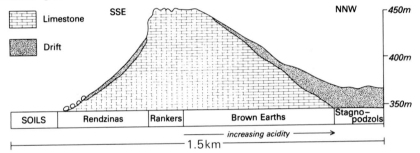

Figure 6.2   Diagrammatic representation of the topographic
              sequence of soils over limestone in N.W. Yorkshire

Wales

Much of the limestone in North Wales is covered by drift,
producing gently to moderately sloping country, with both brown
earths and argillic brown earths, in which limestone forms a
small but significant part outcropping on slope crests and
steeper slopes. Pavements with rankers and other karstic features are found, however, on the limestone platform in Clwyd.
Here, joints are filled with a stoneless yellowish brown clay,
buried by till and thought to be pre-glacial (Thompson 1978).
The character of soils in Pembroke and the Gower Peninsula is
determined mainly by Irish Sea drift, although the deeper soils
incorporate some silty drift. However, pockets of red soil,
which exhibits oriented clay and many ferri-manganiferous concretions when examined in thin section, are considered interglacial (Ball 1960, Crampton 1965). In south Glamorgan, there
are isolated cappings of paleo-argillic brown earths on plateau-
like areas where limestone is close to the surface; these soils
grade into stony soils in glacial and glaciofluvial drift as the
soil cover becomes deeper. The Coalfield Uplands of South Wales
have a very different soil pattern. The narrow limestone outcrop

consists of a line of hills, with bare rock, scree and rankers, interrupted by shallow drift-filled depressions with stagno-humic gley soils and stagnopodzols.

South-west England

Limestone forms part of the Mendip hills and there are isolated outcrops protruding from the Mesozoic cover around Bristol and also in the Forest of Dean. Pavements and glacial landforms are lacking, but soils are often very shallow and there are gorges with much rock and scree. On the Mendip plateau, the thickness of both rock residue and aeolian silt cover is very variable. Argillic horizons are poorly developed where the silt cover is thick, but more marked where there is an under-lying finer residue. Red clay sometimes extends down fissures in the limestone. Soils often have a red colour as Carboniferous strata are stained by iron from overlying Triassic rocks, since removed by erosion. There are some podzolic soils, which were probably once more extensive. In the Forest of Dean, rock out-crops have mainly shallow soils, although some brown calcareous earths have been mapped.

The Peak District

There are no limestone pavements, the surface being soil-covered as this area escaped the most recent glaciation. The plateaux are mainly covered by brown earths and rankers in stoneless silty drift, occasionally incorporating some small patches of till. In places the drift is cherty where the parent rock has been silicified. Steep-sided valleys are covered by mainly shallow soils with frequent scree and bare rock. Red clay is sometimes in pipes in the limestone, but may be derived from more argillaceous limestone (Cazalet 1968) rather than from relatively undisturbed residue.

CONCLUSIONS

There are several distinct patterns of soil formation over Carboniferous Limestone although solution of the rock provides only a limited thickness of residual soil-forming material. Shallow soils predominate on pavements and steep slopes. Brown earths form in till or aeolian silt overlying limestone. Their base status reflects the depth of the drift; their particle-size, mineralogy, colour and stone content reflect its nature and probable source. Clay translocation is rare in the wet uplands of northern England, but common in lower land elsewhere. In parts of the Mendips, the Peak District and South Wales un-affected by the last glaciation there are extensive areas of paleosols, at least partly formed in an interglacial period.

Acknowledgements

The assistance of several colleagues in supplying as yet unpublished information about their recent soil mapping is gratefully acknowledged.

REFERENCES

Avery, B.W. 1980. Soil Classification for England and Wales. *Soil Surv. Tech. Monogr.,* **14**.

Ball, D.F. 1960. Relic-soil on limestone in South Wales. *Nature,* **187**, 497–498.

Barratt, B.C. 1973. Macro- and micromorphology of soils developed in a region of karst topography near Malham, Yorkshire, England. *New Zealand Soil Bureau Scientific Report* **14**.

Bryan, R.B. 1970. Parent materials and texture of Peak District soils. *Zeitschrift fur Geomorph.,* **14**, 262–274.

Bullock, P. 1971. The soils of the Malham Tarn area. *Field Stud.,* **3**, 381–408.

Cazalet, P.C.D. 1968. Investigation of the profile characteristics, development and distribution of the soils of part of the Southern Pennines. Unpubl. Ph.D. thesis, Univ. London.

Clayton, K.M. 1966. The origin of landforms of the Malham area. *Field Stud.,* **2**, 359–384.

Colborne, G.J.N. 1981. Soils in Gloucestershire III: Sheet SO61 (Cinderford). *Soil Surv. Rec. No.73.*

Crampton, C.B. 1961. An interpretation of the micro-mineralogy of certain Glamorgan soils: the influence of ice and wind. *J. Soil Sci.,* **12**, 158–171.

Crampton, C.B. (ed.) 1965. Summer meeting at Swansea, programme and guide to the excursions. *British Soc. Soil Sci.,* Unpublished.

F.A.O. - UNESCO 1974. Soil Map of the World. 1:5 000 000. Vol. 1 Legend. (Unesco, Paris)

Findlay, D.C. 1965. The soils of the Mendip district of Somerset. *Mem. Soil Surv. Great Britain.*

Furness, R.R. and King, S.J. 1972. Soils in Westmorland I: Sheet SD58 (Sedgwick). *Soil Surv. Rec. No. 10.*

George, H. 1978. Soils in Northumberland I: Sheet NZ07 (Stamfordham). *Soil Surv. Rec. No. 53.*

Hall, B.R. and Folland, C.J. 1970. Soils of Lancashire. *Bull. Soil Surv. Great Britain.*

Piggott, C.D. 1962. Soil formation and development on the
    Carboniferous Limestone of Derbyshire I: Parent materials.
    Journal of Ecol., **50**, 145-156.

Smithson, F. 1953. The micro-mineralogy of North Wales soils.
    Journal of Soil Sci., **4**, 194-210.

Soil Survey Staff 1975. Soil taxonomy, a basic system of soil
    classification for making and interpreting soil surveys.
    Agric. Handbook U.S. Dep. Agric. No. 436, (Washington D.C.)

Sweeting, M.M. 1972. *Karst Landforms.* (Macmillan, London)

Thompson, T.R.E. 1978. Soils in Clwyd II: Sheet SJ17 (Holywell).
    Soil Surv. Rec. No. 50.

Address of the Author:

              D.M. Carroll,
              Soil Survey of England and Wales,
              Block 7, Government Buildings,
              St. George's Road,
              Harrogate,
              North Yorkshire, HG2 9ER,
              United Kingdom

7

Effets de la néotectonique dans les karsts Mediterranéens

J. Nicod

RÉSUMÉ

La plupart des massifs calcaires entourant la Méditerranée et faisant partie de la 'Chaine Alpine' (*sensu lato*) ont connu des épisodes de soulèvement au cours du Néogène et du Quaternaire, postérieurement à la mise en place des grandes unités charriées.

1 - La forte énergie du relief ainsi acquise s'est traduite par des mouvements de détente, spécialement sur le front des escarpements, exemple des Audibergue ou sur les bords des canyons antécédents (ex. des pharangis de Crète).

2 - Des jeux en distension et en coulissement ont facilité le développement des circulations hydrogéologiques, et l'évolution des poljés: par exemple El Yammouné (Liban), Cerknica (Slovénie, d'après les travaux de P. HABIC' *et al*.); rejeu du grand accident longitudinal du poljé de San Gregorio (Monte Marzano) lors du tremblement de terre d'Irpinia (1980).

3 - Dans les karsts littoraux mouvements néotectoniques et variations eustatiques du niveau marin se combinent pour aboutir à des systèmes hydrologiques complexes du type Cephalonie et de certains poljes du littoral dalmate.

Sur un plan méthodologique, on rappellera les recherches effectuées en Italie sur la déformation des cavités, par mesure de l'inclinaison successive des stalactites (F.FORTI *et al*.); et l'étude du compartement des aquiféres lors des séismes.

SUMMARY

Most of the limestones blocks surrounding the Mediterranean and belonging to the Alpine Range have experienced rising episodes during the Neogene and the Quaternary, subsequent to the setting in place of the main thrusted units.

1 - The strong energy of the relief thus acquired explains a good many of the expanded movements, particularly on scarp faults (Audibergue example), or on the borders of antecedent canyons (Crete 'pharangis' example).

2 - Slackening in tectonic activity facilitated the spreading out of hydrogeological circulations and polje evolution: for example, El Yammoune (Lebanon), Cerknica (Slovenia, from works of P. HABIC' *et al.*) or the recurrent faulting of the great longitudinal ground feature of San-Gregorio Polje (Monte Marzano) during the Irpinia earthquake (1980).

3 - In littoral karsts, neotectonic movements and eustatic sea-level changes combine to result in complicated hydrogeological systems, such as the Cephalonia type, or some poljes of the Dalmatian shore.

From the methodological point of view, Italian researchers have put us on the right track, as much concerning studies of deformation of the geometry of cavities, by measurements of successive inclinations of stalactites (F. FORTI *et al.*), as by analysis of the aquifers reactions to seismic events.

INTRODUCTION

Les Karsts méditerranéens se caractérisent par une très grande disparité de formes et de degré d'évolution. Parmi les facteurs déterminants: purissance variable des séries calcaires, intensité plus ou moins grande de la fracturation, très grande inégalité des précipitations, caractères différents des périodes froides du Quaternaire, d'une région à l'autre, héritages paléo-karstiques, le rôle de la Néotectonique doit être envisagé. La plupart des massifs calcaires entourant la Méditerranée et faisant partie de la chaine alpine (*sensu lato*) ont connu des épisodes de soulèvement au cours du Néogène et du Quaternaire, postérieurement à la mise en place des structures charriées. Certains continuent de subir une activité tectonique traduite par une séismicité élevée. Tout un courant de l'Ecole Géographique française, à la lumière de nombreux travaux sur le domaine méditerranéen tend à prendre en compte dans l'évolution géomorphologique l'incidence des phénomènes tectoniques récents ou actuels; par ailleurs plusieurs karstologues et hydrogéologues Italiens (F. Forti, P. Celico) se sont particulièrement penchés sur le rôle direct des séismes.

ROLE DE L'ENERGIE DU RELIEF ACQUIS PAR LE JEU DE
LA NEOTECTONIQUE: DISTENSION ET DECOMPRESSION

C'est un fait désormais acquis que l'orogénèse (mio-) plio-quaternaire (et même à partir de l'Oligocene dans le domaine pyrénéo-provençal) a eu comme effet général de soulever des structures charriées mises en place antérieurement.

De telles unités, jusqu'alors soumises à un régime de compression se sont trouvées en situation de distension. Par ailleurs, en raison de l'énergie du relief en accroissement, des phénomènes de décompression ont été provoqués par les processus érosifs tels que le recul des escarpements et le creusement des canyons antécédents comme ceux de la Majella étudié par J. Demangeot 1965 ou les pharangis de Crête (J.C. Bonnefont 1977, G. Fabre et R. Maire 1983). Dans l'ensemble la distension a favorisé l'évolution karstique profonde, les phénomènes de détente (décompression) plus localisés, l'évolution superficielle, mais les deux facteurs jouent dans le même sens.

  i) Un exemple la karstification de l'escarpement
     de chevauchement de l'Audibergue (Alpes Maritimes)
     (Figure 7.1).

La zone centrale présente un système de dolines nivales, situées sur la crête vers 1500-1600m, remarquablement déterminé par la fracturation. Les dolines sont dyssimétriques en fonction du fort pendage N des calcaires du Jurassique supérieur; elles sont alignées sur des fractures de direction N à N 20°E, transverses par rapport à la direction générale de l'escarpement, donc par rapport au plan de chevauchement. Le système de fractures est lié à la mise en place de l'unité chevauchante, lors de la phase tectonique fini-miocène. La fracturation reste ouverte, pour deux raisons:

- *rejeu tectonique:* des plans de friction de même direction affectent aussi les brèches quaternaires, fortement cimentées (en particulier sur la N 85, près de la cote 1042 à l'W d'Escragnolles) et d'origine déjà sismique.

- *Décompression* d'ordre morphologique, en raison de la vigueur de l'escarpement (250 m en moyenne), mais l'ensemble de l'Audibergue est perché de près d'un millier de mètres par rapport à la reculée de la Source de la Siagne. Cette détente a permis, surtout en période froide ou lors des séismes[1] l'alimentation des tabliers de brèches.

---

[1]cf. les discussions sur le 'nettoyage' lors des secousses sismiques, aes blocs, portions de falaises, etc... en situation instable, au Colloque 'Effets des Séismes sur les reliefs de forte énergie', Nice 26-28 mai 1983 (Mediterranee 2-1984).

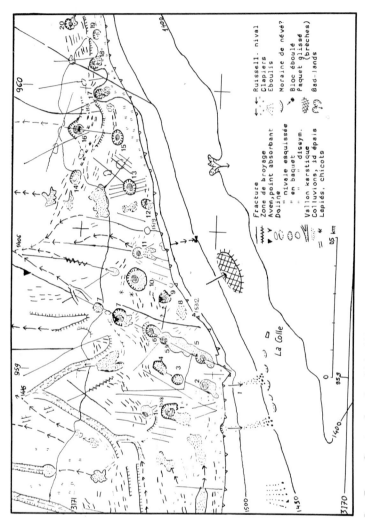

Figure 1. La Zone Centrale de l'Audibergue

Figure 1. The Central Zone of Audibergue
Key: Fracture – Shatter zone – Shaft, swallow hole – Doline – Snow doline –
Bucket doline (Kübel) – id, asymmetric – Karst dell – Colluvium – Grikes; tors –
Snow melt – Stone field – Screes – Protalus rampart – Rock fall – Rock slides
(breccias) – Badlands

Le rôle de la décompression est encore plus sensible dans le cas de l'alignement E-W de dolines et de bogaz de la Bergerie de Biron (Montagne de Thiey) au pied de l'escarpement E de l'Audibergue, et plus proche encore de la reculée de la Siagne.

Ces effets de détente se retrouvent sur le front d'escarpe-de chevauchement sous formes de couloirs et de fentes de décollement (Ph. Renault, 1967); ils sont amplifiés s'il y a des roches plastiques sous-jacentes (Baou des Glacières à la Sainte-Baume), comme sur le front des méga cuestas; mais le jeu de la tectonique récente n'est pas exclu.

ii) L'évolution des écailles - bastions calcaires isolés

Elles correspondent généralement, dans le système alpin à de petites unités de calcaires massifs ou de dolomies, intensément tectonisés lors de leur mise en place, et portées en altitude par des mouvements récents. Bastions isolés, ils sont soumis au jeu de la distension, de la décompression par recul des parois, et disparition des glaciers, enfin aux mouvements différentiels liés au tassement ou au soutirage des assises plastiques qui leur servent souvent de semelle. De grands couloirs ou bogaz découpent leur surface, fonctionnent comme puits à neige et passent en profondeur à des avens 'boite aux lettres'. Y. Quinif (1967) a décrit ce type de couloirs et d'avens dans les Karsts haut-alpins algériens. Dans les Alpes françaises du Sud, le Marguareis, la Grande Séolane, Chabrières, éléments isolés et disloqués de la zone briançonnaise, présentent ce type d'évolution. Au Marguareis des miroirs frais indiquent un rejeu tectonique très récent; à Chabrières, au N-W d'Embrun la célèbre 'Oucane' déjà étudiée par E.A. Martel se présente comme un système de fractures ouvertes dans les calcaires dolomitiques triasiques de cette écaille, très haut perchée (2300 m) au-dessus des marnes noires de la Vallée de la Durance (Serre-Ponçon).

iii) Conséquences de l'antécédence des canyons

Le creusement des grands canyons est commandé en totalité ou en partie par le soulèvement des massifs calcaires, horsts ou qu'ils entaillent; les exemples sont très nombreux et spectaculaires: Canyons de la Majella dans l'Apennin central (J. Demangeot, 1965) de ou de la Macédoine occidentale, des Pharangis de Crete, du Rhummel à Constantine, etc... Si le cas du Verdon est plus complexe (alternance de tronçons surimposés dans les secteurs synclinaux et antécédents dans les anticlinaux), il reste que le creusement est largement guidé par le système de fractures. En effet, dans la plupart des cas, l'antécédence est *dirigée* par les accidents tectoniques qui jouent du fait du soulèvement; les failles tendent à s'ouvrir et commandent à la fois la circulation souterraine et le creusement subaérien.

Par ailleurs la phénomène de détente entraîne l'évolution des parois par éboulement de pans entiers, et se manifeste sur les lèvres par développement de lapiés de fracture (*Kluftkarren*) et même fentes de décollement.

Le réalisation du canyon de l'Aniene à Tivoli constitue un cas différent. D'après J. Raffy (1983), le soulèvement de la bordure de l'Apennin calcaire, dans le contexte de distension et de volcanisme du Latium voisin, a entraîné une karstification intense (en partie liée à l'afflux des eaux thermales riches en CO_2 hypo-volcaniques), permettant le développement d'un cours souterrain, dont le canyon actuel dérive par effondrement des voûtes. De même les grandes accumulations de travertins de la Sabine et du Latium, dont celle de Bagni Albule en contre-bas de Tivoli sont en rapport avec ces phénomènes hydrothermaux, liés à la distension et au volcanisme, spécialement depuis le début du Quaternaire moyen.

Si le soulèvement est modéré, circulation hypogée et sub-aérienne interfèrent et constituent le niveau de base dynamique (G. Fabre et J. Nicod, 1978). Dans le cas contraire, il y a déconnection, le creusement linéaire est plus rapide que l'aménagement des drains affluents (d'où des déversements en cascade); par ailleurs dans le massif, de part et d'autre du canyon les circulations verticales se développent, et recoupent les anciennes circulations phréatiques: Y. Quinif (1976b) a mis en rapport avec elles les grottes perchées du Constantinois; observation analogue dans le canyon de la Gola de Fascette, au SE du massif du Marguareis[2]. Un autre exemple est donné par L. Brancaccio; la grotte de San Michele, dans le Canyon de Tusciano (Apennin Campanien) développée suivant la fracturation N 180 et N 90, a été tronquée et suspendue par des failles N 135 et N 45 (M. Baggioni Lippmann, 1981).

NEOTECTONIQUE ET DEVELOPPEMENT DES POLJES KARSTIQUES

Il s'agit d'un problème délicat, car les conditions d'évolution des poljés sont complexes, tant du point de vue hydrogéologique (problème des barrages karstiques), que paléo-géomorphologique (longue durée, apport de colluvions et alluvions).

- *Les jeux en extension et en coulissement* facilitent en général les circulations karstiques et expliquent l'allongement des poljés suivant les zones de broyages et les accidents actifs. Rappelons quelques cas typiques:
- le poljé d'El Yammoune (Liban) sur l'accident W de la Beqaa, élément du système de fractures entre la plaque arabique et celle de la Méditerranée orientale; les eaux souterraines s'écoulent vers le N, selon cet accident, en direction de la Source de l'Oronte (J. Besancon, 1968);
- le poljé de Zaffaraya, dans les Cordillères bétiques, allongé sur un accident majeur entre deux unités tectoniques:
- les poljés du Xeromeros d'Acarnanie, liés à *l'halocinèse* des calcairés cataclasés associes au gypse (B. Bousquet, 1975).

---

[2]Communication d'Y. Quinif au Colloque d'Imperia, mai 1982, et excursion sur le terrain.

Mais deux cas sont plus probants encore. En Slovénie, dans le poljé de Cerknica, R. Gospodaric' et P. Habič' (1978) ont montré qu'une des failles directrices affecte les cailloutis Wurmiens du fond du poljé. Dans le poljé de San Gregorio, dans l'Apennin de Campanie, une faille axiale localisant le ponor principal (Figure 7.2) joue lors du tremblement de terre d'Irpinia, le 23 novembre 1980, et un important *scarplet*, déd-nivellant les colluvions du fond du poljé[3]. L'effet hydrogéo-logique des secousses a été net: on a constaté un accroissement important du régime des aquifères, comme déjà lors du séisme du 23 juillet 1930 (P. Celico, 1981).

L'effet de cloisonnement dû à la surrection

Plusieurs auteurs ont envisagé le rôle du soulèvement actif dans l'individualisation des poljés, l'écoulement subaérien ne pouvant suivre la montée du (ou des) blocs. Pour J.J. Dufaure (1977, p. 36) c'est essentiellement le cas des poljés corinthiens, situés dans une zone intensément soulevée au cours du Quaternaire (+ de 1 mm/an), mais correspondant aussi à des structures favor-ables. Des renversements de drainage, un coude de capture dans le poljé de Féneos témoignent de cette évolution. Mais dans certains cas, un faible soulèvement suffit: témoins les plaines de Mollaoi, et celle de Niata en Laconie (p. 35). Dans le Taurus méridional, N. Güldali (1976) a envisagé aussi le rôle de la tectonique récente dans le cloisonnement du système de poljés de Kestel. De même M. Baggioni-Lippmann (1981) a montré dans l'Apennin de Campanie, le rôle de la Néotectonique dans l'indivi-dualisation des unités structurales, la désorganisation du réseau hydrographique pliocène, et le développement des poljés - en particulier celui de San Gregorio, déjà cité, isolé de l'écoule-ment normal exoreique par l'encaissement du Platano dans ses gorges antécédentes (Figure 7.2).

La génèse tectonique des poljés-grabens

Le cas inverse existe, celui du fossé d'effondrement trans-formé en poljé. L'Apennin en présente au moins deux exemples: En Campanie, le Valle di Diana fossé tectonique remblayé, à exutoire karstique (M. Baggioni-Lippmann, 1981, p.53), et surtout le bassin d'Avezzano (Lago Fucino), situé vers 650 m, et déter-miné essentiellement par l'inversion tectonique (J. Raffy, 1981 1983). Ses contours coincident avec des fractures, en particulier sur le rebord NE, entre Celano et Gioia un accident a joué lors du séisme du 13 janvier 1915: un miroir de 3 m de rejet est apparu sur le tracé de la faille, tandis que des fissures paral-lèles s'ouvraient dans la plaine (p. 70). L'auteur considère que l'inversion tectonique commence au Villafranchien, et que la dépression est parfaitement constituée au début du Pléistocène supérieur (Lac Fucino 2, 850 m, Riss-Würm?). Au Néo-Würm le con-tour actuel du bassin est réalisé (Lac Fucino 3, 700 m) et le niveau du lac actuel asséché y est emboité.

---

[3]Communication de M. Panizza au Colloque 'Effets des séismes sur les reliefs de forte énergie', Nice, 26-28 mai 1983, et renseignements oraux de Mme Lippmann. Cf. Panizza M., 1982. Introduction to the morphotectonics problems; Proceedings of the I.G.U. Morphotectonics Working Group, Rio Claro, Brazil, 1982.

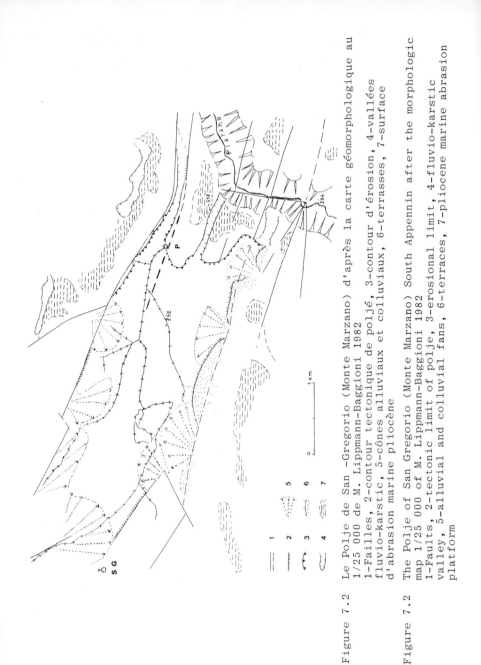

Figure 7.2   Le Polje de San -Gregorio (Monte Marzano) d'après la carte géomorphologique au
1/25 000 de M. Lippmann-Baggioni 1982
1-Failles, 2-contour tectonique de poljé, 3-contour d'érosion, 4-vallées
fluvio-karstic, 5-cônes alluviaux et colluviaux, 6-terrasses, 7-surface
d'abrasion marine pliocène

Figure 7.2   The Polje of San Gregorio (Monte Marzano) South Appennin after the morphologic
map 1/25 000 of M. Lippmann-Baggioni 1982
1-Faults, 2-tectonic limit of polje, 3-erosional limit, 4-fluvio-karstic
valley, 5-alluvial and colluvial fans, 6-terraces, 7-pliocene marine abrasion
platform

Photo 1   Le Grand Canyon du Verdon, dans le champ de faille de
           la Mescla.   Rôle des phénomènes de détente (J. Nicod, 1968)

Photo 1   The Great Canyon of Verdon, in the fault field of the
           'Mescla'. Impact of release phenomena

Photo 2   Ouvala de Valle Enchiausa, dans le Massif de l'Oserot-
           Tête de Moyse (Frontière franco-Italienne), dans une zone
           de tectonisation intense et active.   L'ouvala est dominée
           par l'arc externe d'un glacier rocheux.   Ces glaciers
           rocheux sont liés à l'intense fracturation des dolomies
           de la zone briançonnaise et à la séismicité active
           (J. Nicod, 1975)

Photo 2   Uvala of the 'Valle Enchiausa' in the Oserot-Tête de
           Moyse range, in intensive and active tectonic zone.
           Rock-glaciers proceeded from intensive faulting and
           effect of seismicity, in dolomites of the 'briançonnaise'
           zone

Au cours de ces phases l'hydrologie karstique s'est réalisée mais elle n'a pas été le moteur du système. Le problème est le même en Macédoine. Les deux lacs de Prespa et d'Ohrid sont des lacs de Graben, et le premier se déverse dans le second par une circulation hypogée, inversement le second est surtout alimenté par des sources karstiques ce qui joint à la mobilité du fond (zone de séismicité intense) lui permet d'échapper au comblement sédimentaire: on a le un bel exemple de dépressions tectono-karstiques (J. Nicod et M. Chardon 1983). Citons également dans la péninsule hellénique le lac de Kastoria, à exutoire karstique (L. Faugeres, 1977), et surtout le lac Copais, fossé d'effondrement drainé par des ponors. Dans tous les cas ces dépressions sont d'origine tectonique, mais le système hydrologique est karstique: ce qui souligne le rôle indirect de la tectonique, facilitant en phase de distension ces circulations souterraines.

NEOTECTONIQUE ET KARST LITTORAL

Le littoral des massifs calcaires constitue une zone d'instabilité (J.J. Blanc, 1975). D'une part de nombreux littoraux ont un caractère tectonique, ils correspondent à des failles que déterminent leur tracé; souvent ces failles sont actives, particulièrement dans les Balkans; le littoral dalmate, au niveau du Mosor, de Dubrovnik et du Montenegro, les iles ioniennes, la péninsule du Mani, la Crète etc... Le jeu de ces accidents, combiné avec les variations eustatiques du niveau marin, et les alternatives de compression et de détente qu' elles entrainent, permet l'évolution des falaises par éboulement (J.J. Blanc, 1975: ce qui n'exclut pas le rôle des séismes) mais aussi l'évolution du karst profond.

Il en est résulté le développement des exutoires littoraux ou sous-marins, ceux-ci dans la majorité des cas sont situés à *faible profondeur*, donc dans la zone de battement des variations eustatiques, et ont fonctionné comme exutoires subaériens pendant les phases régressives (recensement et bibliographie in J. Nicod, 1982). Mais la part de la tectonique est certaine dans de nombreux cas. La carte dressée par J.C. Bonnefont (1977, Fig. 4) montre la localisation des *almyros* (sources littorales saumâtres) dans les secteurs instables du littoral, spécialement ceux en affaissement. Les recherches effectuées sur les vruljés de Dalmatie (M. Breznik, 1973) donnent la preuve qu'un grand nombre de fissures correspondant à des exutoires multiples sont englobées par le système eau douce - eau marine. Or ces fissures sont en relation avec les phénomènes de détente, et souvent des failles actives. Ainsi les 7 sources sous-marines d'Aurisina dans la baie de Trieste, correspondant avec le Timaro comme exutoire de la Reka souterraine, sont sur un accident du champ de faille d'Udine, actif comme de récents séismes du Frioul l'ont montré (mai, septembre, 1976). Le groupe de Senj exutoire des poljés d'Otocak et de Lika est constitué de 70 sources littorales, 30 sources sous-marines et quelques *inversacs*, sur 300 m de côte près de Jurjevo: cette concentration exceptionnelle ne peut qu'avoir une origine néotectonique. La source sous-marine de Morinj dans la baie de Kotor, alimentée par le massif

puissamment arrosé de l'Orjen, se trouve sur une faille majeure
active du Monténégro (M. Breznik, p. 168). Des résurgences
aussi importantes que la source sous-marine d'Aghios Georgios,
près de Kiveri, recevant les eaux du ponor de Nestani, dans le
poljé de Tripolis, et actuellement captée, ou l'Almyros Irakliou
en Crète, alimentée par le massif du Psiloritis (M. Breznik,
p. 169), sont localisées de même sur des accidents majeurs. Le
cas extrême est celui de la circulation hydrogéologique exceptionnelle de l'Ile de Céphalonie, des 'Moulins de la Mer'
d'Argostoli, aux sources littorales et sous-marines du côté
opposé de l'île, qui ne peut se comprendre sans des phènomènes
hydrodynamiques actifs (hypothèse de Maurin et Zötl), or ces
derniers exigent un système de conduits important, déterminés
par les phénomènes de détente liés à l'instabilité tectonique de
l'île (cf. perturbations du régime hydrologique par le séisme de
1953, B. Bousquet 1977, p 57).

Dans les secteurs en distension géologique, le développement du karst profond à partir de la zone littorale, peut se
propager loin à l'intérieur: on rappellera l'exemple classique
du Lac rouge (Cerveno Jezero) en bordure du poljé d'Imotski,
sondé sur près de 250 m jusqu'à la cote 44 m et altestant
l'existence de cette zone de karstification profonde (J. Roglic
1974). Enfin, pour être complet il faudrait envisager le rôle
de la régression messinienne - crise de salinité -, et des effets
techniques et morphologiques (creusement des canyons) consécutifs:
problème des formes et exutoires karstiques immergés sous des
tranches d'eau supérieures aux régressions glacio-eustatiques,
que l'on commence à recenser (U. Sauro, 1982).

Ainsi dans l'ensemble, il est nécessaire de prendre en
compte le rôle de la néotectonique dans l'évolution des karsts
méditerranéens. Toutefois, il faut se garder d'exagerer ce
rôle, et *procéder à des mesures*. Dans ce domaine, les chercheurs
italiens nous ont montré la voie, tant en ce qui concerne les
études sur les déformations de la géométrie des cavités, par
mesure des inclinaisons successives des stalactiques (F. Forti
et collab) que par l'analyse des réactions des aquifères aux
séismes.

REFERENCES

Baggioni-Lippmann, 1981. Néotectonique et géomorphologie dans
    l'Apennin Campanien (Italie méridionale). *Rev. Géol. dyn.*,
    23(1), 41-54.

Besancon, J. 1968. Le poljé de Yammouné. *Hannon III*, Beyrouth,
    1-61.

Blanc, J.J. 1975. Ecroulement de falaises et chutes de blocs
    du littoral rocheux de la Provence Occidentale. *Géol. Méd.*,
    2(2), 75-90.

Bleahu, M.D. 1974. Morfologia Carstica (sp.II,4), ed. Stiinti-
    fica, Bucuresti, 588p.

Bonnefont, J.C. 1977. La Néotectonique et sa traduction dans le paysage géomorphologique de l'île de Crète. *Rev. Geog. Phys. Géol. dyn.*, 19(1), 93–108.

Bousquet, B. 1975. La Grèce Occidentale, interprétation morphologique de l'Epire, de l'Acarnanie et des îles Ioniennes *These, Paris,* 1974, 585pp, 11 cartes h.t.

Breznik, M. 1973. The origin of brakish karstic springs and their development, *Geologija, Razprave in Porocila,* 16, 83–186.

Celico, P. 1981. Relazioni tra idrodinamica sottorranea e terramoti in Irpinia (Campania). *Rend. Soc. Geol., It,* 4, 103–108.

Cucchi, F., Forti, F., Semeraro, R. 1979. Indizi di Neotectonica in cavita del Val Rosandra (Trieste). *Atti e Memoire della Commissione Grotte 'Eugenio Boegan',* 18, 1978, 105–109

Demangeot, J.J. 1965. Géomorphologie des Abruzzes adriatiques. *Mém. et Doc. CNRS,* (cf. 621–640).

Dufaure, J.J. 1977. Néotectonique et morphogenèse dans une péninsule méditerranéenne, le Péloponèse. *Rev. Geogr. Phys. Géol. dyn.,* 19(1), 27–58.

Fabre, G. et Nicod, J. 1978. Niveaux de base actuels dans les principaux canyons du Languedoc oriental et des Plans de Provence. *Int. Journal Spéléol.,* 10, 279–290.

Fabre, G. et Maire, R. 1983. Néotectonique et morphogenèse insulaire en Grèce: le massif du Mont Ida (Crète). *Méditerranée,* 2, 39–49.

Faugères, L. 1977. Recherches géomorphologiques en Grèce septentrionale (Macédoine centrale, Macédoine Occidentale), *Thèse Paris,* 4, 1975, (H. Champion, Paris), 2 vol.

Forti, F. 1977. Rapporti tra terremoti e carsismo nello regionale Friuli-Venezia Giulia, *Atti 4 Conv. Reg. Speleo. Trentino-Acro,* 32–45.

Forti, F. et Postpischl, D. Derivazione di dati neotectonici. *CNR, Progetto Finalizzato Geodinamica,* No 251 et 356.

Gams, Iv. 1978. The poljé, the problem of definition. *z. Geomorph. N.F.,* 22(2), 170–181.

Gospadaric' R., Habic', P. 1978. Karst phenomena of Cerknisko Polje. *Acta carsologica, Ljubljana,* 8(1), 162pp.

Güldali, N. 1970. Karstmorphologische Studien im Gebiet des Poljesystem von Kestel (W Taurus). *Tubinger Geogr. Studien,* 40, 104p.

Habic', P. 1982. Kraski relief in tektonika (karst Relief and tectonics). *Acta Carsologica, Ljubljana,* 10, 27–44.

Julian, M. 1984. Karst alpins et Neotectonique in Karsts des Alpes Francaises. *Karstologia,* 3, p. 76.

Julian, M. et Nicod J. 1984. Un karst subalpin mediterraneen: la region Audibergue-Mons (A.M. Var). *Karstologia,* 3, 52–59.

Letourneur, J. et Dayre, M. 1981. Aspects physico-mécaniques et incidences géotechniques de la décompression. *Bull. Ass. Géogr. Fr.*, **478**, 133–138.

Lhenaff, R. 1978. Poljés et structures chariées (Cordillères Bétiques). *Rev. Géogr. alpine*, **3**, 299–307.

Lippmann-Baggioni, M. 1982. Karst et néotectonique, Monte Marzano (Italie méridionale). *Mém. et Doc. de Géographie, CNRS, Phénomènes karstiques*, **3**, 33–43.

Marre, A. et Quinif, Y. 1981. Le Djebel Guerioun, évolution quaternaire d'un massif calcaire des hautes plaines constantinoises (Algérie). *Méditerranée*, **4**, 3–13.

Martin, J. 1981. Le Moyen Atlas Central, étude morphologique (Th. Paris, 1977), *Notes et Mémoires Serv. Géol. Maroc, Rabat*, 445pp.

Nicod, J. 1979. Sur le rôle de la tectonique et des variations des circulations karstiques dans l'évolution des poljés. *Ann. Soc. Géol. Belgique*, **102**, 87–93.

Nicod, J. 1982. Niveaux de base regressifs et formes karstiques submergées. *Mém. no.4 de l'Association Francais Karstologiques, karsts littoraux*, 67–74.

Nicod, J. et Chardon, M. 1983. Notes sur la morphotectonique et l'évolution du relief de la Macédoine Occidentale yougoslave. *Méditer.*, **3**.

Pezzi, M.C. 1976. Morfologia carstica del sector central de la cordillera subbetica (Tesis). *Cuad. Geogr. Univ. Granada*, S.M.2.

Quinif, Y. 1976a. Contribution à l'étude morphologique des karsts algériens de type haut alpin. *Rev. Géogr. Phys. Géol. dyn.*, **2**, **17(1)**, 5–18.

Quinif, Y. 1976b. Grottes perchées du Constantinois, relations avec la Néotectonique. *Bull. Soc. Hist. Nat. Afrique N, Alger*, **66(3-4)**, 1975, 117–126.

Raffy, J. 1981. Orogenèse et dislocations quaternaires du versant tyrrhénien des Abruzzes (Italie Centrale). *Rev. Géol. dyn. Géogr. phys.*, **23(1)**, 55–72.

Raffy, J. 1983. Le versant tyrrhénien de l'Apennin central. *Th. Paris (1979)*, 442pp.

Renault, Ph. 1967. Contribution à l'étude des actions mécaniques et sédimentologiques dans la spéléogenèse. *Ann. de Spéléo.*, 22–23.

Roglic', J. 1974. Les caractères spécifiques du karst dinarique. *CNRS, Mém. et Doc.*, **15**, Phénomènes karstiques II, 269–278.

Sauro, U. 1982. Materiali el problemi per uno studio paleografico delle regioni carsiche italiane. *Lavori della Societa Ital. Biogeografia*, **7**, 1978, 467–513.

8

Geological structure: an important factor controlling karst development

Song Lin Hua

SUMMARY

The effect of geological structures on karst development has been systematically studied. It is possible that geological structure is more important for karst development than the lithology of carbonate rocks, types of hydrocirculation, pCO_2 and climatic factors such as temperature and precipitation. The nature of regional tectonics determines the spatial distribution characteristics of carbonate rocks and karst development. The arrangement of formations affects the spatial location of karst, which is generally in more soluble rocks near the contact zone between two kinds of lithology. Synclines commonly constitute the collecting and storing structures of karst water, and surface and subsurface karst often develops. Anticlines usually form the dividing structures between surface and subsurface water. When the rocks are fractured and destroyed by tectonic movements karst may develop well. The axial parts of folds are the places where stress concentrates, and deformation is strong; there the zone of karst water abounds and karst develops. It is obvious that most branches and main passages of underground drainage systems, poljes, and big springs are connected with fractures and correlate with faults. The existence of deep and big faults promotes deep water circulation and karst development.

RÉSUMÉ

Il se peut que la structure géologique joue un rôle plus important
pour le développement du karst que la lithologie des roches carbonates, la circulation des eaux, le pCO_2 et les facteurs climatiques (températures et précipitations). Le type de tectonique
régionale détermine les caractéristiques spatiales des roches
carbonatées et le développement du karst. Il est fréquent que
les synclinaux constituent des zones receuillant et emmagasinant
les eaux karstiques et par la même possèdent des phénomènes
karstiques bien développés en surface aussi bien que sous terre.
Les anticlinaux sont souvent des axes de partage entre les eaux
superficielles et souterraines. Lorsque les roches sont frac-
turées et intensément triturées par les mouvements tectoniques,
le karst peut être bien développé. Les axes des plis sont les
endroits où les contraintes sont les plus fortes et le broyage
tectonique le plus intense. Il s'en suit que les eaux karstiques
y sont abondantes, permettent au karst de se développer. Il est
certain que la plupart des galeries souterraines, des poljes et
des grandes sources sont guidés par des fractures et des failles.
La présence de failles profondes et importantes facilite la circulation profonde des eaux et le développement du karst.

INTRODUCTION

Karst is the result of long term physical-chemical reactions between water and soluble rocks. Many workers have done a great
deal of work to study the effect of factors like chemical composition, texture of carbonate rocks, water circulation and
hydrodynamic conditions, and pCO_2, temperature and precipitation
on karst development. With the progressive increase of hydrogeological surveys, water conservation, and hydroelectric power
projects in karst areas, karstologists, hydrogeologists, geomorphologists and others have been giving close attention to the
control of geological structures over karst development, water
seepage, and the relationship between the structures and the
distribution of karst water. Han (1980) described the water
bearing conditions of geological structures. Song *et al.,*
(1983) examined the relationship between geological structures
and karst development and karst underground drainage systems.
Xiao (1981) particularly studied neotectonic fissure water and
suggested that many underground streams in South China, and many
of the famous big karst springs, such as Nianziguan Spring,
Lungziei Spring and Baotuo Spring in the north, are all controlled by neotectonic fissures. The control of geological structures over karst development is stressed in this paper.

INFLUENCE OF REGIONAL TECTONICS

Regional tectonic units reflect the nature of regional tectonic movements which completely dominate the sedimentary features, metamorphic degree, deformation and distribution of rocks.

In the geoplatform and pene-geoplatform areas, the earth crustal movements uplift and subside stably. Since the Sinian period, thick shelf carbonate sediments have been deposited on the platform (Group of Karstology, 1979). For instance, Sinian-Triassic dolomite and limestone form about 75-85% of the 6500-11 000 m of marine sediments which have been deposited on the Guizhou Plateau, principally in the Vanjin and Jiangnan paleolands (Yang, 1982). The limestones and dolomites were folded and faulted in several tectonic movements. All these factors determine karst development and distribution in these units.

In the geosynclines the earth's crust has strongly subsided, and thick sediments, including carbonate rocks which change greatly in both thickness and phases, were rapidly deposited. They have been metamorphosed to different degrees, and seriously folded in sharp tectonic movements. Karst is therefore generally distributed in small areas. However, after the subsidence, the earth's crust movements became more epeirogenic, and uplifted or subsided in geoplatforms: thick and pure limestones and dolomites were deposited over large areas. For example, several thousand metres of limestones and dolomites of Devonian-Permian age occur in western and northern Guangxi, where typical tropical Fenglin and Fengzung are well developed, especially in the Guilin tower karst area.

ARRANGEMENT OF STRATIGRAPHY

The aspect of stratigraphy which affects the spatial location of karst development is the relationship between soluble and insoluble rocks. For instance, where the soluble rocks touch insoluble rocks, karstification develops on the soluble rocks near the contact. In Figure 8.1, T_{1m}^1 represents lower Triassic Maoqiaopu limestone and T_{1y}^3 the lower Triassic Jerjitan purple red shale. Karst depressions, sinkholes, ponds and windows of underground streams all occur along the contact zones. Extension of the groundwater channels are coincident with the strike of the rocks.

Sandy shales often lie underneath the limestones and make up the karstification base of the limestone and the lower boundary of karst water circulation. In limestones near the contact zone, groundwater flow concentrates and karstification is strong, causing groundwater passages and caverns to be well developed. The Jigongyan cave and the main course of the Niaoshuiyan drainage system in Dejiang County are developed in the base of Permian limestone laid down upon Silian sandy shale.

167

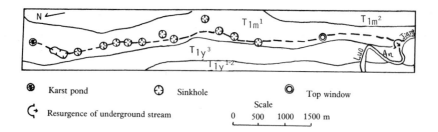

Figure 8.1   Underground stream developed along the contact between Maoqiaopu limestone (T_{1m}^1) and Jergitan shale (T_{1y}^3) in Meitan region, Guizhou Province

Palmer (1981) has studied the caves in limestone covered by permeable sandstones in the United States.

FRACTURES CONTROLLING KARST DEVELOPMENT

Fractures are the result of rock deformation. The porosity of sediments is greatly decreased during the diagenetic process. For example, the porosity of chalk (soft and fine grained limestone) is about 0.7, but the massive hard limestone is just less than 0.01. The fractures in limestone greatly improve the hydro-circulating conditions and water storage capacity. Downing *et al.*, (1979) stated that the permeability of a medium with a porosity of 0.3-0.4 varies in the range of 0.0001 m/d-0.001 m/d, but with fissured porosity 0.0001, it reaches up to 1-100 m/d in the fissures. Limestones containing original porosity water are regarded as primary aquifers, and limestones with fissured permeability are regarded as secondary aquifers.

Any changes of limestone texture could cause variations in the hydrogeological properties. Fracture zones are the areas of transmission and storage of groundwater. Compressive, tensional and shear fractures are formed as the result of rock deformation. Generally as a result of compressive fractures space becomes reduced and fracture fragments get cemented; compression fractures constitute, therefore, aquicludes and impermeable structures. However, tensional fractures expand rock space and make for high porosity; they create good conditions for groundwater, thus making a better transmission medium and water-bearing structure. With shear fractures, some are transmissive, others are not. The direction of geomechanics and porosity of carbonate rocks change in time and space. A fault subject to tectonic forces several times over will be resurrected and complex. Therefore, some compressive faults may change into shear or tension structures, or one part may be compressed and another become tensional.

In many areas, fractures essentially control karst development and spatial distribution. For instance three-tensile faults in Dejiang anticline make the dolomite karst develop much better;

whereas the pore (vadose) water-bearing capacity and karst is
poorly developed in general in north Guizhou (Zhang, 1979). In
Dejiang three underground drainage systems and valleys or poljes
of 0.5-0.8 km wide are developed along the three faults (Song et
al., 1983). Figure 8.2 shows the funnels, depressions and
underground drainage systems distributed along faults in the
Zhengan District, Guizhou Province.

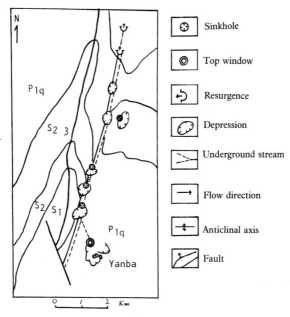

Figure 8.2   Underground stream develop along the fault in
              Zhengan District, Guizhou Province

The result of fractures promoting hydrocirculation enables
karst development to be found far below the regional drainage
base. A good example is the conduit flow and cave filling with
fluvial sands and gravels up to 10 m deep, which occurs along
the faults F20, 220 m below the Wujiang river bed (Li, 1981).

In an area with long-term intermittent uplifting, the fault
always predominates over karst water circulation along the fault
belts. In an uplifting stage, karst water circulates and karstification proceeds downwards. Vertical karst features such as
deep canyons, shafts, and sinkholes may be formed. In a relatively stable stage, the drainage base and hydrocirculation
are also at a relatively stable stage. Karstification is predominantly lateral, producing big basins and valleys and reducing
the limestone hills; it also enlarges the rooms of the subsurface
karst such as channels and caverns. The single or dendritic
drainage pattern transforms into a network pattern. When uplift
alternates with the more stable state, multi-levels of geomorphology and caverns are formed. The different levels of

caverns are connected with vertical features like shafts and sinkholes. When such karstification mechanics are focused on in the fault zone, layered karst features are formed by intermittent uplifting movements. The Longtan polje is developed along the Xingchang fault and there are three levels of water channels; the first is the surface stream which flows for several days after heavy rain; the second, 10-30 m beneath the stream, is the flood passage in the normal rainy season; the third, 90 m below the groundsurface, is full of karst water all the time. All three levels are connected with sinkholes, as shown in Figure 8.3.

Joints play an important role in karst development. Much corrosion is carried out along tensile joints, and this enlarges the rooms of caverns; this helps the limestone absorb more surface water. The distribution and extension of many caves are controlled by the strike of joint sets (Figure 8.4). The pillars of the stone forest in Lunan have resulted from rainwater dissolving pure and thick massive Permian limestones along cross-set vertical joint fissures. Under the stone forest, subterranean drainage systems are developed.

At the intersection of faults or joints, large negative landforms such as basins and valleys occur; the long axis of the valley may correspond with the principal joint set, as shown in Figure 8.5.

EFFECT OF FOLD STRUCTURES

Different types of folds affect karst development. Anticlinal structures generally form watersheds. Rainwater which falls on the surface of anticlines (or seapage water) flows away on two sides from the rock surface at the crest of the formation. Thus an anticline like Dushan forms the natural divide of both surface and subsurface water. However, in the process of folding, the differential movement of materials and the action of

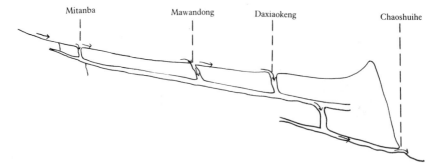

Figure 8.3 Three levels of water channels develop along Kingchang fault, Dejiang, Guizhou Province

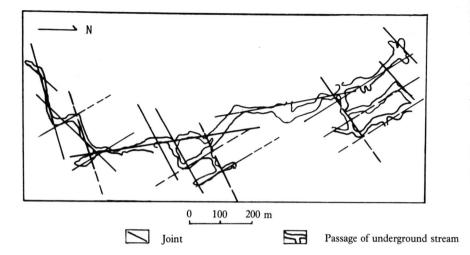

Joint   Passage of underground stream

0   100   200 m

Figure 8.4   Relationship between passages of Shantan underground stream and joint sets, Zhijin County,
Guizhou Province

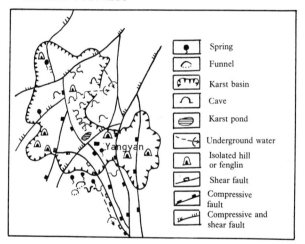

Spring

Funnel

Karst basin

Cave

Karst pond

Underground water

Isolated hill
or fenglin

Shear fault

Compressive
fault

Compressive and
shear fault

Figure 8.5   Relationship between fractures and karst development in Hongyan area, Dao County, Hunan Province.
(After Zhang Yude, 1982)

geomechanics usually causes tensile fractures to form in the
cores of anticlines, and also in secondary cracks and joints.
Therefore, surface and subsurface karst, such as poljes, valleys
and basins for instance, might develop quite well.

171

Synclines are the natural collecting and storing structures of ground water. Limestone, dolomite and other soluble rocks in synclines are commonly corroded by karst water, which causes high karstification in limestones. The typical tropical tower karst in Guilin is developed in a synclinal basin (Chen, 1982). Because of the stability of the earth's crust in the Guilin area, the strong lateral movement of karst water in the syncline creates limestone towers, 40-150 m high, with a Fenglin plain and Fenglin valley by the side of the Lijiang river; while the Fengzung landscape develops on the anticlines on the sides of the Guilin syncline. Another example is the stone forest, with an area of 400 km^2, near Lunan in Yunnan Province; this has developed in the lower Permian Qixia and Maokou limestones in a syncline.

The concentration of run-off in synclines forms independent and completely subterranean drainage systems, like the Niao-shuiyan and Renshuiyan systems in the Shaqi syncline, Dejiang County; and also in the Qingping drainage system in the Qingping syncline of Wuchuan County, in Guizhou Province.

In the plunging parts of anticlines, the stress and strain in the formations are more complicated than that in other parts. There are two main kinds of stress, one which is parallel to the geoforces and the other vertical to the geoforces. Many radial fractures and joint fissures coincide with the dip of the beds and determine the paths and directions of karst water flow. Karst water in the plunging part of an anticline is characterized by radial dividing and, as a result, radial underground drainage systems and surface features are produced.

The situation at the pitching points of synclines is similar to the plunging parts of anticlines. Table 8.1 shows the karst ratio of the total cavern length of drilling core and total length of the drilling core, expressed as a percentage, in the pitching parts of Tuanpiao syncline, Jin County, Liaoning Province.

CONCLUSIONS

Geological structure is an important factor in controlling karst development. It can improve the conditions of karst water bearing and storage in limestone and dolomite; promote deep hydro-circulation; and determine the karstification intensity and the characteristics of karst distribution in space.

The pattern of regional tectonics basically effects the regional distribution of karst. Under the action of regional tectonic forces fold and fracture structures are formed.

Synclines generally constitute the collecting and storing structure of karst water and are strongly karstified; here, surface and subsurface karst are well developed. Anticlines commonly form a water divide, leading the surface and subsurface water away at their crests, particularly if fractures are few.

172

Table 8.1   Comparison of karstification ratios in the boreholes in Jin Syncline, Liaoning Province (in *Karst Research of China,* 1979, p.81)

Borehole No.	Location in geological structure	Distance from syncline axis (m)	Distance from anticline axis (m)	Karstification ratio at -76 m a.s.l. (%)
P1	South flank, Dalianpao syncline	650	1440	0.09
P2	South flank, Dalianpao syncline	300	1225	3.4
P3	South flank, Tuanpiao syncline	450	900	11.1
P4	North flank, Tuanpiao syncline	300	1600	6.5
P5	South flank Tuanpiao syncline ⎰Tilting	240	1125	17.0
P6	North flank Tuanpiao syncline ⎱part of syncline	500	1800	18.0

If the anticlines are fractured, then anticlines become water-bearing structures and karst may develop. The axial parts of folds, especially those plunging and pitching, are places where karst develops and where karst water is stored.

Comparing fractures with folds, fracture structure is more important in the control of karst development and water bearing. The primary passages of subsurface drainage systems, poljes, big karst springs and valleys are almost always determined by fractures. The deep fault is a fundamental necessary condition of karst water deep circulation and deep karst development.

REFERENCES

Chen Wenjun, 1982. Brief introduction to karst geology of Guilin. In: *Selected Papers from the Second All-China Symposium on Karst Sponsored by the Geological Society of China, 1978, Guilin, Guangxi, The People's Republic of China,* (Beijing: Academic Press).

Downing, R.A., Pearson, F.J. and Smith, D.B. 1979. The flow mechanism in the chalk based on radio-isotope analyses of ground water in the London Basin. *Journal of Hydrology,* **40**, 67-83.

Group of Karstology, Institute of Geology, Academi Sinica, 1979. *Karst Research of China,* (Beijing: Academic Press).

173

Han Zhongshan, 1980. On the karst water-bearing structures in the Western part of Hunan and in the Eastern part of Guizhou Province. *Hydrogeology and Engineering Geology,* 3, 32-37.

Li Maoqin, 1981. The deep karsts in Wujiang valley at Wujiangdu Dam Site. *Proceedings of the Eighth International Congress of Speleology,* (Bowling Green, Kentucky), 732-34.

Song Linhua, Zhang Yaoguang *et al.,* 1983. Karst development and the distribution of karst drainage systems in Dejiang, Guizhou Province, China. *Journal of Hydrology,* 61, 3-17.

Xiao Nanshen, 1981. The neotectonic fissure water. *Hydrogeology and Engineering Geology,* 4, 22-25.

Yang Minde, 1982. The geomorphological regularities of karst water occurrences in Guizhou Plateau. *Carsologica Sinica,* 1, 81-91.

Zhang Qianfu, 1979. Karst development and aboundability in North Guizhou. (Unpublished).

Additional reference:

Palmer, A.N. 1981. *A Geological Guide to Mammoth Cave National Park,* (Zephyrus Publications), 196pp.

9

Morphometric variables of drainage basins and their relationship with surrounding lithotectonic zones

Ravinder Kumar

SUMMARY

Eighteen morphometric variables of third-order drainage basins of
two limestone zones were studied. The basins lie to the north (a
zone associated with phyllite and slate) and south of the Chenab
river in Kud, Kashmir Himalaya. The data were subjected to
principal component analysis by the IBM 360/44 computer. The
aim was to investigate the manner in which variables interact in
a downstream direction within the drainage basins of a particular
zone, and their relationship with the surrounding litho-tectonic
zones, of the Murree (sandstone and shale), the Salkhala (schist
and quartzite), and the Murree Thrust (between the Murree and the
Limestone formations) in an area covering about 700 sq km.
    It has been observed that the variance (examined in the con-
text of varimax rotated components) can be explained by each variable with respect to a particular principal component, and the
total variance explained by each principal component of one zone
with respect to the other. These variations also explain the
association of a few variables with one principal component in
one zone, and with another principal component in another zone.
It is therefore concluded that the morphometric variables of the
drainage basins are controlled by litho-tectonic variation.

RÉSUMÉ

Dix huit indices morphométriques de bassins versants de troisième
ordre ont été étudiés. Les bassins sont situés dans deux zones
calcaires au nord (une zone de phyllites et d'ardoises) et au sud
de la rivière Chenab près de Kud (Cachemire, Himalaya). On s'est
servi d'un ordinateur IBM 360/44 pour calculer le PCA (Principal
Component Analysis) et examiner comment les indices des bassins
versants de chaque zone réagissent réciproquement vers l'aval.
On a étudié aussi les relations entre ces indices et des zones
lithotectoniques. Les zones choisies sont le Murree (grès et
marnes), la Salkhala (schistes et quartzites) et le Murree Thrust
(entre le Murree et les formations calcaires). Ces zones couvrent
à peu près 700 km².

Les résultats statistiques montrent qu'il y a des variations
dans la variance (examinées dans le contexte des composantes
tournées du varimax) des variables etudiées qui s'expliquent par
des raisons géomorpholgiques. On conclut que les indices morphométriques des bassins versants sont controlés par des variations
litho-tectoniques.

INTRODUCTION

In the past a number of workers have examined the statistical
relationship between fluvial variables in a bivariate manner.
However, the total downstream interdependent behaviour of the
relevant variables in a fluvial system is not revealed by using
this approach. Snyder (1962), Wong (1963), Matalas and Reiher
(1967), Mather and Doornkamp (1970), Andrews and Estabrook
(1971), Haan and Allen (1972), Abrahams (1972; 1980) and White
(1975), have employed multivariable statistical methods to
examine the interaction between geomorphic and hydrological properties of drainage basins of a stream order or network. Doornkamp and King (1971), and Mithal *et al.*, (1974) analysed the
third order drainage basins of Uganda (using factor analysis)
and Garhwal Himalaya (using principal component analysis) respectively, and gave different groups of variables. Williams
(1971; 1972a; 1972b), McDonald (1975; 1976), and Day (1976,
1978) have done morphometric analysis of karst in tropical areas.
Onesti and Miller (1974) employed principal component analysis
to define patterns of variation among variables for data grouped
by stream order, and examined the downstream trend in the degree
of integration between critical variables. They suggested that
in higher order streams, less variations and greater inter-
dependency between fluvial variables would exist (established by
principal component analysis), since the natural constraints
imposed on the system in its headwater reaches are lessened as
order increases.

White and White (1979) related the properties of a set of
measurements on the Appalachian karst on the fluvial character
of the drainage basins and to the hydrologic setting of the
karstic drainage basins. They stated that although the internal
relationship between doline (sinkhole) measures are very well

ordered, no relationship could be found between the doline measure and various measures of the drainage pattern. Factor analysis, as well, indicated that stream pattern measures were independent of doline measures.

In the present paper attempts are made to find the relationship of morphometric parameters of the third order drainage basins (see Appendix 9.1) of the two limestone zones around Kud. This is done in terms of the actual correlations between the variables and the derived principal components, also the way in which these correlations vary amongst themselves as well as with the surrounding lithotectonic zones (see Appendix 9.2).

DATA COLLECTION

The area, about 700 sq. km in extent, is included in the Survey of India topographic sheet No. 43 0/8 between latitudes N 33°0' and 33°15' and longitudes E 75°15' and 75°30' in Kashmir. It forms a part of the Lesser Himalayan zone. This topographic sheet, with a scale of 1:50 000 and a 20 m contour interval, is used as the base map for the present study. Linear measurements are made with the help of a map tracer (rotameter), and the aerial measurements with a planimeter. Relief of the basin is measured with the help of epidiascopic enlargements. The area has been divided into five zones (Appendix 9.2) depending on the lithotectonic variations (Ravinder Kumar, 1977). The morphometric variables (Appendix 9.1) of the third order drainage basins (following Horton's, 1945, modified method by Strahlar, 1952) of each zone are determined, and then subjected to IBM 360/44 computers of the University of Delhi for principal component analysis.

The analysis is carried out in two sections. The first is concerned with a consideration of principal components of the original data, where the focus is on trends in the magnitude of eigen values for third order streams. The second treats the rotated components (varimax criteria) of the data. An effort is made to discuss components in terms of original variables and compare the results between stream order. It has been decided to forgo a detailed interpretation of various principal components in favour of examining the rotated components, which appear to present a clear picture of the structure of the original variables. The rotated components were derived by rotating all the 18 components to the varimax solution. Significantly loaded variables are taken to be those whose loading values are greater than or equal to 0.50.

INTERPRETATION

Great Limestone (South) zone

Five independent principal components are associated with this zone and they account for 89.1% of the total variance. The rotated principal components according to varimax criteria reveals that principal component 1 is connected with frequency of first and second order streams; lengths of first, second and third order streams; length, area and relief of the basin; and the bifurcation ratio (Rb_2), and accounts for 49.4% of the total variance (Table 9.1). The higher interrelationship of all the independent parameters in this zone suggest that all of them together played a major role in the development of the drainage basins.

Table 9.1   Principal component matrix (% of variance)

Principal Component	Great Limestone (S) zone	Great Limestone (N) zone	Murree zone	Thrust zone	Salkhala zone
1	49.4	53.2	47.2	53.3	57.1
2	14.8	19.5	25.0	20.7	17.5
3	9.9	13.0	10.8	12.5	9.9
4	8.2	6.6	7.1	7.2	8.2
5	6.8	3.2	5.8	5.0	4.0

Principal component 2 is associated with stream frequency, drainage density and drainage texture, and accounts for 14.8% of the total variance. This shows that higher values of stream frequency and drainage density are responsible for finer drainage texture.

Relief, ruggedness number, and basin shape are the functions of principal component 3, and account for 9.9% of the total variance. The direct relationship of basin relief and ruggedness number in this zone suggests that relief is mainly responsible for the ruggedness of the area. Higher values of relief are responsible for more rugged area. They together are indirectly related with the basin shape, indicating that more relief and greater ruggedness produces an elongated basin.

Principal component 4 is associated with bifurcation ratio (Rb_1) and basin slope, and accounts for 8.2% of the total variance. Inverse relationship between the bifurcation ratio and basin slope suggests that with the increases in one parameter the other decreases.

Length ratios (LR_1 and LR_2) are connected with principal component 5 which accounts for 6.8% of the total variance. An inverse relationship between LR_1 and LR_2 indicates that the zone is characterised by higher lengths of first and third order streams and lower length of second order streams.

Great Limestone (North) zone

The Great Limestone zone, north of the Chenab, is assoc- iated with four independent principal components which account for 92.3% of the total variance (Table 9.1). The varimax rotated principal component matrix (Figures 9.1, 9.2 and 9.3) suggest that principal component 1 is associated with the fre- quency of first order streams; lengths of first, second and third order streams; length, area and relief of the basin; bifurcation ratio (RB_1); stream frequency, drainage density and drainage texture; and ruggedness number. It accounts for 53.2% of the total variance. Direct relationship amongst all the above parameters, except stream frequency, drainage density and drain- age texture, indicates that an increase in any parameter in-

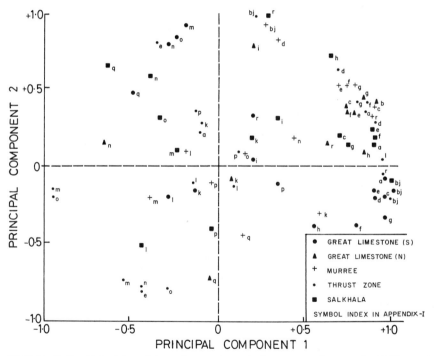

Figure 9.1   Relationship of morphometric parameters of different lithotectonic zones with respect to principal components 1 and 2

179

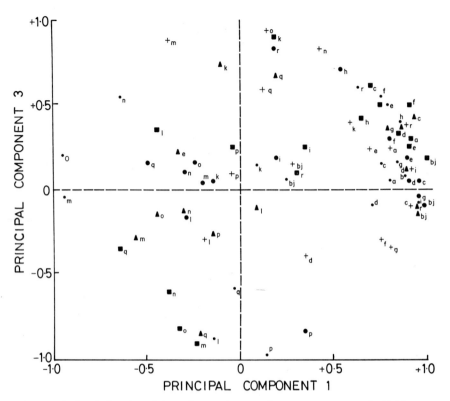

Figure 9.2   Relationship of morphometric parameters of different
             lithotectonic zones with respect to principal
             components 1 and 3

creases the other parameters. The inverse relationship with
stream frequency, drainage density and drainage texture suggests
that the comparatively coarse drainage texture in this zone is
only because of their (rest of the parameters) high values.

Principal component 2, which accounts for 19.5% of the total
variance, is associated with frequency and length of second order
streams, bifurcation ratio (Rb_2) and basin slope. Indirect
relationship of basin slope with bifurcation ratio (Rb_2), frequency and length of second order streams, indicates that the
high basin slope in the zone is only responsible for the low
values of these parameters.

Basin area, length ratio (LR_2), drainage density, basin
shape and slope, and ruggedness number are connected with principal component 3 and account for 13.0% of the total variance.
Except for length ratio (LR_2) and basin shape, all the parameters
are also associated with the other components, suggesting that
they have a factorial complexity of two, and have more than one
theoretical dimension. Lengths of second and third order streams

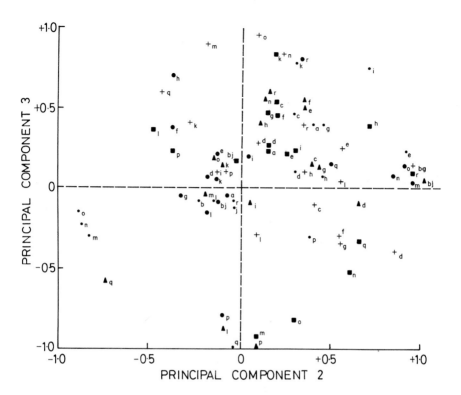

Figure 9.3 Relationship of morphometric parameters of different
lithotectonic zones with respect to principal
components 2 and 3

together are responsible for the basinal shapes of the region.

Principal component 4 accounts for 6.6% of the total variance, and is connected with length ratio (LR_1), length of first
order streams and ruggedness of the area (Figures 9.1, 9.2 and
9.3). The last two parameters have more than one theoretical
dimension, and they have some effects on length ratio (LR_1).

Murree Formation zone

In this zone five independent principal components account
for 95.9% of the total variance (Table 9.1). Principal component
1 is associated with the frequency of first order streams;
lengths of first and third order streams; length, relief and area
of the basin; bifurcation ration (Rb_1) and ruggedness number
(Figures 9.1, 9.2 and 9.3) It accounts for 47.2% of the total
variance. The frequency and length of second order streams are
almost independent to the parameters of principal component 1,
though they are directly proportional to them, as indicated by
their relationship with respect to principal component 2, but
to a small extent. This suggests that the increase in frequency

of first order streams hardly increases the frequency of second order streams. This further suggests that in the third order basins of this zone most of the first order streams join directly to the higher (second and third) order streams, which does not affect the increase of the order and length of the streams.

Principal component 2 is mainly associated with the frequency and length of second order streams, the bifurcation ratio (Rb_2), and to a lesser extent, with the frequency of first order streams, length of third order streams, and length and area of the basin. It accounts for 25.0% of the total variance.

According to Strahler (1964) the studies of many stream networks confirm the principle that in a region of uniform climate, rock type, and stage of development, the bifurcation ratio tends to remain constant from one order to the next. Values of bifurcation ratio between 3 and 5 are characteristic of natural stream system. But the average value of bifurcation ratio (Rb_2) in this region is 2.889 (Ravinder Kumar and Verma, 1977), suggesting that the frequency of second order streams is most probably controlled by the joint planes which are quite common here (Verma and Ravinder Kumar, 1978). The length of second order streams (Figures 9.1, 9.2 and 9.3) is directly related to frequency of second order streams; therefore, it appears that these two parameters are dependent to a lesser extent on the other parameters associated with principal component 2.

Stream frequency, drainage density, drainage texture and basin slope are associated with principal component 3 and account for 10.8% of the total variance. Their close relationship suggests that the slope factor in the Murree zone plays a major role in the development of stream frequency, drainage density and drainage texture. Lower values of basin slope in this zone are responsible for the coarse drainage texture.

Length ratio (LR_1) and basin shape are directly proportional to each other and are associated with principal component 4. They account for 7.1% of the total variance. This suggests that lower values of length of first order streams and higher values of length of second order streams will result in an elongated drainage basin. But in this zone higher values of length of first order streams and lower values of length of second order stream suggest that the drainage basins will be more circular.

Length ratio (LR_2) is connected with principal component 5 and accounts for only 5.8% of the total variance, suggesting that with respect to all the parameters, it plays only a minor role in the development of the drainage basins.

Thrust zone

The results of principal component analysis indicate that four independent components account for 93.7% of the total variance in the data (Table 9.1). Component 1 is associated with frequency of first and second order streams; lengths of first and second order streams; basinal length, area and relief; bifurcation ratio (Rb_2) and ruggedness number. It accounts for

53.3% of the total variance. This suggests that, except for the length of third order streams, all the independent morphometric parameters and ruggedness number of the region are very much dependent upon one another. Increase in any of the above mentioned parameters increases the others. Ruggedness of the region is mainly due to the higher values of these parameters.

Principal component 2 is associated with the length of third order streams, bifurcation ratio (Rb_1), stream frequency, drainage density and drainage texture, and accounts for 20.7% of the total variance. This indicates that the finest drainage texture (in comparison with the rest of the zones) found in this region is the result of the higher values of the above parameters.

Principal component 3 accounts for 12.5% of the total variance and is connected with bifurcation ratio (Rb_1), length ratio (LR_1), and basin slope (Figures 9.1, 9.2 and 9.3). It reveals that the steepness of the basin slope in the region is responsible for the higher values of frequency and length of first order streams, and the lower values of frequency and length of second order streams.

Length ratio (LR_2) and basin shape are related to principal component 4, which accounts for 7.2% of the total variance. This indicates that the basin shape in the region is controlled by the combined effects of lengths of second and third order streams.

Salkhala Formation zone

Morphometric parameters of third order drainage basins of the Salkhala zone are characterised by four independent principal components which account for 92.7% of the total variance. Principal component 1 accounts for 57.1% of the total variance (Table 9.1), and is associated with frequency of first and second order streams; lengths of first, second and third order streams; length, area and relief of basins; bifurcation ratio (Rb_2) and basin slope. The higher interrelationship of all the independent parameters (Figures 9.1, 9.2 and 9.3), similar to that of the Great Limestone (South) area, suggests that they played the major part in the evolution of the drainage basins. The inverse relationship of the independent parameters with basin slope suggests that high basin slope is mainly responsible for the lower values of most of the independent parameters of the region.

Principal component 2 accounts for 17.5% of the total variance, and is related to relief, ruggedness, basin slope and drainage density. This suggests that higher values of relief and drainage density, and steeper slopes in the region are responsible for the more rugged area.

Principal component 3 is associated with the length of first order streams; length ratio (LR_1); stream frequency, drainage density and texture; and accounts for 9.9% of the total variance. The inverse relationship of stream frequency, drainage density and texture (Figures 9.1, 9.2 and 9.3) with length of first order streams and length ratio (LR_1) suggests that coarse drainage texture in the region is explained by the longer first order streams.

Basin shape and bifurcation ratio (Rb_1) are related to principal component 4, which accounts for 8.2% of the total variance. This suggests that the present shape of the basins in the region are the result of the combined effects of the number of first and second order streams.

CONCLUSION

It has been concluded from the above discussion that in almost all the cases the independent parameters, i.e. frequency of first and second order streams; lengths of first, second and third order streams; length, area and relief of the basins, are associated with principal component 1 which accounts for the maximum variance in the data. It suggests that these parameters play a major part in the development of the third order drainage basins, irrespective of any lithologic or tectonic variations. But at the same time, variations in the variance explained by each parameter with respect to a particular principal component, and the total variance explained by each principal component of one zone with respect to the other zone, is due to lithotectonic controls. These variations also explain the association of a few parameters with one principal component in one zone and with another principal component in another zone.

This further suggests that the groups of parameters of third order drainage basin differentiated by Doornkamp and King (1971), and Mithal *et al.*, (1974) in their respective areas, do not always hold good as there are controlling factors involved in it.

Finally it is concluded that lithotectonic variations play their role in the formation of the drainage system of an area.

Acknowledgements

The author is thankful to Professor V.K. Verma, Department of Geology, University of Delhi for his able guidance in the present work. Dr S.C.D. Sah, Director of the Wadia Institute of Himalayan Geology, is acknowledged for providing necessary facilities. Shri S.M. Luthra (presently Director of the Computer Centre, University of Hyderabad) and Mrs Geeta Bhowmick of the Computer Centre, University of Delhi are also acknowledged for their help in computerization of the data.

REFERENCES

Abrahams, A.D. 1972. Factor analysis of drainage basin properties: evidence for stream abstraction accompanying degradation of relief. *Water Resources Research*, **8(3)**, 624-633.

Abrahams, A.D. 1980. A multivariate analysis of chain lengths in natural channel networks. *Journal of Geology,* **88(6)**, 681-696.

Andrews, J.T. and Estabrook, G. 1971. Applications of information and graph theory to multivariate geomorphological analysis. *Journal of Geology,* **79**, 207-221.

Day, M.J. 1976. The morphology and hydrology of some Jamaican Karst depressions. *Earth Surface Processes,* 1, 111-129.

Day, M.J. 1978. Morphology and distribution of residual limestone hills (mogotes) in the Karst of northern Puerto Rico. *Geological Soceity of America Bulletin,* **89**, 426-432.

Doornkamp, J.C. and King, A.M. 1971. *Numerical analysis in Geomorphology: an introduction.* (London: Edward Arnold).

Haan, C.T. and Allen, D.M. 1972. Comparison on multiple regression and principal component regression for predicting water yield in Kentucky. *Water Resources Research,* 8(6), 1593-1596.

Matalas, N.C. and Reiher, B.J. 1967. Some comments on the use of factor analysis. *Water Resources Research,* 3(1), 213-223.

Mather, P.M. and Doornkamp, J.C. 1970. Multivariate analysis in geography with particular reference to drainage basin morphometry. *Transactions of the Institute of British Geographers,* **51**, 163-187.

McDonald, R.C. 1975. Observations on hill slope erosion in tower Karst topography of Belize. *Geological Society of America Bulletin,* **86**, 255-256.

McDonald, R.C. 1976. Hill slope base depressions in tower Karst topography of Belize. *Zeitschrift fur Geomorphologie,* Supplement **26**, 98-103.

Mithal, R.S., Prakash, B. and Bajpai, I.P. 1974. Drainage basin morphometric study of a part of the Garhwal Himalaya. *Himalayan Geology,* 4, 195-215.

Onesti, L.J. and Miller, T.K. 1974. Patterns of variation in a fluvial system. *Water Resources Research,* 10(6), 1178-1186.

Ravinder Kumar, 1977. *Studies on some aspects of Geomorphology around Kud, Kashmir Himalaya (with a Statistical Approach),* (Unpublished Ph.D. Thesis, University of Delhi).

Ravinder Kumar and Verma V.K. 1977. Lithotectonic control on the morphometric parameters of the drainage basins around Kud Kashmir Himalaya. *Chayanica Geologica,* 3(2), 147-165.

Snyder, W.M. 1962. Some possibilities for multivariate analysis in hydrologic studies. *Journal of Geophysical Research,* 67(2), 721-729.

Strahler, A.N. 1952. Hypsometric (area - altitude) analysis of erosional topography. *Geological Society of America Bulletin,* 63, 1117-1142.

Strahler, A.N. 1964. Quantitative geomorphology of drainage basins and channel networks. In: *Handbook of Applied Hydrology,* ed. V.T. Chow, 4-39.

Verma, V.K. and Ravinder Kumar, 1978. Role of tectonics in the evolution of drainage system around Kud, Kashmir Himalaya. In: *Tectonic Geology of Himalaya,* ed. P.S. Saklani, 269-286.

185

White, E.L. 1975. Factor analysis of drainage basin properties: Classification of flood behaviour in terms of basin geomorphology. *Water Resources Bulletin,* 11, 676-687.

White, E.L. and White, W.B. 1979. Quantitative morphology of Landforms in carbonate rock basins in the Appalachian Highlands. *Geological Society of America Bulletin,* 90, 385-396.

Williams, P.W. 1971. Illustrating morphometric analysis of Karst with examples from New Guinea. *Zeit. fur Geomorph.* 15, 40-61.

Williams, P.W. 1972a. The analysis of special characteristics of Karst terrains. In: *Spatial Analysis in Geomorphology,* ed. R.J. Chorley, (London), 135-163.

Williams, P.W. 1972b. Morphometric analysis of polygonal Karst in New Guinea. *Geological Society of America Bulletin,* 83, 761-796.

Wong, S.T. 1963. A multivariate statistical model for predicting mean annual flood in New England. *Annals of Association of American Geographers,* 53, 298-311.

APPENDIX 9.1

The symbols and morphometric parameters used

Symbols used in the diagrams	Morphometric parameter		
a	Frequency of first order streams		$- \quad F_1$
b	Frequency of second order streams		$- \quad F_2$
	Frequency of third order streams		$- \quad F_3$
c	Length of first order streams		$- \quad L_1$
d	Length of second order streams		$- \quad L_2$
e	Length of third order streams		$- \quad L_3$
f	Length of the basin		$- \quad L$
g	Area of the basin		$- \quad A$
h	Relief of the basin		$- \quad R$
i	Bifurcation ratio	$- Rb_1$	$= F_1/F_2$
j	Bifurcation ratio	$- Rb_2$	$= F_2/F_3$
k	Length ratio	$- LR_1$	$= L_1/L_2$
l	Length ratio	$- LR_2$	$= L_2/L_3$
m	Stream Frequency	$- SF$	$= (F_1 + F_2 + F_3)/A$
n	Drainage Density	$- DD$	$= (L_1 + L_2 + L_3)/A$
o	Drainage Texture	$- DT$	$= SF \times DD$
p	Basin shape	$- B.Sh.$	$=$ Diameter/L
q	Basin Slope	$- B Sl$	$= R/L$
r	Ruggedness number	$- RN$	$= DD \times R$

APPENDIX 9.2

Lithotectonic zones of the area

Zone   I - Region comprising of the Great Limestone Formation (south of the Chenab) consisting mainly of limestone of Permo-Carboniferous age.

Zone   II - Region comprising of the Great Limestone Formation (north of the Chenab) in which along with limestone, phyllites and slates of the Eocene age also occur.

Zone III - Region comprising of the Murree Formation, consisting of purple and grey sandstones associated with shales.

Pseudo - conglomeratic at the base.
Age   - Oligocene-Miocene.

Zone   IV - Region comprising the Thrust zone (between zones I and III).

Zone   V - Region consisting of the Salkhala Formation, made up of mica-schist, garnetiferous mica-schist, carbonaceous schist and quartzite of Precambrian age.

187

10

Karst and structure in tropical areas: the Malagasy example

G. Rossi

SUMMARY

Madagascar is a favoured country for the study of karst phenomena. All along the west coast, from Ankarana to Mahafaly plateau, karsts cover about 30 000 km². The limestone plateau are developed in gently sloping monoclines. Their extent reaches about 1700 km, from latitude 12°S to the tropic of Capricorn. But, in spite of this extension in latitude, the climates in which they are situated offer common characteristics: they are all tropical climates with a long dry season. The total rainfall decreases southwards, from 2200 mm in Ankarana to less than 600 mm in Mahafaly plateau. The dry season lasts for five months in Ankarana, and for eight months in the south. These karsts are consequently situated in climates varying from the tropical with a very high total rainfall, to the subarid. There are very few geomorphologic studies about this enormous karst group. The studies we conducted from 1971 to 1977 have enabled us to analyse Ankarana (1974), Narinda (1975), Namoroka (1977), Bemaraha (1982), and Kelifely (1984). The relief of Malagasy limestone displays tropical karst landscapes, from the classic plateau with dolines to the extraordinary tsingy, including all types of hill karsts. These types are seldom pure and, in most cases, different types are closely alike or even imbricate; this leads us to deal with some aspects of the delicate problem of the origin of these forms.

RÉSUMÉ

Madagascar est un pays remarquable pour l'étude des phénomènes karstiques. Tout au long de la côte occidentale, de l'Ankarana au plateau Mahafaly, la superficie des karsts est d'environ 30 000 km². Les plateaux calcaires se développent sur les revers à pendage modéré des unités monoclinales. Cette extension atteint près de 1700 km, du 12°5 au tropique de capricorne. Mais, en dépit de ce large dispositif zonal, les climats qui les concernent montrent une assez grand homogénéité: dans tous les cas il s'agit de climats tropicaux à longue saison sèche. La tranche des précipitations décroît en direction du Sud, de 2200 mm en Ankarana à moins de 600 mm sur le plateau Mahafaly. La saison sèche, qui s'étend sur cinq mois dans Ankarana, atteint huit mois dans le Sud. Ces karsts sont donc situés sous des climats allant du type tropical à fortes précipitations annuelles au type subaride. Les études géomorphologiques concernant ce vaste domaine karstique sont peu nombreuses. Les recherches menées de 1971 à 1977 nous ont permis les analyses suivantes: Ankarana (1974), Narinda (1975); Namoroka (1977), Bemaraha (1982) et Kelifely (1984). Les reliefs calcaires malgaches forment un ensemble de paysages karstiques tropicaux allant de la forme classique du plateau à dolines aux extraordinaires tsingy, couvrant tous les types de karsts à buttes. Il arrive que les modelés soient homogènes mais, le plus fréquemment, il y a des passages et même des imbrications de formes; ce phénomène nous fournit des données sur le problème délicat de l'origine de ces formes.

We will consider here some aspects of the structural influences on the Malagasy group forms (Table 10.1). The synthesis of our observations on the problem of limestone solution in tropical areas has been published previously (Rossi, 1976).

THE TSINGYS

The Tsingys (Rossi, 1974) are forms which show, structurally, the most outstanding features. Lithologically, they are always linked with pure limestones, which are either not or only feebly dolomitic, and crystalline or subcrystalline. They are also very lightly porous, and often arranged in metric or decimetric beds, forming rigid and thick table-like masses. These rigid tables react to all tectonic movements by fracturing, and it is the density of the vertical fracturation which is the other *sine qua non* condition in the appearance of these forms. The fracturing can be open or scarcely visible diaclases, with decimetric or metric spreading, and forming a suborthogonal or lozenge-shaped network; other dispositions are rare. It is from this network that characteristic forms in the shape of very sharp 'blades' or 'needles' develop. The spacing of the stratification joints is also a constant fact, and the evolution of the tsingy is achieved through solution and, therefore, through lowering in height and surface reduction, as well as through the overhanging of top blocks, which eventually topple over. (Figure 10.1)

190

Table 10.1 Structural conditions for the appearance of elementary karst forms

	Limestone faciès	+ dolomites	Porosity	Fracturation	Thickness above impervious	Subterranean networks
Tsingy	Crystalline	no	very low 1-2%	intense	indifferent	important if thick
Kuppens	Clayey to crumbly	yes	very high <40%	indifferent	moderate (in decametres	rare
Kegels	Clayey	yes	high	indifferent	moderate to high (100 m)	rare
Mogotes	Compact	yes	very low (1%)	eventual	moderate to high (100 m)	feebly extended
Doline in 'verre de montre'	indifferent	yes	very variable (5-35%)	indifferent	weak	probably of less importance
Doline-puits	compact	yes	indifferent	eventual	moderate (in decametres)	important
Dolines-entonnoirs	compact	?	indifferent	eventual	moderate (in decametres	important

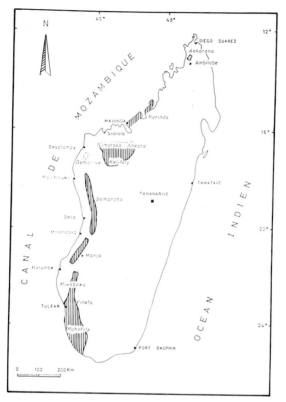

Figure 10.1   Localisation map

Photo 10.1   Tsingy table-like plateau of the Bemaraha showing
important vertical fracturation (vertical view at
1:25 000)

Photo 10.2   The tsingy of the Ankarana plateau

Examples of this type of relief are very rare other than those at Madagascar (Figure 10.1), where it is found in the Bemaraha (Photo 10.1), Namoroka, Ankarana (Photo 10.2) and in the Bemarivo. It has been mentioned by Tricart (1960) in Brasil, Verstappen (1964) in New Guinea, Wilford and Wall (1965) in Sarawak, Cooke (1973) in Tanzania and by us in North Mombasa (Kenya). Where the authors give indications on this topic, we notice that they are always concerned with the same structural conditions.

A point neglected by most of the authors and which we consider fundamental is the influence of porosity. Since these limestones are very slightly porous, water does not penetrate into the rock mass; it flows almost wholly at the surface. The solution, facilitated by very great purity of the rock, is consequently wholly superficial and laminar; and it is this fact that explains the great development of lapiés, needles and vertical grooves on the tsingy flanks and the general aspect of the tsingy. The great purity of the limestone explains at the same time their solutional susceptibility and the absence of decalcification residue; for these forms crop out without any pedologic cover. This raises a major genetic problem: tsingys are forms resulting from direct solution by rainwater. It is the drops of rainwater which, on reaching the rock, flow along the slopes and dissolve the calcium carbonate almost instantaneously (Rossi, 1976).

THE DOLINE PLATEAUX

Doline plateaux, the 'causses', seem to be feebly represented in the tropical area; they are however probably not often mentioned because these forms are common. In Madagascar we find some, essentially in the Mariarano region, Kelifely - Ankara, Soaserana - Manja region and in Mahafaly plateau (Battistini, 1964)

193

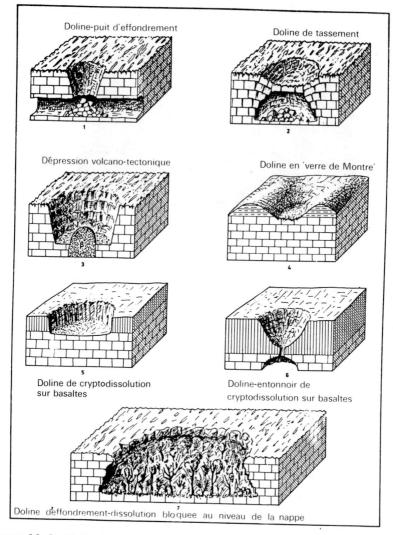

Figure 10.2   Main types of dolines
1. Doline-puit (well shaped doline) above subterranean network
2. Doline en 'verre de montre' resulting from collapses above
   a subterranean network
3. Tectonic doline around a basaltic plug (Ankarana)
4. Doline en 'verre de montre' resulting from solution
5. Doline-puit (well shaped doline) on thin non calcareous level
6. Doline entonnoir (funnel shaped doline on thick non calcareous level)
7. Collapse doline (well shaped type). The bottom is at the
   watertable level. Important lateral solution.

Dolines always appear when lithology presents a karstifiable series overlying relatively impervious levels. But such lime-stone series can be petrographically very different. Thus, we have observed dolines in dense limestones, clayey limestones, dolomitic limestones and in calcareous dolomites. However, a particular stratigraphic disposition seems to correspond to each type of form.

The dolines in 'verre de montre'

Their density is greatest in limestones with a dolomitic, porous and clay-like tendency, such as those of northwest Kelifely or the Mariarano region. This can be explained by the fact that these solutional forms develop easily on dolomites, which are susceptible to superficial solution. In all cases the karstifiable layer is not very thick, and it lies upon a level serving as a relative impermeable layer on which the dissolution is blocked up.

The most schematic case is that of Mariarano where the dolomitic limestones of the doline floor overlie compact lime-stones, which are slightly clayey. When this layer is reached solution operates laterally and the doline gradually widens, according to the process clearly analyzed by Rakoto-Ramiarantsoa (1975) in the Majunga region where the structural situation is identical.

The localization of these dolines obey tectonic critera, and the case of their being aligned on fractures is classic; but in dolomitic limestones it is often impossible to bring out pre-ferential alignments. It seems evident that the hollowing of zones more susceptible to solution occurs, for example in more dolomitic areas (in a petrographically non-homogeneous series), as is the case in the lagoonal facies of Mariarano when the dolo-mitic series is homogeneous. As in northwest Kelifely, the sur-face of the plateau is riddled with dolines so that the inter-fluves are limited to narrow compartments and we then obtain a karst landscape in 'nid d'abeilles' (honeycomb-like landscape) (Photo 10.3).

The imbrication of forms can exist when the impervious level, often marly, is relatively thin. It is then easily cleared away and karstification is renewed; another type of doline then being able to dig into the bottom of the initial form, depending upon the thickness and nature of the subjacent bedrock. This type of depression is also found in other lime-stones, often impure, compact or clayey; it usually constitutes the only significant form of karst (Ankara, Soaserana) (Photo 10.4), but lithological disposition always shows the existence of impervious levels intercalated in the karstifiable series. In the literature, examples of doline plateaux are not abundant; we can mention Kouilou (Renault, 1959) and Yucatan (Corbel, 1959). In Kouilou, the author mentions frequent clayey inter-calations and silicified levels within the limestone series.

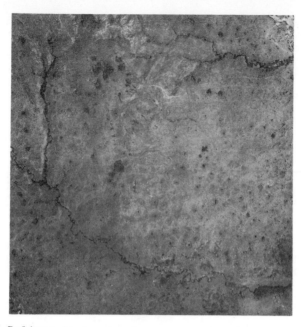

Photo 10.3 Dolines in 'verre de montre' of the Kelifely karst
showing a honeycomb-like landscape (vertical view at 1:40 000)

Photo 10.4 Tectonic doline of the Ankarana plateau

Finally, dolines in 'verre de montre' are a common dissolution form, which can appear practically in any type of limestone. They only reach significant densities in rocks sufficiently porous and susceptible to solution, such as chalky dolomites, and in this case, the layer must be thin; if not, other
types of landscape can appear.

'Dolines-entonnoirs' (funnel-shaped dolines)

The examples offered by the Kelifely, the Mahafaly plateau
and Narinda karst show that they can be either forms resulting
from piping or from sinking. They appear practically in any
type of limestone, provided it is thickly bedded. In Narinda
and in the centre of Kelifely, their density is important and
they determine the relief. In Narinda, the beds tend to be
dolomitic and the alignment of depressions along the fracture
directions is very plain. Because of their genesis, it does not
seem adequate to establish any relation between this form and a
determined lithological type. On the contrary, it is often
found in topographic locations where the piping is considerable
(strips of plateau, canyon edges, and above networks of subterranean water courses).

In Narinda, once the karst floor is reached, these dolines
develop by lateral solution and by base enlargement. Being
coalescent, they give Karstgassen (karst streets) which finally
isolate groups of mogotes. It is in Kelifely that we have found
many examples of dendritic karst composed of a succession of
'dolines-entonnoirs', generally small and aligned on a hierarchic
subterranean hydrographic network. These depressions, sometimes
coalescent, show outlines of small canyons and they often have
a pear-shaped flat section; as the gully is orientated in the
direction of flow this leaves no room for doubt as to their
origin. They appear where the karstifiable layer above the
aquifer is not very thick (ranging in decametres) (Photo 10.5).

The 'doline puits' (well-shaped dolines)

These exist in the Kelifely and in the Mahafaly plateau.
They are typical forms resulting from collapse above subterranean
networks. However when their bases are at watertable level they
can develop by lateral solution, and we can observe a development
from a 'doline-entonnoir' to a 'doline-puits'. In regard to
their origin, they appear to be able to form in any type of
limestone provided that the thickness above the aquifer is not
too considerable, and that the aquifer is characterized by the
development of a significant subterranean cave network. When
their density is considerable, as in some Kelifely sectors, they
can be coalescent and result in isolating plateau strips or even
buttes, which are characterized by a rugged outline and abrupt
edges. In this case, lateral solution at the watertable level
plays an important role, as can be proved by the steepness of
the butte sides (Photo 10.6).

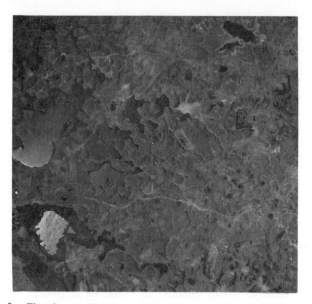

Photo 10.5   The kuppenkarst of Mariarano, Narinda (vertical
view at 1:25 000)

Photo 10.6   Mogotes and karstrandebene in the karst of
Narinda

Tectonic dolines of the tsingy table-lime masses
==

The beds of crystalline limestones, chiefly in the Ankarana
and the Namoroka, and to a lesser degree the Antsingy of
Bemaraha, are affected by dolines of diverse forms, but which
are all closely linked with tectonics. One of the best examples
is the extraordinary hexagonal collapse-dolines of the Ankarana.
They are often situated at the crossing to two or more fractures,
and they are forms resulting from solutional collapse. In the
first stage they are created by collapse, following which they
evolve; secondly, solution occurs at the watertable level, thus
resulting in depressions of various forms.

Summarising, we can group dolines into two major categories:
i) dolines resulting from solution, whose aspect is always close
to the type 'verre de montre'. They can appear in most types
of limestone, but they are preferentially located on limestones
very susceptible to solution, such as dolomitic limestones,
provided that this easily karstifiable layer is not too thick,
(i.e. the watertable must be located sufficiently near the surface). ii) depressions resulting from piping or from collapse,
linked to the presence of a thick karstifiable series and with
subterranean flow ordered according to a cave network; this
network must be sufficiently important to cause either a suction
or collapse that can have repercussions at the surface. These
networks are, of course, guided by directions of fracturation.
Since the evolution of these surficial forms depends directly
upon the type and the importance of subterranean drainage, they
are relatively independent of lithology.

But in any case, plateaux with dispersed dolines exist only
where karstifiable levels are not very thick and are separated
by intercalations of more or less impervious rocks, or on impure
limestones on which they are the only karst form.

THE KARST BUTTES

Amongst all the elementary forms of tropical karsts, karst buttes
raise the most problems of definition. If the terms kuppen,
kegel, mogote, or turm are used to designate broad families of
forms many buttes are not included in the classification; besides
these so-called 'pure' types, there exist many transitional forms
which are arbitrarily ranged in either category.

Similar problems arise in characterizing associations of
forms. If the limit between doline plateaux and cockpits can
be determined from the density of closed depressions and from
their coalescence or non-coalescence, several varieties of
cockpit exist, conditional upon the aspect of the depressions
and of the karstic hills. Furthermore, the descriptions given
by authors who have worked in tropical areas confirm both the
variety of forms and the lack of precision in terms used.

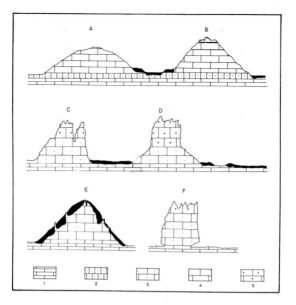

Figure 10.3   Main types of karst buttes
    A. Typical kuppenkarst (Mariarano example)
    B. Kegelkarst (Bemaraha example)
    C-D Two types of mogotes (Narinda example)
    E. Kegel fossilised by clay residue
    F. Turm resulting of lateral solution by the seasonal
       watertable (Namoroka example)
    1. Impervious limestones
    2. Limestones with little dolomite content
    3. Dolomitic limestones
    4. Dolomite
    5. Massive karstic limestones In black: clay and sand residue

     Consequently, we propose here a classification of elementary
forms, based upon the most commonly used terminology. It is
this terminology that will be used henceforth in this work.

Kegels (cones): limestone buttes with a conical or truncated
     form, and whose rectilinear, regularly sloping sides
     produce an open angle with the karst floor. The best
     example can be found in the Philippines in Barol
     Island (Voss, 1970).

Kuppens (coupoles): limestone buttes in a form with a nearly
     flat dome, with regular and convex sides, a slightly
     rounded top, and producing a more or less open angle
     with the karst floor. The best examples can be seen
     in Narinda karst, in Bemaraha.

Mogotes: limestone buttes with an irregular form, with a
     flat, rounded or indented top. The sides, often in-
     dented, have variable and irregular slope, but which
     are generally steep. The best example is the famous

200

Sierra de Los Organos in Cuba (Lehmann *et al.*, 1956). The variations of form of this type can be important.

Turm (towers): limestone buttes with a flat, rounded or irregular top, with subvertical and regular sides meeting the karst floor at an almost orthogonal angle (Photo 10.7). Its prototype can be found in southwest China (Guilin Region).

A further source of problems is that it is rare to find precise indications concerning the petrographic types of limestone, its chemical composition and porosity and the relief to which they correspond. This lack does not facilitate comparisons or the solution of questions encountered in studying these strange landscapes.

Kegels

In Malagary, kegels (cones) exist in two regions: Narinda and Bemaraha. In Narinda, they correspond to a homogeneous series of dolomites (55-67% $CaCO_3$, compact and lightly porous (3-5%) limestones. The bed of massive limestone, which plays the role of a hard layer, maintains the steepness of the dolomitic sides and the individualization of the hills which result in the first stage, in a landscape of cones. When the hard limestone cap has disappeared, the lowering of the dolomitic sides gives rise to kuppen, which are more or less flattened, (Photo 10.8). In the Bamaraha some kegels have a base diameter of 300 m and a height of 100 m, and their form is extraordinarily regular. They form small massifs in which dry valleys and dolines separate several smaller kuppens.

Photo 10.7   The turmkarst of the southern part of the Ankarana plateau. Example of evolution of a mogotes landscape

201

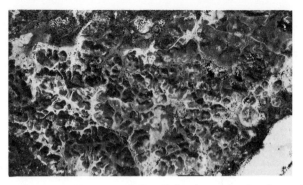

Photo 10.8   The kegelkarst of Narinda (vertical view at 1:25 000)

In a limestone series, valleys or closed depressions progressively individualize plateau fragments, these latter being
slowly divided into karstic hills.   The existence of marly
intercalations which, for a while, allow a subaerial flow
accounts for the formation and the frequency of dry valleys or
valleys with a temporary run-off.

A series of sections shows, with some approximation, an
equivalent succession of thin beds of dense limestone interrupted by levels of clay limestones and marls.   The analyses give:

	$CaCO_3$	$MgCO_3$	Clayey residue	Porosity
Maximum value	87%	13%	18%	21%
Minimum value	61%	1%	4%	1%
Average value	73%	6%	9%	8%

In spite of some observed variations, all these limestones
have common characteristics.   There is little dolomite in their
composition, except to the east where it increases locally without any noticeable influence on relief; they are relatively pure
limestones, often compact and clayey; their porosity, variable
according to beds, is generally low.   But the fact that seems
fundamental is the existence of frequent impervious intercalations.   It is this original characteristic that can explain
the peculiar aspect of the buttes and their formation process.
Contrary to what has been observed in the Narinda karst, we have
not noticed the generalized presence on top of particularly massive limestone beds or recrystallized calcite crusts, and it
does not seem that there is a systematic progressive evolution
from the stage of kegels to that of kuppen.   The appearance of
either form seems to be the result of the density and the disposition of depressions and valleys, rather than the result of
evolution.   However, there exist, particularly along the Antsingy,
buttes capped with massive or crystalline limestones; in this
area, the sides are particularly steep.   When this resistant cap
has disappeared, the steepness of the sides decreases, the top

become rounded and the lowering of the sides proceeds until another resistant bed is reached. At this moment, the altitude of the top becomes stable and the side slope tends to increase.

Examination of these resistant beds shows that they are relatively impervious limestones, whose porosity is always low, less than 5%. Consequently, their karstification is slower than that of subjacent beds whose porosity is more important. The sides recede more rapidly than the top altitude decreases, and as a consequence the sides straighten. When there are several impervious beds on a karst hill, which is frequent in the Bemarah the evolution of the sides becomes more complex. Their profile is irregular, with the inferior part a steep slope and the superior part a gentle slope. The slope changes correspond to an outcrop of a relatively impervious bed.

There appears to be a relationship between the slope of the sides and the rock porosity. Broadly speaking, the higher the rock porosity, the more gentle the slope of the sides. This is inferred from the results below:

Slope	Maximum Porosity	Minimum Porosity	Average	Median
10°	21%	10%	15.2%	18.5%
11–20°	20%	8%	14.5%	13.5%
21–30°	18%	6%	10.7%	10.5%
31–40°	12%	1%	5.6%	6%
4°	9%	1%	4.5%	4%

The sides of the hills have small ledges, dips and small terraces dependent upon the nature of the outcropping limestone bed. Thus ledges develop in low porous limestones (1-5%): these are mostly dense compact limestones, always slightly clayey, and with varying compositions - 80-87% $CaCO_3$ + 0-4% $MgCO_3$ + 8-18% clay residue.

These forms have often been described in the literature. Thus, Pfeffer (1969) mentions them in Jamaica in very pure limestones; Birot, Corbel and Muxart (1968) speak of pure clayey limestones in Puerto Rico. Williams (1972) specifies in the Darai hills in New Guinea, that typical kegels appear when crystalline limestone beds directly overlie clayey limestones. Voss (1970) describes the landscape of Thousand Hills in Barol Island (The Philippines) in very pure limestones, weakly dolomitic, homogeneous and fine-grained. On the whole, it seems that typical cones, whose best example can be found in Barol (see Voss's remarkable photographs), occur in limestones which are chemically rather different but always sufficiently porous, homogeneous, moderately thick, and overlying an impervious level which serves as the floor to the karst evolution.

On the other hand, a character often mentioned by authors is the presence of either a bed of massive and compact limestone on the top, or calcite recrystallization phenomena, resulting in the formation of a more resistant level on the kegel top (Monroe, 1964). We consider the existence of this resistant level important, because it also helps to maintain the steepness of the sides; it is this level which probably explains the sub-equality of the tops, a character pointed out by many authors, (see photo 10.4).

Kuppens

Kuppens are the most frequent type of karstic hills; we have observed them in Malagasy, Mariarano, Kelifely, Bemarivo, Bemaraha, Manja, Mikoboka and in Mahafaly, but the best example is that of Mariarano. They correspond, in the cases we observed, to chalky limestones, or to crumbly dolomites, i.e. they always correspond to very porous rocks (20-37%). They are usually homogeneous, forming a moderately thick series (some tens of metres) above a relatively impervious level. When a certain heterogeneity is indicated by differences in porosity, the aspect of kuppens changes. Thus at Mariarano, outcrops of compact (50% $CaCO_3$ + 45% $MgCO_3$) and feebly porous (3-5%) dolomites show dips or even walls on the side of the coupole.

In the Kelifely, even small lithological differences are visible in the form of the sides. The beds of the dense lime-stones '80-87% $CaCO_3$ + clayey residue) or those of compact dolo-mites (74-80% $CaCO_3$ + 17-24% $MgCO_3$) show regular sides, whereas very porous (12-19%) limestones and compact dolomites show gentle and blunt forms. It is a fact that when lithological conditions are favorable, coupoles occur systematically, even on small-scale outcrops. (photo 10.9)

Photo 10.9   The cockpit karst of Narinda and the polje of Amboaboaka with isolated mogotes (vertical view at 1:25 000)

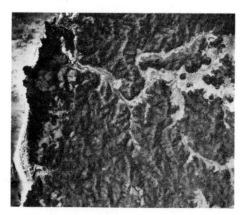

Mogotes

Generally we call 'mogotes' buttes of irregular form which cannot be classified in any of the above types. One of the most famous mogote landscapes is that of the Sierra de Los Organos in Cuba (Lehmann et al., 1956). We have observed some in Narinda, in the Kelifely and on small areas in the Bemaraha. It appears to be possible for mogotes to occur in either homogeneous or heterogeneous carbonate series; the limestones must be pure, lightly porous and the thickness above the aquifer moderate-about some tens of metres.

The numerous observations we have made at Narinda and Kelifely show that in a heterogeneous series, the detailed relief of the mogote is dependent upon lithology. Lightly porous rocks have regular slopes, cliffs and steep sides. In homogeneous series, there may be pure dense limestones (95-99% $CaCO_3$) which are compact and weakly porous (3-5%), or dolomites (55-61% $CaCO_3$ + 31-40% $MgCO_3$) which are also massive, compact and lightly porous (3-6%). When crystalline limestone beds crop out, they develop into tsingy according to the purity and the porosity of the rock.

Many authors have been concerned with this type of form, frequently found in tropical areas. Unfortunately, even if the descriptions are numerous, studies relating to lithology in detail are rare. The works conducted by Monroe (1963), Lehmann (1953; 1954), Panos and Stelcl (1968), Pfeffer (1969), Miotke (1973), Voss (1970), Gerstenhauer (1960), Enjalbert (1964) and Lasserre (1961) amongst others, confirm our observations. Mogotes, sometimes called 'kegels', are not linked with a closely determined petrographic type, but with pure compact carbonate rocks. In any case, they appear only when the watertable is blocked at an almost constant level because their evolution requires lateral solution.

Genetic and evolutional problems of buttes

It is possible to distinguish two categories of forms: kuppens and kegels on the one hand, mogotes and turms on the other. Their genesis and evolution do not seem to be dependent on the same processes.

Kegels and kuppens Lithologically, this group appears in similar conditions: chalky limestones or dolomites, which are very porous. The initial evolution is achieved through the intermediary of shallow dolines, the type in 'verre de montre'. In these very porous soft series, the localization of depressions does not seem to obey essentially tectonic criteria, but may obey some slight petrographical differences linked with sedimentation. This is true for dolomites and it is probably the same case with chalky limestones. These dolines in 'verre de montre' can develop into 'dolines-entonnoirs', because the sides which are protected by the hard top layer recede less rapidly that solution on the bottom: if piping occurs landscape of kegels develops.

This first stage of evolution does not present any major problems. It has been considered by many authors, particularly by Lehmann (1953). However, it is the next stage that raises discussion. In fact, once the karst floor is reached, kegels and kuppens do not develop toward forms with subvertical sides of the mogote type; this is very clear in Narinda as well as in Bemaraha and in Kelifely. The impervious level is slowly removed, but the sides do not straighten up from solution at the base. In the case of kegels, they remain parallel to themselves as long as the top resistant level remains; once this level has disappeared, the sides tend to lower and consequently we have kuppens. In all cases, the junction with the karst floor remains concave and makes an open angle, and there are corroded sides in some places within the rock.

Unfortunately it is not possible for want of precision in other studies, to know whether this example can be generalized, but the photographs by Voss (1970) show an analogous situation. This proves that in such a type of rock the evolution by pellicular solution is more rapid on the sides than the solutional sapping at the base, and personally, we do not think that it is possible to consider the kuppen or kegel landscape as an initial stage in the evolution of the mogote forms. Mogotes appear only in precise lithological conditions, have their own individuality, and their own evolutional cycle.

Mogotes In the first stage of evolution, the trenching of the limestone surface by diverse types of depressions, often aligned on fractures, gives a landscape of cockpit type. Depending on the type of depression: linear, 'dolines-puits', 'dolines-entonnoirs', or 'dolines en baquet', themselves determined mostly by structure, the cockpit landscape shows considerable variation. Photographs of the Caribbean Isles, as well as in Far East, show that we cannot speak of 'a cockpit landscape' but rather of 'cockpit landscapes'; the Kelifely is an example of a variety which is overlooked in classification.

When a level exists on which the downward movement of depressions is blocked, the evolution in the second stage is carried on essentially by lateral solution, forming notches at the base of the side (fusshöhle). To the karstic processes are added mechanical phenomena of mass falling; all these processes resulting in buttes with irregular form, but whose sides are very steep or subvertical. When the foot is regularly and frequently flooded by the watertable, the process can result in forming a turm karst, which appears then as an advanced stage in the karst evolution.

The process of evolution is the opposite of that in typical kuppens and kegels. The causes of this are structural in origin; the limestones in which mogotes occur are generally massive and less porous than those in which kegels and kuppen are found. In kegels and kuppens the sides are eroded less rapidly than solution at the watertable level.

206

This evolution, primarily envisaged by Lehmann and then by many other researchers, results in formation of karstic corrosion plains (karstrandebene). However it is important to note the existence of a constant base level; moreover, it is likely that the best isolated mogote karsts overlying a karstrandebene are those that are blocked with an impervious level. The example of the Narinda region is therefore significant because it exhibits all the evolutional stages, from the cockpit to the assemblage of residual blocks within a corrosion plain.

In some cases a karst cycle may result in a corrosion plain. However, such a cycle could only occur in structurally homogeneous sectors which would probably be very localized. Such a theory cannot be generalised because, due to lithological variations and tectonic influences on a larger scale, such a reconstitution appears to be speculation; we do not know, as a matter of fact, any example of a generalized 'karstic surface' affecting an important massif as a whole.

A common problem: localization Localization of forms is a problem that has been particularly treated by Verstappen (1960; 1964) and by Corbel and Muxart (1970). These authors emphasized the fact that, in some cases, the mogote can be pre-formed when sedimentation takes place, (for example under the form of a coral-reef), and the subsequently resurrected by solution or differential erosion. This has been clearly proved by Verstappen. But besides these examples, which nevertheless seem exceptional, localization of mogotes depends generally upon that of the closed depressions. The latter (and examples are abundant) follow tectonic directions, particularly distinct when limestones are highly compact and dense. Apart from these classic cases, it seems that the variations of facies, even if they are not very important, can play a determining role. In this regard the disposition of depressions, and therefore that of buttes, is often said to be anarchical and it escapes any tentative reduction to mathematical models, such as those proposed by Williams (1972).

At this level, only extremely detailed work and abundant analyses of samples could provide reliable proof. However, our analyses have shown that petrographic microvariations are very frequent in limestone series and that they produce variations in porosity. There often exist significant differences in porosity between two samples identical in appearance, and these variations sometimes occur over lateral distances of some hectometres. As for vertical discontinuities of facies, they are also well known.

These phenomena are very clear in dolomitic series. Owing to the character of dolomitization, which is often irregular being a process of variable intensity in space and time, series tending to be dolomitic show rapid and frequent variations in chemical composition and in porosity within one bed or the adjacent beds. On the other hand, dolomitization could have been achieved vertically inside a calcareous mass and resulted in 'colonnes de dolomitisation' (Nicod, 1971). In addition, and we have observed this case in Narinda, buttes can rapidly change their aspect depending upon the character of the rock; in heterogeneous series, localization is necessarily anarchical because it is under the control of local conditions of sedimentation and dolomitization.

Finally, apart from some particular cases, localization of closed depressions is linked with the facility of water penetration and piping. It can be in a fractured zone, or in a subterranean network, or in a sector of higher porosity. The first two cases seem to be more frequent in massive rocks, whereas the third case appears mainly in limestones or dolomites whose aspect is chalky or pulverised, in which tectonic directions are not well expressed.

The two groups of forms (kuppens and kegels; mogotes and turms) therefore do not seem to have genetic links. We think that their formation and their evolution which, in both can result in localized levellings, obey structural and more particularly lithological criteria.

In very porous calcareous rocks landscapes develop whose forms are rounded, soft and have valleys, resulting in kuppens and kegels; whereas massive, compact, less porous calcareous rocks, give landscapes of mogotes and turm karst.

CONCLUSIONS: ON THE ROLE OF STRUCTURAL FACTORS

Thus, most of the surface forms in tropical karsts seem to be determined by precise structural conditions according to the type of relief. Some structural factors may play a fundamental role. The influence of the calcareous rock porosity in temperate areas is a factor that several authors have stressed, particularly Sweeting (1965) and Nicod (1971). In fact, due to very important superficial solution, porosity plays a fundamental role in tropical areas. Indeed, it is the differences of porosity which control variations in surface forms.

In very porous rocks, which absorb significant quantities of water, solution seems to be carried on uniformly at the surface of the rock mass, while within the rock solution builds up to a considerable depth. The result is a diffuse solution, somewhat granular, affecting the whole form in question; as a consequence, we have blunt forms and the absence of sharp or 'vigorous' forms. This phenomenon is further developed because fractures are usually not well expressed in such soft limestones, and consequently, do not constitute planes of preferential water penetration.

Inversely, in compact or crystalline, and weakly or very weakly porous limestones, water infiltration and therefore downward solution in the rock is very slow and reduced. It is even negligible in the case of crystalline limestones. Consequently, solution is essentially pellicular and it is due mostly to surface run-off. It also occurs along vertical or oblique fissures and diaclases, and to a lesser degree, along stratification joints, i.e. along the planes of easy penetration of water. It is these hard brittle limestones which best exhibit fractures and dense networks of diaclases. These two factors: solution at the rock surface only, and importance of the fracturisation network, account for vigorous indented forms and the importance of surface sculptures, of which tsingys are a striking illustration.

We should distinguish soft, porous limestones and dolomites in which infiltration is achieved in the mass, and hard, compact and weakly porous limestones in which penetration is achieved essentially along fracturisation planes. Porosity in calcareous rocks raises many problems because their behaviour is extremely variable. Thus very pure limestones, such as those of the karst floor in Narinda (98% $CaCO_3$), behave as relatively impermeable (porosity 1-3%) in comparison with the dolomitic limestones in mogotes. As for dolomites, their behaviour is also one of the most variable, for instance the Mariarano friable dolomites are very highly porous (<40%), but the Moramba compact dolomites (Narinda) have a porosity ranging only from 3 to 4%.

Nicod (1971) has considered this problem. He thinks that dolomites are generally more porous than limestones, by reason of their genesis. Globally, this point is accurate. We have noticed that dolomitic limestones, or some dolomites such as those in Mariarano coupoles or in the west Kelifely are, with chalky limestones, the most porous rocks that we have found. But there remains the case of the Moramba compact calcareous dolomites, which are very slightly porous.

On the whole, it seems that porosity determines the mode and importance of water penetration and consequently, the mode and importance of solution. In this we agree with Nicod (1971) when he states: 'we then reach an essential hypothesis, it is the unequal porosity that explains the unequal solution in dolomites'. Personally we think that this remark could be extended to limestones too; it is the unequal porosity that principally explains the differences in the landforms.

The lithological disposition of different layers plays an important role; the presence of non-calcareous impervious levels and the thickness of karstifiable series above this level are two other determining factors. Thus, a thin calcareous layer overlying an impervious level allows only the formation of shallow dolines. Landscapes of typical mogotes require the existence of a moderately thick series above the beds which block the downward movement of water. Finally, the tectonics are another factor, and the more compact and more rigid the rocks, the more important the tectonic influence. Fractures and diaclases allow high permeability of the rock mass, by facilitating water penetration along privileged zones, and by increasing the karstifiable surface along these zones. The extreme case is that of the tsingy, but the examples of alignments of dolines or kegels in the Bemaraha are also significant.

Tectonics also play a major role in localizing subterranean networks. For a long time this role has been evident in temperate countries, and if the existence of important networks in tropical area has been long denied, it is certainly because such regions are not well known. In tropical areas we now have many examples; some 40 km of Ankarana galleries; the important networks mentioned by Cooke (1973) in the Tanga massif in Tanzania; the outlines of canyons resulting from the coalescence of 'dolines-puits' in the Kelifely; the zone of 'dolines-puits' in the Mahafaly plateau; the important resurgences of the southwest Madagasgan karsts, to mention but a few.

Furthermore, it seems necessary to correct the point of view held by some authors, namely Renault (1959) or Corbel (1959), who think that the systems of cavities are not well developed in tropical areas. What is true, is that in rocks which are lightly susceptible to tectonic influences such as chalky limestones, these networks are feebly developed, and consequently, in the regions of kuppens or kegels, significant cavities are rare. But it is not the same case in brittle limestones, such as the thick bedrocks of crystalline limestones of the Ankarana type. In addition, important networks can develop only if the thickness of limestones above the general watertable is considerable. Consequently, the absence of well-developed networks in such regions of buttes is not surprising.

These authors have sometimes held that the absence of large subterranean networks comparable with those of temperate areas is a zonal character of tropical karsts. We think the idea erroneous. The existence or absence of these networks is linked to structure, and not to climate. As proof, regions of chalk in temperate countries are by no means remarkable for their cavities; and conversely, the existence of developed networks in tropical areas is a fact. On the other hand, in temperate areas, it is in massive, thick limestones such as those in Pre-Alps that the most important systems of caves are found.

Consequently, structure is a fundamental factor in determining landforms. Indeed there exists a deterministic relationship, since the same structural conditions in the same climatic area reproduce the same family of forms; the example of the tsingy tables is in this regard particularly important. Obviously the infinite possibilities of structural combinations on regional as well as on local scales do not permit this determinism to be strict; but, incontestably, there exist close relationships. The multiplication of regional morphological studies should permit one to specify the links that we have simply sketched in this work.

This 'structuralist' position does not exclude the importance of solutional phenomena. Structure is a frame, an outline sketch, inside which these phenomena operate, as in the case of differential erosion processes (Rossi, 1976). Variety in karst forms are determined by structure, but it is the influence of bioclimatic factors which account for the elaboration of forms, and for the differences observed between tropical and temperate areas. In fact, what characterizes tropical karst, as opposed to temperate karst, is essentially the hypertrophy of forms; it is responsible for the extraordinary variety of tropical karstic hills landscapes. And this is due to the predominant - and not exclusive - character of superficial solution in comparison with the temperate area. Morphology helps us to keep in mind some realities, and particularly that it is neither in Alaska nor in Slovenia, but in South East Asia, West Indies, New Guinea or in Madagascar that we can observe the most impressive surface karsts.

Acknowledgements

I would like to thank Dr M.M. Sweeting who was kind enough to review the final draft of this paper.

REFERENCES

Battistini, R. 1964. *L'Extrême-Sud de Madagascar*. (Paris: Ed. Cujas).

Birot, P. 1966. *Le Relief Calcaire*. (Paris: Centre de Documentation Universitaire).

Birot, P. Corbel, J. and Muxart, R., 1968. Morphologie des Régions Calcaires à la Jamaique et à Porto-Rico. *Mem. et Doc. du C.N.R.S.*, 4, (Paris).

Cooke, H.J. 1973. A tropical karst in North-East Tanzania. *Zeitsch. f. Géom.*, 17(4), (Berlin - Stuttgart).

Corbel, J. 1959. Karsts du Yucatan et de la Floride. *Bull. Ass. Géogr. Fçais*, 283, (Paris).

Corbel, J. and Muxart, R., 1970. Karsts des zones tropicales humides. *Zeitsch F. Géom.*, 11(4), (Berlin - Stuttgart).

Cvijic, J. 1961. La géographie des terrains calcaires. *Ac. Serbe des Scien. et des Arts*. (publié d'après un manuscrit antérieur à 1927). (Zagreb.)

Enjalbert, H., 1964. Phénomènes karstiques au Mexique et au Guatemala. *Bull. Ass. Géogr. Frçais*, (Paris).

Gerstenhauer, A. 1960. Der tropische karst in Tabasco. *Zeitsch f. Géom, Suppl. 2*, (Berlin - Stuttgart).

Lasserre A. 1961. *La Guadeloupe, étude géographique*. (Thèse, Bordeaux).

Lehmann, H. 1953. Der tropische Kegelkarst in Westindien. *Verh dt. Géogr. Tags.*, 29.

Lehmann, H. 1954. Die Karstphänomenen in verschiedenen Klimazonen. *Erdkunde*, 8.

Lehmann, H. Krömmelbein, K. and Lötscher, W., 1956. Karst-morphologische, geologische und botanische Studien in der Sierra de los Organos auf Cuba. *Erdkunde*, 10.

Miotke, F.D. 1973. Die Tieferlegung der Oberflachen zwischen Mogoten in Puerto Rico. *Geogr. Zeitsch*, 32.

Monroe, W.H. 1963. Geology of the Camuy Quagrangle, Puerto Rico. *United States Geological Survey, Bulletin*.

Monroe, W.H. 1964. Origin and interior structure of mogotes of northern Puerto Rico. *Intern. Congr. Geogr.*, (London).

Nicod, J. 1971. Quelques remarques sur la dissolution des dolomies. *Bull. Ass. Géogr. Français,* 389-390, (Paris).

Nicod, J. 1972. *Pays et paysages du calcaire,* (Paris: Presses, Universitaires Francaises).

Panos, V. and Stelcl, 1968. Problems of the conical karst in Cuba. *IV Congrès Intern. Spéléo.,* (Ljubljana).

Renault, Ph. 1959. Le karst du Kouilou. *Rev Géogr. de Lyon,* **34(4).**

Rossi, G. 1974. Morphologie et évolution d'un karst en milieu tropical sec: l'Ankarana. *Mém et Doc. du C.N.R.S.,* **15,** (Paris).

Rossi, G. 1975. Le karst de Narinda. *Madagascar, Revue de Géographie,* **27,** Tananarive.

Rossi, G., 1976. Karst et dissolution des calcaires en milieu tropical. *Zeitsch f. Geom. Suppl. 26,* (Berlin - Stuttgart).

Rossi, G. 1977. Le karst du Namoroka. *Rev. Géom. Dyn.,* **3,** (Paris).

Rossi, G. 1977. *L'Extrême-Nord de Madagascar.* (Thèse, Edisud, Aix-en-Provence).

Rossi, G. 1982. Le karst du Bemaraha. *Mémoires et Documents du C.N.R.S.* Phénomènes karstiques 3. (Paris).

Sweeting, M.M., 1965. Denudation in Limestone Regions: A Symposium. *The Geographical Journal,* **5,** p. 132.

Tricart, J. and Cardoso da Silva T., 1960. Un exemple d'évolution karstique en milieu tropical sec: le morne de Bom Jesus da lapa. *Zeitsch f. Geom.,* **4(1),** (Berlin - Stuttgart).

Verstappen, H. Th. 1960. Some observations on karst development in the Malay Archipalago. *Journal of Tropical Geography,* **14.**

Verstappen, H. Th. 1964. Karstmorphology of the Star Mountains, Central New Guinea. *Zeitsch. f. Geom.,* **8(1).**

Voss, F. 1970. Typische Oberflächenformen: tropischer Kegelkarst auf den Philippinen. *Geogr. Zeitsch.,* **59(3).**

Wilford, G.E. and Wall, J.R. 1965. Karst topography in Sarawak. *The Journal of Tropical Geography,* **21.**

Williams, P.M. 1972. Morphometric analysis of polygonal karst in New Guines. *Geological Society of America Bulletin,* **5,** p.83.

11

Stable isotopes - an investigation into their application in karst hydrology in the U.K., with special reference to the Malham area, North Yorkshire

H.A. Brown, M.M. Sweeting and R.L. Otlet

SUMMARY

Natural variations in stable isotopes in the hydrological cycle
have provided valuable information in many areas worldwide, and
most successfully where extremes of climatic seasonality or relief exist. The project reported here was initiated to assess
the viability of the technique in the UK. Oxygen isotope results
are presented for the Malham area, North Yorkshire. The isotopic
input signal in monthly precipitation was found to be only weakly
seasonal, although the range of variations is significantly
(approximately 100 times) larger than the estimated measurement
error. A finer structure was revealed at shorter timescales, and
this may be of relevance for detailed hydrological tracing,
especially if suitable input 'spikes' could be predicted reliably.
Variations of input with altitude, however, were found to be
erratic. Monthly samples of ground and surface waters exhibited
relatively smaller $\delta^{18}O$ variations, indicating early mixing and
storage of waters in the soil and/or upper karstic zone, with
some evidence of the persistance of winter recharge. The complexity of the mixing process is exemplified in an examination
of a storm hydrograph at Waterhouses Spring, where the marked
chemical response is distinct from the small isotopic variations
observed. In contrast with the smoothing of the input signal in
groundwater, a robust, naturally enhanced and clearly seasonal
isotope signal was discovered in the waters of Malham Tarn (a
natural lake), and this suggests a useful application in the study
of leakage from, and interconnections with, surface storage water
bodies. It is concluded that although the isotope technique reveals information not obtainable by conventional hydrological
methods, it is unlikely that it could ever be used in isolation
and is more correctly regarded, therefore, as a new 'dimension'
rather than a new direction in karst hydrology.

RÉSUMÉ

Les variations naturelles des isotopes stables du cycle hydrologique
ont fourni des renseignements importants dans diverses régions du
monde, et la plupart des résultats significatifs ont eu lieu dans
les régions à saisons ou reliefs contrastés. Le projet que l'on va
décrire a pour but de tester cette technique appliquée au milieu de
Royaume-Uni. Les résultats des isotopes d'oxygène sont donnés pour
la région de Malham, au nord du Yorkshire. On a trouvé que les
variations isotopiques de la pluie mensuelle étaient faibles selon la
saison bien que l'ampleur de ces variations soit plus grande (à
peu près 100 fois) que l'erreur d'estimation des mesures. Pour des
périodes moins longues on a décelé plus de détails. Ceux-ci
pourraient être utiles pour des traçages hydrologiques, surtout si
des pics convenables pouvaient être prévus avec certitude.
Cependant les variations isotopiques selon l'altitude étaient variables. Les échantillons mensuels des eaux de fond et de surface ont
montré des variations $\delta^{18}O$ moins prononcées ce qui laisse entendre
que des eaux sont mélangées et enmagasinées dans le sol et/ou
la zone supérieure du karst. Il y a également des indications en
faveur d'une reconstitution hivernale des nappes. On souligne la
complexité des processus de mélange des eaux par l'examen d'un
hydrographe à la résurgence de Waterhouses, où les variations
chimiques sont nettement différentes des variations isotopiques
observées. Les variations isotopiques des eaux de fond sont à
comparer avec les résultats des variations isotopiques saisonnières
bien nettes et naturellement marquées, des eaux de Malham Tarn
(lac naturel). Ceci nous montre une application utile pour l'étude
des pertes et les liens avec les réservoirs naturels de surface.
La technique des isotopes donne des résultats qui ne pourraient
pas être obtenus par les autres moyens conventionnels de l'hydrologie. Pourtant il n'est pas souhaitable qu'on puisse utiliser
cette technique de façon isolée sans recourir conjointement à ces
derniers. On devrait considérer cette technique davantage comme
une nouvelle dimension que comme une nouvelle direction dans le
domaine de l'hydrologie karstique.

INTRODUCTION

Variations in the stable isotopes of oxygen (^{18}O and ^{16}O) and
hydrogen (^{1}H and ^{2}H, protium and deuterium) in waters throughout
the hydrological cycle provide a tool available to hydrologists
in the form of a 'natural tracer'. Variations occurring over
time and space have been exploited successfully in both areas
of karst and of non-karst. In general, however, the successful
use of the technique has relied upon the study area exhibiting
either extremes of climatic seasonality, as for example in the
Sahara (Conrad and Fontes, 1970), or extremes of relief, as in
the Swiss Jura (Seigenthaler *et al.*, 1983). Such extremes are
not found in the UK and in consequence the development of the
stable isotope technique has been slower, and although there is
some knowledge of the input signals (i.e. the stable isotope

patterns in precipitation), investigations regarding their exploitation and possible limitations have not been carried out in detail. The research project reported here was therefore initiated to examine the general viability of the technique in the UK.

The work refers to a study carried out in the Malham area, North Yorkshire, involving the systematic monitoring of natural waters, principally for oxygen isotope variations. In this paper a brief explanation of the principles underlying the use of the stable isotopes generally will be given, and the experiment design outlined. Results of isotope analyses of natural waters will be examined for the Malham area. Although the final interpretation of the results with respect to karst hydrology must remain tentative, requiring more detailed analysis, an assessment is made regarding the contribution of the technique towards a 'new direction' in karst hydrology.

STABLE ISOTOPE NOTATION AND PROPERTIES

Isotope abundance ratios are normally expressed as a difference (delta) from the comparable ratio of the international reference, Standard Mean Oceanic Water (after Craig, 1961), in units of parts per thousand (per mil or $°/_{oo}$); thus a measured oxygen isotope ratio for a water sample (x) with respect to the SMOW standard is referred to as $\delta^{18}O_{SMOW}$ where:

$$\delta^{18}O_{SMOW} = \frac{[R_x - R_{SMOW}]}{R_{SMOW}} \times 1000 \ (°/_{oo})$$

and R is the ratio $^{18}O/^{16}O$ of the sample (x) or reference (SMOW), as indicated.

Oxygen isotope ratios are measured using light element, precision mass spectrometers. In this study a VG Micromass 602E was used. Each sample is measured as CO_2 gas, prepared by equilibration with the water at 25°C, according to the standard technique of Epstein and Mayeda (1953).

The fractionation, or partitioning of isotopes between two substances with different isotope ratios, commonly occurs at phase changes and is dependent upon temperature and the degree to which equilibrium is achieved (Hoefs, 1973). On thermodynamic considerations it may be anticipated that precipitation will be isotopically lighter (having more negative $\delta^{18}O$ values) in winter months than in summer months, and also will become isotopically lighter with increasing altitude (and decreasing temperatures) in a given area. Studies verifying these effects are summarised by Yurtsever and Gat (1981).

Given a clear input signal, at the chosen scales of space and time, stable isotopes are attractive as tracers since they offer certain specific advantages over many artificial tracers.

These are:

i) They are the constituents of water and therefore travel at the same speed.
ii) They are conservative; that is interaction with the medium through which they pass is minimal under most conditions.
iii) They are not toxic.
iv) Their input is areal; in other words, the rainfall itself.

In light of these advantages and the known exploitation of stable isotopes elsewhere, it seemed important not to neglect their possible application in studies of UK karst hydrology.

EXPERIMENTAL DESIGN

The primary objectives of the study were to investigate the following two questions; firstly, is a seasonal and/or altitudinal pattern identifiable in the stable isotope input of precipitation over the UK?, and if this is the case, secondly, is the signal sufficiently strong to survive mixing in hydrological systems and so be potentially valuable in karst and other hydrological studies?

It was considered important in such a pilot study to choose a field area which would provide fast throughput times to minimise signal attenuation, adequate relief to enable examination of isotope effects, and also a known hydrological regime to verify the stable isotope results (as had also been noted by Bakalowicz *et al.*, 1974). The Malham area satisfied these requirements. The area, shown in Figures 11.1 and 11.2, consists predominantly of horizontal karstified limestone and has an

Figure 11.1a   Location of study area

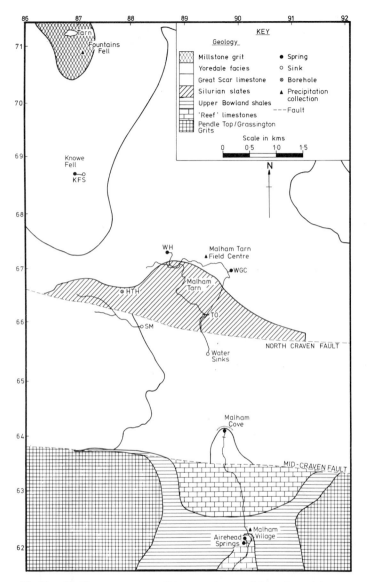

Figure 11.1b   Malham area geology and sampling locations
(KFS = Knowe Fell sinking stream, WH = Waterhouses
Spring, WGC = West Great Close Spring, TO = Tarn
Outflow, HTH = Higher Tren House, SM = Smelt Mill
sink)

217

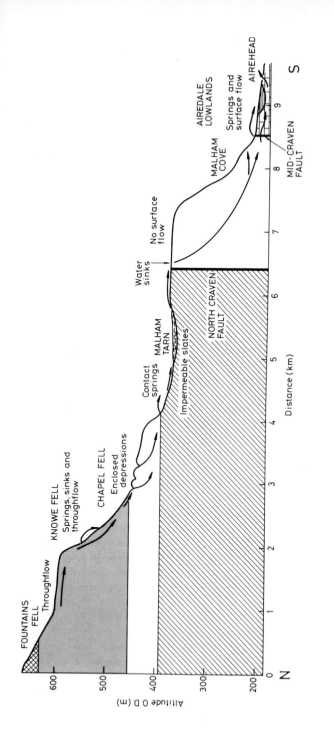

Figure 11.2 The cascading hydrological system of the Malham area: a diagrammatic section from Fountains Fell, through Knowe Fell and Malham Tarn, to Airehead Springs

altitudinal range of 185 to 657 m O.D. It has been the subject of conventional hydrological studies since the nineteenth century. Original tracing and flood pulse studies by Tate (1879) and by Howarth *et al.*, (1900) in the Malham area have been reexamined, and further experiments made by Smith and Atkinson (1977).

The principle connections in the lower part of the system are between the Tarn Outflow stream sinking at Water Sinks, and Airehead Springs; and also between Smelt Mill sinking stream and Malham Cove (Smith and Atkinson, *op. cit.*). The flow between these points is normally rapid, turbulent and confined to conduits. An observed intermittant overflow between the systems may be due to a restriction in a minor passage leading from Water Sinks to Malham Cove. Above the level of Malham Tarn (a natural lake) no artificial tracing has been undertaken, and directions of drainage are uncertain.

A programme of systematic sampling to investigate the $\delta^{18}O$ input signal in precipitation, and its correlation with surface waters over short and extended timescales was carried out over a 28 month period. Precipitation was collected monthly, weekly and also within storms. Monthly collecting stations were at Fountains Fell, Malham Tarn Field Centre (Malham Tarn House) and Malham village at altitudes 657 m, 395 m and 185 m respectively (shown in Figure 11.1). Results are reported here using Meteorological Office storage gauges as sample collectors. Weekly samples were obtained from accumulations of precipitation emptied daily from a reporting raingauge by the meteorological observer at Malham Tarn Field Centre. Within-storm rainfall sampling was normally carried out using an automatic rainfall sampler purpose-built by Rock and Taylor Ltd.

Ground and surface water samples were collected on a monthly basis, with more intensive sampling at Waterhouses Spring over selected storm periods. An attempt was made to intercept components of the cascading system discussed above and identified in Figure 11.2.

RESULTS AND DISCUSSION

As seen in Figure 11.3, the $\delta^{18}O_{SMOW}$ values in monthly rainfall from the three collection stations are seen to follow a definable structure, although exhibiting only weak seasonal trends, with all values falling within the range -4 to -13°/$_{oo}$, or approximately 100 times the estimated measurement error (at 1σ). The standard deviations of monthly input (e.g. σ of 1.47°/$_{oo}$ at Fountains Fell for n=25) are typical of a mid-latitude maritime area, and much smaller than those found in continental climates, e.g. Vienna (σ 3.40°/$_{oo}$, n=36, for 1973-75; I.A.E.A., 1979). Input variations over the Malham area tend to reflect particular synoptic conditions, for example heavy snow over the study area in March 1982. Drifting snow and its subsequent melt into the collector at the Malham village site is known to have contributed to the extremely negative $\delta^{18}O$ value here for precipitation in December 1981.

219

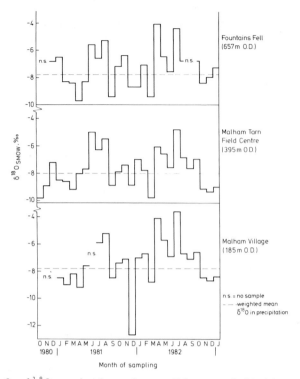

Figure 11.3 $\delta^{18}O$ variations in monthly precipitation samples
collected at three stations within the Malham
area, each at a different altitude (Fountains Fell,
Malham Tarn Field Centre and Malham village)

Weekly sample measurements (Figure 11.4) appear erratic
and reveal a wider range of values, approximately $15°/_{oo}$ over
a two-year period, the detail of which is unobserved in a single
month's collection.   Such short timescale effects may be valuable in certain hydrological cases where the throughput of rainwater is rapid and possibilities for storage and mixing limited,
as in urban runoff hydrology.   However, the most significant
deviations in input from annual average isotope values which are
also associated with large precipitation events (thus providing
a clear tracer 'spike') are rare and as yet difficult to predict.   It appears that snow, which is frequently isotopically
light, may, on melting, provide the most well-defined natural
tracer for studies in the UK.   Isotopic responses of surface
water to snowmelt have been investigated elsewhere, e.g. in the
Canadian Rockies by Sklash *et al.*, (1976) but are complicated by
the processes of snowpack development where the melt is gradual.

Within-storm measurements of precipitation reveal even finer
structure.   In Figure 11.5 a $5°/_{oo}$ range is seen over 1.3 days
where samples were taken two hourly.   These short period variations, although interesting in terms of meteorological dynamics,

may prove difficult to exploit as tracer spikes.

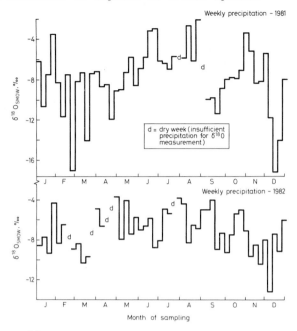

Figure 11.4 $\delta^{18}O$ variations in weekly precipitation samples collected at Malham Tarn Field Centre

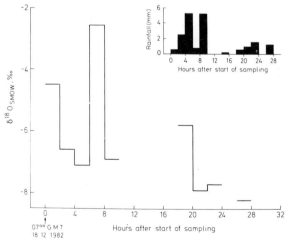

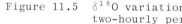

Figure 11.5 $\delta^{18}O$ variations in precipitation collected over two-hourly periods, on the site of AERE Harwell, Oxfordshire

221

It was considered important to investigate the relationships between isotopic input and climatological variables, since a correlation could be used to estimate mean $\delta^{18}O$ values at sites or for periods where actual stable isotope data do not exist. A linear regression was carried out between $\delta^{18}O$ in precipitation at Malham Tarn Field Centre and mean temperature and total precipitation records from the adjacent meteorological station. Results are given below for both monthly and weekly time periods.

Monthly precipitation

$$\delta^{18}O_{SMOW} = -8.80 + 0.18(T_m) \qquad r = 0.60 \qquad n=25$$

$$\delta^{18}O_{SMOW} = -6.03 - 0.01(P_m) \qquad r = 0.64 \qquad n=26$$

Weekly precipitation

$$\delta^{18}O_{SMOW} = -9.44 + 0.28(T_w) \qquad r = 0.50 \qquad n=98$$

$$\delta^{18}O_{SMOW} = -6.17 - 0.04(P_w) \qquad r = 0.39 \qquad n=98$$

where T_m, T_w are monthly and weekly mean temperatures (°C), and P_m, P_w are monthly and weekly precipitation totals (mm).

Correlations of both monthly and weekly $\delta^{18}O$ values in rainfall with air temperature and precipitation amounts are seen to be quite weak, especially when compared with more continental areas, such as Locarno, Switzerland, where a correlation coefficient (r) of 0.82 between $\delta^{18}O$ values and monthly temperature data was observed (Seigenthaler and Mather, 1983). The so-called 'temperature' and 'amount' effects, described by Dansgaard (1964) and examined over Europe by Rosanski et al., (1982) are, therefore, hardly applicable in this area. It appears, however, that air mass characteristics may dominate stable isotope values in precipitation over the UK, and further investigations, including an assessment of storm trajectories (e.g. after Lawrence et al., 1982) are required to provide a predictive base for tracing purposes.

The effect of altitude on isotopic input appears erratic over the study area, reflecting perhaps the minor importance in this area of stationary orographic rainfall, upon which this effect depends. An average depletion rate of 0.11°/oo/100m is discernable however in the summer months, from Malham village to Fountains Fell, although this rate is slightly lower than any in the worldwide range of values reported by Yurtsever and Gat (1981), of 0.15 to 0.5°/oo/100m.

On examination of ground and surface waters (Figure 11.6), a rapid smoothing appears to occur, shown by a subdued and variable response in these waters to the isotopic input of rainfall. The waters appear to exhibit an average baseflow value of approximately -7.8°/oo, which is in close agreement with the weighted isotopic mean in precipitation, shown in Figure 11.3, and is reflected in the fairly constant isotope values in Higher Tren House borehole (Figure 11.6c).

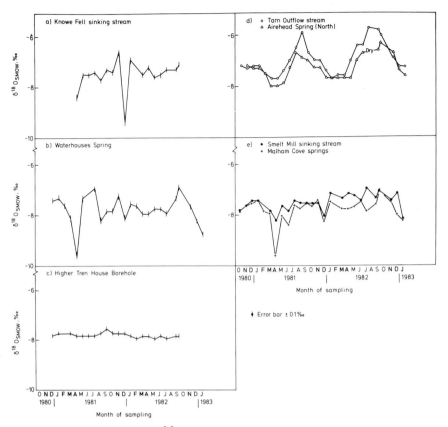

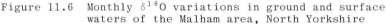

Figure 11.6   Monthly $\delta^{18}O$ variations in ground and surface
waters of the Malham area, North Yorkshire

In the correlation matrix (Table 11.1) Knowe Fell sinking
stream, representing the top of the cascading system, shows a
poor correlation (average r=0.43) with rainfall values for each
month preceding sampling.   These are further reduced at Waterhouses Spring (average r value with precipitation, 0.23), but a
higher correlation between the aforementioned sink and the spring
(r=0.60) is seen to exist, although no direct link between them
can be established using this technique.   More detailed examination of the monthly plots, together with the geochemical and
hydrological data available, are required to explain the short
term deviations which appear to be frequently associated with
snowmelt events (e.g. at Knowe Fell sinking stream, January 1982).
A thick cover (0.2-1.5 m) of peat and/or glacial drift is known
to exist over much of the upper part of the catchment (Bullock,
1971), where water may be stored and mixing take place, prior to
entering the karstic zone. $\delta^{18}O$ data from cave drips below bare
limestone and samples taken of soil moisture will assist in the
assessment of possible mixing in a zone of epikarst, as already
indicated in several isotope studies (Bakalowicz *et al.*, 1974,

223

Table 11.1 Correlation matrix of monthly $\delta^{18}O$ values in natural
waters of the Malham area, North Yorkshire

		FF	MT	MV	KF	WH	TO	AH	n
(FF)	Fountains Fell Precipitation at 657m O.D.	-	.84**	.79**	.35	.30	.58*	.33	25
(MT)	Malham Tarn Field Centre Precipitation at 395m O.D.		-	.83**	.27	.15	.57*	.28	28
(MV)	Malham village Precipitation at 185m O.D.			-	.67*	.23	.58*	.34	24
(KF)	Knowe Fell Surface water				-	.60	.21	.29	18
(WH)	Waterhouses Surface water					-	.34	.54	25
(TO)	Tarn Outflow Surface water						-	.88**	27
(AH)	Airehead Spring (north) Surface water							-	25

Correlation coefficients (r) are significantly different from zero:

** at the 99.9% confidence level

* at the 99.5% confidence level

n is the number of samples measured for $\delta^{18}O$ in each data set.

French Pyrenees; Goede *et al.,* 1982, Tasmania), although again
the definition of the input signal in the UK will limit future
investigations.

Unexpectedly, the most well-defined seasonal signal is
found in Malham Tarn, which is fed by streams from the upper
catchment, although only a weak correlation has been found between the previous month's rainfall and these waters, represented
by Waterhouses Spring. This spring provides a major tributary
to the Tarn, amounting to approximately 45% of all contributions
by discharge. The definition of this signal is assumed to be
due to evaporation, despite the lack of seasonal temperature
extremes in the area. Measurements of monthly deuterium/hydrogen
ratios for the Tarn (not shown) reveal similar variations, and
this would not occur were the effect due solely, for example, to
the precipitation of $CaCO_3$ in the Tarn (reported by Pentecost,
1981). Figure 11.7 shows a scatter plot of $\delta^{18}O$ versus δD values
for both the Tarn Outflow water and for Fountains Fell precipitation. The slopes of regression lines fitted through the data
sets, however, are hardly distinguishable (only Fountains Fell
computed regression is shown, for clarity), as might otherwise
be expected of a strongly evaporative effect. Exact estimation
of evaporation rates by isotopic means (e.g. after Zimmerman,
1979), is dependent upon parameters for which inadequate data
exists and some are not directly measurable. Further experimentation however, using the methods of Alison and Leavy (1982)

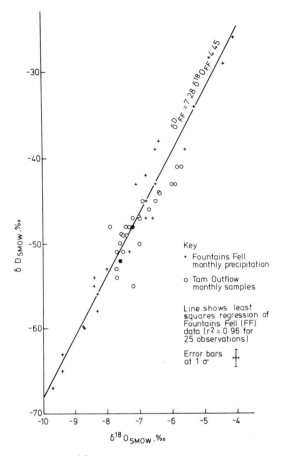

Figure 11.7　Plot of $\delta^{18}O$ versus δD for Fountains Fell monthly precipitation and for Tarn Outflow monthly stream-water samples.

and of Zuber (1983), may assist in an indirect parameterisation. Without that data, estimates of evaporation are liable to errors of over an order of magnitude.

The naturally labelled Tarn water is clearly identified in the lower altitude springs at Airehead, where first times of artificial tracer arrival after input at Water Sinks of between 6.5 hours and 43 hours have been found by Smith and Atkinson (1977). Isotope results are presented here for the largest and northern-most spring in a group of three in close proximity, the isotopic, hydrological and chemical responses of which are very similar. In periods of summer low flow, isotopic differences between the Tarn Outflow water and Airehead Springs are the largest, indicating the larger proportion of a stored baseflow contribution to the latter's discharge.

As a first approach, a simplistic mass balance equation of the following form was used to estimate the baseflow component:

$$\delta_B Q_B + \delta_{TO} Q_{TO} = \delta_{AH} Q_{AH} \qquad (1)$$

where δ and Q are isotopic composition and discharge respectively, and where subscripts B, TO, AH refer to baseflow, Tarn Outflow and Airehead Spring water respectively. However the total discharge of the Tarn does not feed solely to this spring, the discharge of which is normally lower than the Tarn, therefore to apportion the sources of water a modified equation is needed. If a unit discharge at Airehead is assumed, and a proportion X is contributed by water from the Tarn, then

$$\delta_{AH} = (X)\delta_{TO} + (1-X)\delta_B \qquad (2)$$

When δ_B is attributed a constant value of $-7.8°/_{oo}$, baseflow contributions to Airehead are found to be 29% in December 1981, and 82% in May 1982. These are comparable with figures found by Smith and Atkinson (1977) using artificial tracers, when all the springs at Airehead were taken together. At certain times, however (April, May and June 1981), negative baseflow contributions are computed using this method. A proposed explanation is illustrated by examination of Figure 11.6e, which shows a direct comparison of Smelt Mill sinking stream and Malham Cove spring $\delta^{18}O$ results over 27 months. A persistance for several months of isotopically light winter recharge (from May to July 1981), entering the system below the sinking stream and being detectable at Malham Cove is inferred from the Malham Cove results. These plot well below the corresponding Smelt Mill $\delta^{18}O$ values during this period, indicating baseflow $\delta^{18}O$ values more negative than the 'normal' $-7.8°/_{oo}$ value. Such an effect would contradict the constant isotopic baseflow assumption of the mass balance calculation (2), and it is suggested that it accounts for apparent negative baseflow contributions in certain months. It is of interest to note, however, that the persistance of winter recharge could not have been seen using conventional hydrological techniques.

An example of the short-period response of Waterhouses Spring to storm rainfall is shown in Figures 11.8, 11.9 and 11.10. The curves of conductivity and Ca^{2+} concentrations (Figure 11.9) are characterised by a slight increase at the onset of the hydrograph response (Figure 11.8), possibly due to displacement of fissure storage, followed by dilution curves which correspond to the two discharge peaks.

The response in $\delta^{18}O$ values, shown in Figure 11.10, is less marked, hardly exceeding experimental errors for many samples, and is more difficult to explain. From 0 to 23 hours after the start of sampling, 51 mm of rain fell with an average $\delta^{18}O$ of $-6.1°/_{oo}$, i.e. isotopically heavier than the initial spring water which was at $-7.5°/_{oo}$. An isotopic response to this might have been expected at the spring, but is not clearly seen over the observation period. It is noted that isotope values relating to the initial rising limb of the hydrograph are erratic. From 23 to 38 hours, an average input of $-7.2°/_{oo}$ in 14.3 mm rainfall is also difficult to detect. However, from 36 to 62 hours, a

226

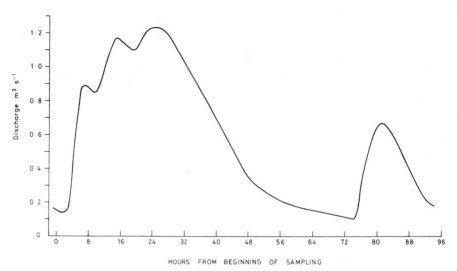

Figure 11.8   Hydrograph response at Waterhouses Spring to storm rainfall, 30 September to 4 October 1981

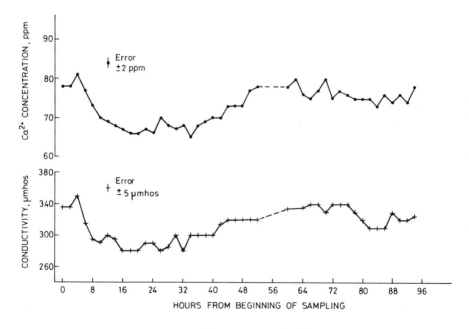

Figure 11.9   Response in Ca^{2+} concentration and conductivity at Waterhouses Spring to storm rainfall, 30 September to 4 October 1981

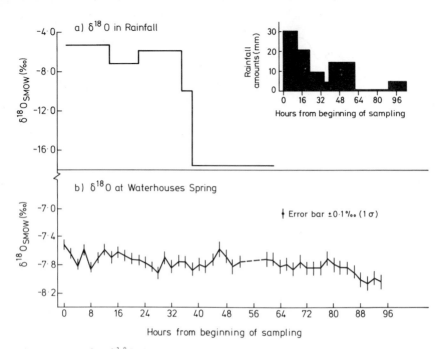

Figure 11.10 $\delta^{18}O$ input in rainfall and isotopic response at
            Waterhouses Spring, 30 September to 4 October
            1981.

very light isotopic input of $-17.6°/_{oo}$ in 14.7 mm might account
for the falling isotope levels in the spring, approximately 40
hours later, towards the very end of the observation period.
The interpretation is made more difficult because the rainfall
averages apply only to a single collection point, whereas stream
water is derived from a wide area, and also the stream samples
are spot measurements, not weighted for discharge amounts.

    A possible explanation of the lack of $\delta^{18}O$ variation at the
spring is that the water undergoes a complexity of mixing and
displacement in the catchment area. This may take place in a
zone in the aquifer above that where preferential flow paths are
evidenced by the response of chemical parameters, which are more
dependent upon process dynamics. Merot *et al.*,(1981) similarly
found hidden complexity in hydrograph response after analysis
for stable isotopes and attributed this, in a non-karst area,
to releases from different hydrological reservoirs.

    The extent of the averaging effects is unexpected and demon-
strates the power of the isotope technique in providing information which could not be obtained by conventional hydrological
methods.

CONCLUSIONS

In principle, the stable isotope technique has great potential in karst hydrology, in its provision of a label of water origin. In practice in the UK, however, its use is limited by the inadequate definition of the seasonal input signal, and erratic altitudinal patterns.

It is suggested that its main use will be at a short time-scale (over weeks or days), in studies investigating the dynamics of the unsaturated zone where the initial mixing of the signal is occurring. To enable such studies, it would be of great value to be able to predict the isotope signals in precipitation (both rain and snowfall), and this would be helped by more detailed studies with respect to synoptic conditions.

The discovery of a robust, naturally enhanced isotope signal from Malham Tarn suggests a useful application in the study of leakage from, and interconnections with, surface storage water bodies.

Finally, the comment is made that caution must be exercised in the interpretation of stable isotope data in isolation, as data will always be best understood when examined together with conventional hydrological information. In this respect, the stable isotope technique may be viewed, perhaps, as providing not a new direction, but an additional dimension, in karst hydrology.

Acknowledgements

Thanks are extended to the staff of Malham Tarn Field Centre who collected monthly precipitation samples from the Fountains Fell collector, and also to the Yorkshire Water Authority and to the National Trust for permission to site equipment on their land. The research was carried out while one of the authors (HAB) was in receipt of a NERC award (GT4/80/AAPS/38), which is gratefully acknowledged.

REFERENCES

Allison, G.B. and Leavy, F.W. 1982. Estimation of isotopic parameters using constant feed pans. *Journal of Hydrology,* **55**, 151-161.

Bakalovicz, M., Blavoux, B. and Mangin, A. 1974. Apports du traçage isotopique naturel à la connaissance du fonctionnement d'un système karstique - teneurs en oxygène-18 de trois systèmes des Pyrenées, France. *Journal of Hydrology,* **23**, 143-158.

Bullock, P. 1971. The soils of the Malham Tarn area. *Field Studies,* **3(3)**, 381-408.

Conrad, G. and Fontes, J.Ch. 1970. Hydrologie du Sahara nord-occidental. In: *Isotope Hydrology,* Proceedings of the Symposium, Vienna, 1970, (Vienna: IAEA), 405-419.

Craig, H. 1961. Isotopic variations in meteoric waters. *Science,* 133, 1702-1703.

Dansgaard, W. 1964. Stable isotopes in precipitation. *Tellus,* 16, 436-468.

Epstein, S. and Mayeda, T.K. 1953. Variations of the $^{18}O/^{16}O$ ratio in natural waters. *Geochimica et Cosmochimica Acta,* 4, 213-224.

Goede, A., Green, D.C. and Harmon, R.S. 1982. Isotopic composition of precipitation, cave drips and actively forming speleothems at three Tasmanian cave sites. *Helectite,* 20(1), 17-28.

International Atomic Energy Agency, 1979. World Survey of isotope concentration in precipitation (1972-1975). IAEA Technical Report no. 192 (Vienna: IAEA)

Hoefs, J. 1973. *Stable isotope geochemistry. Minerals, Rocks and Inorganic Materials,* 9, (Berlin: Springer-Verlag) 140pp.

Howarth, J.H., Fennel, C.W., Bean, J.A., Branson, F.W., Ackroyd, W., Coulthard, T., Kendall, P.F. and Carter, W.L. 1900. The underground waters of north-west Yorkshire. *Proceedings of the Yorkshire geological and polytechnic Society,* 14, 1-44.

Lawrence, J.R. Gedzelman, S.D., White, J.W.C., Smiley, D. and Lazov, P. 1982. Storm trajectories in the eastern US: D/H isotopic composition of precipitation. *Nature,* 296, 638-640.

Merot, Ph., Bourget, M. and le Leuch, M. 1981. Analyse d'une crue a l'aide du traçage naturel par l'oxygène-18 mesuré dans les pluies, le sol et le ruisseau. *Catena,* 8, 69-81.

Pentecost, A. 1981. The tufa deposits of the Malham district, North Yorkshire. *Field Studies,* 5, 365-387.

Rosanski, K., Sonntag, C. and Munnich, K.O. 1982. Factors controlling stable isotope composition of European precipitation. *Tellus,* 34, 142-150.

Siegenthaler, V. and Mather, H.A. 1983. Dependence of $\delta^{18}O$ and δD in precipitation on climate. In: *Palaeoclimates and Palaeowaters,* IAEA Advisory Group Meeting, Vienna, 1982, (Vienna: IAEA), 37-51.

Siegenthaler, U., Schotterer, U. and Muller, I. 1983. Isotopic and chemical investigations of springs from different karst zones in the Swiss Jura. In: *Isotope Hydrology in Water Resources Development,* Proceedings of the Symposium IAEA, Vienna, 1983, (Vienna: IAEA), in press.

Sklash, M.G., Farvolden, R.N. and Fritz, P. 1976. A conceptual model of watershed response to rainfall, developed through the use of oxygen-18 as a natural tracer. *Canadian Journal of Earth Sciences,* 13, 271-283.

Smith, D.I. and Atkinson, T.C. 1977. Underground flow in cavernous limestones with special reference to the Malham Area. *Field Studies,* 4, 597–616.

Tate, T., 1879. The source of the River Aire. *Proceedings of the Yorkshire geological and polytechnic Society,* 7, 177–187.

Yurtsever, Y. and Gat, J. 1981. Atmospheric waters. In: *Stable Isotope Hydrology,* IAEA Technical Report, 210, (Vienna: IAEA), 103–142.

Zimmerman, U. 1979. Determination by stable isotopes of underground inflow and outflow and evaporation of young artificial groundwater lakes. In: *Isotopes in Lake Studies,* (Vienna: IAEA), 87–94.

Zuber, A. 1983. On the environmental isotope method for determining the water balance components for some lakes. *Journal of Hydrology,* 61, 409–427.

12

Stormflow characteristics of three small limestone drainage basins in North Island, New Zealand

J. Gunn and B. Turnpenny

SUMMARY

The small experimental basin approach, rarely used in karst areas, formed the basis for an examination of subterranean streamflow characteristics in three New Zealand catchments. Two of the basins lie to the west of Waitomo Caves and the third is south of Port Waikato. In the Waitomo basins, which are entirely autogenic with no surface drainage, the subterranean streams receive both diffuse percolation recharge and concentrated recharge from closed depressions. By way of contrast the Port Waikato basin has mixed lithologies and the subterranean stream is recharged mainly by allogenic streamsinks with smaller diffuse inputs of both allogenic and autogenic percolation. The Waitomo basins were instrumented for 14 months and the Port Waikato basin for 8 months. Storm hydrographs from each basin were analysed using time-based separation techniques, and stormflow parameters were evaluated in accordance with the methods of surface water hydrologists. Stormflow duration and time to peak are similar in all three basins, but the Port Waikato stream has a higher stormflow yield and peakflow magnitude and a lower antecedent baseflow than the two Waitomo streams. These differences may be accounted for by the allogenic recharge and by the low storativity of both the Port Waikato limestones and the overlying soils. There are also differences between the stormflow yields, peakflow magnitudes and antecedent baseflows in the two Waitomo basins and these are ascribed to human modifications (mainly forest clearance) which have increased the storage capacity of one basin. A more general comparison of the stormflow parameters with published figures from surface drainage basins indicates that the three limestone basins are not anomalous but form part of a continuum of natural hydrological systems. Hence it is suggested that karst hydrologists should pay greater attention to the concepts and methodology of surface water hydrology.

RÉSUMÉ

Les méthodes conçues pour étudier l'hydrologie des bassins versants expérimentaux n'ont pas été souvent utilisées dans les régions karstiques. On s'est servi de ces méthodes pour examiner l'hydrologie souterraine de trois bassins hydrologiques de Nouvelle-Zélande. Deux de ces bassins se trouvent à l'ouest des grottes de Waitomo et le troisième au sud de Port Waikoto. Dans les bassins autogènes de Waitomo il n'y a aucun cours d'eau de surface. Les rivières souterraines reçoivent les eaux d'infiltration et des eaux plus concentrées issues des dolines. Cependant le bassin versant de Port Waikato se compose de lithologies différentes et la rivière souterraine est alimentée essentiellement par des pertes allogènes bien qu'elle reçoive aussi de petits apports éparpillés d'eaux d'infiltration d'origine à la fois allogène et autogène. Les bassins de Waitomo ont été étudiés pendant 14 mois et celui de Port Waikato pendant 8 mois. Les Hydrographes de crues de chaque bassin expérimental ont été analysés par des techniques de séparation dites 'time-based' et les indices de crues ont été évalués selon les méthodes classiques des hydrologues. Le temps de passage des crues et les débits maxima sont à peu prés les mêmes pour les trois bassins, mais les crues du bassin de Port Waikato sont plus volumineuses et leurs débits maxima plus élevés. Il faut ajouter que l'écoulement d'étiage du bassin de Port Waikato est moins important que ceux des deux rivières des bassins de Waitomo. On peut expliquer ces différénces d'une part par des apports d'eaux allogènes et d'autre part par la lithologie des calcaires de Port Waikato et la nature des sols, ce qui détermine la capacité des réserves d'eau. Il y a des différences également entre les volumes d'eaux apportées par les crues et les valeurs maximales des débits et des niveaux d'étiages dans les deux bassins de Waitomo. On les explique par l'influence anthropique (le déboisement des terre est la cause essentielle) qui a augmenté la capacité des réserves d'un de ces bassins. Le comparaison entre ces résultats et ceux d'autres bassins hydrologiques non-karstiques montre que les résultats des trois bassins karstiques ne sont pas anormaux mais font partie des variations normales du système hydrologique. On pense donc que les hydrologues classiques devraient prêter davantage attention aux théories et méthodes de ceux qui étudient l'hydrologie en surface.

234

INTRODUCTION

In a major review of progress in Australasian karst studies
Williams (1978, p 260) noted that: "The fact that 'karst has
long constituted an almost autonomous field within the scientific
study of scenery' (Jennings, 1967, p 256) has been to its dis-
advantage, and will become even more so if comparative isolation
limits the application of a wide range of ideas and techniques
now being developed in geomorphology in general." It may be
argued that 'autonomy' has also prevailed in karst hydrology
where there has been an almost obsessive concern over the nature
of limestone drainage, and in particular the type of groundwater
ciculation which prevails and the applicability of the water
table concept. Jennings (1971) has summarised the main details
of the controversy which, as Smith *et al.*, (1976) have noted,
generated more heat than light. More recent studies, based to
a large extent on water tracing and chemical analysis of karst
risings, have shown that karst systems span a continuum from
aquifers dominated by diffuse recharge and slow phreatic fissure
flow to systems in which substantial point inputs from allogenic
streamsinks flow through large vadose conduits. Most karst
aquifers lie between these two extremes receiving both diffuse
recharge and point-recharge from streamsinks or from closed
depressions (Gunn, 1983). Hence, underground flow includes both
diffuse fissure flow and conduit flow components and these
interact to form a single integrated system similar to that of
surface drainage basins (Smith *et al.*, 1976). In view of this
similarity it might be expected that karst hydrologists would
look to developments in drainage basin studies in order to advance their understanding of karst systems. The merits of this
form of 'hydrological bias' to karst studies were outlined by
Newson (1972) and demonstrated in a study of solutional and
mechanical erosion in limestone catchments on the Mendip Hills,
England (Smith and Newson, 1974). However, there have been few
such studies and on the whole the International Hydrological
Decade (1965-74), which provided a major stimulus to data collection and analysis in surface basins, appears to have had relatively little impact on karst studies. One of the major
features of the IHD was the adoption of the small experimental
basin approach as a basis for investigations of storm runoff
production and drainage basin dynamics (Ward, 1971; 1975).
Another important advance was the replacement of subjective,
genetic methods of hydrograph separation by the objective, time-
based technique first proposed by Hewlett and Hibbert (1967).
The choice of 0.0055 l/s/ha/h as the slope of the separation line
originally related to conditions in forested basins in the
eastern United States, but it is now widely used because it allows
a ready comparison of hydrograph parameters that have been computed on a uniform basis for drainage basins in different hydrologic regions (Walling, 1971; Gregory, 1974; Harr, 1977; Cheng
et al., 1977; Pearce and McKerchar, 1979; Taylor, 1982). The
failure of karst hydrologists to make use of these new approaches
may be attributed primarily to the groundwater bias and in
particular to the conceptual and physical difficulties in defining

the watersheds of underground drainage basins. However this is
not always an insurmountable problem as water tracing techniques
have been used to identify the boundaries of subterranean drainage basins in several karst areas (Atkinson and Drew, 1974;
Hess and White, 1974; Quinlan and Rowe, 1977; Gunn, 1982). Hence
it was hypothesised that those karst systems in which vadose
conduit flow predominates form part of a continuum of natural
hydrological systems, and that they are therefore amenable to
analysis by the normal techniques of surface water hydrology.
Testing of this hypothesis formed part of wider investigations
in the Waitomo (Gunn, 1978) and Limestone Downs (Turnpenny,
1979) areas of New Zealand. This paper presents the results of
the hydrological studies and compares them with published data
from non-carbonate surface basins in New Zealand.

THE STUDY AREAS

Limestones outcrop widely in New Zealand, from Waiomio in the
north of North Island to Te Anau in the south of South Island
(Williams, 1982). The two study areas, Waitomo and Limestone
Downs, are situated in west central North Island (Figure 12.1).
Both karsts are formed on Oligocene Landon Series limestones,
the most widely outcropping carbonate rocks in New Zealand, but
their climate and physiography differ markedly and will be described separately.

     The regional geology of the Waitomo district has been dis-
cussed by Barrett (1967), Nelson (1973), and Nelson and Hume
(1977). In the area studied the Te Kuiti Group limestones total
approximately 100 m in thickness and are gently dipping, strongly
jointed, flaggy and well bedded. Three formations are recognised: firstly, the Otorohanga Limestone, secondly, the Waitomo
Sandstone and thirdly, the Orahiri Limestone (Figure 12.2).
They are underlain by the Aotea sandstone, which forms the local
base level for drainage, and overlain by 2-6 m of Pleistocene
tephra (Ward, 1967; 1972; Pain, 1975) which form the soil parent
material. The solum is classified as a yellow-brown loam and
has characteristic properties of friability, deep humic topsoil
and slippery, non-sticky clay (Gibbs, 1968). The area is
characterised by warm humid summers and mild wet winters. Rainfall is evenly distributed throughout the year with no three
month season accounting for more than 30%, or less than 20%, of
the annual total. Mean annual temperature is about 11.6°C, and
mean annual precipitation is approximately 2370 mm with monthly
totals ranging from 50-440 mm (Gunn, 1978). The present day
vegetation over most of the area is essentially improved cattle
and sheep pasture with a few patches of trees, scrub and ferns
on the steeper slopes. These are vestiges of the original dense,
evergreen Podcarp - mixed hardwood rain forest which once covered
the area (Holloway, 1959) but which now survives only in pockets.
The dominant landform is the closed depression and in many areas
the depressions interlock to form a cellular polygonal karst
network (Williams, 1978). Within the polygonal karst areas
there are no perennial surface streams but the depressions act
as local centres of drainage, channeling overland flow, through-

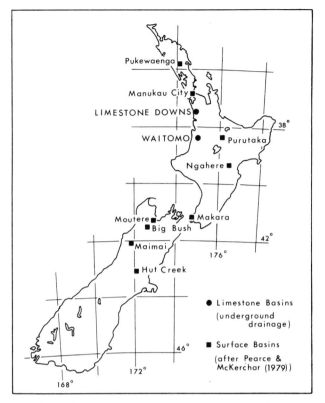

Figure 12.1   Location of study areas (in capitals) and of
catchments studied by Pearce and McKerchar (1979)

flow and subcutaneous flow into subterranean drainage systems
(Gunn, 1981).   As a result of this concentration of autogenic
recharge most underground water movement is through large vadose
conduits many of which are accessible to cavers (Hobson 1976;
Gunn 1979).

The regional geology of the Limestone Downs area has been
described by Waterhouse (1974) and Rogers and Grant-Mackie (1978).
In contrast to the Waitomo district only one limestone unit, the
Waimai Limestone (90% $CaCO_3$, 7% SiO_2), outcrops in the area
studied.   This unit is approximately 10 m in thickness, gently
dipping, strongly cross-bedded, flaggy and crystalline.   It is
underlain by a calcareous sandstone (40-50% $CaCO_3$) and overlain
by a calcareous siltstone (50-60% $CaCO_3$) and by indurated Pleistocene sands (Figure 12.2).   The soils are yellow-brown earths
on the Oligocene lithologies and yellow-brown sand soils on the
Pleistocene.   Both are well drained and the development of ironpans in the B horizon of the sand soils encourages rapid throughflow.   The mean annual temperature is similar to that in the
Waitomo district, as are the natural and cleared vegetation, but
mean annual precipitation is markedly lower at 1200 mm.   The

Figure 12.2   Stratigraphic columns for study areas

landforms also differ as the thin limestones have a limited outcrop and do not support closed depressions. Surface streams,
having their origins on the Awhitu Sands and Te Akatea Siltstone,
sink soon after crossing onto the limestone and flow through
shallow vadose caves before rising. Hence the characteristic
surface landforms are stream-sinks and dry valleys. The concentrated allogenic recharge is supplemented by diffuse allogenic
and autogenic percolation inputs which give rise to abundant
spelothems.

EXPERIMENTAL BASINS

In areas of impermeable rocks with surface drainage, where topographic divides form catchment boundaries, it is possible to delimit drainage basins on topographic maps and to examine the
physical characteristics of several basins before selecting one
which is 'representative' of the hydrological region. In karst
areas this approach is not possible because. of the unknown
relationship between surface topography and underground drainage.
Hence an alternative approach was devised for the present study
and to facilitate future small basin experiments in karst areas.
Following initial reconnaissance representative research areas
were identified and in each area a rising or a junction point on
an underground stream was selected as the experimental basin
outlet. Discharge measurements were made at the outlet points,

and the area contributing flow to them was defined by water
tracing experiments. When these experiments had been completed
the catchment boundaries were mapped and drainage basin area
computed. Hydrological measurement and boundary definition may
therefore proceed at the same time.

At Limestone Downs one research area was identified and
within it the Puriri Cave resurgence was selected as the experimental basin outlet. Puriri Cave has approximately 1000 m of
accessible passage and represents an extreme form of vadose
development, the 'through-cave' (Warwick, 1976, p 74). Water
from the two main allogenic stream-sinks may be followed through
the cave to the resurgence (Figure 12.3) obviating the need for
water tracing. However, several abandoned stream-sinks lie on
the floors of the two dry valleys which continue beyond the present day sinks. These older sinks operate intermittently during
periods of intense or prolonged rainfall and they were therefore
traced in order to establish the contemporary catchment of the
cave system. A 90° sharp crested V-notch weir and autographic
stage recorder were installed immediately downstream of the

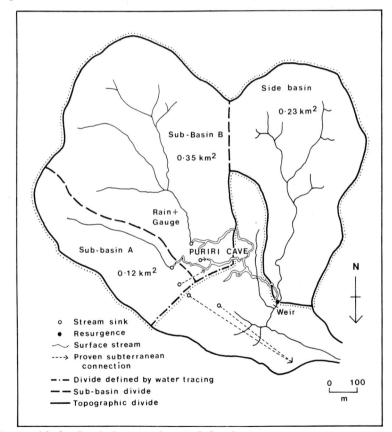

Figure 12.3 Puriri experimental basin

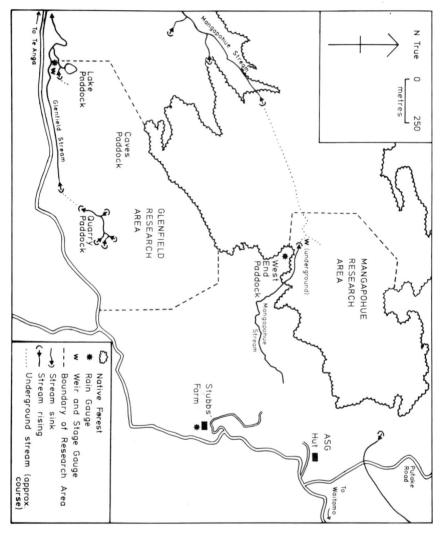

Figure 12.4 Mangapohue and Glenfield research areas

resurgence and an autographic rainguage was sited approximately
centrally within the basin (Figure 12.3). The total area contributing flow to the weir is 70 ha, 47 from the Puriri resurgenc
and 23 from the ephemeral Side Catchment which is tributary to
the Puriri stream at the resurgence (Figure 12.3). Measurements
of both rainfall and discharge commenced in January 1979 and
continued for eight months.

   Two research areas were identified in the Waitomo district,
Mangapohue which is clothed in dense native rain forest and
Glenfield where the natural vegetation has been replaced by improved pasture. In the Glenfield area the most suitable basin
outlet was the resurgence of the Glenfield stream from Wierd
Cave (Figure 12.4), and in the Mangapohue area the chosen site
was the Cymru stream at its junction with the main stream in
Mangapohue Cave (Figure 12.4 and Figure 12.5). Both research
areas are polygonal karsts with no allogenic stream-sinks, and
initially it was hoped that the paths taken by drainage water
from each depression could be determined by water tracing using
fluorescent dyes. Unfortunately attempts to trace water from
smaller depressions with no obvious outlet and from some depressions in the Glenfield area whose outlets were partially blocked

Figure 12.5   Autographic stage recorder and 90° V-notch weir at
             the outlet of the Cymru experimental basin in
             Mangapohue Cave

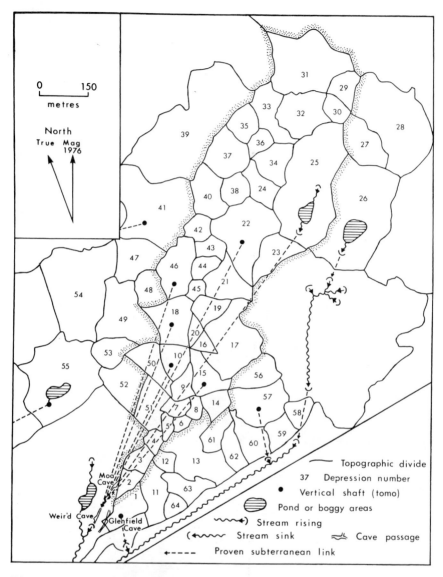

Figure 12.6   Depression boundaries and water tracing experiments
in the Glenfield research area (boundary of
experimental basin is stippled)

242

by soil and vegetable debris proved unsuccessful. However 11 successful traces were carried out in the Glenfield area (Figure 12.6) and 34 in the Mangapohue area (Figure 12.7), with mean linear velocities of 100-300 m/h. In using these results to delimit the areas draining to the Cymru and Glenfield streams two assumptions were made: firstly, that all water entering a depression drains to the same outlet and secondly, that those

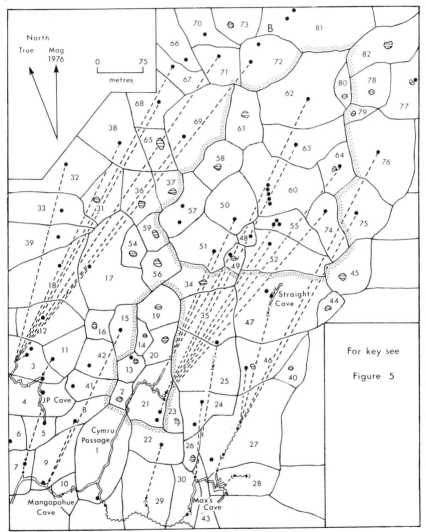

Figure 12.7 Depression boundaries and water tracing experiments in the Mangapohue research area (boundary of Cymru experimental basin is stippled)

243

depressions which could not be traced contribute flow to the same outlet as their nearest down-dip neighbour. Support for these assumptions is provided firstly by the successful water tracing experiments as each depression was traced to one, and only one, outlet point, and secondly by a hydrological study of the depressions (Gunn, 1981) which showed that they channel flow to an outlet area from where it is transmitted as shaft flow or vadose flow to the underground drainage network. Having made these assumptions the depressions contributing flow to the Cymru and Glenfield streams were identified, basin boundaries were delimited (Figures 12.6 and 12.7) and basin areas calculated as 9.54 and 38.05 ha respectively. Inputs to the two experimental basins were estimated from three autographic rain gauges (Figure 12.4) and streamflow output was monitored by sharp crested 90° V-notch weirs and autographic stage gauges (Figure 12.5). Measurements commenced on 1 February 1976 and continued for 14 months. As a check on the accuracy of the basin area and hydrometric measurements water balances were computed for the groundwater year 3 April 1976 to 2 April 1977, which was chosen so as to begin and end when water storage was at a minimum (Table 12.1). Potential evapotranspiration was computed using a version of the Thornthwaite (1954) formula recommended for use in New Zealand by Toebes (1968). Since soil moisture measurements indicated that moisture contents were >75% field capacity for most of the year it was assumed that actual evapotranspiration equalled the potential estimate. Change in storage was estimated from analysis of general basin recession curves. The imbalance in the Glenfield basin is extremely small (-7mm, Table 12.1), and although the imbalance in the Cymru basin is larger (+45mm) it is still within the potential measurement errors for precipitation and discharge data (± 7.5% and ± 5%). However it is thought that the imbalance may be due to actual evapotranspiration in the Cymru basin exceeding the Thornwaite estimate as has been observed in other forested basins in New Zealand (Ibbitt, 1971). These results suggest that the errors in the basin area, precipitation and discharge data are small, although the possibility of discrepancies in individual measurements being fortuitously complementary cannot be excluded.

Table 12.1 Water balance components

Component	Cymru Basin (9.54 ha)	Glenfield Basin (38.05 ha)
Rainfall (mm)	2366	2341
Runoff (mm)	1630	1650
Evapotranspiration (mm)	693	693
Change in storage[1] (mm)	+2	-5
Imbalance (mm and % of rainfall)	+45 (1.9%)	-7 (0.3%)

[1] From analysis of general basin recession curves

GENERAL DISCHARGE CHARACTERISTICS

As a basis for comparison of the three experimental basins their general discharge characteristics (Table 12.2) and flow duration curves (Figure 12.8) were computed. For consistency in separation of stormflow (quick flow) and delayed flow the time-based technique of Hewlett and Hibbert (1967) was used (Figure 12.9). Two response factors, Rp (the fraction of total precipitation yielded as stormflow) and Ry (the fraction of total yield which is stormflow), were computed (Table 12.2). The Cymru and Glenfield basins have similar mean discharges, minimum instantaneous discharges and runoff/rainfall ratios, but the Cymru basin has a somewhat higher discharge variability (30/70 ratio) and markedly higher maximum instantaneous discharge and stormflow yield, the latter being reflected in higher Rp and Ry ratios. Rainfall inputs to the Puriri basin are less than half those of the Waitomo basins, whilst evapotranspiration is approximately the same and this gives rise to lower runoff percentage, mean discharge and minimum instantaneous discharge. However, discharge variability (30/70 ratio) is much higher and Puriri also has higher Rp and Ry ratios indicating a greater production of stormflow per unit rainfall.

Table 12.2 General discharge characteristics

	Cymru Stream 3 Apr 1976 -	Glenfield Stream 2 Apr 1977	Puriri Stream 7 Jan 1979 - 16 Aug 1979
Mean discharge (l/s/ha)	0.52	0.52	0.15
Max. instantaneous discharge	9.41	3.26	7.47
Min. instantaneous discharge	0.13	0.13	0.01
Runoff/Rainfall (%)	68.9	70.5	39.5
30/70 Ratio[1]	2.7	2.5	8.4
Stormflow[2] (mm)	272.9	131.8	177.1
Delayed flow[2] (mm)	1357.4	1518.0	177.8
Response ratio[3] Rp(%)	11.5	5.6	19.7
Response ratio[3] Ry(%)	16.7	8.0	50.0

[1] Ratio of discharge equalled or exceeded 30% of time to that equalled or exceeded 70% of time

[2] Defined in table 12.3

[3] Defined in text (after Hewlett and Hibbert, 1967)

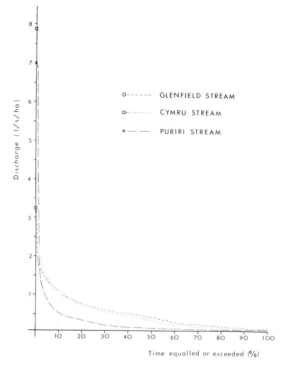

Figure 12.8   Flow duration curves

STORM HYDROGRAPH ANALYSIS

In small drainage basins the size and shape of storm hydrographs
are controlled by precipitation characteristics and runoff
generation mechanisms, and storm hydrograph analysis may therefore provide information on these mechanisms.   In particular it
has been suggested that the proportion of rainfall yielded as
stormflow during a single event provides an estimate of the proportion of the basin contributing to stormflow (Hewlett, 1974;
Harr, 1977).   Many hydrograph shape indices have been derived
for the traditional but inconsistent genetic methods of hydrograph separation (Linsley *et al.*, 1975), and several have been
redefined by Hewlett and Helvey (1970) and Cheng *et al.*, (1977)
to conform to the time-based separation technique (Figure 12.9;
Table 12.3).   These indices, together with the stormflow ratio
introduced by Gunn (1978), were adopted for the present study.
During the study periods there were 70 storm events yielding
more than 0.025 mm stormflow in the Cymru basin, 60 in the Glenfield basin and 33 in the Puriri basin.   The disparity between
the number of events in the two Waitomo basins is thought to be
due to minor rainfalls (<15mm) which can produce small but

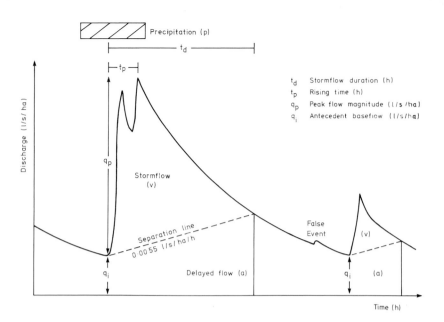

Figure 12.9   Hydrograph separation parameters (modified from Hewlett and Helvey, 1970); for parameter definitions see Table 12.3

significant amounts of stormflow from the Cymru basin (<1mm), but usually produce insignificant amounts (<0.025mm) in the Glenfield basin.

STORM HYDROGRAPH CHARACTERISTICS

Comparison of the storm hydrograph indices for the three basins (Table 12.4) yields the following results:

i) td (stormflow duration) and tp (time to peak).   All three basins have similar means and ranges.

ii) v (stormflow yield).   All three basins have similar ranges and although the mean at Puriri is higher than Cymru, which in turn is almost double Glenfield, the differences are non-significant (α = 0.05) due to the high standard deviations.

iii) qp (peakflow magnitude).   Puriri and Cymru have similar ranges and although the mean at Puriri is higher the difference is non-significant (α = 0.05).   However the range at Glenfield is much smaller and the mean is significantly lower than both Cymru (α = 0.05) and Puriri (α = 0.01).

iv) a (delayed flow during storm event).   Cymru and Glenfield have almost identical means and ranges but both means are significantly higher (α = 0.05) than the Puriri mean.

247

Table 12.3   Stormflow parameters used in the study

Parameter	Symbol and Unit of measurement	Definition
Rainfall amount	p, mm	The depth of gross rainfall during a storm that is considered to cause the stormflow event
Stormflow amount	v, mm	The streamflow volume that lies above the hydrograph separation line divided by the drainage basin area
Delayed flow	a, mm	The streamflow volume that lies below the hydrograph separation line divided by the drainage basin area
Stormflow duration	td, h	The time period from the initial hydrograph rise to when the hydrograph separation line intersects the falling limb of the hydrograph
Time to peak	tp, h	The time period from the initial hydrograph rise to the occurrence of the peak discharge
Antecedent base-flow	qi, l/s/ha	The discharge prior to the hydrograph rise caused by a rainstorm
Peak flow magnitude	qp, l/s/ha	The maximum instantaneous discharge during a stormflow event minus the antecedent baseflow
Hydrologic response ratio	rh	The ratio of stormflow amount to rainfall amount expressed as a percentage
Stormflow ratio	rv	The ratio of stormflow amount to total streamflow amount during the storm event, expressed as a percentage

v) qi (antecedent baseflow). The Glenfield mean is significantly higher than that of the Cymru basin ($\alpha = 0.05$) and both means are significantly higher than that of Puriri ($\alpha = 0.01$).

vi) rv (stormflow ratio). This proved to be the most discriminating index, as the means for all three basins differ significantly from each other ($\alpha = 0.01$).

The similarity of td and tp indicates that the autogenic inputs from closed depressions in the Waitomo basins are not significantly slower than the allogenic inputs to Puriri Cave from the two large stream-sinks. This emphasises the importance of closed depressions as sources of rapid recharge to limestone aquifers (Fox and Rushton, 1976; Gunn, 1983). The higher stormflow ratio and lower antecedent baseflow in the Puriri basin, together with the high degree of discharge variability shown by the 30/70 ratio (Table 12.2), are indicative of low storativity within the basin. This may be related to pedogenic conditions within the allogenic stream catchments as ironpans within the

248

Table 12.4 Statistics for storm hydrograph indices

Parameter[1]	Cymru Basin (n = 70)			Glenfield Basin (n = 60)			Puriri Basin (n = 33)		
	mean	s.d.	range	mean	s.d.	range	mean	s.d.	range
v	4.29	9.40	0.04 - 45.8	2.34	6.24	0.03 - 33.2	5.38	9.61	0.03 - 40.4
a	6.03	9.12	0.26 - 37.6	6.14	9.28	0.18 - 36.7	2.30	3.17	0.03 - 14.5
qp	0.91	1.50	0.04 - 8.0	0.37	0.57	0.04 - 3.0	1.51	2.33	0.04 - 7.3
qi	0.43	0.27	0.13 - 1.1	0.55	0.31	0.14 - 1.4	0.15	0.15	0.01 - 0.7
td	25.5	29.40	3.4 - 134.8	22.24	27.12	3.2 - 125.0	24.0	22.49	4.8 - 79.7
tp	6.5	9.88	1 - 55	5.8	8.74	1 - 58	7.4	10.10	1 - 57
rv	26.3	17.14	1.91 - 68.3	14.4	11.20	2.34 - 57.6	48.0	25.24	4.31 - 85.6

[1] For parameter definitions see Table 12.3

sand soils and heavy clay soils on the siltstone discourage percolation and encourage rapid runoff as overland flow or throughflow. Karstification of drainage in the lower part of the basin does not appear to have increased storage or to have changed the expected hydrological response. Hence it would be possible to infer from the discharge characteristics that the underground drainage is no more than 'a surface stream with a roof', even if speleological proof of this was not available. The higher storage in the Waitomo basins is a function of the greater thickness and permeability of superficial deposits and of the well developed subcutaneous zone (upper zone of weathered limestone) where water may be stored for at least 11 weeks (Gunn, 1981). However there are significant differences between the two basins as the forested Cymru basin has a more flashy response (higher qp, rv, v) and lower storage (qi) than Glenfield (pasture). These differences are the exact antithesis of those observed in surface basins when forest is removed (Hewlett and Helvey, 1970; Hornbeck, 1973), but they are still thought to be a consequence of human activities. When the Glenfield area was cleared of forest, soil and vegetal debris accumulated at the bottom of depressions and many outlets became partially blocked or constricted. Stormflow generated within these depressions takes longer to move from the basal outlet area to the underlying conduits than is the case where outlets are open. Visual evidence of this effect is provided by small ponds which develop in some affected depressions, particularly during intense or prolonged storms. An initial estimate of the delay caused by obstructions may be obtained by comparing the mean percentage stormflow yields of Cymru and Glenfield for different storm durations (Table 12.5). During relatively short duration storm events (<20 hours) a unit input of rainfall into Glenfield produces, on average, less than half the stormflow which would be yielded by the same input into Cymru basin. However, as storm duration increases so does relative yield, so that the average stormflow yield per unit input from Glenfield during longer duration events (>50 hours) is almost 80% of that from Cymru (Table 12.5). These results suggest that stormflow generated in depressions with obstructed outlets takes from approximately 20-50 hours longer than normal to reach the drainage basin outlet. As a consequence it only contributes to the basin stormflow response during longer events, and at other times the hydrograph rise and stormflow response is generated entirely within depressions with open outlet areas. Hewlett (1974) and Harr (1977) have suggested that rh also provides an estimate of the proportion of a drainage basin which contributes to stormflow. The mean value for Cymru is almost double that of Glenfield (Table 12.5), but rh rises with stormflow depth, and for events yielding over 1 mm stormflow the Glenfield percentage contributing area is 80% of that in the Cymru basin. This supports the hypothesis of a delayed response and further suggests that during small events obstruction of outlet reduces the efficiency of the Glenfield basin by almost 50%, whereas for larger events the reduction is only 20% as partially blocked depressions begin to contribute to stormflow. The overall increase in rh from 1.88-15.61 in Cymru and from 0.84-12.67 in Glenfield is probably due to a growth of contributing areas within closed depressions in a manner analagous to the variable source area (Hewlett and Hibbert, 1967) and dynamic contributing volume (Jones, 1979) concepts in 'normal' drainage basins.

Table 12.5   Hydrologic response ratio (rh) for different storm durations and stormflow yields

| Storm duration (h) | rh (%) | | rh Glenfield as a % |
	Cymru	Glenfield	of rh Cymru
<10	2.58	1.19	46.1
10 - 19.9	4.29	2.10	49.0
20 - 49.9	9.80	6.08	62.0
≥50	24.80	19.60	79.0
Stormflow amount (mm)			
<0.1	1.88	0.84	44.7
0.1 - 0.99	3.38	2.09	61.8
>1	15.61	12.67	81.2
All events	8.28	4.30	51.9

COMPARISONS WITH SURFACE BASINS

Although a comprehensive network of representative and experimental basins was established in New Zealand during the IHD (Toebes, 1965; Toebes and Morrissey, 1970) the only published data on storm hydrograph characteristics are contained in a review by Pearce and McKerchar (1979) which draws on earlier work by Pearce et al., (1976). Pearce and McKerchar (1979) were primarily concerned with the generation of storm runoff in nine drainage basins (Figure 12.1), none of which are located in areas of carbonate rocks. Their data permitted the computation of five indices: V, mean stormflow depth; V_{max}, the maximum stormflow depth from a single event; V_{min}, the minimum stormflow depth from a single event; Rp, total stormflow as a percentage of gross rainfall; and Ry, total stormflow as a percentage of total runoff. The results, and those for the three limestone basins described in the present study, have been tabulated in order of decreasing V (Table 12.6). It is apparent that the stormflow yield indices for the limestone basins lie within the range encountered on other lithologies. As expected, the Puriri basin lies at the upper end of this range and its Ry value in particular is exceeded by only one other basin. By way of contrast the more typically karstic Waitomo basins lie closer to the bottom of the range on account of their greater storage capacity. Pearce and McKerchar (1979) also examined the relationship between stormflow depth and the proportion of net rainfall yielded in rainfall for five basins and their data were used to compute rh values which may be compared to those for the Cymru and Glenfield basins (Table 12.7). The rh values suggest that the proportion of the

Table 12.6   Stormflow yields for 12 New Zealand drainage basins

Site	Area(ha)	Storm Events	$\bar{V}$ (mm)	V_{max} (mm)	V_{min} (mm)	Rp (%)	Ry (%)
* Hut Creek	22.1	62	18.2	167.0	1.0	32.8	49.5
* Maimai Basins (6)	1.6- 4.6	924	14.1	187.0	0.5	38.9	64.4
* Ngahere Basin	52.0	31	13.4	141.0	0.1	15.8	24.7
* Pukewaenga Basin	38.9	34	7.8	70.0	0.3	21.0	43.5
Puriri Basin	70.0	33	5.4	40.4	0.1	19.7	50.0
* Makara Basin 11	7.4	25	5.4	12.8	0.1	11.0	40.8
* Moutere Basin 5	7.0	23	4.8	28.5	0.1	9.9	39.8
* Manukau Basin	30.1	21	4.5	65.0	0.3	7.3	·20.0
Cymru Basin	9.5	70	4.3	45.8	0.1	11.6	16.8
* Big Bush Basins (4)	4.8-20.2	254	4.1	58.0	0.1	12.2	28.7
Glenfield Basin	38.1	60	2.3	33.2	0.1	5.5	7.7
* Purutaka Basin	22.5	4	1.7	3.5	0.7	0.4	1.7

* Source: Pearce and McKerchar (1979)
Hut Creek data relate only to events yielding >1mm stormflow

Table 12.7   Relationship between stormflow yield and proportion of gross storm rainfall in stormflow for 7 New Zealand drainage basins

Basin	Stormflow yield (mm)				
	0.1-0.99	1.0-4.99	5.0-14.99	15.0-29.99	30.0-59.99
	Mean proportion of gross storm rainfall yielded as storm flow (%)				
Pukewaenga*	10.6	23.8	34.3	48.3	
Hut Creek*		11.3	22.0	37.0	46.0
Maimai*	4.1	11.1	29.9	41.2	54.5
Cymru	3.4	8.1	18.0	26.8	38.2
Big Bush*	2.6	9.0	18.5	40.4	40.4
Moutere*	2.6	8.1	18.1	34.6	
Glenfield	2.1	7.9	13.5	27.0	30.4

* Source: Pearce and McKerchar (1979)

Cymru basin contributing to stormflow in low-medium yield events
(<15 mm stormflow) is similar to that in non-karst basins; but
for higher yield events the percentage contributing area is
somewhat smaller than in the non-karst basins. One possible
interpretation is that expansion of the stormflow contributing
area in closed depressions is initially rapid and then slows
down. This in turn may be related to subcutaneous flow which
appears to be transmitted less rapidly than overland flow and
saturated throughflow, but more rapidly than unsaturated throughflow and 'base flow'. Although obstruction of depression outlets
in Glenfield has reduced stormflow yields below those in the
natural Cymru basin the rh values do not differ markedly from
those of the surface basins, although they do lie outside the
observed ranges. Hence it may be concluded that the three
limestone basins are not anomalous but form part of a continuum
of natural hydrologic systems.

CONCLUSIONS

The small experimental basin approach and time-based hydrograph
separation techniques have been used to analyse the subterranean
streamflow characteristics of three New Zealand catchments. Two
of the basins studied (Cymru and Glenfield) are situated in an
area of polygonal karst where recharge is entirely autogenic.
The third (Puriri) lies in an area of fluviokarst where recharge
is primarily from allogenic streamsinks. Stormflow duration and
time to peak are similar in all three basins, emphasising the
rapidity with which polygonal karsts can respond to recharge
despite the absence of surface drainage. The fluviokarst basin
has higher mean stormflow yield, peakflow magnitude and stormflow ratio, but lower antecedent baseflow and delayed flow than
the polygonal karst basins. These differences are thought to
relate more to the near surface hillslope hydrology than to
conditions within the mass of limestone. Pedological conditions
in the Puriri basin encourage rapid runoff as overland flow and
throughflow and there is limited storage in the soil and non-
carbonate bedrock. By way of contrast the deeper, more permeable
soils and superficial deposits in the polygonal karst have a
greater storativity and the subcutaneous zone also provides an
important store. Stormflow generation mechanisms in karst depressions are still incompletely understood, but an initial
model may be proposed on the basis of storm hydrograph analysis
and previous research on depression hydrology (Gunn, 1981; 1983).
During short duration events and the initial stages of longer
events stormflow is generated close to depression outlet areas
where soil moisture contents are highest (Gunn and Trudgill,
1982; Figures 12.2 and 12.3), probably in the form of saturated
throughflow. As the storm progresses the saturated wedge expands upslope particularly along topographic lows which form
small valleys. Overland flow may be generated by return flow or
precipitation onto the saturated area. Subcutaneous flow may
also contribute to stormflow during larger events by a pulse
flow mechanism, although its average flow-through time in the
depressions studied is 2-10 weeks (Gunn, 1981). Once it reaches
the outlet area stormflow is channelled underground by vertical

shafts and then moves through solutionally enlarged conduits to the basin outlet. Hence the hydrological response of the polygonal karsts is a function of three factors: storm rainfall characteristics; stormflow generation mechanisms within depressions; and stormflow transmission to subterranean streams. The influence of the third factor is particularly apparent in the Glenfield area where obstruction of depression outlets during land clearance operations has reduced stormflow yields and peakflow magnitudes and increased delayed flow and antecedent baseflow.

The extent of the information gained by the hydrological studies, together with the broad similarities between the storm hydrograph characteristics of the karst basins and those of basins on non-carbonate rocks in New Zealand, supports the hypothesis that 'those karst systems in which vadose conduit flow predominates form part of a continuum of natural hydrological systems'. Systems with phreatic conduit flow may also lie within this continuum, and Atkinson (1977) has divided the hydrograph from Cheddar Spring, a phreatic rising in southwest England, into 'quickflow' and 'base flow' components using an arbitrary method rather than the time-based technique. Recognition that karst systems form part of a hydrological continuum should lead to a greater use by karst hydrologists of the concepts and techniques developed in drainage basin studies. It may also encourage a more balanced treatment of karst in hydrology and fluvial geomorphology texts, rather than the present situation where it is completely omitted from some texts (Ward, 1975; Dunne and Leopold, 1978) while in others the treatment is best described as 'cautious and usually inadequate' (Williams, 1978, p 260). However, it should also be noted that the more traditional techniques of groundwater hydrology may still be of use in some karsts, particularly where flow is more diffuse in narrow fissures or through primary pores.

Finally, it is hoped that the present study will provide a stimulus for further work on the storm hydrograph characteristics of karst systems, and that this will both complement the detailed work which has been undertaken on recession curves (Mangin, 1975; Bakalowicz and Mangin, 1980) and also lead to more realistic mathematical models such as those of Dreiss (1982; 1983).

Acknowledgements

The research which forms the basis of this paper was undertaken while the authors were Ph.D. (J.G.) and M.A. (B.T.) students at the University of Auckland and we gratefully acknowledge the support and guidance of our supervisor, Professor P.W. Williams. Thanks are also due to the Association of Commonwealth Universities for providing J.G. with a Commonwealth Scholarship and to Catherine Gunn for drawing the figures.

REFERENCES

Atkinson, T.C. 1977. Diffuse flow and conduit flow in limestone terrain in the Mendip Hills, Somerset (Great Britain). *Journal of Hydrology,* 35, 93-110.

Atkinson, T.C. and Drew, D.P. 1974. Underground drainage of limestone catchments in the Mendip Hills. In: *Fluvial Processes in Instrumented Watersheds,* eds. K.J. Gregory and D.E. Walling, (London: Institute of British Geographers, Special Publication, 6), 87-106.

Bakalowicz, M. and Mangin, A. 1980. L'aquifère karstique. Sa définition, ses caractéristiques et son identification. *Mem. h. ser. Soc. Geol. France,* 11, 71-79.

Barrett, P.J. 1967. Te Kuiti Group in the Waitomo - Te Anga Area. *New Zealand J. Geol. Geophys.,* 10(4), 1009-1026.

Cheng, J.D., Black, T.A. and Willington, R.P. 1977. The stormflow characteristics of a small, steep and forested watershed in the Coast Mountains of south-western British Columbia. *Proc. Canadian Hydrol. Symp., Edmonton,* 300-310.

Dreiss, S.J. 1982. Linear kernels for karst aquifers. *Water Resources Research,* 18(4), 865-876.

Dreiss, S.J. 1983. Linear unit-response functions as indicators of recharge areas for large karst springs. *Journal of Hydrology,* 61(1/3), 31-44.

Dunne, T.D. and Leopold, L.B. 1978. *Water in Environmental Planning,* (San Francisco: Freeman), 818pp.

Fox, I.A. and Rushton, K.R. 1976. Rapid recharge in a limestone aquifer. *Groundwater,* 14(1), 21-27.

Gibbs, H.S., 1968. Volcanic-ash soils in New Zealand. *DSIR Inform. Ser.,* 65.

Gregory, K.J. 1974. Streamflow and building activity. In: *Fluvial Processes in Instrumented Watersheds,* eds. K.J. Gregory and D.E. Walling, (London: Institute of British Geographers, Special Publication, 6), 107-122.

Gunn, J. 1978. *Karst hydrology and solution in the Waitomo District, New Zealand.* Unpublished Ph.D. thesis, University of Auckland.

Gunn, J. 1979. Caves and shafts on Stubbs Farm, Waitomo. *New Zealand Speleological Bulletin,* 6, 221-237.

Gunn, J. 1981. Hydrological processes in karst depressions. *Z. Geomorph. N.F.,* 25(3), 313-331.

Gunn, J. 1982. Water tracing in Ireland. A review with special reference to the Cuilcagh karst. *Irish Geography,* 15, 94-106.

Gunn, J. 1983. Point-recharge of limestone aquifers - a model from New Zealand karst. *Journal of Hydrology,* 61(1/3), 19-29.

Gunn, J. and Trudgill, S.T. 1982. Carbon dioxide production and concentrations in the soil atmosphere: A case study from New Zealand volcanic ash soils. *Catena*, 9(1/2), 81-94.

Harr, R.D. 1977. Water flux in soil and subsoil on a steep forested slope. *Journal of Hydrology*, 33(1), 37-58.

Hess, J.W. and White, W.B. 1974. Hydrograph analysis of carbonate aquifers. *Penn. State Univ. Inst. for Res. on Land and Water Resources, Res. Publ.*, 83.

Hewlett, J.D. 1974. Comments on letters relating to 'Role of subsurface flow in generating surface runoff, 2, Upstream source areas' *Water Resources Res.*, 10(3), 605-606.

Hewlett, J.D. and Helvey, J.D. 1970. Effects of forest clear-felling on the storm hydrograph. *Water Resources Res.*, 6(3), 768-782.

Hewlett, J.D. and Hibbert, A.R. 1967. Factors affecting the response of small watersheds to precipitation in humid areas. In: *Forest Hydrology*, eds. W.E. Sopper and H.W. Lull, (Pergamon, Oxford), 275-290.

Hobson, D. 1976. The Waitomo Caves dossier. *New Zealand Speleological Bulletin*, 5(100), 585-621.

Holloway, J.T. 1959. Pre-European vegetation in New Zealand. In: *A Descriptive Atlas of New Zealand*, ed. A.H. McLintock, (Wellington: Government Printer), 23-25.

Hornbeck, J.W. 1973. Storm flow from hardwood forested and cleared watersheds in New Hampshire. *Water Resources Research*, 9(2), 346-354.

Ibbitt, R.P. 1971. Development of a conceptual model of infiltration. *N.Z. Min. of Works, Hydrol. Res. Prog., Report 5*.

Jennings, J.N. 1967. Some karst areas of Australia. In: *Landform Studies from Australia and New Guinea*, eds. J.N. Jennings and J.A. Mabbutt, (Canberra: A.N.U. Press), 256-292.

Jennings, J.N. 1971. *Karst*. (Canberra: A.N.U. Press), 252pp.

Jones, J.A.A. 1979. Extending the Hewlett model of stream runoff generation. *Area*, 11(2), 110-114.

Linsley, R.K., Kohler, M.A. and Paulus, J.L.H. 1975. *Hydrology for engineers*, 2nd Edition, (New York: McGraw-Hill).

Mangin, A. 1975. Contribution a l'etude hydrodynamique des aquifères karstiques. Thèse Doct. *Annales de Spéléologie*, 29(3), 283-332; 29(4), 495-601; 30(1), 21-124.

Nelson, C.S. 1973. *Stratigraphy and sedimentology of the Te Kuiti Group in Waitomo County, South Auckland*. Unpublished Ph.D. thesis, University of Auckland.

Nelson, C.S. and Hume, T.M. 1977. Relative intensity of tectonic events revealed by the Tertiary sedimentary record in the North Wanganui Basin and adjacent areas, New Zealand. *New Zealand J. Geol. Geophys.*, 20(2), 369-392.

Newson, M.D. 1972. Merits of a hydrological bias to karst erosion studies. *Trans. Cave Res. Grp.*, 14(2), 118-124.

Pain, C.F. 1975. Some tephra deposits in the south-west Waikato area, North Island, New Zealand. *New Zealand J. Geol. Geophys.*, **18(4)**, 541-550.

Pearce, A.J. and McKerchar, A.J. 1979. Upstream generation of storm runoff. In: *Physical Hydrology - New Zealand Experience.* eds. D.L. Murray and P. Ackroyd, (New Zealand Hydrological Society, Wellington), 165-192.

Pearce, A.J., O'Loughlin, C.L. and Rowe, L.K. 1976. Hydrologic regime of small, undisturbed beech forest catchments, north Westland. *Proc. Soil & Plant Water Symp., D.S.I.R. Inf. Ser.,* **126**, 150-158.

Quinlan, J.F. and Rowe, D.R. 1977. Review of the physical hydrology of the Central Kentucky karst. In: *Hydrologic problems in karst regions,* eds. R.R. Dilamarter and S.C. Csallany, (Bowling Green: Western Kentucky University Press), 50-63.

Rodgers, L.A. and Grant-Mackie, J.A. 1978. *Aspects of the geology of the Port Waikato Region,* (Geology Department University of Auckland).

Smith, D.I., Atkinson, T.C. and Drew, D.P. 1976. The hydrology of limestone terrains. In: *The Science of Speleology,* eds. T.D. Ford and C.H.D. Cullingford, (London: Academic Press), 179-212.

Smith, D.I. and Newson, M.D. 1974. The dynamics of solutional and mechanical erosions in limestone catchments on the Mendip Hills, Somerset. In: *Fluvial Processes in Instrumented Watersheds,* eds. K.J. Gregory and D.E. Walling, (London: Institute of British Geographers, Special Publication, 6, 155-167.

Taylor, C.H. 1982. The effect on storm runoff response of seasonal variations in contributing zones in small watersheds. *Nordic Hydrology,* **13**, 165-182.

Thornthwaite, C.W. 1954. A re-examination of the concept and measurement of potential evapotranspiration. *Publ. in Climatology,* **7**.

Toebes, C. 1965. The planning of representative and experimental basin networks in New Zealand. *Int. Assn. of Sci. Hydrol., Symp. of Budapest, Publ.* 66.

Toebes, C. 1968. Computation of the potential evapotranspiration by the Thornthwaite method. *N.Z. Min. of Works, Handbook of hydrol. proc.,* 14.

Toebes, C. and Morrissey, W.B., 1970. Representative basins of New Zealand. *N.Z. Min. of Works, Misc. Hydrol. Publ.,* **7**.

Turnpenny, B.W. 1979. *Temporal variations in stream solute concentrations.* Unpublished M.A. thesis, University of Auckland.

Walling, D.E. 1971. Streamflow from instrumented catchments in south-east Devon. In: *Exeter essays in geography,* eds. K.J. Gregory and W.L.D. Ravenhill, (Exeter: University of Exeter Press), 55-81.

Ward, R.C. 1971. Small watershed experiments. *Hull University Occasional Publications in Geography,* **18**.

Ward, R.C. 1975. *Principles of hydrology,* 2nd Edition, (London: McGraw Hill).

Ward, W.T. 1967. Volcanic ash beds of the lower Waikato basin, North Island, New Zealand. *New Zealand J. Geol. Geophys.,* **10**, 1109–1135.

Ward, W.T. 1972. Pleistocene ash in the Waikato basin. *New Zealand J. Geol. Geophys.,* **15**, 678–685.

Warwick, G.T. 1976. Geomorphology and Caves. In: *The Science of Speleology,* eds. T.D. Ford and C.H.D. Cullingford, (London: Academic Press), 61–125.

Waterhouse, B.C. 1974. Type and standard localities, Papakura Limestone. *New Zealand J. Geol. Geophys.,* **17**, 487–490.

Williams, P.W. 1978. Interpretations of Australasian Karsts. In: *Landform evolution in Australasia,* eds. J.C. Davies and M.A.J. Williams, (Canberra: ANU Press), 259–286.

Williams, P.W. 1982. Karst in New Zealand. In: *Landforms of New Zealand,* eds. J. Soons and M.J. Selby, (Auckland: Longman Paul), 105–126.

13

Groundwater flow in the lowland limestone aquifer of eastern Co. Galway and eastern Co. Mayo, western Ireland

C. Coxon and D.P. Drew

SUMMARY

The western part of the central lowland of Ireland in eastern County Galway, eastern County Mayo and County Roscommon, is an area of sub-dued topography rarely rising over 60 m a.s.l. It is underlain by Carboniferous limestone mantled with varying thicknesses of glacial and fluvioglacial material. The landforms are in part of glacial origin and in part karstic, and include many turloughs (seasonal lakes). Techniques from karst hydrology (e.g. dye tracing) and from conventional geohydrology (e.g. water table mapping from borehole data) have been used in the area. These have demonstrated that the groundwater hydrology is intermediate in type between a non-karstic diffuse flow aquifer, and the conduit dominated groundwater flow system characteristic of most karstic terrains.

RÉSUMÉ

La partie occidentale des pays-bas de l'Irlande Centrale (l'est du Comté de Galway, l'est de celui de Mayo et celui de Roscommon) est une région au relief peu élevé où les sommets atteignent rarement une soixantaine de mètres. Les calcaires carbonifères sous-jacents sont recouverts par des dépôts glaciaires et fluvio-glaciaires. La morphologie est en partie d'origine glaciaire et en partie d'origine karstique, et possède de nombreuses mares temporaires ('turloughs'). Les techniques de l'hydrologie karstique (tracage par colorants) et de l'hydrologie conventionnelle (cartographie de la nappe phréatique à partir des forages) ont été utilisés dans cette région. Elles nous ont montré que l'hydrologie souterraine se compose d'un système intermédiaire entre des aquifères perméables et des aquifères per-méables en grand qui caractérisent la plupart des terrains karstiques.

INTRODUCTION

The western part of the central lowland of Ireland, including parts of Counties Galway, Mayo and Roscommon, is underlain by a partly karstified aquifer of Carboniferous limestone. Over an area of some 2500 km^2 drainage is partly or wholly subterranean. The dominant landforms are those resulting from glaciation; karstic features being confined to sinkholes, springs, closed depressions and caves, none of these being noticeable elements of the landscape. Thus, unlike other lowland karsts such as those of the Yucutan, Nullabor or Indiana, all of which exhibit distinctive karstic landforms, the limestone lowland of western Ireland is karstic only if the term is defined hydrologically.

It may be that the absence of distinctive karstic landforms is due to the glacial derangement of drainage and the mantle of drift resulting from glaciation. Williams (1970) and Mitchell (1980), suggest that an ancient, possibly Tertiary, karst landscape was partially obliterated by Pleistocene processes.

The nature of the area and of surface-groundwater interaction is such that neither the conventional techniques of karst hydrology nor non-carbonate rock groundwater investigation by themselves yield a full understanding of hydrological processes. Therefore, relevant techniques from both approaches have been applied to the study of the area.

GEOLOGY AND GEOMORPHOLOGY OF THE WESTERN LOWLANDS

The area described in this paper is shown in Figure 13.1. To the west are the large lakes of Corrib and Mask and the outcrop of non-calcareous rocks. To the east, karstification decreases as the cover of drift and raised bog increases. Much of the area lies between 0 and 60 m a.s.l. and has a subdued topography dominated by the landforms of glacial and fluvioglacial deposition, particularly eskers and kames. Areas of marsh and raised bog occur between esker ridges. In areas of thinner drift, particularly close to the major lakes, limestone scarps up to 20 m high occur, as do areas of limestone pavement.

Although the glacial drift of the area is derived entirely from carbonate rocks, its texture varies from the coarse sands and gravels of eskers and kames to compact clay-rich lodgement till. The area is underlain by highly fractured sub-horizontal Carboniferous limestones. To the east and north the limestones become less pure and limited information from borehole yields suggests that secondary permeability declines accordingly.

Drainage in the southern part of the area is directly to the Atlantic Ocean (Galway Bay), but further north Loughs Mask and Corrib function as local base levels.

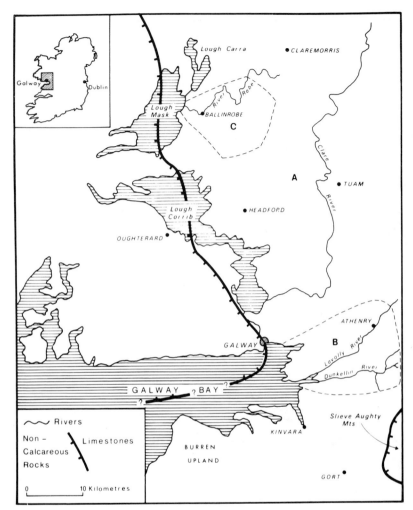

Figure 13.1   The location of the study area within western
Ireland showing the case study areas: (A) mid
River Clare basin, (B) Dunkellin - Lavally
catchments, (C) Hollymount area. Inset, Ireland,
showing the location of the study area

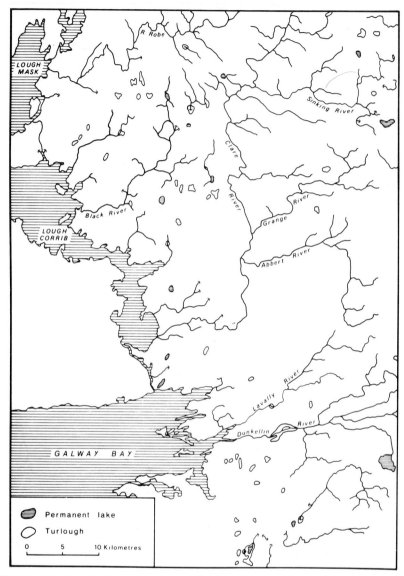

Figure 13.2a   Surface water hydrology of the study area.
                (a) Present day drainage patterns and active
                turloughs

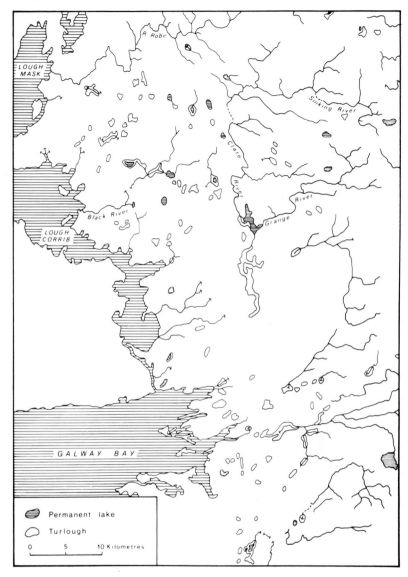

Figure 13.2b   Surface water hydrology of the study area.
              (b) The probable drainage pattern and
              distribution of turloughs prior to arterial
              drainage in the nineteenth century

263

HYDROLOGY OF THE WESTERN LOWLANDS

Surface water

Surface drainage is almost absent from the south of the area between Gort and Kinvara. Streams originating on the Devonian rocks of the Slieve Aughty Mountains sink at or near the limestone contact, to reappear at the intertidal springs of Kinvara. Northeast of Galway City the catchment of the Clare River which drains into Lough Corrib, includes much of the central area of the western lowlands, whilst to the north and south are the smaller basins of the Rivers Robe and Dunkellin-Lavally respectively. However, even within this north-central area are extensive zones which lack integrated surface drainage, for example the area east of Galway (c. 300 km²) and south of Ballinrobe (c. 200 km²).

The present day drainage network (Figure 13.2a) is to some extent a manmade rather than a natural system: the product of successive schemes of arterial drainage designed to reduce winter flooding of agricultural land in the region. Figure 13.2b is an attempt to reconstruct the pattern of drainage in the area prior to the initiation of arterial drainage in the early 19th century. Such a map is necessarily of uncertain accuracy due to the lack of documentary and cartographic evidence. However it is certain that few of the major rivers of the area had a natural outfall to the sea or the lakes. Much of the stream network shown in Figure 13.2a is a storm runoff system and is inactive during summer baseflow periods.

Groundwater

The limestones of the western lowland form an aquifer of highly variable productivity, as is indicated by borehole yields which range from zero to 1500 m³/day. Recharge to this aquifer has three components:

i) Direct recharge of precipitation, particularly in areas underlain by coarse textured regolith.

ii) Sinking streams, of which more than 100 are known in the area. However, these sinking streams are largely ephemeral and their flow rarely exceeds 50 litres/sec. Hence they do not comprise a significant proportion of total recharge.

iii) Line recharge from the beds of the major rivers. Several of the rivers of the area are seasonally influent over short, well-defined reaches. For example the Clare River loses some 20% of its flow in a 0.5 km reach in summer, whilst the tributary Sinking River loses 80% of its water over a similar distance. In some instances (the Lavally and Dunkellin rivers for example) the entire flow sinks through the river bed leaving the downstream section of channel dry.

Under winter conditions the major rivers of the area are effluent, but in summer discharge of groundwater is confined to springs which occur in two distinct environments. First are the intertidal or submarine resurgences (for example at Kinvara) along the eastern and southern shores of Galway Bay. Second are a series of springs which are located some distance inland, commonly at the edges of boggy areas or at the foot of limestone scarps. It may be that this latter group are associated with former higher water levels in Loughs Corrib and Mask.

A further groundwater phenomenon, though one that manifests itself as a landform, is the turlough or seasonal lake. Turloughs are shallow hollows up to 5 km² in area, which become lakes for 5-11 months of the year but are dry for the remainder of the time. Hydrologically, turloughs behave in a manner similar to that of poljes (Gams, 1978) and may contain discrete sinkholes and springs, or may fill and empty via estavella. However there is no evidence that they bear any genetic resemblance to poljes. Some turloughs, for example the Rahasane Turlough on the course of the Dunkellin River, function solely as stream sinks and contain no springs, although morphologically they are indistinguishable from turloughs with springs or estavella.

Originally there were a large number of turloughs in the area under consideration (Figure 13.2b), but drainage schemes have greatly reduced the number that retain their natural hydrological characteristics.

An example of the groundwater hydrology of the area and its interaction with surface water is given in Figure 13.3 (Drew, 1976) for the central part of the Clare River basin. The data were obtained by field mapping, water tracing and by discharge measurement over a two-year period. The lack of accordance between surface and groundwater flow patterns is apparent. Groundwater flow is dominantly east to west linking separate river basins, as for example the Clare River and Black River. Underground flow rates are within the range 10-65 m/hour and are localized within zones of relatively high permeability. True cavernous groundwater flow is not known from the area shown in Figure 13.3 but occurs in the areas immediately to the north and south.

THE CASE STUDIES

Introduction

Two smaller areas within the western limestone lowlands have been studied in greater detail. Their location is shown in Figure 13.1. The first area (referred to as the Lavally-Dunkellin area) lies to the east of Galway Bay, and covers approximately 180 km². The second area (referred to as the Hollymount area) lies to the east of Lough Mask, and to the south of the Robe river, and covers approximately 150 km².

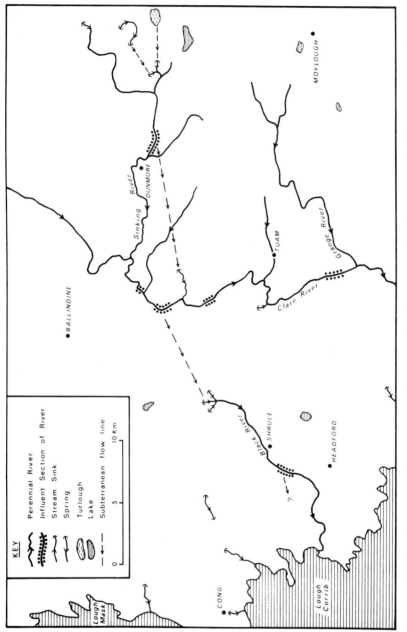

Figure 13.3   Surface water – groundwater relationships in the area of the western central lowland adjacent to Lough Corrib

The two areas are thought to represent different aspects of the hydrology of the western lowlands. Both are areas of gently undulating land, containing several turloughs, with springs at the periphery, but the Lavally-Dunkellin area contains rivers which are largely the creation on the 19th century drainage engineers, whereas the Hollymount area is devoid of surface rivers.

Both areas have been studied using techniques from both karst hydrology and traditional geohydrology. The information obtained from these approaches is discussed below.

The Lavally-Dunkellin area

Prior to arterial drainage both the Lavally and Dunkellin rivers sank underground some distance from the sea. During the 19th century the channels were extended downstream of the sinks to the sea at Galway Bay, and thus the lower sections of the streamcourses are artificial. Groundwater recharge occurs from the influent beds of the rivers and also by direct infiltration of precipitation. However aquifer discharge, particularly in the summer, is localized at a series of coastal springs (Figure 13.4) indicating a degree of concentration of groundwater flow.

Figure 13.5 shows groundwater contours over the area under high (winter) and low (summer) water conditions. The lack of accord between groundwater patterns and surface channels is apparent. Even under winter conditions direct groundwater-surface water interaction is apparent only in the upper (natural) part of the river channels.

Figure 13.4 shows groundwater flowlines constructed according to conventional hydrogeological practice from the water-table maps (Figure 13.5). Predictably, the flow lines converge on the major springs but the pattern of flow suggests that the magnitude of groundwater flux is unequal over the area. Narrow (0.5-1.0 km wide) bands of concentrated flow exist presumably corresponding to zones of very high permeability. One such zone occurs to the north of the Dunkellin River, close to the surface water divide between the Dunkellin and Lavally rivers. The existence of such channels of high transmissivity is supported by the results of water tracing in the area by Drew (1984) which indicated little lateral diffusion of tracer between input and output.

Thus the pattern of groundwater flow in these catchments may be considered as transitional between that in a non-karstic fissured aquifer and that typical of fully karstified aquifers. Although a coherent watertable surface does exist and true conduit, direct input-to-output flow is absent, the high degree of anisotropy and heterogeneity of permeability indicated by the flow patterns is characteristic of karstified carbonate aquifers.

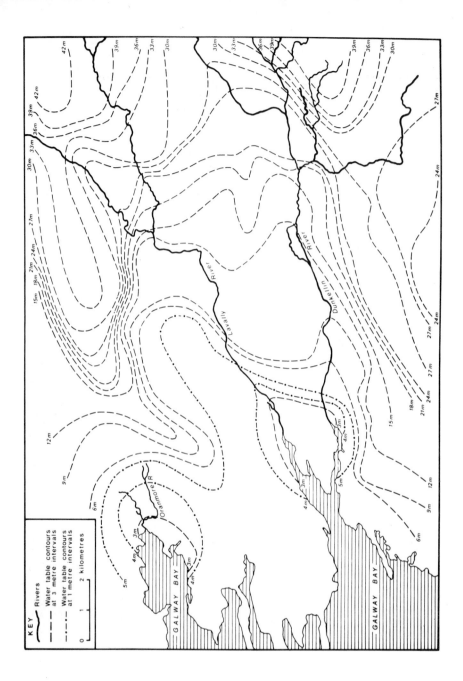

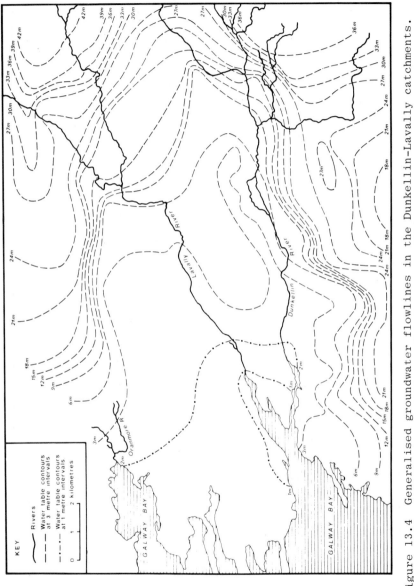

Figure 13.4   Generalised groundwater flowlines in the Dunkellin-Lavally catchments. (a) Winter conditions, (b) Summer conditions

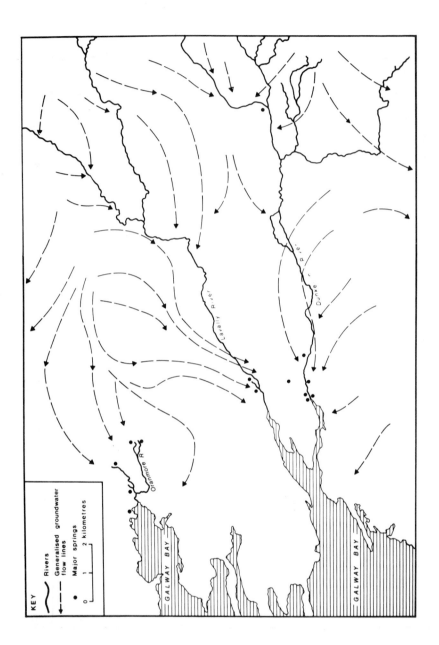

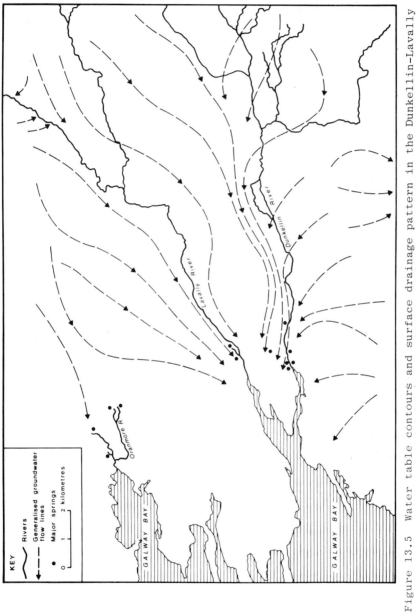

Figure 13.5   Water table contours and surface drainage pattern in the Dunkellin-Lavally catchments: (a) Winter conditions (b) Summer conditions

The Hollymount area

Introduction This area lies mainly between 30 and 50 m a.s.l.
The drift cover is very variable: in the east, where there are
drumlinoid features, it is at least 20 m thick, while in some
places it is absent, and patches of limestone pavement occur.

The natural hydrological features of the area are shown on
Figure 13.6. The most noticeable features are the turloughs:
in an area of approximately 150 km^2, there are 12 turloughs which
have an area greater than 10 ha, the largest one being approximately 150 ha in area. A series of risings around the edge of
the area discharge into the Robe River, and Loughs Mask and
Corrib. In addition, two permanent risings (Cregduff and Fountainhill) occur in the two largest turloughs. The water from
each of these formerly sank at the far end of the respective
turlough, but the Cregduff turlough is now linked with the Robe
by an artificial channel, and the Fountainhill turlough is
similarly linked with Cross risings, so that now only some of
the flow from the risings sinks at the swallow holes.

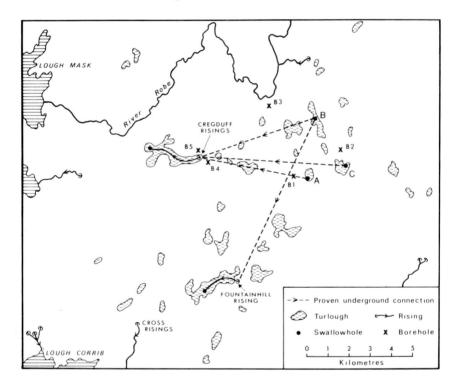

Figure 13.6   Natural hydrology of the Hollymount study area,
showing the results of water tracing experiments

Some of the other turloughs in the area have also been affected by drainage schemes, particularly those in the southern half of the area, which have been linked with the Cross risings by a drainage channel, cut 8 m deep in places (this channel is shown on Figure 13.2a). However, the northern part of the area, on which the present study concentrates, is as yet largely un-affected by drainage attempts, and in the 30 km^2 area to the east of Cregduff risings, active turloughs cover 160 ha (i.e. 5% of the area). These turloughs fill and empty mainly by estavella; they flood within about a week, usually in October, and empty more gradually, the majority being dry usually by the end of June.

Water tracing experiments The absence of sinking rivers in the Hollymount area means that the only opportunity for water tracing is provided by the turloughs, which can generally be traced in early summer, when water levels fall sufficiently low to enable tracers to be added to the water flowing down the swallow hole.

Three turloughs in the area have been traced – these are shown on Figure 13.6. The results of the traces are summarised in Table 13.1.

Table 13.1   Summarised results of water tracing in the Hollymount area

Input	turlough A	turlough B	turlough C
Output	Cregduff risings	Cregduff risings	Cregduff risings
Tracer (weight)	Na fluorescein (7 kg)	Leucophor P.B.S. (4.5 kg)	Na fluorescein (10 kg)
Conc. at output	10^{-5} g/l	? (cottonwool detectors)	$>10^{-2}$ g/l
Average linear velocity	5-10 m/hr	47-123 m/hr	79-103 m/hr
Flow conditions	low (August 1982)	high (May 1983)	medium (June 1983)

The emergence of dye from turlough A at Cregduff in a pro-longed wave in very low concentrations – the peak of 10^{-5} g/l was not reached until 40 days after input – suggests the possi-bility of dispersed fissure flow. The velocity is of the same order of magnitude as that quoted for fissure flow in the East Yorkshire Chalk by Foster and Milton (1974). However, it should be noted that such low velocities have also been found in true karst conduit systems under very low flow conditions (Stanton and Smart, 1981), and that this trace was carried out under such conditions.

The traces from the other two turloughs to Cregduff pro-duced velocities which are an order of magnitude greater than that from turlough A. It can also be seen from Table 13.1 that the dye from turlough C produced a much greater peak concentra-tion than that from turlough A. Thus the results from the second two traces are more characteristic of flow in typical karst areas such as the Mendip Hills, or the White Limestone in Jamaica (Smith *et al.*, 1976), or of concentrated flow in solutionally widened fissures in the Chalk (Atkinson and Smith, 1974).

A small amount of the tracer from turlough B was picked up on cottonwool detectors at Fountainhill rising (see Figure 13.6), between 9 and 14 days after input (linear velocity = 24-37 m/hr): the significance of this is discussed later. The absence of any fluorescence on detectors at two other risings over this period, and at Fountainhill rising for two months subsequently, makes it improbable that the fluorescence here was due to a background source.

Application of conventional geohydrological techniques   Water levels in 30-35 boreholes in the area were measured on 12 occasions over one year, and an attempt was made to draw water-table contours using these data. It was found to be impossible to draw contours which accommodated all of the boreholes. In some cases, the 'misfit' points (about 15% of the total) were due to drawdown from pumping for water supply, and in other cases they were low-yielding wells, implying that they were located in zones of low permeability. If these 'misfit' points were ignored, generalised contours could be drawn.

The pattern of contours is reasonably constant throughout the year. Figure 13.7 shows the maps for December 1982 and May 1983. It can be seen that a feature of both maps is the trough running westwards across the area, implying a convergence of flow lines on Cregduff. The trough appears to have a northern and southern branch, suggesting the presence of two main flow lines.

The maps were drawn without reference to the turlough water levels, so it is of interest to note that the water levels in the main turloughs in the area, which are shown on the maps, coincide roughly with the groundwater table as indicated by the boreholes.

A continuous record of water levels from four boreholes in the area is shown in Figure 13.8 (the location of the boreholes is shown in Figure 13.6). It can be seen that the response of each borehole to rainfall is different, both in magnitude and in sensitivity to individual rainfall events. This is thought to be partly due to the variable drift cover. For example, B1 has virtually no drift cover, and responds to every rainfall event, whereas B2 has 21 m of glacial drift, which presumably buffers out some of the minor fluctuations. However, it is also thought to reflect the great variability of the aquifer itself in terms of transmissivity and storativity, seen for example in the great difference in behaviour between B1 and B4 (both with thin drift cover). Caliper logging of these boreholes was carried out. This is a method used by geohydrologists to determine the degree of fissuring, and thus estimate the permeability (Parizek and Siddiqui, 1970). The caliper logs of these nominally 15 cm diameter boreholes showed that B1 had no notable fissures, its diameter varying between 15 and 17 cm, while at the base of

274

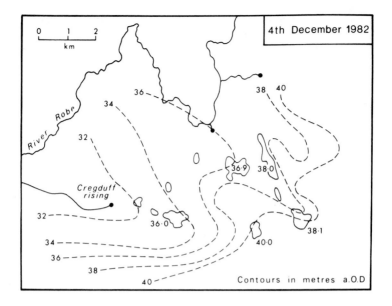

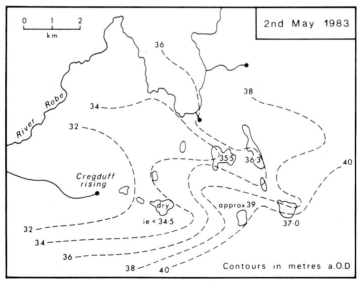

Figure 13.7   Watertable contours in the Hollymount area.
(a) December 1982, (b) May 1983

275

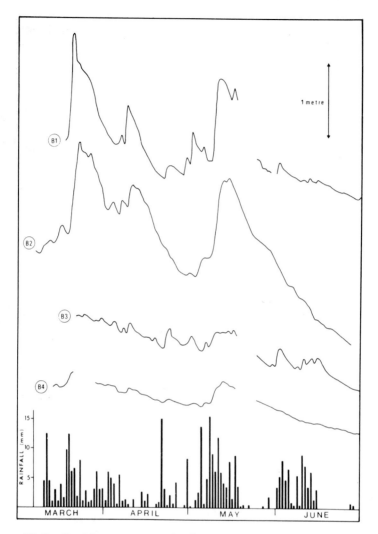

Figure 13.8 Continuous record of water levels in four boreholes
in the Hollymount area, from 1 March to 30 June
1983, and daily rainfall for the same period

B4 (24 m below the ground surface) the diameter increased to
>65 cm. Pump tests were also carried out on the boreholes;
again a traditional method in geohydrology, to calculate the
permeability of the aquifer. Because this aquifer does not conform to the ideal conditions assumed, the figures obtained cannot
be taken as exact, but they can be used for comparative purposes.
Thus, the estimates of specific capacity obtained, less than 48
litres/hr/m of drawdown for B1, and c. 10 000 litres/hr/m for B4,
imply a great difference in permeability.

Thus, the much more subdued response to rainfall of B4, seen on Figure 13.8, reflects the fact that it is in a much more permeable area than B1. It can be seen from Figure 13.6 that it is located near to Cregduff risings, and is presumably in the zone of higher permeability running towards Cregduff implied by the watertable maps. The narrowness, or discontinuous nature of this zone, and the great spatial variability of permeability implied by the differing yields of B1 and B4, is further illustrated by the presence of an 83 m deep borehole (B5 on Figure 13.6). It is north of Cregduff risings, less than 1 km from B4, and is reported to have gone dry after only 360 litres was pumped out, implying an even lower permeability than at B1.

The indication from the caliper log of B4 that water enters at 24 m below the ground surface (while the water level in the borehole is 3-4 m below the ground surface) implies that at this point the aquifer is confined by overlying layers of more massive rock. Well drillers' reports from other wells in the area suggest that several areas are confined in this way - or possibly in some cases by glacial drift. Thus the permeability of the rock varies vertically as well as horizontally, from very high to virtually zero.

Discussion The study methods described above employ the techniques of karst hydrology and conventional geohydrology respectively, so it is of interest to see how the information obtained compares.

Examination of the May watertable map shows that the flow lines implied by the contours (following the normal assumptions of groundwater mapping) would all converge on Cregduff, which corresponds well with the arrival of dye from all three traces at this rising. However, the arrival of a small amount of tracer at Fountainhill rising from turlough B, which was mentioned above, is not so easily accounted for, as the generalised contours would suggest that it was impossible for any water to flow in this direction. This implies that the watertable map as drawn is to some degree incorrect. Either the interpolation between the data points is inaccurate, or alternatively the watertable is much more discontinuous than the maps imply, and an almost infinite number of data points would be required to illustrate its actual configuration.

The fact that there are 'misfit' points which were ignored in drawing the maps, at least some of which are not due to pumping for water supply, suggests that the watertable is at least partly discontinuous. The other borehole data presented above, which provide evidence of great variation in permeability both laterally and vertically, bear out this idea. Thus, the implication is that the aquifer has a degree of anistropy and heterogeneity more characteristic of a karstic aquifer than a non-karstic fissure flow aquifer.

CONCLUSIONS

From the above evidence, a number of general conclusions about the hydrology of the western Irish limestone lowlands can be drawn. There is evidence for the presence of a watertable, to a greater extent than in most karst areas. However, it appears to be to some degree discontinuous, and is certainly more irregular than, for example, that of a chalk aquifer. The range of groundwater flow velocities obtained from water tracing, is approximately between 5 and 120 m/hr. It is uncertain whether the lowest velocities observed imply dispersed fissure flow, but the higher velocities must indicate a concentration of flow, at least in a network of widened fissures, if not in true caverns. Evidence for narrow zones of concentrated flow is also provided by the watertable maps; while borehole data show the extreme variability of permeability over short distances both laterally and vertically. Where an artificial surface drainage network has been superimposed on the natural pattern of turloughs and risings, the surface and groundwater flows are generally unrelated, and the catchments may not correspond at all.

Thus, although the surface features of the area are largely non-karstic (being glacial depositional forms, and artificial drainage networks), the underground flow system is at least semi-karstic, being highly anisotropic, with narrow zones of concentrated flow, and concentrated outputs (i.e. springs).

However, the extent to which the hydrology of the area can be understood is dependent on the reliability and relevance of the evidence which the techniques used provide. The water tracing techniques provide unambiguous data concerning discrete input to output flow routes, but yield no information about the behaviour of diffuse recharge water. In addition, it is not known whether turloughs (the tracer input sites) are simply 'windows' into groundwater flow, or whether they represent atypical groundwater-surface water conditions. Thus under these circumstances, water tracing may be near the limits of its validity as a technique.

Conventional groundwater techniques, such as pump testing of boreholes, and borehole logging, provide a useful indication of the great and highly localised variations in permeability of the limestone, and in the Hollymount area they correlate well with the results of water tracing. However, it is not possible to quantify permeability and storativity with any degree of confidence using the commonly accepted methods.

Discrepancies between groundwater flow paths predicted from watertable mapping and those derived from water tracing experiments appear to occur in the Hollymount area. Therefore it may be that true watertable conditions are more complex and fragmented than shown by the isopleths constructed from the limited number of data points available, with discrete conduit-type flow systems being superimposed upon diffuse regional groundwater flow patterns. Resolution of this problem would require the establishment of a dense network of observation boreholes, together with the use of highly sensitive water tracing experiments involving sampling over long periods of time.

REFERENCES

Atkinson, T.C. and Smith, D.I. 1974. Rapid groundwater flow in fissures in the Chalk: an example from south Hampshire. *Q. Jl. Engng. Geol.*, **7**, 197-205.

Drew, D.P. 1976. Hydrogeology of the north Co. Galway - south Co. Mayo lowland karst area. *Proceedings of the 6th International Congress of Spelaeology, Olomouc, Czechoslovakia,* 57-61.

Drew, D.P. 1984. The effect of human activity on a lowland karst aquifer. In: *Hydrogeology of karstic terrains, case histories,* eds. G. Castany, E. Groba, E. Romijn (Hanover : International Association of Hydrogeologists - UNESCO), 195-199.

Foster, S.S.D. and Milton, V.A. 1974. The permeability and storage of an unconfined Chalk aquifer. *Hydrol. Sci. Bull.*, **19(4)**, 485-500.

Gams, I. 1978. The polje: the problem of definition. *Zeit. fur Geom. N.F.*, **22(2)**, 170-181.

Mitchell, G.F. 1980. The search for Tertiary Ireland. *Journal of Earth Sciences, Royal Dublin Society,* **3**, 13-33.

Parizek, R.R. and Siddiqui, S.H. 1970. Determining the sustained yields of wells in carbonate and fractured aquifers. *Groundwater,* **8(5)**, 12-20.

Smith, D.I., Atkinson, T.C. and Drew, D.P. 1976. Limestone Hydrology. In: *The Science of Speleology,* eds. T.D. Ford and C.H.D. Cullingford, (London: Academic Press), 179-212.

Stanton, W.I. and Smart, P.L. 1981. Repeated dye traces of underground streams in the Mendip Hills, Somerset. *Proceedings of the University of Bristol Spelaeological Society,* **16(1)**, 47-58.

Williams, P.W. 1970. Limestone morphology in Ireland. In: *Irish Geographical Studies,* eds. N. Stephens and R.E. Glasscock, (Belfast), 105-124.

14

Karst water temperatures and the shaping of Malham Cove, Yorkshire

A.F. Pitty, J.L. Ternan, R.A. Halliwell and J. Crowther

SUMMARY

Fluctuations in karst water temperatures from 15 sampling sites in the Malham area of northwest Yorkshire are presented. Springs draining into Malham Tarn have narrow temperature ranges (standard deviations = 0.12 to 0.22°C), with a mean value of 7.39°C. The possibility of lake water, formerly ponded beneath and behind glacier ice, being periodically released by advection is discussed. The role of such abrupt, large-scale releases in the shaping of spectacular limestone landforms in the vicinity is considered.

RÉSUMÉ

Les variations de température, relevées à quinze endroits d'échantillonnage dans la région de Malham au nord-ouest du Yorkshire, sont presentées. Les eaux des résurgences qui s'accumulent au Malham Tarn présentent des variations de température peu élevées (déviation de standard = 0.12 à 0.22°C) avec une moyenne de 7.39°C. La possibilité de relâcher de temps à autre les eaux d'un lac, qui sont retenues en contrebas ou derrière un glacier, par des processus d'advection, est discutée. L'importance de ces lâchages brusques et volumineux quant au développement de la spectaculaire morphologie karstique des alentours est discutée.

INTRODUCTION

Malham is a mecca for students of mysterious underground drainages, and for visitors who flock to admire the sheer splendour of the limestone cliffs of Malham Cove and Gordale Scar, and the surrealism of the limestone pavements. The relief of the area is illustrated (Figure 14.1), together with selected features of the solid and drift geology. These features are considered in relation to discussion of temperatures of karst waters in the area, which are the focal point of the following account. The location of water sampling points is indicated (Figure 14.1), together with the standard deviation of the karst water temperatures. These values are 'best estimates', based on 24 fortnightly observations for sites 1, 2, 3, 4, 6, 7 and 8 (J.L.T.) and on 12 monthly observations for sites 5, 6, 9 and 10 (J.C. and R.A.H.) and for sites 10, 12, 13, 14 and 15 (A.F.P.). Site 6 was observed independently in two sampling schemes. The value quoted of 0.22°C (Figure 14.1), measured by Ternan (1972) compares with that of 0.20°C from observations shared by Crowther and Halliwell (unpublished).

KARST WATER RISINGS AROUND MALHAM TARN

Malham Tarn is the only permanent lake on limestone in the UK. It occupies an elongated tract of irregular but low relief to the north of the North Craven Fault. Much of the lower central zone of this tract is underlain by an inlier of Silurian slates. There are, however, higher elevations along much of the sides of this tract and it is commonly referred to as the 'Tarn-Great Close Mire basin'. This 'basin' has the appearance of a headwater area of a valley formerly leading eastwards along the line of the fault. The present-day valleys of the Watlowes and Gordale Beck are narrow notches in the low interfluve to the south and may have developed later. Great Scar Limestone makes up much of the ground around the inlier and of the higher land to the north. The limestone is flat-lying or dips slightly to the north. There are traces of a former sandstone capping on Parson's Pulpit, to the northeast, and thin sandstones and shale bands begin to occur in the Yoredale Series on the higher slopes of Knowe Fell, to the northwest.

A string of karst risings occur at, or close to, the northern margin of the impermeable inlier. The very narrow temperature range at sites 3, 4 and 6 (standard deviation = 0.12 to 0.22) demonstrates that these issues are essentially springs of diffuse percolation water from limestone strata only. This reflects the general paucity of cave development in the area, since major resurgences in northwest Yorkshire have water temperature fluctuations with standard deviations of 1.80°C or more (Pitty *et al.*, 1979, p.159). Site 5, downstream from the main supply inlet to Malham Tarn at site 4, demonstrates how groundwater temperatures begin to adjust to the ambient air temperatures.

Beginnings of this adjustment are unavoidable features of measurements at sites 1, 2 and 7, due to their very low discharge in summer months, and too marked at site 8 to make a value worth quoting. Mean water temperatures for the eight sites in this string of risings is 7.39°C, ranging from 7.24°C at site 3, to 7.61 at the Tarn inlet (site 4).

SURFACE FLOWS NEAR THE NORTH CRAVEN FAULT

The area between the North Craven and Mid-Craven Faults is predominantly Great Scar Limestone, with extensive areas of bare limestone pavement and low cliffs or 'scars' defined by master joints. There are small faults which form features like Langscar, to the west of Watlowes, while Gordale '... has doubtless been determined by a crack with a similar north-north-westerly trend' (Garwood and Goodyear, 1924, p.225). The Great Scar Limestone is flat-lying or dips slightly to the north. However, the higher land to the west of Smelt Mill sink is a more steeply inclined dipslope of limestone, with Black Hill prominent as a small sandstone outlier and with thin sandstones and shales of the Yoredale Series on the higher ground. Smith and Atkinson (1977, p.604) are mistaken in mapping this area as Bowland Shales, as this is specifically a 'basin' facies, occurring only to the south of the Mid-Craven Fault.

Because the limestone between the two faults is dominated by master joints and small fractures, surface flows of water sink soon after crossing the North Craven Fault, although some flow persists throughout Gordale Beck. All four water-sampling points along this zone have similar water temperature fluctuations, with standard deviations ranging between 4.10 and 4.28°C. These values obviously reflect the rapid adjustment of water temperatures to air temperatures. However, the adjustment is not complete, as suggested by the widening of standard deviations from 4.17°C at the Tarn outlet (site 9) to 4.28 at the Water Sinks (site 11). The chemical characteristics of these three flows is different. Correlation coefficients for calcium hardness fluctuations are $r = -0.36$ for sites 10 and 11, $r = 0.43$ for sites 10 and 12, and $r = -0.01$ for sites 11 and 12 (Pitty, 1968, p.116).

RESURGENCES NEAR MALHAM VILLAGE, SOUTH OF THE MID-CRAVEN FAULT

Water from the Smelt Mill Sink probably follows the southeasterly direction of master joints and small faults to re-emerge at the foot of Malham Cove. That from Water Sinks travels to Airehead, possibly following a similarly joint-controlled direction towards Grey Gill before turning southwest. Only a hypothetical straight line linking these two pairs of sink-resurgence systems supports the much quoted interpretation that these systems 'cross underground'. This interpretation gives an unnecessarily convoluted impression of karst groundwater behaviour in this locality, now clarified by the detailed re-examination by Smith and Atkinson

283

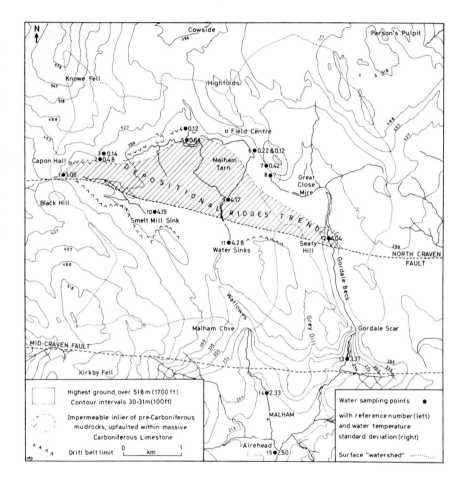

Figure 14.1   Location of water-sampling points and selected
features of the geology, relief, and drainage of
the Malham Tarn area

284

(1977) of the original tracer experiments by Howarth *et al.,*
(1900).

The intermediary values for water temperature fluctuations
at sites 13, 14 and 15 (standard deviations of 3.37°C, 2.33°C
and 2.50°C, respectively) are typical of headstream waters that
have re-emerged from underground conduits, although both sites
13 and 14 are some distance downstream from actual resurgence
points. However, the standard deviation of 2.50°C at Airehead
represents precisely the damping effect of underground flow on
the variability of 4.28°C at the Water Sinks (site 11).

GLACIATION, WATER PALEOTEMPERATURES, AND FLUVIOGLACIAL FEATURES

Opinions range widely about the glacial conditions in the north-
west Yorkshire limestone tract during glacial maxima. Noting
relict flora in 'refuges' on some peaks, Raistrick (1933, p 263)
suggested that some peaks over 600 m a.s.1. could have been
nunataks at maximum glaciations. King (1976, p 108) concludes
that ice was local in origin and that ice erosion was strongly
localised. In contrast, postdictions from a computer model
suggest a thickness of ice of 200-600 m above even the highest
peaks in the vicinity of Malham (Clayton, 1981, p 404).

Since limestone areas often reveal glacial sequences which
differ from those of adjacent lowlands on less permeable terrain
(Pitty, 1979), it is worth discussing the possible inter-
relationships between former glacier ice, lake ice, and water
paleotemperatures of the springs in the Tarn-Great Close Mire
basin. More specifically, the possible characteristics of a
former, larger Malham Tarn during such episodes could be significant in the interpretation of the geohydrological and geomorphological history of the locality. Mean air temperatures
at about 5-6°C lower than the present day are commonly suggested
(Emiliani, 1955; Coope, 1962). Subtracting this estimated drop
from the present-day mean for the main spring water supplying
Malham Tarn (site 4) leaves a mean value of 1.38-2.38°C above
zero. Since three standard deviations span the width of a population of normally distributed data, a further subtraction (of
0.12 x 1.5 = 0.18°C) still leaves a difference of 1.1-2.1°C
above freezing point for the coolest postdicted issues of groundwater. Given the very small temperature differences that are
involved, it is noteworthy that Malham Tarn Field Centre has a
mean temperature 0.3°C higher than would be expected from extrapolations from climatological stations in adjacent lowlands
(Manley, 1979, p 88). This is probably due to the south-facing
orientation of the northern flank of the Tarn-Great Close Mire
Basin. In addition, there is commonly a time lag of about three
months between antecedent air temperatures and that of emerging
water from springs (Pitty, 1976). Thus, karst water emerging
during autumn retains a little of the thermal energy from the
preceding summer. And regardless of the conditions at glacial
maxima, it seems clear that a delicate dynamic equilibrium between ice front and emerging karst groundwater would have pre-

vailed for long periods at Malham Tarn.

Landforms and deposits in the Tarn-Great Close Mire basin indicate that the area was ice-covered, but with much water present too. Clark (1967, p 480) stated that, 'There is much evidence of the movement of water and of glacio-fluvial deposition beneath ice', and enthusiastically mapped all channel forms, including the heads of Gordale and Watlowes, as subglacial features. His mapping of an outer limit to water-deposited drift around Malham Tarn (Figure 14.1) has been extended around Great Close Mire by Calloway (Clayton, 1981). Within this broader extent of drift, there are rather irregular heaps of bedded, water-deposited material south of the Tarn, interpreted as kames (Clayton, 1966, p 365). These form a strip of ridges running en echelon across much of the southern flank to the basin (Figure 14.1). These are not necessarily glacier-ice features; they have some similarities with ice-pushed ridges which characterise present day frozen shores, like those described in arctic Canada by Owens and McCann (1970).

SELF-DUMPING OF ICE-PONDED DRAINAGE
AT TEMPERATURES A FRACTION ABOVE ZERO

Staff from the Malham Tarn Field Centre have collected climatological data from the summit of Fountains Fell (668 m O.D.) which indicate that the present-day mean annual temperature of the highest summit in the vicinity of Malham Tarn is 4.6°C (Manley, 1979, p 87). This confirms how close glacial maxima temperatures would have been to zero in the Tarn-Great Close Mire basin, some 270 m lower. In that narrow temperature range where lake water exists alongside or beneath glacier ice, periodically lake water may be spectacularly drained by self-dumping mechanisms. Either water volume may become sufficient to float the ponding ice wall, as suggested for ice-ponded lakes in Iceland (Thorarinsson, 1939); or, at much smaller volumes than those required to float ice, fractionally small increases in water temperature slightly enlarge a subglacial drainage tunnel (Liestøl, 1956). The volume of ice melted from such tunnel walls in a given moment is a function of the total volume of water that has passed through (Gilbert, 1971, p 354). Thus, even a slightly enlarged tunnel admits greater volumes of flow which, in turn, accelerate the enlargement of the tunnel. This positive feedback loop self-accelerates rapidly, since it is the coldest, ice-contact water which drains through first, so that Liestøl-type drainage results in floods as catastrophic in scale as those of Thorarinsson-type lake emptying. These phenomena are quite common at critical latitudes at the present day. For example, in the region around 'Hazard Lake' in Yukon Territory, over 150 basins are, or have been, ice-dammed (Clarke, 1982, p 6). Very small temperature scales are involved in such drainage waters. For example, lake water temperatures of only 0.25, 0.9 and 0.15°C were required to explain the tunnel enlargement that drained ice-dammed Summit Lake in British Columbia in the autumns of 1965, 1967 and 1968, respectively (Gilbert, 1971, p 355). In the classic Icelandic example of Grimsvötn, water temperature at the tunnel outlet in the 1954 flood was 0.05°C (Nye, 1976). In Iceland, such floods from subglacial lakes are termed 'jökulhlaups'. Geothermal heat is commonly significant in enlarging the subglacial tunnels of 'jökulhlaups'. These are, therefore, a special case, rather than being typical of the more general type of lake drainage, with water heated by solar radiation alone

Both types of self-dumping of ice-ponded water can be envisaged in the Tarn-Great Close Mire basin, depending on the severity of glacial conditions at the time. In either case, significant trends in water temperatures, away from the concentration of springs on the north side of the Tarn, must be supposed. In colder conditions, glacier ice may have been sealed to bedrock, particularly on the southern side of the basin, away from the source of relatively warm spring water. In contrast, to the north, spring waters could have maintained a lake alongside glacier ice which either drained over an adjacent col or, occasionally, developed sufficient hydrostatic head to 'float' the glacial ice. In less cold conditions, with the sole of a glacier approaching melting-point temperatures, spring water warmth could maintain and, occasionally, enlarge sub-ice tunnels. Either mechanism, however, may have been less common in the Great Close Mire catchment where, at the present day at least, springs are negligible. The wide range of temperature fluctuations at site 9 also suggest that subsurface contributions to stream flow are insignificant.

Since any type of discharge is a function of drainage area, the order of magnitude of a flood of subglacial water draining from the Malham Tarn watershed can be estimated. A conservative estimate can be ensured by considering only water draining from beneath the ice. Walder and Hallet (1979) have shown that cavities account for as much as 20-40% of the ice-rock interface beneath small cirque glaciers; such cavities would be drained in Thorarinsson-type outbursts. In fact, Hodge (1974) has estimated that water stored at the beds of the Nisqually and South Cascade glaciers, which was released in 'jökulhlaups', corresponded to a water layer about 1 m in depth. In the case of subglacial Malham Tarn area the remains of the kame complex suggest a subglacial area of at least 4.5 km² (Figure 14.1). Finally, self-dumping is usually complete within 1 or 2 days (Marcus, 1960), with at least a 100-fold increases in discharge, compared with average summer flows, being common (Clague and Mathews, 1973). Combining these orders of magnitude suggests that a Thorarinsson-type outburst from beneath Malham Tarn ice would involve at least 4.5 million m³ of water, released in 1 or 2 days at a rate of 26-52 cumecs. This compares with present-day discharge from the Tarn which is usually in the order of 0.25 to 0.5 cumecs.

ORIGIN AND SHAPING OF MALHAM COVE AND GORDALE SCAR CANYON

Malham Cove, a large amplitude horeshoe shape in plan and with a vertical drop of about 100 m (Waltham, 1974, p 376) has been repeatedly interpreted as a dry waterfall. Even comparisons with the form of Niagara have been drawn by guidebook authors, keen to catch the tourist's eye (Halliwell, 1979, p 36). Nonetheless, the catchment of only some 13 km^2 above the Cove has always appeared to be too small in comparison with the dimensions of the Cove. Clearly, the hypothesis of formerly repeated 'jökulhlaup'-like outbursts from the area around the Tarn seems a possibility and would offer an adequate mechanism to explain the enigma of the Cove. However, it is important to stress that several attributes, shared by the Cove and by Gordale Scar Canyon alike, are due to at least four other factors. Firstly, the occurrence of both features is due to the presence of the Mid-Craven Fault, even if this pre-Namurian feature is not exhumed along its full length (Hudson, 1930, p 317). Secondly, impressive vertical scale, considering the comparatively low altitude at which they occur, appears to be due to geologically more recent reactivation of movement along the fault. Trotter (1929, p 167) suggests that uplift in the northern Pennines occurred in the late Tertiary. He describes streams crossing the fault scarp above the Vale of Eden that '...are in the initial stages of development, and have not as yet seriously modified the watershed', which he attributes to the recentness of the fault scarp (Trotter, 1929, p 179). Thirdly, the development of both features has involved recession from the actual line of the fault by some 600-700 m (Figure 14.1). Fourthly, both are sheer cliffs to their bases, possibly due to the close proximity to the surface at these levels of the sub-limestone basement, recorded as exposed in the 19th century at the entrance to Gordale (Davis and Lees, 1878, p 38). This more resistant, impermeable rock arrests downcutting and favours the re-emergence of groundwaters which tend to flush loose debris away from the base of the cliffs.

Despite these similarities, the striking difference in general shape between the rounded Cove and the canyon-like approach to the waterfalls in Gordale is little discussed. The linear recession along the Gordale Scar Canyon is, in part, guided by small faults, a feature not present at the Cove. It may also be due to the exposure of low cliffs of slates in the upper reaches of Gordale Beck, where it is incised into the pre-Carboniferous basement near site 12 (Figure 14.1). There is no comparable source of abrasives to aid stream erosion, by mechanisms like pothole-drilling for example, downvalley from Malham Tarn. Indeed, even sand-sized abrasives from relics of the former sandstone caprocks would settle out in a lake basin. Thus, linear recession of the waterfalls at Gordale would be favoured by the abrasiveness of a sediment load compared with the more sediment-free flows down Watlowes. Thus simple reasons for the major difference in form between Cove and Canyon can be offered. The several factors that account for some of these similarities recur along the length of the Craven Faults. The distinctive feature of the Malham area remains that these two large forms, considering their relatively low altitude, occur downvalley from the unique feature in the UK of a lake basin on limestone.

CONCLUSION

The distinctive features of the karst springs which supply Malham Tarn are their mean annual water temperatures, and their very narrow range of fluctuations. These suggest continued karst spring flow during portions of glacial episodes. Release of thermal energy from relatively warm lake water is the dominant factor contributing to subglacial tunnel enlargement. Therefore, former 'jökulhlaup'-like outbursts from the Tarn basin are postulated. The occurrence downvalley of two large semi-relict waterfalls is consistent with this possibility.

Acknowledgement

The first-named author is indebted to co-authors for contributing data and for commenting on an earlier draft of this paper. However co-authors do not necessarily agree with parts of the interpretation advanced, nor are they responsible for any defects in its exposition.

REFERENCES

Clague, J.J. and Mathews, W.H. 1973. The magnitude of jökulhlaups. *Journal of Glaciology,* 12, 501-504.

Clark, R. 1967. A contribution to glacial studies of the Malham Tarn area. *Field Studies,* 2, 479-491.

Clarke, G.K.C. 1982. Glacier outburst floods from 'Hazard Lake', Yukon Territory, and the problem of flood magnitude prediction. *Journal of Glaciology,* 28, 3-21.

Clayton, K.M. 1966. The origins of the landforms of the Malham area. *Field Studies,* 2, 359-384.

Clayton, K.M. 1981. Explanatory description of the landforms of the Malham area. *Field Studies,* 5, 389-423.

Coope, G.R. 1962. A Pleistocene coeopterous fauna with arctic affinities from Fladbury, Worcestershire. *Quart. J. Geol. Soc.,* 118, 103-123.

Davis, J.W. and Lees, F.A. 1878. *West Yorkshire: An Account of its Geology, Physical Geography, Climatology and Botany,* (London: L.Reeve), 414pp.

Emiliani, C. 1955. Pleistocene temperatures. *Journal of Geology,* 63, 538-578.

Garwood, E.J. and Goodyear, E. 1924. The Lower Carboniferous succession in the Settle district and along the line of the Craven Faults. *Quart. J. Geol. Soc.*, **80**, 184-273.

Gilbert, R. 1971. Observations on ice-dammed Summit Lake, British Columbia, Canada. *Journal of Glaciology*, **10**, 351-356.

Halliwell, R.A. 1979. Gradual changes in the hydrology of the Yorkshire Dales demonstrated by tourist descriptions. *Trans. Br. Cave Res. Assoc.*, **6**, 35-40.

Hodge, S.M. 1974. Variations in the sliding of a temperate glacier. *Journal of Glaciology*, **13**, 349-369.

Howarth, J.H. *et al.*, 1900. The underground waters of North-West Yorkshire. *Proc. Yorks. Geol. Soc.*, **14**, 1-44.

Hudson, R.G.S. 1930. The Carboniferous of the Craven reef belt, the Namurian unconformity at Scaleber, near Settle. *Proc. Geol. Assoc.*, **41**, 290-322.

King, C.A.M. 1976. *Northern England.* (London: Methuen), 213pp.

Liestøl, O. 1956. Glacier-dammed lakes in Norway. *Norsk Geog. Tidsskr.*, **15**, 122-149.

Manley, G. 1979. Temperature records on Fountains Fell, with some Pennine comparisons. *Field Studies*, **5**, 85-92.

Marcus, M.G. 1960. Periodic drainage of glacier-dammed Tulsequah Lake, British Columbia. *Geographical Review*, **50**, 89-106.

Nye, J.F. 1976. Water flow in glaciers: jökulhlaups, tunnels and veins. *Journal of Glaciology*, **17**, 181-207.

Owens, E.H. and McCann, S.B. 1970. The role of ice in the Arctic beach environment with special reference to Cape Ricketts, southwest Devon Island, Northwest Territories, Canada. *American Journal of Science*, **268**, 397-414.

Pitty, A.F. 1968. Some notes on the use of calcium hardness measurements in studies of cave hydrology. *Trans. Cave Res. Group GB.*, **10**, 115-120.

Pitty, A.F. 1976. Water temperatures in the limestone areas of the central and southern Pennines. *Proc. Yorks. Geol. Soc.*, **40**, 601-612.

Pitty, A.F. 1979. Underground contributions to surface flow, as estimated by water temperature variability. In: *Geographical Approaches to Fluvial Processes*, ed. A.F. Pitty, (Norwich: Geobooks), 163-172.

Pitty, A.F., Halliwell, R.A., Ternan, J.L., Whittel, P.A. and Cooper, R.G. 1979. The range of water temperature fluctuations in the limestone waters of the central and southern Pennines. *Journal of Hydrology*, **41**, 157-160.

Raistrick, A. 1933. The glacial and post-glacial periods in West Yorkshire. *Proc. Geol. Assoc.*, **44**, 263-269.

Smith, D.I. and Atkinson, T. 1977. Underground flow in cavernous limestones with special reference to the Malham area. *Field Studies*, **4**, 597-616.

Ternan, J.L. 1972. *Karst water studies in the Malham area, north of the Craven Faults.* Unpublished Ph.D. thesis, University of Hull.

Thorarinsson, S. 1939. The ice-dammed lakes of Iceland with particular reference to their values as indicators of glacier oscillation. *Geog. Annaler,* **21**, 216-242.

Trotter, F.M. 1929. The Tertiary uplift and resultant drainage of the Alston Block and adjacent areas. *Proc. Yorks. Geol. Soc.,* **21**, 161-180.

Walder, J. and Hallet, B. 1979. Geometry of former subglacial water channels and cavities. *Journal of Glaciology,* **23**, 335-346.

Waltham, A.C., ed. 1974. *Limestones and caves of North-west England.* (Newton Abbot, Devon: David and Charles), 477pp.

15

Datations ^{14}C de concrétions de grottes Belges: vitesses de croissance durant l'Holocène et implications paléoclimatiques

M. Gewelt

RÉSUMÉ

Neuf concrétions issues de grottes belges ont été datées par [14]C. La correction des âges ^{14}C, due à la dilution de l'activité initiale par du carbone mort issu de la dissolution de bedrock, est discutée et le facteur de dilution q = 0,85 a été provisoirement adopté. Les vitesses de croissance, calculées sur base des datations ^{14}C, varient, pour 8 stalagmites holocènes, de 0,22 à 9,29 cm/100 ans. Les volumes moyens de la calcite précipitée sont de 6 cm³/100 ans au minimum et de 128 cm³/100 ans au maximum. Les vitesses de croissance calculées pour un plancher stalag- mitique sont faibles (0,24 cm/100 ans en moyenne), en partie à cause de plusieurs interruptions de croissance. Un arrêt du concrétionnement d'au moins 20.000 ans a été trouvé au sein d'une stalagmite. Les facteurs influençant les vitesses de croissance et expliquant leur grande variabilité sont discutés. D'autre part, plus de 50 nouvelles datations ^{14}C ont été utilisées pour dresser un premier histogramme de la répartition des dates ^{14}C de concrétions prélevées dans des grottes belges. Cela nous a permis de mettre en évidence une interruption (ou tout au moins un fort ralentissement) de la croissance des concrétions durant la période comprise entre 30.000 et 10.000 ans BP. Une inter- prétation paléoclimatique est donnée à cet arrêt du concrétionne- ment ainsi qu'à la reprise très active de la précipitation de la calcite durant l'Holocène.

SUMMARY

Nine speleothems from Belgian caves have been dated by means of
^{14}C. The ^{14}C conventional ages must be corrected by a correction
factor (q) due to the dilution of the initial activity by
'infinitely old' carbon coming from the limestone dissolution.
Various ways of estimating this dilution factor are discussed
and we finally adopt (temporarily) the q = 0.85 value. Vertical
growth rates, calculated on the basis of ^{14}C ages, range,
for eight Holocene stalagmites, from 0.22 to 9.29 cm.100 yr^{-1}.
The mean vertical growth rate of a flowstone is low (0.24 cm.100
yr^{-1}) and this is partly due to some growth hiatus. One of the
stalagmites shows a growth hiatus of at least 20.10^3 years. The
factors explaining the great variability of the growth rates are
discussed. In addition, more than 50 new ^{14}C dates have been
used to make a first histogram of the ^{14}C dates repartition in
speleothems from Belgian caves. Evidence has been found of an
interruption - or at least of an important slowdown - of
speleothems growth during the period between 30.10^3 (our ^{14}C
dating limit) and 10.10^3 years BP. A paleoclimatic interpretation is given to explain this growth interruption together
with the active CaCO$_3$ precipitation during the Holocene.

INTRODUCTION

Depuis les premières datations ^{14}C de concrétions de grottes
(Franke, 1951; Franke *et al.*, 1958; 1959; Broecker et Olson,
1959; Broecker et Walton, 1959; Broecker *et al.*, 1960), de nouvelles méthodes de datations ont été développées et appliquées
à la calcite stalagmitique. L'une de ces méthodes (^{230}Th/^{234}U),
qui permet de dater les concrétions jusqu'à environ 350.000 ans
BP, vient de faire l'objet d'une étude qui reprend un très grand
nombre de datations de concrétions (Hennig *et al.*, 1983). Néanmoins, la méthode du ^{14}C présente un intérêt indéniable pour la
datation des concrétions Holocènes.

Les datations ^{14}C de concrétions stalagmites provenant de
grottes belges sont encore très rares: au nombre d'une dizaine,
elles ont été effectuées par E. Gilot à l'Université de Louvain-
la-Neuve (communication écrite de B. Bastin) et par M.A. Geyh à
Hanovre. Ces premières datations ^{14}C ont été publiées par
Bastin (1982) et par Gewelt (1981) pour l'une des stalagmites
(RSMV). Aussi, pour tenter de combler ce vide relatif et surtout
pour comparer les données belges avec celles de l'étranger, nous
avons entrepris une campagne de mesures ^{14}C dans des concrétions
stalagmitiques belges. Les résultats de 24 nouvelles datations
de stalagmites et d'un plancher stalagmitique sont présentés ici
et sont utilisés pour estimer les vitesses de croissance de 9
concrétions stalagmitiques Holocènes. De plus, un premier
histogramme des datations ^{14}C de concrétions belges a été dressé
en utilisant plus de 50 nouvelles datations ^{14}C (Gewelt, inédit).

La publication de ces résultats constitue donc un premier bilan
provisoire des datations ^{14}C effectuées en Belgique sur des
concrétions de grottes.

ORIGINE ET CONTEXTE DES ECHANTILLONS ETUDIES

Localisation des grottes

Les grottes dans lesquelles ont été prélevées les concrétions étudiées sont localisées sur la Figure 15.1, qui montre
également la répartition des formations carbonatées du Paléozoïque. Cinq des six grottes ou des concrétions ont été prélevées se développent dans les calcaires dévoniens et principalement dans le Frasnien. L'Abîme de Comblain-au-Pont s'ouvre
quant à lui dans les Calcaires carbonifères du Viséen.

Les concrétions analysées

Seuls sont repris ici les échantillons dont les datations
ont été utilisées pour le calcul des vitesses de croissance.
Plusieurs autres échantillons sont encore en cours d'étude et
les résultats seront publiés ultérieurement.

a) CPL2 à Comblain-au-Pont   Cet échantillon représente une
carotte de calcite (Figure 15.2) forée dans un plancher stalagmitique prolongeant celui qui recouvre les sédiments qui ont
comblé un ancien siphon. L'échantillon est localisé quelques
mètres en amont de la salle des échos dans l'Abîme de Comblain-
au-Pont. Le prélèvement a été effectué en collaboration avec
le Dr. G. Koch, du Centre d'Etude de l'Energie Nucléaire (C.E.N.)
au moyen d'un carottier électrique décrit plus loin (Figure 15.4).
Le plancher stalagmitique échantillonné est relativement friable
et les strates de calcite sont entrecoupées par des lits argileux
de faible épaisseur qui témoignent de plusieurs interruptions
de croissance. Celles-ci sont représentées par des hiatus (h)
sur la Figure 15.2.

b) RSMII à Remouchamps   Stalacto-stalagmite prélevée en place
dans le 'Réseau du 5 Février' de la Grotte de Remouchamps. La
concrétion se développait sur une coulée stalagmitique de paroi
peu épaisse (2 à 3 cm). La partie supérieure de la concrétion
se termine par une stalactite soudée à la stalagmite sous-
jacente. L'ensemble forme une petite colonne de 27 cm de haut.
La stalagmite inférieure a été étudiée par Gewelt (1978) au
point de vue des variations des δ^{18}O et δ^{13}C. Ces dernières
mesures ont donc été réutilisées pour la normalisation des
activités ^{14}C.

c) RSMV à Remouchamps   Stalagmite de plus de 60 cm de hauteur
prélevée en place à plus de 250 m de l'entrée de la grotte de
Remouchamps. Cette stalagmite, qui se présente comme un cierge
de diamètre presque constant (5 à 6 cm), a été étudiée sur le
plan des variations de δ^{18}O - δ^{13}C par Gewelt (1978 et 1981).
Trois datations ^{14}C ont été effectuées par Geyh à Hanovre
(communication écrite de M.A. Geyh à Y. Quinif); elles ont servi

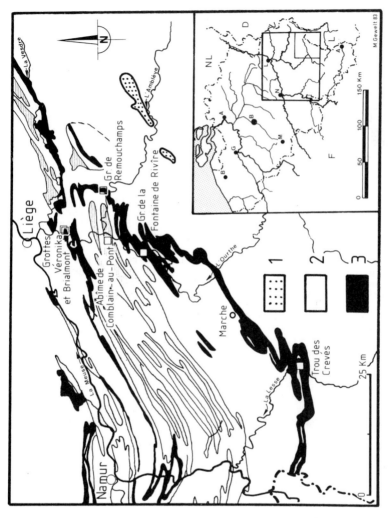

Figure 15.1   Localisation des grottes étudiées dans les formations carbonatées du paléozoïque du sud de la Belgique. D'après Ek (1976), légèrement modifié. 1. Permien (Poudingue à ciment carbonaté); 2. Calcaires carbonifères; 3. Calcaires du Dévonien moyen et supérieur

CPL 2

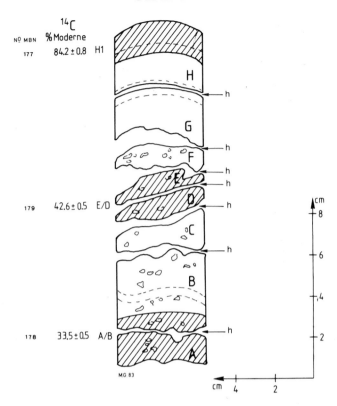

Figure 15.2   Datations ^{14}C d'une carotte (CPL 2) forée dans
un plancher stalagmitique de l'Abîme de
Comblain-au-Pont.   h = hiatus

à étayer des interprétations paléoclimatiques basées sur les
isotopes stables (Gewelt, 1981) et sur l'analyse palynologique
(Bastin, 1982).

d) RSM8 à Remouchamps   Stalagmite prélevée non en place dans la
Salle des Ruines de la Grotte de Remouchamps.   La partie supérieure de la concrétion n'a pas été retrouvée.   En coupe longitudinale, on aperçoit très bien une rupture de croissance,
d'ailleurs soulignée par de la calcite de couleur noire.   Cet
hiatus sera aussi confirmé par les datations ^{14}C que nous avons
effectuées: une interruption de croissance d'au moins 20.000 ans
y a été mise en évidence! Une moitié de cette concrétion a été
fournie à B. Bastin pour qu'y soit réalisée l'analyse pollinique.

297

e) RSM6 à Remouchamps Petite stalagmite (17 cm de haut) prélevée non en place dans la salle de Schiste. On retrouve à la base de la stalagmite des fragments de schistes calcareux caractéristiques de cette partie de la grotte, ce qui atteste que la concrétion s'est bien développée dans cette salle.

f) BSM1 à Tilff Morceau inférieur d'une stalagmite en place prélevée dans la grotte de Brialmont. La structure interne de la stalagmite montre que le concrétion devait être beaucoup plus haute, son diamètre n'étant pas à la mesure de sa hauteur car la concrétion originale a été recouverte par une deuxième génération de calcite. L'ensemble de la concrétion est constitué de calcite poreuse de couleur blanche.

g) FRSM9 à Hamoir Grande stalagmite, haute de plus de 1,60 m, prélevée en place dans la Grotte de la Fontaine de Rivîre, avec l'aide de J. Godissart. Cette stalagmite en forme de cierge a un diamètre très constant (environ 6,5 cm); elle se développait sur la paroi nord de la salle du lac, à une quinzaine de mètres au-dessus du niveau de l'eau. Une moitié de la concrétion a été donnée à B. Bastin en vue de l'analyse pollinique.

h) VKSM1 à Tilff Stalagmite prélevée non en place par A. Briffoz sur les alluvions du petit ruisseau souterrain de la grotte Véronika. A la base de la concrétion, on retrouve, cimentées dans la calcite, de petites poches de sédiments graveleux. La stalagmite, qui mesure 30 cm de haut, doit probablement s'être développée sur, ou à proximité, des alluvions où elle a été retrouvée descellée.

i) TCSM1 à Wavreille Stalagmite prélevée non en place (et en deux parties) dans le Trou des Crevés, avec l'aide de C. Ek et Y. Quinif. La partie supérieure de la stalagmite (Figure 15.3) montre clairement que la stalagmite principale est partiellement recouverte par une stalagmite secondaire qui la recouvre latéralement. Cette deuxième stalagmite, ainsi que l'inclinaison de l'axe de croissance de la stalagmite principale, peuvent sans doute s'expliquer par de légers décalages du point d'alimentation ou par un déplacement latéral de la concrétion. La Figure 15.3 montre également en coupe longitudinale les fines zones de croissance superposées. Les traces circulaires sont les traces de forages effectués en vue d'analyses des variations des isotopes stables du carbone et de l'oxygène ($\delta^{13}C$ et $\delta^{18}O$).

METHODOLOGIE

Prélèvements

Afin de réduire au maximum l'impact des prélèvements sur le patrimoine souterrain, ce sont des stalagmites déjà descellées de leur substratum qui sont préférentiellement choisies. De plus, nous prélevons également des échantillons de calcite par carottage. Le carottier électrique utilisé (Figure 15.4) est muni d'un foret diamanté qui fournit des carottes de 30 cm de long et de 4,5 cm de diamètre. Un système d'allonge permet

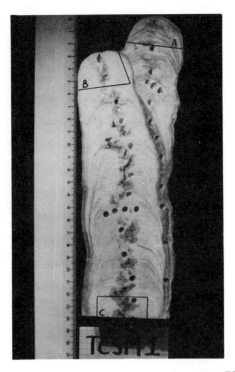

Figure 15.3 Partie supérieure de la stalagmite TCSM 1 du Trou
des crevés (Wavreille). Analyses ^{14}C: A = MBN 233,
B = MBN 232, C = MBN 236 (voir Tableau 15.1).
Photo: M. Gewelt

d'effectuer des forages plus profonds (60 à 90 cm). L'appareil
représenté sur la Figure 15.4 est au travail sur un plancher
stalagmitique dans l'Abîme de Comblain-au-Pont. Au total, trois
carottes ont été prélevées dans cette grotte; l'échantillon
CPL2 (Figure 15.2) est un exemple d'une carotte obtenue par ce
système de prélèvement.

Analyse ^{14}C

Les échantillons de calcite sont soumis à l'analyse ^{14}C
par comptage β^- en scintillation liquide du benzène synthétisé
à partir du CO_2 produit par acidolyse du carbonate. De 30 à 50
g de calcite sont nécessaires pour l'analyse. La synthèse
du benzène s'effectue suivant la chaîne de réactions :

$$CO_3^= \xrightarrow{H^+} CO_2 \xrightarrow{Li(600°C)} Li_2C_2 \xrightarrow{H_2O} C_2H_2 \xrightarrow[\text{(catalyseur)}]{V_2O_5} C_6H_6$$

Figure 15.4   Carottier électrique forant le plancher stalagmitique CPL 2 (Abîme de Comblain-au-Pont).
Photo: M. Gewelt

La rampe de synthèse utilisée au Centre d'Etude de l'Energie
Nucléaire à Mol est assez semblable à celle décrite par Fontes
(1971).   Le comptage des échantillons de benzène (auxquels on
ajoute le scintillant Butyl PBD à raison de 8 mg/g de C_6H_6)
s'effectue dans un spectromètre à scintillation liquide Inter-
technique SL30 spécialement adapté.   Le bruit de fond de
l'appareil est fourni par le comptage d'un flacon de benzène
'mort' de poids équivalent à celui de l'échantillon.   Tous nos
échantillons de calcite ont subi un prétraitement à l'HCl qui
élimine les parties superficielles (5 à 10% du poids initial de
l'échantillon) susceptibles d'être contaminées.   Les échantillons
sont ensuite lavés à l'eau bidistillée, séchés à l'étuve et
stockés dans des flacons hermétiques en polyéthylène.

VALIDITE DES AGES ^{14}C

Expression de l'erreur

Deux expressions de l'erreur sur l'âge ^{14}C sont utilisées (Tableau 15.1). La première représente la déviation standard calculée sur le nombre total d'impulsions enregistrées par le spectromètre à scintillation liquide. Cette erreur, prise au niveau de ± σ est en général utilisée dans l'expression des âges ^{14}C conventionnels.

On peut également utiliser une expression de l'erreur plus élevée qui permet de mieux appréhender l'incertitude sur les âges ^{14}C et qui est représentée par l'écart quadratique moyen calculé sur plusieurs séries de mesures de 100 minutes chacune. On procède donc à des comptages alternatifs de 100 minutes de l'échantillon et du bruit de fond.

Estimation de l'activité initiale

Pour exprimer les âges ^{14}C conventionnels, on a utilisé la procédure de normalisation préconisée par Stuiver et Polach (1977): lorsque le δ^{13}C est mesuré (vs PDB), on normalise l'activité ^{14}C de l'échantillon par

$$A_{\text{éch. norm.}} = A_{\text{éch.}} \left(1 - \frac{2(25 + \delta^{13}C)}{1000} \right);$$

lorsque δ^{13}C n'est pas mesuré, on utilise la valeur moyenne du δ^{13}C des concrétions stalagmitiques (-8 ±2°/$_{\circ\circ}$) (Stuiver et Polach, 1977), ce qui revient à ajouter 275 ± 50 ans aux âges ^{14}C bruts. Il est d'autre part bien connu que les âges ^{14}C conventionnels doivent être corrigés lorsque leur contenu ^{14}C initial diffère de celui de l'atmosphère (effet du réservoir). Dans le cas des concrétions stalagmitiques, l'activité initiale est, dès la précipitation, diminuée par rapport à l'activité ^{14}C spécifique de l'atmosphère. En effet, le mode même de formation des concrétions implique une dilution du contenu ^{14}C initial, due à la présence, dans la calcite précipitée, de carbone radioactivement 'mort' (quant à son contenu en ^{14}C) provenant de la dissolution du bedrock. On a en effet la réaction:

$$CaCO_3 + CO_2 + H_2O \underset{b}{\overset{a}{\rightleftarrows}} Ca^{2+} + 2\ HCO_3^{-} \tag{1}$$

a: dissolution du bedrock $CaCO_3$ avec participation du CO_2 dissous dans l'eau

b: précipitation (formation de concrétions) à partir du bicarbonate et du calcium contenus dans l'eau.

L'activité ^{14}C initiale doit donc être corrigée d'un facteur q qui quantifie cette dilution du ^{14}C (Vogel, 1970; Geyh, 1972).

$$A_{\text{éch.}} = A_o.q.e^{-\lambda t}$$

ou $A_{\text{éch.}}$ = Activité ^{14}C de l'échantillon

$A_o.q$ = Activité ^{14}C initiale

A_o = Activité ^{14}C du CO_2 atmosphérique à l'époque du concrétionnement, qui est censée être représentée par l'activité du carbone moderne (95% act. du standard NBS)

λ = constante radioactive du ^{14}C = $\dfrac{\ln 2}{T}$ et T est la période 'conventionnelle' du ^{14}C (5568 ans)

t = âge de l'échantillon (ans BP).

La dilution de l'activité initiale influence donc les âges ($t = -\dfrac{1}{\lambda}.\ln\dfrac{A}{A_o.q}$) de la façon indiquée sur la Figure 15.5.

Les valeurs de q indiquées sur cette figure sont données à titre d'exemple. Δt représente la correction à retrancher aux âges ^{14}C conventionnels.

En réalité, on pourrait concevoir une valeur de q = 0,5 qui représenterait les conditions stoechiométriques de l'équation (1). Dans ce cas, 50% de carbone présent à la précipitation de la calcite proviendrait de la dissolution du bedrock et 50% viendrait du CO_2 atmosphérique. Cette valeur extrême de q est rarement rencontrée dans les concrétions et l'on peut envisager plusieurs façons d'estimer le facteur q:

1°) On peut comparer de la calcite actuelle avec le contenu actuel en ^{14}C de l'atmosphère et de la biosphère. En France, la part du CO_2 d'origine atmosphérique présent dans une stalagmite a été estimée à 65% (q = 0,65) (Labeyrie et al., 1967). Nous

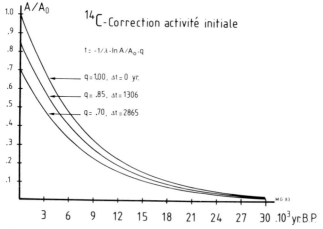

Figure 15.5 Décroissance radioactive du ^{14}C (T = 5568 ans) et correction Δt à soustraire aux âges ^{14}C conventionnels en fonction de différents facteurs de dilution (q)

avons tenté les mêmes déterminations dans des concrétions de grottes belges en utilisant l'activité ^{14}C au sommet de stalagmites ou de planchers, comparée à l'activité ^{14}C du sucre de Tirlemont en 1981 (MBN 164: 121,6 ± 0,7%):

MBN 177 (CPL2-HI):   84,2 ± 0,8% du moderne, q = 0,69

MBN 204 (EPL4):   87,9 ± 0,7% du moderne, q = 0,72

MBN 209 (FRSM9-1/B):   83,7 ± 0,7% du moderne, q = 0,69

Ces valeurs de q sont à interpréter avec prudence car la calcite actuelle intègre une série de niveaux de calcite d'âges récents mais différents. Or, l'activité ^{14}C du CO_2 atmosphérique a beaucoup varié ces dernières années (effet Suess et, à partir des années cinquante, effet des explosions nucléaires). De plus, même si l'on était certain de l'age exact de la calcite prélevée, il faut encore tenir compte de la valeur du CO_2 atmosphérique prise pour le calcul de q. En effet, le CO_2 présent dans les eaux souterraines provient principalement du CO_2 du sol qui n'est pas issu des végétaux de l'année mais de la décomposition des végétaux tombés depuis 2 ans en moyenne (Labeyrie *et al.*, 1967). Il faut de plus postuler que la valeur de q est restée constante dans le passé, ce qui n'est pas certain.

2°) En comparant les activités ^{14}C de travertins avec celles de matières végétales associées, Thorpe *et al.*, (1981) trouvent la meilleure correspondance en utilisant un facteur de dilution dû au bedrock de q = 0,85 ± 0,05. Grâce à des séquences de datations dans des travertins en Angleterre, il avait déjà été démontré l'inadéquation du facteur q = 0,5 (Thorpe *et al.*, 1980). Cette méthode de comparaison est difficile à appliquer aux stalagmites qui ne contiennent que très peu de matières organiques datables.

3°) Les modèles de balance de masse (Pearson, 1965; Pearson et Hanshaw, 1970), basés sur l'analyse des $\delta^{13}C$ des différentes sources de carbone contribuant à la précipitation des carbonates, sont principalement utilisés à la 'datation' des eaux souterraines. Appliqués à la datation des travertins, (Thorpe *et al.*, 1981), ils paraissent fournir des corrections trop importantes. Utilisés pour la correction des datations des concrétions stalagmitiques, ils fournissent également des valeurs de q voisines de 0,5 (par ex. Ek *et al.*, 1981), ce qui paraît être, au vu des autres résultats, une correction trop importante dans la plupart des cas.

Cette surestimation de la correction due à la dilution doit probablement être recherchée dans le fait qu'en général ces modèles considèrent que la dissolution du $CaCO_3$ s'effectue en système fermé. Dans le cas des concrétions de grottes, il doit très probablement y avoir un échange entre les bicarbonates dissous et le CO_2, particulièrement dans le cas d'un système ouvert qui est toujours en contact avec la source de CO_2 (on se reportera à la discussion de Fontes, 1980, sur les différents modèles en système ouvert ou fermé). Ceci doit donc augmenter les valeurs du facteur q et donc diminuer la correction à apporter aux âges [14]C. Signalons qu'une étude statistique (Vogel, 1970) du contenu [14]C d'eaux souterraines a fourni un facteur de dilution dû au bedrock carbonaté de q = 0,85 ± 0,05.

4°) Comparaisons des datations ^{14}C avec d'autres données, par exemple la palynologie (étude en cours avec Bastin). L'analyse pollinique des concrétions (Bastin et al., 1977; Bastin, 1978) fournit en effet des spectres polliniques caractéristiques, en particulier pour l'Holocène (Bastin, 1982). Dans la mesure où des spectres polliniques se répètent dans plusieurs concrétions, les sous-âges définis par l'étude des pollens peuvent être comparés aux datations ^{14}C et éventuellement servir à estimer la correction à apporter aux âges ^{14}C.

Nous comptons également entreprendre des comparaisons entre âges ^{14}C et âges ^{230}Th/^{234}U. Ceci vient d'être effectué dans une stalagmite d'une grotte de la province du Cap, en Afrique du Sud, par Vogel (1983).

Pour l'Holocène, il trouve un très bon agrément entre les âges ^{14}C et ^{230}Th/^{234}U en retranchant 1500 ans aux dates ^{14}C (ce qui correspond à un facteur q = 0,83) et en les calibrant ensuite avec la courbe de Suess (1970).

En l'absence de mesures complémentaires, nous utiliserons ici le facteur de dilution q = 0,85 qui nous paraît être assez généralement vérifié. Il a en effet été trouvé dans de la calcite stalagmitique formée avant les explosions nucléaires (Broecker et Olson, 1959). La valeur q = 0,85 ± 0,05 a également été trouvée par Geyh (1970b) en comparant un histogramme de datation ^{14}C dans des concrétions avec un histogramme de datation ^{14}C dans des matières organiques. Les pics des deux histogrammes montraient un décalage d'environ 1300 ans pour l'Holocène et de 800 à 1000 ans pour la fin du Pléistocène. La valeur q = 0,85 peut donc être considérée comme plausible pour la datation des concrétions (Geyh, 1970a) et elle avait d'ailleurs déjà été trouvée par Franke et al., (1958, cité dans Geyh, 1972) et par Geyh et Schillat (1966); elle est également utilisée par Talma et al. (1974). Le choix du facteur de dilution adopté (q = 0,85) conditionne évidemment les interprétations des âges ^{14}C. La correction utilisée ici est donc susceptible d'être modifiée ultérieurement si de nouveaux résultats montraient qu'un autre facteur de dilution doit être utilisé. Il est en effet possible que le facteur q ait varié dans le passé en fonction des vicissitudes du climat.

RESULTATS ET DISCUSSION

Vitesse de croissance verticale

Les résultats des datations ^{14}C sur lesquels sont basés les calculs des vitesses de croissance verticale sont reportés dans le Tableau 15.1.

(1)   MBN = Mol, Section Mesures Bas Niveau (Dr G. Koch). Centre
      d'Etude de l'Energie Nucléaire (CEN/SCK). B - 2400 Mol,
      Belgique. Hv = Hannover, Niedersächsisches Landesamt für
      Bodemforschung (Dr M.A. Geyh).
    * Publié dans Gewelt (1981) et Bastin (1982).

(2)   Localisation: C = Abîme de Comblain-au-Pont; R = Grotte de
      Remouchamps; B = Grotte de Brialmont (Tillf); FR = Grotte
      de la Fontaine de Rivîre (Hamoir); VK = Grotte Véronika
      (Tillf); TC = Trou des Crevés (Wavreille).

      Type de concrétion: SM = Stalagmite; PL = Plancher
      stalagmitique.

(3)   Date de la fin du comptage.

(4)   % du moderne = A/A_0 x 100.
      A = Activité ^{14}C de l'échantillon (en $cpm.g^{-1}$ de carbone).
      A_0 = Activité ^{14}C du carbone moderne représentée par 95%
          de l'activité ^{14}C de l'acide oxalique du standard NBS.

      ± 'erreur conventionnelle' = déviation standard calculeé
      sur le nombre total d'impulsions.

      ± 'écart quadratique moyen sur n. mesures de 100 min.'
      = erreur calculée sur une série de n mesures de 100 min.
      chacune, effectuées sur l'échantillon et sur le bruit
      de fond.

$$s = \sqrt{\frac{\sum\limits_{1}^{n} (N_i - \bar{N})^2}{n-1}}$$

      N_i = nombre de coups. 100 min^{-1}

      $\bar{N}$ = moyenne du nombre de coups total

      n = nombre de périodes de comptage
      de 100 min. En général, 15 < n < 30.

(5) $\delta^{13}C = \left[\dfrac{^{13}C/^{12}C \ \text{éch.}}{^{13}C/^{12}C \ \text{std.}} - 1 \right] .1000$, exprimé en $^o/_{oo}$ vs PDB.

(6)   Age ^{14}C conventionnel, calculé avec la période de Libby
      (T = 5568 ans). Ces âges ont été calculés en normalisant
      les activités ^{14}C en fonction des $\delta^{13}C$ (quand ceux-ci sont
      disponibles). Dans les autres cas, nous avons utilisé le
      $\delta^{13}C$ moyen (- 8±2$^o/_{oo}$), ce qui revient a ajouter 275± 50 ans
      aux âges ^{14}C bruts (Stuiver et Polach, 1977).

(7)   Ages ^{14}C corrigés pour la dilution du ^{14}C due à la dissolu-
      tion du bedrock.

$$t = -\frac{1}{\lambda} \ln \frac{A}{A_0 .q} \qquad (ici, \ q = 0,85)$$

Table 15.1 Résultats des datations ^{14}C de concrétions stalagmitiques holocènes utilisés pour le calcul des vitesses de croissance

N° labo. (1)	N° échantillon (2)	Date mesures (3)	^{14}C (% moderne) ± 'erreur conventionnelle' ± 'écart quadrat.' moyen sur n. mesures de 100 m.' (4)	$\delta^{13}C$ °/°° vs PDB (5)	âge ^{14}C conventionnel ± 'erreur conventionnelle' (6) (ans B.P.)	âge ^{14}C corrigé pour la dilution due au bedrock (q = 0,85) ± 'écart quadratique moyen' (7) (ans B.P.)	Localisation schématique des prélèvements
MBN 177	CPL2-H1	22.03.82	84,2 ± 0,8 ± 3,1	–	1660 ± 85	350 +300 −290	sommet du plancher (hiatus)
MBN 179	CPL2-E/D	26.03.82	42,6 ± 0,5 ± 1,9	–	7130 ± 110	5820 +370 −350	'milieu' du plancher (hiatus)
MBN 178	CPL2-A/B	22.03.82	33,5 ± 0,5 ± 1,6	–	9060 ± 130	7750 +390 −380	base du plancher
MBN 182	RSMI/E	16.04.82	67,6 ± 0,7 ± 2,5	−10,4	3390 ± 90	2080 +300 −290	sommet de la stalagmite
MBN 183	RSMI/D	19.04.83	64,3 ± 0,7 ± 2,5	−10,5	3780 ± 95	2470 +320 −310	'milieu' supérieur
MBN 184	RSMI/B	22.04.82	61,9 ± 0,7 ± 2,7	−10,2	4100 ± 95	2790 +360 −340	'milieu' inférieur
MBN 180	RSMI/A	31.03.82	59,7 ± 0,6 ± 2,8	−10,6	4380 ± 85	3070 +390 −370	base de la stalagmite
Hv 9686*	RSMV/I	18.04.80	53,3 ± 1,1	−11,3	5055 ± 175	3750	sommet
Hv 9685*	RSMV/C	18.04.80	29,0 ± 0,6	−10,0	9940 ± 160	8630	'milieu' (hiatus)
Hv 9684*	RSMV/A	18.04.80	24,9 ± 1,0	−10,7	11.175 ± 335	9870	base
MBN 200	RSM8/F2	25.10.82	34,5 ± 0,4 ± 1,4	–	8830 ± 100	7520 +330 −320	partie supérieure
MBN 192	RSM8/B1	15.06.82	27,2 ± 0,3 ± 1,4	–	10.740 ± 95	9430 +430 −400	'milieu' inférieur (hiatus)
MBN 188	RSM8/A	04.05.82	00,6 ± 0,2 ± 0,7	–	> 30.000 B.P.		partie inférieure
MBN 225	RSM6/A	07.04.83	61,7 ± 0,5 ± 2,7	–	4150 ± 85	2850 +365 −350	sommet
MBN 190	RSM6/C	14.05.82	27,4 ± 0,4 ± 2,0	–	10.680 ± 130	9370 +610 −570	base

Table 15.1 (cont.)

MBN 197	BSM1/E	26.07.82	41,8 ± 0,3 / 2,3	-	7280 ± 70	5970 +460 / -430	partie supérieure
MBN 195	BSM1/A	05.07.82	34,6 ± 0,3 / 2,2	-	8800 ± 80	7490 +530 / -500	base
MBN 209	FRSM9-1/B	14.12.82	83,7 ± 0,7 / 2,8	-	1700 ± 80	390 +280 / -270	sommet
MBN 224	FRSM9-2'/B	25.03.82	77,5 ± 0,7 / 3,1	-	2320 ± 85	1020 +335 / -320	
MBN 213	FRSM9-3/B	28.12.82	66,0 ± 0,6 / 2,2	-	3610 ± 85	2300 +280 / -270	'milieu'
MBN 206	FRSM9-5/B	26.11.82	55,7 ± 0,7 / 3,0	-	4970 ± 110	3660 +440 / -420	
MBN 204	FRSM9-5/A	26.11.82	48,8 ± 0,6 / 1,8	-	6040 ± 110	4730 +300 / -290	base
MBN 217	VKSM 1/C	03.03.83	83,0 ± 0,7 / 3,1	-	1770 ± 80	470 +300 / -290	sommet
MBN 211	VKSM 1/A	21.12.82	76,4 ± 0,6 / 2,4	-	2400 ± 80	1130 +260 / -250	base
MBN 233	TCSM 1/A	08.06.83	53,0 ± 0,5 / 2,1	-	5380 ± 90	4070 +335 / -330	sommet 2
MBN 232	TCSM 1/B	03.06.83	52,5 ± 0,6 / 2,8	-	5450 ± 110	4140 +435 / -415	sommet 1
MBN 236	TCSM 1/C	23.06.83	45,5 ± 0,5 / 2,4	-	6600 ± 100	5300 +440 / -420	partie inférieure

Table 15.2 Vitesses de croissance verticale et volumes de
calcite précipitée dans des concrétions
stalagmitiques holocènes datées par ^{14}C

N° éch.	Age ^{14}C (q = 0,85) (ans B.P.)	Vitesse de croissance (cm/100 ans)	Vitesse moyenne pondérée (cm/100 ans)	Volume moyen de calcite (cm³/an)	Localisation
CPL2-H1	350 ± 85				
		0,14			
CPL2-E/D	5820 ± 110		0,24	-	Abîme de Comblain-au-Pont
		0,35			
CPL2-A/B	7750 ± 130				
RSMII/E	2080 ± 90				
		1,03			
RSMII/D	2470 ± 95				
		2,13	1,58	0,18	Grotte de Remouchamps
RSMII/B	2790 ± 95				
		1,11			
RSMII/A	3070 ± 85				
RSMV/I	3750 ± 175				
		0,86			
RSMV/C	8630 ± 160		1,04	0,23	Grotte de Remouchamps
		1,46			
RSMV/A	9870 ± 335				
RSM8/F2	7520 ± 100				
		1,20	1,20	0,21	Grotte de Remouchamps
RSM8/B1	9430 ± 95				
RSM6/A	2850 ± 85				
		0,22	0,22	0,06	Grotte de Remouchamps
RSM6/C	9370 ± 130				
BSM1/E	5970 ± 70				
		0,99	0,99	0,78	Grotte de Brialmont (Tilff)
BSM1/A	7490 ± 80				
FRSM9-1/B	390 ± 80				
		5,90			
FRSM9-2'/B	1020 ± 85				
		4,14			
FRSM9-3/B	2300 ± 85		4,04	1,28	Grotte de la Fontaine de Rivîre (Hamoir)
		3,22			
FRSM9-5/B	3660 ± 110				
		2,49			
FRSM9-5/A	4730 ± 110				
VKSM1/C	470 ± 80				
		4,03	4,03	1,14	Grotte Véronika (Tilff)
VKSM1/A	1130 ± 80				
TCSM1/A	4070 ± 90				
		9,29			
TCSM1/B	4140 ± 110		3,87	0,53	Trou des Crevés (Wavreille)
		1,55			
TCSM1/C	5300 ± 100				

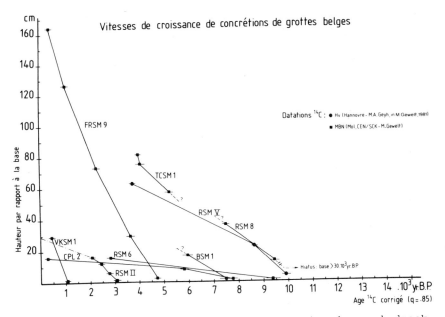

Figure 15.6 Ages ¹⁴C corrigés pour la dilution due au bedrock
(q = 0,85) et vitesses de croissance de concrétions
stalagmitiques holocènes issues de grottes belges

Les huit stalagmites et le plancher stalagmitique ont été
datés par ¹⁴C en plusieurs endroits étagés sur leur hauteur.
Comme le montre le Tableau 15.1, les résultats ¹⁴C sont en
parfaite concordance stratigraphique, l'activité ¹⁴C décroissant
du sommet vers la base des concrétions. Dans certains cas
(RSMII par exemple), les datations effectuées sur des couches
stratigraphiquement très proches peuvent se superposer dans les
limites des erreurs de mesure.

Pour la mesure des distances entre points datés, on a
utilisé le centre des échantillons analysés et pour le calcul des
vitesses, on a postulé des vitesses de croissance constantes
entre les datations (ce qui évidemment n'est pas nécessairement
exact, les vitesses pouvant varier au sein d'une même concrétion).

Le Tableau 15.2 fournit les résultats des vitesses et des
volumes de croissance calculés à partir des datations au radiocarbone. Des vitesses moyennes de croissance ont également été
calculées sur l'ensemble de chaque concrétion, en pondérant les
vitesses de croissance en fonction de la hauteur de calcite
entre deux dates. Les volumes de calcite précipitée ont été
calculés en prenant le diamètre moyen des stalagmites et en les
assimilant à des cylindres.

Le Tableau 15.2 montre que les vitesses ae croissance sont
assez variables. Les valeurs maximales des vitesses de croissance sont de 9,29 et 5,90 cm/100 ans, tandis que les vitesses
minimales sont 0,14 et 0,22 cm/100 ans. Les vitesses moyennes
pondérées varient de 0,22 à 4,04 cm/100 ans. Les volumes moyens
de calcite précipitée varient quant à eux de 0,06 à 1,28 cm³/an.
Les différentes datations relatives aux concrétions étudiées ont
été reportées en fonction de la hauteur par rapport a la base
(Figure 15.6). Les droites joignant les points datés offrent
donc une image des taux de croissance de chaque concrétion pendant le laps de temps considéré. Plus la pente de droite est
redressée, plus la vitesse de croissance est rapide. Les traits
interrompus indiquent que la concrétion n'est pas complète, soit
que son sommet n'ait pas été retrouvé (et donc daté) ou bien que
sa base soit encore en cours d'analyse ou encore qu'elle
soit plus vieille que 30.000 BP (RSM 8). Le trait d'axe prolongeant RSM II indique que la concrétion se formait encore au
moment du prélèvement. L'échelle des âges ^{14}C utilisée est
corrigée pour un facteur de dilution q = 0,85 (voir ci-dessus).

Les vitesses les plus rapides s'observent dans les deux
stalagmites (VKSM 1 et FRSM 9) les plus jeunes (depuis environ
2500 BP jusqu'à la période actuelle). Il semble que les
vitesses élevées s'accompagnent d'une précipitation de calcite
vacuolaire, en tout cas dans VKMS 1 où les vacuoles sont très
nombreuses. Cette observation serait à mettre en relation avec
la dynamique de la cristallisation de la calcite.

Les vitesses peuvent varier au sein d'une même concrétion,
par exemple pour FRSM9 et RSMV. On observe également des ruptures dans les vitesses de croissance, vers 2500 BP pour FRSM 9
(la croissance étant plus rapide après cette date et jusqu'à la
période actuelle) et vers 8600 BP dans RSM V où l'on remarque
un ralentissement depuis cette date jusqu'au sommet de la
stalagmite, vers 3700 BP Les autres concrétions étudiées paraissent avoir des vitesses de croissance relativement constantes.

Le sommet de trois stalagmites n'est pas subactuel: on
détecte donc ici un arrêt de croissance, certain pour RSMV (vers
3700 BP) qui était en place, probable pour les deux autres
stalagmites (TCSM1 et RSM6) qui ont été prélevées non en place.
Dans ce dernier cas, il est également possible, s'il n'y a pas
eu d'arrêt de croissance, qu'on date l'époque de l'écroulement
des deux stalagmites, c'est-à-dire 4000 BP (TCSM1) et 2800 BP
(RSM 6).

Un autre arrêt de croissance, au sein même d'une stalagmite
celui-là, a été détecté: RSM8 montre en coupe une couche de
croissance de calcite ocre, avec de petits cristaux de calcite
aciculaires. Cette couche paraît caractéristique d'une interruption de croissance; elle est surmontée d'une couche de calcite
noire qui marque la reprise du concrétionnement. Cette couleur
noire est assez rare dans les stalagmites holocènes que nous
avons étudiées jusqu'ici et elle nous paraît être le signe d'un
important apport de matière organique qui était stockée dans la
fissure d'alimentation pendant l'interruption de croissance de
la concrétion. Cette interruption a duré au minimum 20.000 ans,

les datations ^{14}C effectuées de part et d'autre de l'hiatus ayant donné, au-dessus, environ 9500 BP (date approximative de la reprise du concrétionnement) et au-dessous de l'hiatus, plus de 30.000 ans BP.

Les vitesses de croissance lentes s'observent dans CPL2, RSM6 et également en RSM II (trait d'axe sur la Figure 15.6).

Pour CPL 2, l'explication des vitesses lentes calculées tient principalement dans le nombre important d'arrêts de croissance de la calcite (voir les hiatus sur la Figure 15.2). Ces hiatus se marquent par des passées argileuses de faible épaisseur (de l'ordre du centimètre). Dans certains cas, la calcite recouvrant la phase de sédimentation antérieure montre des veines de calcite en relief qui paraissent être des remplissages de fentes de dessication de l'argile. Bien que ces interruptions de croissance suffisent à expliquer les faibles vitesses de développement vertical du plancher, il est concevable que les planchers stalagmitiques aient en général une vitesse de croissance verticale moindre que celle des stalagmites, notamment pour des raisons d'épaisseur de film d'eau et de comportements cinétique et dynamique. Dans le cas des stalagmites, la précipitation de calcite peut être plus rapide car les gouttes d'alimentation éclatent au point de chute, ce qui permet probablement un dégazage plus facile et plus rapide du CO_2 de la solution et facilite la précipitation du $CaCO_3$. L'étude théorique de Dreybrodt (1980; 1981) a d'ailleurs démontré théoriquement que les coulées stalagmitiques de paroi ont une vitesse de croissance inférieure à celle des stalagmites.

La faible vitesse de croissance mesurée dans RSM 6 (0,22 cm/100 ans) ne semble pas due à une interruption de croissance: aucun hiatus n'a été identifié dans cette stalagmite. Il faut probablement en chercher la cause dans le mode de formation de la concrétion qui s'est développée sous une faible épaisseur de schiste calcareux. L'eau venant de sol traverse uniquement ces schistes avant d'arriver au plafond de la Salle de Schiste (grotte de Remouchamps). Cette formation géologique doit sans doute être soumise à une dissolution moindre qu'un calcaire pur. Aussi, le potentiel de reprécipitation du $CaCO_3$ des eaux arrivant dans cette salle doit-il probablement aussi être moindre, ce qui expliquerait la faible vitesse de croissance de RSM 6.

La stalacto-stalagmite RSM II a été datée en plusieurs points, du moins dans la partie stalagmite de la concrétion. La vitesse moyenne de croissance de la stalagmite (qui constitue les 20 premiers cm de la colonne) est assez élevée: 1,58 cm/100 ans. Alors que les 7 derniers cm (constitués d'une stalactite) montrent, par interpolation graphique sur la Figure 15.6 (trait d'axe), une vitesse beaucoup plus faible depuis le sommet daté de la partie stalagmitique, jusqu'à la période actuelle (la concrétion était toujours active au moment du prélèvement).

311

Ce ralentissement de la croissance s'explique peut-être par la morphologie en stalactite de la partie supérieure[1].

En ce qui concerne les relations entre les vitesses de croissance et la morphologie des stalagmites, nos résultats ne permettent pas encore de donner une réponse certaine. Il semble cependant que les stalagmites en forme de cierge (H/Ø > 5) peuvent se développer plus rapidement enhauteur que les stalagmites massives (H/Ø < 5).

La majorité des échantillons présentés ici appartient au premier type. Cependant, BSM 1 est une stalagmite plus massive (malheureusement incomplète vers le haut) qui montre, mais de façon peu significative, une vitesse de croissance légèrement inférieure (0,99 cm/100 ans). Cette faible différence doit s'expliquer par le fait que la forme massive de la stalagmite est due à une deuxième génération de concrétionnement qui a recouvert latéralement une stalagmite d'un diamètre originel plus faible.

Ces premières données concernant les vitesses de croissance de concrétions de grottes belges durant l'Holocène peuvent être comparées avec celles obtenues à l'étranger.

En Europe Centrale, Franke (1967) calcule des vitesses de croissance de stalagmites comprises entre 0,5 et 4,5 cm/100 ans. Dans des concrétions holocènes, issues de grottes des mêmes régions, Geyh et Franke (1970) trouvent des vitesses de 0,98±0,7 cm/100 ans et de 1,35±0,1 cm/100 ans. Ces chiffres sont comparables aux nôtres. Pour des stalagmites plus anciennes, les vitesses sont plus réduites (0,15±0,1 cm/100 ans) et en particulier pendant la période comprise entre 17.000 et 35.000 BP, il ne se trouve aucune stalagmite dont la vitesse de croissance soit supérieure à 0,31 cm/100 ans.

En France, Labeyrie *et al.* (1967) trouvent pour un cierge de l'Aven-d'Orgnac des vitesses moyennes de formation comprises entre 2,2 et 4,4 cm/100 ans, ainsi qu'un volume moyen de calcite précipitée de 2,5 cm^3/an. Duplessy *et al.* (1972) analysent plusieurs stalagmites de la Grange Mathieu et de l'Aven d'Orgnac et trouvent des vitesses de croissance variant de 0,6 à 6 cm/100 ans.

Les chiffres obtenus en Belgique (0,22 à 4,04 cm/100 ans) sont donc assez comparables à ceux trouvés en Europe Centrale et en France. Par contre, Harmon *et al.* (1975) citent des vitesses de croissance nettement inférieures, pour des 'long columnar stalagmites' (H/Ø > 5) datées par $^{230}Th/^{234}U$. Ainsi, les

_____

(1) En effet, dès que la stalactite est soudée à la stalagmite, l'eau arrivant par le canal d'alimentation central de la stalactite est bloquée et isolée de l'atmosphère de la grotte, ce qui entrave la précipitation de $CaCO_3$. Celle-ci ne peut plus alors s'effectuer qu'à partir de l'eau ruisselant sur la partie extérieure de la colonne stalagmitique.

vitesses de formation moyennes observées au Mexique sont de 0,41 cm/100 ans, en Virginie occidentale, de 0,18 cm/100 ans, aux Bermudes de 0,12 cm/100 ans et au Kentucky, de 0,04 cm/100 ans. Les stalagmites étudiées (Harmon *et al.*, 1975) ont des âges compris entre 25.000 et 200.000 BP.

Signalons aussi que des calculs théoriques (Dreybrodt, 1980) ont abouti à des vitesses maximales de croissance des stalagmites de 10 cm/100 ans. D'après les données citées plus haut, cette valeur semble bien constituer un maximum qui a d'ailleurs été rencontré dans une stalagmite belge (TCSM 1) : 9,29 cm/100 ans.

La large gamme des vitesses de croissance rencontrée, aussi bien dans une même région qu'entre régions différentes doit être attribuée à la diversité des facteurs influençant de manière directe ou indirecte le concrétionnement et au nombre important de combinaisons possibles entre ces facteurs. On peut notamment citer :

- le climat et la température;
- la quantité, la fréquence et la nature des précipitations atmosphériques;
- la nature et l'épaisseur du sol dans lequel percolent les eaux;
- la teneur en CO_2 de l'air du sol (liée au métabolisme plus ou moins intense de la biomasse);
- la teneur en CO_2 de l'air de la grotte;
- la vitesse de percolation des eaux (influence sur le nombre et la fréquence des gouttes d'alimentation des stalactites et stalagmites);
- la lithologie des roches traversées par les eaux de per- colation (ralentissement des vitesses de croissance pour les schistes calcareux (RSM 6) et effet de la dolomite, du gypse et de la pyrite sur la dissolution).

Ceci ne constitue pas une liste exhaustive des facteurs climatiques, hydrologiques, géologiques et géochimiques influen- çant la vitesse de concrétionnement.

Ces quelques exemples sont mentionnés pour mettre en évi- dence la difficulté de construire un modèle fiable reliant par exemple la morphologie des concrétions et leur vitesse de croissance. En effet, un certain nombre de paramètres régissant la précipitation de la calcite ont varié d'une manière parfois incertaine dans le passé, durant la croissance même des con- crétions.

On soulignera enfin que les interpolations d'âges entre parties de concrétions datées sont très délicates si une analyse microstratigraphique n'est pas effectuée. L'observation détaillée des couches de croissance des concrétions permet en effet le plus souvent de s'affranchir des interruptions de croissance qui peuvent parfois s'être étendues sur une longue période (plus de 20.000 ans en RSM 8).

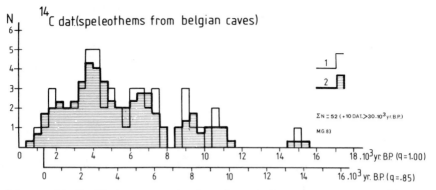

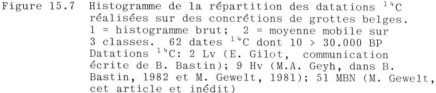

Figure 15.7   Histogramme de la répartition des datations [14]C
réalisées sur des concrétions de grottes belges.
1 = histogramme brut; 2 = moyenne mobile sur
3 classes. 62 dates ^{14}C dont 10 > 30.000 BP
Datations [14]C: 2 Lv (E. Gilot, communication
écrite de B. Bastin); 9 Hv (M.A. Geyh, dans B.
Bastin, 1982 et M. Gewelt, 1981); 51 MBN (M. Gewelt,
cet article et inédit)

Essai d'interprétation paléoclimatique des datations [14]C

    Sur l'histogramme (Figure 15.7), nous avons reporté la
majorité des datations ^{14}C effectuées dans des concrétions de
grottes belges. Aux 24 nouvelles datations publiées ici
(Tableau 15.1), on a ajouté 27 datations (Gewelt, inédit) ainsi
que 9 datations de Hanovre (Hv) publiées dans Bastin (1982) et
Gewelt (1981). Deux datations (Lv861 et Lv862) effectuées par
E. Gilot (communication écrite de B. Bastin) ont également été
utilisées. La construction de l'histogramme a été effectuée en
reportant les datations ^{14}C par classe de 400 ans (ce qui
équivaut environ à 3 σ de l'erreur conventionnelle sur la statistique de comptage). En ordonnée, ce sont les effectifs N
(nombre de datations par classe d'âge) qui ont été représentés.
Deux échelles des âges ^{14}C ont été dessinées; la première représente les âges ^{14}C conventionnels, non corrigés par la dilution
du bedrock (q = 1,00), tandis que la seconde échelle en abscisse
représente les âges ^{14}C corrigés avec un facteur de dilution
q = 0,85. C'est cette échelle corrigée que nous utilisons dans
la discussion. L'histogramme brut a également été lissé par une
moyenne mobile effectuée sur 3 classes (trait gras, Figure 15.7).
Remarquons que l'interprétation peut être sujette à caution
étant donné le nombre relativement faible de datations utilisées
(62) et l'influence possible du choix des concrétions datées.
Ce sont en effet les concrétions d'aspect 'jeune' qui ont été de
préférence analysées étant donné que nous ne disposions que de
la seule méthode de datation par [14]C (limitée à environ 30.000
BP). Il est donc possible que l'échantillonnage soit biaisé.

L'histogramme de la répartition des dates ^{14}C montre
(Figure 15.7):

- absence de datation ^{14}C dans des concrétions de grottes entre
30.000 et 10.000 BP, sauf une vers 15.000 BP (âge ^{14}C non
corrigé). Cette seule datation tombe dans le Dryas I
lorsqu'elle n'est pas corrigée pour la dilution du bedrock
(q = 1,0). Si l'on admet, et cela sera discuté plus loin,
que le Dryas I n'est pas une époque favorable au concrétionnement, il conviendrait de corriger la datation d'environ
1800 ans (q = 0,80) pour qu'elle corresponde au réchauffement
du Bölling. En effet, si le facteur de correction 'normal',
q = 0,85 était utilisé, la formation de la concrétion serait
encore placée à la fin du Dryas ancien.

- 10 datations dépassent la limite de détection (âge supérieur
à 30.000 BP) sans qu'on puisse préciser davantage l'âge par
la seule méthode du ^{14}C. Ces concrétions feront prochainement
l'objet d'analyses ^{230}Th/^{234}U.

- intensification du nombre de dates à partir de l'Atlantique,
avec un maximum entre 2.000 et 3.000 BP, c'est-à-dire environ
à la transition Subboréal-Subatlantique. Les premières dates
trouvées démarrent à environ 10.000 BP. L'absence de datations
entre 6500 et 7500 BP, ainsi que la seule date vers 4500 BP,
ne nous paraissent pas significatives, vu le nombre assez
petit de datations effectuées (62 au total). C'est plutôt la
distribution générale des datations et les maxima qui paraissent significatifs.

L'histogramme montre en tout cas que le concrétionnement
était très faible, voire même interrompu dans les grottes
étudiées en Belgique pendant la période 10.000-30.000 BP. Par
contre, durant l'Holocene les grottes sont le siège d'une importante précipitation de calcite stalagmitique, qui semble être
corrélé avec un adoucissement du climat, car l'augmentation du
potentiel dissolution-reprécipitation du $CaCO_3$ semble bien liée
à une augmentation de la température (Drake et Wigley, 1975).

Diverses causes peuvent être à l'origine des interruptions
de concrétionnement, par exemple:

- absence d'eau de percolation, probablement liée à la présence
d'un pergélisol. L'existence d'un 'permafrost' a été con-
firmée en Belgique par la présence de fentes de gel, notamment
durant le Dryas III et bien sûr pendant le Vistule. La
formation de ces fentes de gel, qui se développent dans un
sol gelé en permanence, implique une température moyenne
annuelle inférieure à -1°C (Pissart, 1976).

- diminution de la teneur en CO_2 d'origine biogénique dans le
sol, durant la période froide. Si la diminution de la température s'accompagne d'une diminution de l'activité biologique,
la pCO_2 du sol diminue également, ce qui réduit donc
l'agressivité de l'eau. Le potentiel dissolution étant réduit,
la capacité des eaux de percolation à précipiter sous terre
de la calcite diminue également. On sait par ailleurs que
la prétendue agressivité intense des eaux de fonte de la
glace, et dans certains cas de la neige, est controuvée, ce

qui a été démontré depuis longtemps par Ek (1964; 1966), Ek et Pissart (1965) et Ek *et al.* (1969).

- réduction de la quantité de précipitations atmosphériques.

- une réduction de la température des grottes jusqu'à une température inférieure à 0°C rendrait le concrétionnement impossible. (eau immobilisée sous forme de glace). Cette hypothèse n'est peut-être pas à exclure pour les périodes de froid intense (Vistule 3?) et de durée suffisamment longue pour que la température de la grotte ait le temps de s'équilibrer avec la température moyenne en surface. Cet équilibrage prend quelques centaines d'années suivant l'épaisseur du toit calcaire surplombant la grotte (Duplessy *et al.*, 1971).

- des grottes noyées par l'eau ou remplies par des sédiments sont également un obstacle majeur au concrétionnement. On sait en effet (Gewelt, 1978) qu'en climat périglaciaire, les grottes peuvent être, au moins partiellement, colmatées par des remplissages sédimentaires. Si ceux-ci atteignent la voûte, le concrétionnement est enrayé, du moins localement. De plus, ces remplissages sédimentaires peuvent jouer le rôle de véritables bouchons, ce qui entraine un remplissage de la grotte par l'eau et impose une reprise de la circulation des eaux en surface, à l'aval des pertes. Si la grotte est noyée durant ces périodes (périglaciaires), le concrétionnement peut également être interrompu. L'observation de formes phréatiques du type 'box-work' dans la zone vadose de certaines grottes-chantoirs paraît d'ailleurs confirmer cette hypothese de cavité noyée (Gewelt, 1978).

De façon inverse, la présence de concrétionnement (Figure 15.7) est l'indicateur de certaines conditions climatiques et hydrologiques:

- absence d'un pergélisol continu;

- température de la grotte supérieure à 0°C;

- grotte remplie d'air (c'est-à-dire non noyée et non colmatée par un remplissage sédimentaire).

Remarquons que la présence d'anciennes concrétions ne reflète pas nécessairement la présence d'un sol avec végétation, notamment si le bedrock contient de la dolomite, du gypse ou de la pyrite (Atkinson, 1983). Les concrétions de Castleguard Cave (grotte située sous le Columbia Ice Field) se forment en effet sans l'intervention de CO_2 biogénique, la grotte étant située sous un glacier. L'étude de Atkinson (1983) montre que la formation des concrétions est due, dans cette grotte, à l'existence de gypse et de dolomite qui permettent de faire intervenir des processus de dissolution incongruente. De plus, l'oxydation de la pyrite présente dans le bed rock peut fournir de l'acide sulfurique et donc favoriser la dissolution. Ces facteurs lithologiques sont prédominants pour la formation des concrétions de Castleguard Cave. Ils surpassent nettement les précipitations dues à l'évaporation et celles dues à la sursaturation de la calcite causée par un léger réchauffement des eaux dans la grotte (Atkinson, 1983). Dreybrodt (1982) a calculé que la précipitation de calcite due à un léger réchauffement des eaux saturées vis-à-vis du $CaCO_3$ entraîne la formation de stalagmites dont la vitesse maximale de croissance est au plus de 10^{-3} cm/an, soit 0,1 cm/100 ans. Ces processus bien réels semblent cependant assez locaux et, en Belgique, nous n'avons pas encore trouvé de concrétion formée par ces mécanismes durant les périodes froides. Au contraire, durant celles-ci, il semble bien qu'il y ait eu un arrêt de croissance des concrétions (Figure 15.7), ce qui sera confirmé ou infirmé par des données ultérieures.

CONCLUSION

Malgré les difficultés d'estimation de la correction à apporter aux âges ^{14}C conventionnels (correction due à la réduction de l'activité initiale par la présence de carbone 'mort' issu de la dissolution du bedrock calcaire), la méthode de datation des concrétions de grottes par le radiocarbone constitue un outil précieux pour la chronologie du Quaternaire récent et plus particulièrement pour l'Holocène. Plusieurs indications nous ont conduit à adopter un facteur de correction de q = 0,85, ce qui se ramène à retrancher environ 1300 ans aux âges ^{14}C conventionnels. Cette correction, provisoirement adoptée ici, pourrait néanmoins être différente suivant les vicissitudes climatiques du passé.

Les analyses au radiocarbone, menées au sein de plusieurs stalagmites et d'un plancher stalagmitique holocènes montrent que les vitesses de croissance sont très variables (de 0,22 à 9,29 cm), ainsi que les volumes de calcite précipitée (de 6 à 128 $cm^3/100$ ans). Les vitesses de croissance peuvent également varier au sein d'une même concrétion. Le nombre important de facteurs (géologiques, géochimiques, hydrologiques et climatiques) régissant la croissance des concrétions explique cette gamme assez large de vitesses de croissance. Cette variabilité des vitesses de croissance est d'ailleurs comparable à celle observée dans des concrétions de grottes d'Europe Centrale et de France.

Les 62 datations ^{14}C effectuées dans des concrétions de grottes belges indiquent que le concrétionnement s'est probablement interrompu durant les périodes froides du Quaternaire. En tout cas, durant la période de 30.000 (limite de notre méthode de datation) à 10.000 BP, nous n'avons trouvé, jusqu'à présent, qu'une seule concrétion. Seules des mesures complémentaires (en cours) sur un plus grand nombre d'échantillons pourront vérifier, avec une statistique suffisante, si les principales tendances, mises en évidence par nos premiers résultats, se confirment.

Remerciements

Ce travail a été partiellement financé par un 'Crédit aux chercheurs' accordé par le FNRS au Professeur A. Pissart que nous remercions vivement. Le Dr C. Ek a bien voulu relire le manuscrit et y apporter des critiques constructives; il nous a

également très efficacement guidé sur le terrain. Qu'il trouve
ici l'expression de notre profonde reconnaissance.

Notre reconnaissance s'adresse également au CEN à Mol et
plus particulièrement au Dr G. Koch qui nous accueille dans sa
section 'Mesures bas niveau', à MM. J. Mermans et F. Verhoeven
pour leur aide au laboratoire, au Dr C. Hurtgen et à M.F. Staes
pour leur assistance lors des prélèvements au carottier. Nous
tenons également à remercier pour leur aide dans le prélèvement
des échantillons, MM. A. Briffoz et J. Godissart et le Dr Y.
Quinif. Il nous est aussi agréable de remercier le Dr B. Bastin
qui a accepté d'effectuer plusieurs analyses polliniques dans
les stalagmites étudiées. Merci aussi à l'Administration
communale d'Aywaille et à MM. A. Herceg et G. Purnelle de la
Société anonyme des Grottes de Remouchamps qui nous ont autorisé
à effectuer des prélèvements d'échantillons dans les grottes de
Remouchamps et de Comblain-au-Pont.

BIBLIOGRAPHIE

Atkinson, T.C. 1983. Growth mecanisms of speleothems in Castle
    guard Cave (Alberta, Canada). *Arctic and Alpine Research,*
    15(4), 523-536.

Bastin, B., Dupuis, C. et Quinif, Y. 1977. Preliminary results
    of the application of quaternary geological methods of
    speleogenetic studies of a Belgian cave. *Proceedings of
    the 7th International Speleological Congress,* Sheffield,
    England, 24-28.

Bastin, B. 1979. L'analyse pollinique des stalagmites: une
    nouvelle possibilité d'approche des fluctuations climatique
    du Quaternaire. *Ann. Soc. Géol. Belg.,* **101**, 13-19.

Bastin, B. 1982. Premier bilan de l'analyse pollinique de
    stalagmites holocènes en provenance de grottes belges.
    Revue belge de Geographie, **106(1)**, 87-97.

Broecker, W.S. et Olson, E.A. 1959. ^{14}C dating of cave forma-
    tions. *N.S.S. Bull.,* **21(1)**, p 43.

Broecker, W.S. et Walton, A. 1959. The geochemistry of ^{14}C in
    fresh-water systems. *Geochimica et Cosmochimica Acta,* **16**,
    15-38.

Broecker, W.S., Olson, E.A. et Orr, P.C. 1960. Radiocarbon
    measurements and annual rings in cave formations. *Nature,*
    185, 93-94.

Drake, J.J. et Wigley, T.M.L. 1975. The effect of climate on
    the chemistry of carbonate groundwater. *Water Resources
    Research,* **11**, 958-962.

Dreybrodt, W. 1980. Deposition of calcite from thin films of
    natural calcareous solutions and the growth of speleothems.
    Chem. Geol., **29**, 89-105.

Dreybrodt, W. 1981. The kinetics of calcite precipitation from thin films of calcareous solutions and the growth of speleothems: revisited. *Chem. Geol.*, **32**, 237-245.

Dreybrodt, W. 1982. A possible mechanism for growth of calcite speleothems without participation of biogenic carbon dioxide. *Earth Planetary Science Letters*, **58**, 293-299.

Duplessy, J.C., Labeyrie, J., Lalou, C. et Nguyen, H.V. 1971. Le mesure des variations climatiques continentales. Application à la période comprise entre 130.000 et 90.000 ans BP. *Quaternary Research*, **1**, 162-174.

Duplessy, J.C., Lalou, C., Delibrias, G. et Nguyen, H.V. 1972. Datations et études isotopiques des stalagmites. Applications aux paléotempératures. *Ann. Spéléol.*, **27(3)**, 445-464.

Ek, C. 1964. Note sur les eaux de fonte des glaciers de la Haute Maurienne. Leur action sur les carbonates. *Revue belge de Géographie*, **88(1-2)**, 127-156.

Ek, C. 1966. Faible aggressivité des eaux de fonte des glaciers: l'exemple de la Marmolada (Dolomites). *Ann. Soc. Géol. Belg.*, **89**, 177-188.

Ek, C. 1976. Les phénomènes karstiques. In: *Géomorphologie de la Belgique. Hommage au Professeur P. Macar*, (A. Pissart, coord., Lab. Géol. et Géogr. phys., Univ. Liège), 137-157.

Ek, C. et Pissart, A. 1965. Dépôt de carbonate de calcium par congélation et teneur en bicarbonate des eaux résiduelles. *C.R. Acad. Sc. Paris*, **260**, 929-932.

Ek, C., Hillaire-Marcel, C. et Trudel, B. 1981. Sédimentologie et paléoclimatologie isotopique dans une grotte de Gaspésie, Québec. *Géographie physique et Quaternaire*, **34(2)**, 317-328.

Ek, C., Gilewska, S., Kaszowski, L., Kobylecki, A., Oleksinowa, K. et Oleksinowna, B. 1969. Some analyses of the CO_2 content of the air in five Polish caves. *Zeit. für Geomorph.*, **13**, 267-286.

Fontes, J.C. 1971. Un ensemble destiné à la mesure de l'activité du radiocarbone naturel par scintillation liquide. *Rev. Géogr. phys. Géol. dyn.*, **13(1)**, 67-86.

Fontes, J.C. 1980. Hydrogéologie: un champ privilégié de l'application des isotopes du milieu: L'"âge" des eaux souterraines. *Implications de l'hydrogéologie dans les autres sciences de la terre*, IHES, Symp. Montpellier (1978), 589-590 et h.t. 1-39.

Franke, H.W. 1951. Altersbestimmungen an Kalzitkronkretionen mit radioactivem Kohlenstoff. *Naturwissenschaften*, **38**, 527-528.

Franke, H.W. 1967. Isotopenverhältnisse im sekundären Kalk − geochronologische Aspekte. *Atompraxis*, **13(8)**, 363-366.

Franke, H.W., Münnich, K.O. et Vogel, J.C. 1958. Auflösung und Abscheidung von Kalk-^{14}C Datierung von Kalkabscheidungen. *Die Höhle*, **9**, 1-5.

Franke, H.W., Münnich, K.O. et Vogel, J.C. 1959. Erste Ergebnisse von Kohlenstoff-Isotopenmessungen an Kalksinter. *Die Höhle,* 10(2), 17-23.

Gewelt, M. 1978. *Géomorphologie et paléoclimatologie isotopique dans le Vallon des chantoirs.* Mémoire de licence en Sc. géographiques, Université de Liège, Fac. Sc., 213pp.

Gewelt, M. 1981. Les variations isotopiques du carbone et de l'oxygène dans une stalagmite de la grotte de Remouchamps (Belgique). Méthodes et premiers résultats. *Ann. Soc. Géol. Belg.,* 104, 269-279.

Geyh, M.A. 1970a. Isotopenphysikalische Untersuchungen an Kalksinter, ihre Bedeutung fur die [14]C Alterbestimmung von Grundwasser und die Erforschung des Paläoklimas. *Géol. Jb.,* 88, 149-158.

Geyh, M.A. 1970b. Zeitliche Abgrenzung von Klimaänderungen mit [14]C Daten von Kalksinter und organischen Substanzen. *Beih. Geol. Jb.,* 98, 15-22.

Geyh, M.A. 1972. Basic studies in Hydrology and ^{14}C and ^{3}H measurements. *Proc. 24th Int. Geol. Conf.,* Montréal, Section 11, 227-234.

Geyh, M.A. et Schillat, B. 1966. Messungen der Kohlenstoff. Isotopenhäufigkeit von Kalksinterproben aus der Langenfelden Höhle. *Der Aufschluss,* 12, 315-323.

Geyh, M.A. et Franke, H.W. 1970. Zur Wachshumsgeschwindigkeit von Stalagmiten. *Atompraxis,* 16(1), 46-48.

Harmon, R.S., Thompson, P., Schwarcz, H.P. et Ford, D.C. 1975. Uranium - Series Dating of Speleothems. *N.S.S. Bull.,* 37, 21-33.

Hennig, G.J., Grün, R. et Brunnacker, K. 1983. Speleothems, Travertines and Paleoclimates. *Quaternary Research,* 20, 1-29.

Labeyrie, J., Duplessy, J.C., Delibrias, G. et Letolle, R. 1967. Etude des températures des climats anciens par la mesure de l'oxygène 18, du carbone 13 et du carbone 14 dans les concrétions des cavernes. In: *Radioactive dating and methods of low-level counting,* (Vienne: IAEA), 153-160.

Pearson, Jr. F.J. 1965. Use of ^{13}C/^{12}C ratios to correct radiocarbon ages of material initially diluted by limestone. In: *Proc. 6th Int. Conf. Radiocarbon and Tritium Dating.* ed. R. Chatters, (Washington: Pulman), 357-366.

Pearson, Jr., F.J. et Hanshaw, B.B. 1970. Sources of dissolved species in groundwater and their effects on carbon-14 dating. In: *Isotope Hydrology,* (Vienne: IAEA), 271-286.

Pissart, A. 1976. Les dépôts et la morphologie périglaciaires de la Belgique. In: *Géomorphologie de la Belgique. Hommage au Professeur P. Macar.* (A. Pissart coord., Lab. Géol. et Géogr. phys., Univ. Liège), 115-135.

Stuiver, M. et Polach, H.A. 1977. Discussion-Reporting of ^{14}C data. *Radiocarbon,* 19(3), 355-363.

Suess, H.E. 1970. Bristelcone-pine calibration of the radio-carbon time-scale 5200 BC to the present. In: *Radiocarbon Variations and absolute Chronology,* ed. I.U. Olsson, (New York: John Wiley and Sons), 303-311.

Talma, A.S., Vogel, J.C. et Partridge, T.C. 1974. Isotopics contents of some Transvaal speleothems and their plaeoclimatic significance. *South African Journal of Science,* 70, 135-140.

Thorpe, P.M., Otlet, R.L. et Sweeting, M.M. 1980. Hydrological implications from ^{14}C profiling of UK tufa. *Radiocarbon,* 22(3), 897-908.

Thorpe, P.M., Holyoak, D.T., Preece, R.C. et Willing, M.J. 1981. Validity of corrected ^{14}C dates from calcareous tufa. *Actes du colloque de l'AGF Formations carbonatées externes, tufs et travertins,* (Paris), 151-156.

Vogel, J.C. 1970. [14]C dating of groundwater. In: *Isotope Hydrology,* (Vienna: IAEA), 225-239.

Vogel, J.C. 1983. [14]C variations during the upper Pleistocene. *Radiocarbon,* 25(2), 213-218.

16

Palynology:
a neglected tool in British cave studies

C.O. Hunt and S.J. Gale

SUMMARY

The application of palynology to the study of cave sediments has
been largely neglected in Britain. This is partly due to the
misconception that pollen is not preserved in the cave environment
and that pollen in cave deposits suffers from vertical mixing. It
is also partly because of the difficulty of extracting pollen from
cave sediments and because mineral sediments, such as those of
caves, give different pollen spectra to those of peats. However,
new techniques have allowed pollen to be more easily extracted
from cave sediments, whilst cave-pollen spectra have been shown to
reflect the same major climatic and ecological changes as those
seen in spectra from other sediments. Recent work on British cave
sediments ranging in age from Rhaetian to Holocene has demonstrated
the use of palynology as a palaeoenvironmental technique, as a
chronological tool, as a means of establishing the provenance of
cave sediments, as a sedimentary-environmental indicator, and as a
method of obtaining environmental information from 'overdug' sites
or museum specimens.

RÉSUMÉ

L'application de la palynologie à l'étude des sédiments de grottes a été plus ou moins negligée en Grande Bretagne. Ceci s'explique en partie par la conception erronée que les pollens se conservent mal dans les grottes et que les pollens des dépôts souterrains subissent des mélanges verticaux. Cela s'explique aussi par les difficultés rencontrées pour extraire les pollens des sédiments des grottes et parce que les sédiments minéraux comme ceux des grottes donnent des spectres polliniques différents de ceux des tourbes. Cependant, des techniques nouvelles ont permis d'extraire plus facilement les pollens des dépôts souterrains et on a montré que les spectres polliniques des grottes reflètent les mêmes changements climatiques et écologiques que ceux des autres sédiments. Les recherches récentes sur des sédiments de grottes britanniques dont l'âge s'étalait du Rhétien à l'Holocène ont démontré l'utilité de la palynologie pour reconstituer les paléoenvironnements, établir les chronologies, découvrir l'origine des sédiments des grottes, préciser l'environnements sédimentaires et obtenir des informations sur l'environnement à partir d'échantillons de musées ou de sites de fouilles abandonnés.

INTRODUCTION

Caves behave as sediment traps for a wide variety of deposits, and as pitfalls or shelters for man and animals. Unlike other terrestrial deposits, however, the sediments laid down in caves are protected from the effects of many subaerial weathering and erosional processes, with the result that long and complex depositional sequences may be preserved in the cave environment. As a consequence, cave sediments in the British Isles have been extensively investigated in order to obtain evidence of palaeoenvironmental conditions both within and outside the cave system (Sutcliffe, 1960; Bull, 1980; Gale, 1984).

In most non-glacial Quaternary deposits, palynology is one of the major palaeontological research tools, providing a detailed account of vegetational sequences which can be interpreted as a palaeoenvironmental or, to some extent, as a chronological record. Despite this, the application of palynology to studies of cave sediments has been largely neglected in Britain. Indeed, several recent reviews dealing with the investigation of cave sediments do not even mention the technique (Jennings, 1971, 171-178; Sweeting, 1972, 173-191; Ford, 1975; Bögli, 1980, 165-199). This is the more surprising since palynology has been successfully used in studies of cave deposits in Switzerland (Knuchel and Rupp, 1954; Bandi et al., 1953), Czechoslovakia (Kneblova, in Prosek, 1958), France (Leroi-Gourhan, 1966), Australia (Martin, 1973), the United States (Peterson, 1976), Israel (Horowitz, 1979), South Africa (Van Zinderen Bakker, 1982), and elsewhere.

FACTORS CONTRIBUTING TO THE NEGLECT
OF PALYNOLOGY IN CAVE STUDIES

The neglect of palynology by many British cave researchers
appears to stem from widespread ignorance about the conditions
under which pollen and other organic-walled microfossils may be
laid down and preserved in caves. Thus, many Quaternary palynologists have the misconception that pollen is not preserved in
calcareous environments (Moore and Webb, 1978, p. 15). Yet
numerous studies, exemplified by those of Davey (1969), who obtained palynomorphs from the Chalk, and Turner (in Kerney et al.,
1980), who obtained pollen from calcareous tufas, have clearly
shown that pollen and other organic-walled microfossils may be
preserved in favourable calcareous environments. It would be
more true to say that pollen is not preserved in strongly-
oxidising aerobic depositional environments. Yet caves contain
many depositional environments where strongly-oxidising conditions are not present.

Cave sediments have also been neglected by many palynologists because such deposits are thought to be too coarse and
porous to prevent the vertical mixing of pollen by infiltration
or suffosion (Collcutt et al., 1981, 36-37). Yet many cave
sediments are very fine-grained (Ford, 1975; Bull, 1980). Moreover, pollen seems to be relatively immobile, even in coarse,
sandy sediments, since it is rapidly bound by soil colloids
(Keatinge, 1983). Thus, even in soil profiles exposed to subaerial processes, downwash is thought to have only a minor effect
on pollen mobility (Keatinge, 1983 and references therein). On
the other hand, the relative absence of bioturbation by earth-
worms and other fauna in caves means that the pollen record in
cave sediments is likely to be better preserved than in most
soils, where biological disturbance is the major transporter of
pollen through the profile (Keatinge, 1983 and references
therein).

Another common misconception is that, since pollen assemblages from mineral sediments are very different to those from
peats, the often very sparse pollen spectra from mineral sediments are unreliable (Faegri and Iversen, 1964, p. 73). These
differences can, however, be mostly ascribed to differences in
the local parent flora and to differences in pollen taphonomy.
Once account has been taken of these factors, pollen assemblages
from mineral sediments can be interpreted in exactly the same
way as those from peats (Dimbleby, 1957; Faegri and Iversen,
1964, p. 119; Keatinge, 1983). Moreover, palynologists working
on pre-Quaternary deposits regard pollen and spore assemblages
from minerogenic sediments as more representative of the regional
pollen-rain than those from organic sediments (Neves, 1961).

Despite the neglect of palynology in cave studies, the
pioneering work of Campbell (summarised in Campbell, 1977) has
clearly shown that palynology is a useful and viable research
tool in British cave studies. Unfortunately, Campbell's work

was flawed in many respects, since it made use of wide sampling-
intervals, small sample sizes and inefficient sample-preparation
techniques. Many of the problems faced by Campbell stemmed from
the difficulties of extracting pollen from inorganic sediments,
the established techniques for which are extremely hazardous.
Since that time, however, advances in sample preparation techniques (summarised by Hunt, 1984) have allowed pollen to be
rapidly, safely and cheaply extracted from larger samples of
inorganic material, thus making it possible to produce pollen
diagrams based on large counts of pollen at small sampling intervals.

INTERPRETATION OF CAVE-POLLEN SPECTRA

Certain difficulties exist in the interpretation of cave-pollen
spectra. Perhaps the most obvious of these is caused by the
nature of the cave-mouth flora, which in temperate regions is
dominated by ferns (Lloyd, 1977). Fern spores are thus strongly
represented in interstadial and interglacial pollen-spectra from
caves. In the Holocene deposits of Kirkhead Cave, Cumbria, UK,
for example, fern spores comprise between 47.8 and 86.7% of the
total pollen and spores (Figure 16.1).

Cave-pollen assemblages might also be considered 'atypical'
because of the nature of the regional pollen-rain in karst areas,
unique biogeographical regions characterised by thin soils and
calcicole floras (Pigott, 1956; Pennington, 1974, p. 111). It
thus seems, for example, that a closed woodland canopy may not
have developed on parts of the Morecambe Bay karst, northwest
England, even during the Holocene forest maximum (pollen zones
VI-VIIa), since grasses and ruderal species are well-represented
in sediments of this age from Kirkhead Cave (Figure 16.1). These
results do not invalidate the pollen analyses from Kirkhead Cave;
however, it is necessary to take vegetational differences into
consideration when comparing results from karst areas with those
from areas of non-calcareous bedrock.

Variations in the rate of inorganic sedimentation in caves
may also cause problems, particularly since rates of deposition
in caves generally appear to be higher during cold stages
(Bakalowicz et al., 1984). As a consequence, pollen is diluted
during cold stages, which are already times of low pollen-
productivity, so that even very large samples contain insufficient
pollen for reliable statistical treatment. On the other hand,
rates of warm-stage inorganic sedimentation may be so low that
successive pollen assemblage-zones may be difficult to distinguish. In Kirkhead Cave, for example, the rate of deposition
during the cold stage of pollen zone III was over three times
that during the succeeding warm-stage pollen zones IV-VIIa
(Gale et al., 1984). In the case of Robin Hood's Cave, Cresswell, UK, bulk samples taken from 100 mm lengths of core were
submitted for analysis, with the result that the rather thin
warm-stage sediments were mixed with adjacent cold-stage sediments and the record blurred (Figure 16.2) (Hunt, in press).
Sampling of the sediments at nearby Pinhole Cave has been at 10 mm

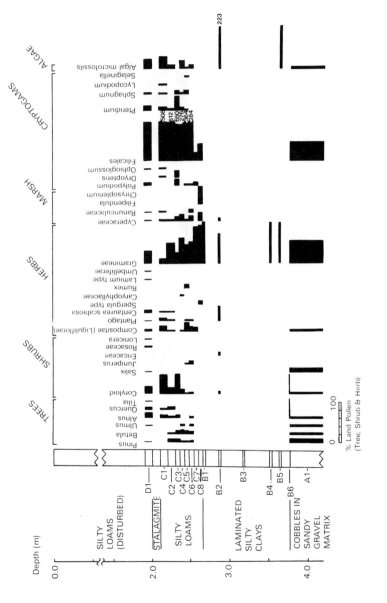

Figure 16.1 Pollen, spore and algal diagram. Kirkhead Cave, Cumbria, UK

327

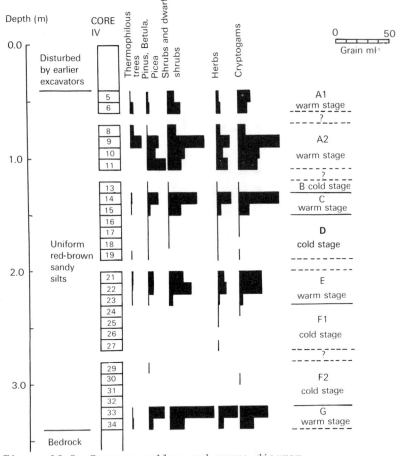

Figure 16.2   Summary pollen and spore diagram.
Robin Hood's Cave, Creswell, UK

intervals in an attempt to overcome this problem (R.D.S. Jenkinson, pers. comm., 1983).

APPLICATIONS OF PALYNOLOGY TO CAVE RESEARCH

Perhaps the most successful application of palynology to British cave research has been in elucidating palaeoenvironmental conditions in studies of otherwise unfossiliferous or poorly-fossiliferous deposits (Hubbard, in Bishop, 1975, p.96; Campbell, 1977; Marshall and Whiteside, 1980; Hunt, in press; Hunt, in Bramwell et al., 1984; Gale and Hunt, 1985). At Westbury-sub-Mendip, Somerset, UK, for example, Hubbard (in Bishop, 1975, p. 96) was able to demonstrate that evidence of early man and a Middle Quaternary mammalian fauna were deposited during zone II of an interglacial.

Secondly, the ecological information obtained by palynology also provides the basis of a dating tool, since assemblages of palynomorphs in cave sediments can be correlated with the record in securely-dated sequences elsewhere. Thus, at Tytherington fissure, Somerset, UK, marine phytoplankton from the fissure deposits not only provided a precise Rhaetian date for the associated Upper Triassic reptilian remains, but also demonstrated that they accumulated in a shoreline situation (Marshall and Whiteside, 1980). At Kirkhead Cave, pollen analysis has enabled Later Upper Palaeolithic implements to be dated (Gale *et al.*, 1984); whilst mammalian remains and a single flint artifact from Steetly Cave, near Cresswell, UK, have been shown by palynological methods to be mid-Holocene in age (Hunt, in Bramwell *et al.*, 1984).

A third application of palynology has been to help establish the provenance of sediments in caves. In Kirkhead Cave, distinctive suites of pre-Quaternary palynomorphs in the deposits show that the sediments had their origin in Irish Sea Till laid down to the south of the cave, rather than in locally-deposited material (Gale and Hunt, 1985). In Robin Hood's Cave, recycled pre-Quaternary palynomorphs are concentrated in the entrance-facies of the cave, suggesting that these sediments have a different source to those deeper in the cave (Hunt, in press). Similar work has been done by Peterson (1976) in the large and complex system of Mammoth Cave, Kentucky, USA, where it was discovered that there were sufficient differences in the flora around different inlets to the system to allow the sediments derived from certain inlets to be identified.

Fourthly, palynology may also be able to throw some light on the detailed depositional environment of some cave sediments. Many entrance-facies sediments contain distinctive spores and cysts, probably of fungi and algae, whose distribution and abundance seem to be environmentally controlled, probably by temperature, and by moisture and light availability. In Kirkhead Cave, for example, a 1.11 m thick unit of laminated silty-clays contains a Quaternary assemblage consisting mainly of algal bodies, including *Spirogyra* spores, *Pediastrum*, and psilate ?algal cysts, together with echinate ?algal cysts. The assemblage suggests deposition in moist, freshwater conditions (Gale and Hunt, 1985). At Robin Hood's Cave, a different assemblage suggests deposition in drier conditions (Hunt, in press).

Finally, the relatively small sample sizes necessary for palynological work allows the analysis of small amounts of *in situ* sediment. This is particularly important in the case of those caves 'overdug' in the 19th and early 20th centuries, or where fragments of sediment adhere to museum specimens of uncertain provenance within a cave. One example of this has been the use of palynology to establish the environment of deposition, and possibly the provenance, of teeth and bones of *Equus* sp. and *Coelodonta antiquitatis* Blumenbach recovered earlier this century (Jenkinson, 1983) from Pinhole Cave, Creswell. The pollen assemblages recovered from the specimens are both typical of warm-stage conditions, but are of rather different types, the

329

former being of interstadial type, and the latter of late-interglacial facies. It should be possible to relate these assemblages to specific pollen zones when the pollen diagram from Pinhole Cave is complete.

CONCLUSIONS

It has been shown that many cave sediments are suitable for palynological investigation. Although cave-pollen spectra may seem unusual, when due account has been taken of the flora found in cave entrances and the peculiarities of karst vegetation, it is apparent that the cave-pollen record reflects the same major climatic and ecological changes seen in spectra from other Quaternary sediments. The results of the small amount of work that has been done in Britain, and the larger body of work from abroad, suggest that, in favourable circumstances, the cave-pollen record may be comparable in quality with that from other depositional environments. The long depositional sequences characteristic of caves make it probable that a detailed palynological history of a considerable part of the Quaternary in Britain will eventually emerge from caves.

REFERENCES

Bakalowicz, M., Sorriaux P. and Ford, D.C. 1984. Quaternary glacial events in the Pyrenees from U-series dating of spleothems in the Niaux-Lombrives-Sabart caves, Ariège, France. *Norsk geogr. Tidsskr.*, **38**, 193-197.

Bandi, H.G., Lüdin, C., Mamber, W., Schaud, S., Schmid, E. and Welten, W. 1953. Die Brügglihöhle an der Kohlholzhalde bei Nenzlingen (Kt. Bern), eine neue Fundstelle des Spätmagdalénien im untern Birstal. *Jahrbuch des Bernischen Historischen Museums,* **32-33**, 45-76.

Bishop, M.J. 1975. Earliest record of man's presence in Britain. *Nature,Lond.*, **253**, 95-97.

Bögli, A. 1980. *Karst Hydrology and Physical Speleology.* (Berlin: Springer-Verlag), 284 pp.

Bramwell, D., Cartledge, K.M., Gilbertson, D.D., Griffin, C.M., Hunt, C.O., Jenkinson, R.D.S. and Samson, C. 1984. Steetly Quarry Cave: a 'lost' interglacial site and Steetly Cave: a 5000 year old badger den. In: *In the Shadow of Extinction: a Quaternary Archaeology and Palaeoecology of the Lake, Fissures and smaller Caves at Cresswell Crags SSSI*, eds. D.D. Gilbertson and R.D.S. Jenkinson, (University of Sheffield: Department of Prehistory Archaeology), 75-87.

Bull, P.A. 1980. Towards a reconstruction of timescales and palaeoenvironments from cave sediment studies. In: *Timescales in Geomorphology,* eds. R.A. Cullingford, D.A. Davidson and J. Lewin, (London: Wiley), 177-187.

Campbell, J.B. 1977. *The Upper Palaeolithic of Britain.*
(Oxford: Clarendon Press), 264 + 376 pp.

Collcutt, S.N., Currant A.P. and Hawkes, C.J. 1981. A further
report on the excavations at Sun Hole, Cheddar. *Proceedings
of the University of Bristol speleaological Society,* 16,
21-38.

Davey, R.J. 1969. Non-calcareous microplankton from the
Cenomanian of England, northern France and north America
Part I. *Bulletin of the British Museum of Natural History
(Geology),* 17, 103-180.

Dimbleby, G.W. 1957. Pollen analysis of terrestrial soils.
New Phytolital, 56, 12-28.

Faegri, K. and Iversen, J. 1964. *A Textbook of Pollen Analysis.*
(Oxford: Blackwell), 237 pp.

Ford, T.D. 1975. Sediments in caves. *Trans. Br. Cave Res.
Assoc.,* 2, 41-46.

Gale, S.J. 1984. Quaternary hydrological development in the
Morecambe Bay karst, northwest England. *Norsk geogr. Tiddskr.,*
38, 185-192.

Gale, S.J. and Hunt, C.O. 1985. The Stratigraphy of Kirkhead
Cave, an Upper Palaeolithic site in northern England.
Proceedings of the Prehistorical Society, 51, in press.

Gale, S.J., Hunt, C.O. and Southgate, G.A. 1984. Kirkhead Cave:
biostratigraphy and magnetostratigraphy. *Archaeometry,* 26,
192-198.

Horowitz, A. 1979. *The Quaternary of Israel.* (New York:
Academic Press), 394 pp.

Hunt, C.O. 1984. Recent advances in pollen extraction tech-
niques: a brief review. In: *Palaeobiological Investigations:
Research Methods, Design and Interpretation,* eds.
N.R.J. Fieller, D.D. Gilbertson and N.G.A. Ralph, (Oxford:
British Archaeological Reports, British Series).

Hunt, C.O. in press. Palynology. In: *Robin Hood's Cave: Geology
and Palaeoecology,* eds. R.D.S. Jenkinson and D.D. Gilbertson,
(University of Sheffield, Department of Prehistory and
Archaeology).

Jenkinson, R.D.S. 1983. *The Archaeology of Cresswell Crags.*
Unpublished Ph.D. thesis, University of Sheffield.

Jennings, J.N. 1971. *Karst.* (Canberra: Australian National
University press), 252 pp.

Keatinge, T.H. 1983. Development of pollen assemblage zones
in soil profiles in southeastern England. *Boreas,* 12, 1-12.

Kerney, M.P., Preece, R.C. and Turner, C. 1980. Molluscan and
plant biostratigraphy of some Late Devensian and Flandrian
deposits in Kent. *Philosophical Transactions Royal Society
of London,* B, 291, 1-43.

Knuchel, F. and Rupp, R. 1954. Altersbestimmung von Höhlensinter
in der Beatushöhle (Schweiz). *Die Höhle,* 5, 5-6.

Leroi-Gourhan, A.   1966.   La grotte de Prélétang (commune de Presles, Isère); II.   Analyse pollinique des sédiments. *Gallia Préhist.*, **9**, 85–92.

Lloyd, O.C.   1977.   Ferns in cave entrances. *Proceedings of the International Speleological Congress,* **7**, 288.

Marshall, J.E.A. and Whiteside, D.I.   1980.   Marine influence in the Triassic 'uplands'. *Nature (London)*, **287**, 627–628.

Martin, H.A.   1973.   Palynology and historical ecology of some cave excavations in the Australian Nullarbor. *Australian Journal of Botany,* **21**, 283–316.

Moore, P.D. and Webb, J.A.   1978.   *An Illustrated Guide to Pollen Analysis.* (London: Hodder and Stoughton), 133 pp.

Neves, R.   1961.   Namurian plant spores from the southern Pennines, England. *Palaeontology,* **4**, 247–279.

Pennington, W.   1974.   *The History of British Vegetation.* (London: English Universities Press), 152 pp.

Peterson, G.M.   1976.   Pollen analysis and the origin of cave sediments in the central Kentucky karst. *Bulletin of the National Speleological Society,* **38**, 53–58.

Pigott, C.D.   1956.   The vegetation of Upper Teesdale in the north Pennines. *Journal of Ecology,* **44**, 545–586.

Prŏsek, F.   1958.   Die Erforschung der Dreiochsenhöhle am Kotŷs-Berg bei Koněprusy. *Anthropozoikum,* **7**, 47–78.

Sutcliffe, A.J.   1960.   Joint Mitnor Cave, Buckfastleigh. *Transactions and Proceedings of the Torquay Natural History Society,* **13**, 1–26.

Sweeting, M.M.   1972.   *Karst Landforms.* (London: Macmillan) 362 pp.

Van Zinderen Bakker, E.M.   1982.   Pollen analytical studies of the Wonderwerk Cave, South Africa. *Pollen Spores,* **24**, 235–250.

17

The formation of caves in granite

B. Finlayson

SUMMARY

The speleological literature contains little on the subject of caves in rocks of granitic composition. Much of what has been written is in the form of exploration reports by local caving groups and is not readily accessible. It is becoming increasingly obvious that caves in granite are more common than previously thought, and that there is some hitherto unrecognised variety in types of caves and modes of origin. Using cave descriptions from the literature and the results of recent field work in eastern Australia and western USA, a preliminary classification of granite caves has been developed. Three classes of granite cave have so far been recognised: (i) boulder caves - accessible openings between boulders in a pile of corestones; (ii) open joint caves - usually stream passages, where the joint along which the cave has developed is roofed by boulders; (iii) closed joint caves - developed along horizontal or near horizontal joints, and the caves are roofed by granite *in situ*. These three classes have been distinguished solely on morphological grounds. Possible modes of origin are discussed in some detail in the paper. Evidence is presented to show that caves in granite can constitute a hazard to engineering operations. Wider dissemination of information regarding cave formation in granite should help to alert engineering geologists to this problem.

RÉSUMÉ

La littérature spéléologique ne discute guère du problème des grottes dans les roches granitiques. La plupart des articles présentent des recherches locales de groupes spéléologiques et sont peu accessibles. Il est de plus en plus évident que les grottes granitiques sont plus fréquentes qu'on ne pensait généralement et qu'il existe des formes et des origines qui n'avaient pas encore été reconnues. Une classification préliminaire des grottes granitiques en trois catégories est proposée à partir des descriptions trouvées dans la littérature karstique et des études faites récemment sur le terrain. Trois types de grottes granitiques ont été discernés: i) grottes de blocs - avec ouvertures pénétrables dans des amas de blocs; ii) grottes à joints ouverts - d'habitude des conduits drainés, où le joint qui a guidé le développement de la grotte est coiffé par des blocs; iii) grottes à joints fermés-développés le long de joints horizontaux ou quasi-horizontaux, elles sont coiffées par le granite en place. Ces trois catégories ont été différenciés uniquement par leur morphologie. Leur genèse éventuelle est discutée dans l'article. On montre que des grottes granitiques peuvent être une source de risques dans les opérations de génie civil. Une plus large information sur la formation des grottes granitiques devrait contribuer à sensibiliser les ingénieurs géologues à ce problème.

INTRODUCTION

In 1980, Claude Chabert considered that:

> 'Il est également prématuré de répertorier les 'grandes' cavités formées par le granite, dans la mesure ou les spéléologues n'y ont pas encore prete attention' (Chabert, 1980, p 111).

This situation now appears to be changing rapidly. Recent explorations in the Greenhorn Caves in California indicate that there is over 1500 m of underground passage, which is more than three times the length of the longest granite cave reported by Chabert. Several new granite caves have recently been reported from eastern Australia by Finlayson (1981; 1982); Twidale (1982) has made the subject respectable by devoting a chapter of his recent book on granite landforms to 'Caves and Tafoni'. Despite this, the literature is not substantial. Many granite caves are known but not described in the literature, and there would seem to be a strong possibility that many more remain to be discovered. The information now coming to light about caves in granite is adding to the understanding of the development of granite landscapes and particularly the potential of subsurface water in this regard. Speleothems from granite caves also hold considerable promise for further investigations of the chemical weathering of granite. Wojcik (1961a; 1961b) has described caves in granite in the High Tatra Mountains and the Karkonosze Mountains of Poland. Some of the Tatra Mountains caves appear to be formed in the spaces between corestones, but others are attributed to

solution along sideritic veins. Shafts and niches in the
Karkonosze Mountains are associated with feldspar-rich zones.

Caves are known in granite country in many parts of the
USA. The granite caves at Lost Creek, Colorado, attained
notoriety when a fatal accident occurred there during its exploration (Arnold, 1980). Boy Scout Cave and McLaughlin Canyon
Caves in Okanogan County, Washington State were described by
Halliday (1963) as being associated with block movements. Enchanted Rock Cave, Texas (Smith, 1974; Kastning, 1976; 1977),
has developed in an inselberg mass by the removal of grus from
weathered joints and is roofed over by dislodged blocks and ex-
foliation sheets. Smith reports that other caves occur on
Enchanted Rock and its flanking hills and that they are described
in the files of the Texas Speleological Survey. A similar,
though smaller cave in North Carolina has been described by
Hedges (1978). Carroll (1978 and pers. comm.) reports fissure
and talus caves in granite in a variety of locations in the
northeast of the United States. Two of the granite boulder caves
in New Hampshire, Lost River Cave and Polar Cave, have been
commercially opened for tours (Gurnee and Gurnee, 1980). Two
extensive cave systems along stream courses are known in California; early stages of the exploration of Cahuilla Creek Caves
were reported by Quick (1972) and an interior photograph faces
page 60 of Halliday's book on American Caves (Halliday, 1974);
while Breisch (1980; 1981) has described the continuing exploration of the Greenhorn Caves.

Shaw (1980) described a cave developed on the flank of a
granite inselberg in Guyana. This cave is formed by the spaces
between massive boulders, and Shaw attributes its development
to the stripping of granular disintegration products or grus
from between corestones. Similar caves are known from elsewhere,
for example Melville's Caves, Victoria, Australia (Matthews,
1979) though these are the only ones described in detail in the
literature.

Elsewhere in Australia, granite caves have long been known
locally but were not reported in the literature until Ollier
(1965) briefly mentioned Labertouche Cave in a general article
on granite weathering in Australia. Labertouche Cave, a stream
passage through boulders, was described in more detail by
Finlayson (1981), who also discussed similar caves at a number
of other locations in Victoria. A cave formed along a joint in
granite in Girraween National Park in southern Queensland has
long been known to local cavers. Pound et al., (1975) published
a map of this cave and it has been further discussed by Finlayson
(1982) who located three more granite caves in the same area.
A cave in the Banana Range, Central Queensland, described by
Shannon (1975) has been widely quoted as an example of a granite
cave (e.g. Twidale, 1982). While it is formed on granodiorite
bedrock, the cave is the result of eluviation beneath a duri-
crusted surface.

Perhaps the most fascinating example is that reported by Morris (1971) from Swanport on the Murray River in South Australia. Here drilling operations to investigate foundations for a new bridge across the Murray encountered cavities from 0.3 m to 5.8 m high in otherwise fresh strong granite. The granite is covered by nearly 10 m of recent alluvium. The cavities which occurred at depths of up to 29 m below the base of the alluvium were found to contain alluvial sediments similar to those overlying the granite. A piece of spring steel was removed from one of them and fresh wood fragments from another. Morris suggested that water from the river above was circulating readily through some of the cavities. Some of these cavities could be explained in terms of granite boulders occupying a former river bed below the alluvium, though this does not account for the deeper cavities which are in granite *in situ*.

In this paper the term granite is used in the general sense of a coarse-grained plutonic igneous rock containing abundant quartz, i.e. encompassing the terms granite and granodiorite as defined by Streckeisen (1976). No work has yet been undertaken to assess whether there is any relationship between cave formation and mineralogical or textural composition of rocks in this broad group, though such an investigation would seem to be warranted.

TYPES OF CAVES IN GRANITE

Perusal of the literature and field observations of granite caves clearly show that a certain variety of cave types exists and that accuracy in communication through the literature might be improved by the development of a classification of granite caves. Twidale (1982) has obviously recognized this need by discussing caves under two subheadings: 'Caves associated with corestones and grus' and 'Caves associated with fractures'. This is a logical subdivision and the classification suggested here follows this pattern but subdivides the two types that Twidale recognized. Halliday (1974) uses the term 'talus caves' to refer to all caves associated with boulders. The classification is set out in Figure 17.1 with examples of each type from the literature.

Type I. Boulder caves

In these the cave space is between boulders. As shown in Figure 17.1, two subdivisions are recognized and the distinction rests largely on the cave's position in the landscape. The boulder pile type generally occurs relatively high up in the local topography, often on ridge crests and the caves are usually quite small, sometimes not becoming completely dark. By contrast, the boulder-filled stream channel type occupies the valley bottoms and the longest known granite caves fall into this group.

(a) Boulder piles These caves result from the stripping of grus from between corestones; the corestones settle and the spaces between them are occasionally large enough to be called caves. The only published map of such a cave, Makatau Cave in

336

Schematic cross-section

Cave type		Examples

I Boulder caves
(a) Boulder pile

Makatau Cave
(Shaw, 1980)

Melville's Caves
(Matthews, 1979)

(b) Boulder-filled
stream channel

Labertouche Cave
(Finlayson, 1981)

II Open joint caves

River Cave
(Pound *et al.* 1975;
Finlayson, 1982)

Enchanted Rock Cave
(Kastning, 1876; 1977)

III Closed joint caves

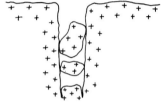

Goebel's Cave
(Finlayson, 1982)

Figure 17.1   Summary of granite cave types

Guyana, is shown here in Figure 17.2 (Shaw, 1980). Many other
examples exist, some very small, but others, such as Melville's
Cave in Victoria (Matthews, 1979), are relatively large, with
passages up to 20 m long (Figure 17.3).

(b) Boulder-filled stream channels   The evidence at present
available indicates that this is the most common cave type.
These caves consist of a stream course in granite bedrock, completely roofed over by boulders. In some cases the boulder cover
is only one layer and the cave beneath does not become completely
dark. In other cases the boulder cover may be up to 60 m thick
and an extensive cave system is developed. Many locations are
known where streams disappear underground in boulder filled
channels in granite terrain but no accessible cave passage has

337

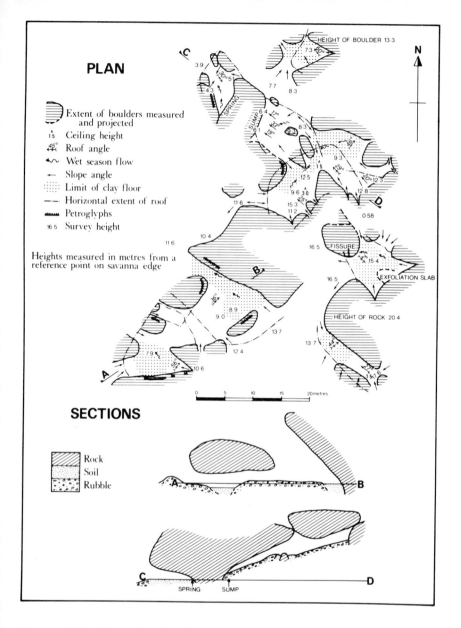

Figure 17.2   Map of a boulder pile cave (Type Ia), Makatau
Mountain, Aishalton, Guyana (After Shaw, 1980)

338

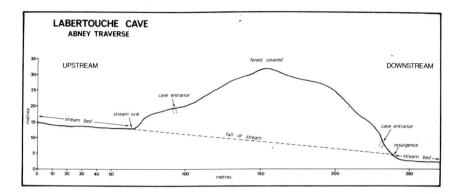

Figure 17.3   Interior of a boulder pile cave (Type Ia),
              Melville's Cave, Victoria, Australia (Photo by
              Rudy Frank)

been found. There appears to be considerable variety among caves
of this type regarding the frequency with which the stream flows
over the surface of the boulders. At one end of the scale there
are those cases where the flow is underground only during baseflow, and even minor peaks of runoff exceed the capacity of the
subsurface channels. At the other extreme there are those caves
where the underground channels accommodate all flow levels. In
these cases a true blind valley is formed. In all cases known
to the author, the stream beneath the boulders flows over
granite *in situ*, and in some cases is incised into joints in the
bedrock.

A particularly well developed example of this cave type is
Labertouche Cave in Victoria, Australia (Figure 17.4; Ollier,
1965; Finlayson, 1981). The cave forms a blind valley with the
crest of the col terminating the valley some 25 m above stream
level. The whole length of the cave (175 m) can be traversed
through the spaces between the boulders. Other examples of this
cave type reported in the literature are Brittania Creek and Mt
Buffalo also in Victoria (Finlayson, 1981); Cahuilla Creek,
California, USA (Quick, 1972); Greehorn Caves, California
(Breisch, 1980); and Lost Creek Caves, Colorado (Allured, 1980).

The precise details of the formation of these caves are not
clear and it is distinctly possible that they have not all formed
the same way. The problem of their origin lies in how the stream

339

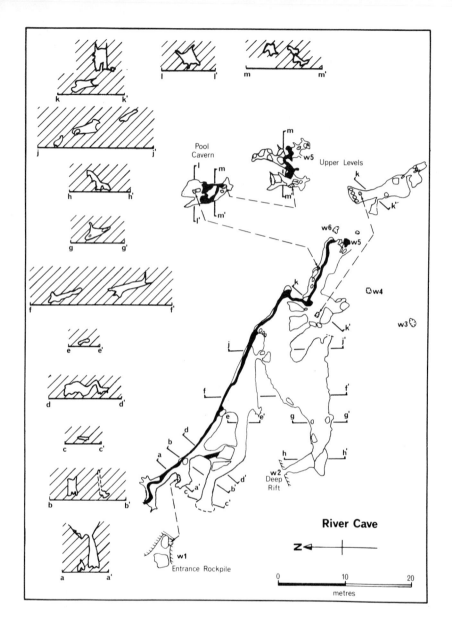

Figure 17.4   Long section of a boulder-filled stream channel
(Type Ib), Labertouche Cave, Victoria,
Australia (After Finlayson, 1981)

340

found its way underneath the boulders and three theories are presented here, the 'prior', 'post', and 'lateral' theories.

Under the 'prior' theory, deep weathering prior to stream incision produced corestones in a grus matrix. This may have taken place under different climatic conditions and almost certainly below some kind of planation surface. Since the weathered grus between the corestones is more easily eroded than the corestones themselves, the stream, during incision, selectively transports the grus, the corestones accumulate and eventually collect so as to cover the stream. A variation on this theory is that the stream moves underground into a subsurface pipe produced by eluviation of the grus.

According to the 'post' theory, the boulders which roof the cave have separated out of the bedrock after stream incision. The stream becomes incised in the joint system of the granite, which gradually breaks up into boulders which collapse together to form a boulder roof over the stream.

The 'lateral' theory suggests that the boulders which form the cave roof have been moved laterally on to the stream by mass movement. The mass failure of a valley side slope would deposit in the stream channel an unconsolidated mixture of fine and coarse grade material. The fine material would be selectively removed leaving the stream flowing through a pile of boulders. Halliday (1963) describes an example of a cave formed in this way: Boulder Creek Cave in Yakima County, Washington State, though the bedrock is not granite.

To date there has not been sufficiently detailed investigation of any of the caves of this type to reliably determine the mechanisms by which they formed.

Type II. Open joint caves

The cave space is a joint or fracture in the granite and is roofed by boulders dislodged during the excavation of the joint. Two published examples of this cave type are Enchanted Rock Cave in Texas (Kastning, 1976; 1977) and South Bald Rock Cave in southern Queensland (Finlayson, 1982). In both cases the cave is in an inselberg mass. Kastning has given an account of the formation of Enchanted Rock Cave in which he suggested that grussification along the fracture began prior to exhumation of the inselberg. The grus was stripped out during exhumation, and blocks from the upper fracture walls and slabs of exfoliated sheets became lodged in the fracture forming a discontinuous cave roof. Essentially the same sequence appears to have occurred at South Bald Rock, though in this case weathering has progressed along two adjacent joints and blocks from between them have tilted and become jammed across the joints thus providing the cave roof.

River Cave at Girraween, southern Queensland, (Figure 17.5; Pound et al., 1975; Finlayson, 1982) is a variation on this type. Here the cave is occupied by a substantial and permanent stream. The cave joint has a dip of approximately 20°. The floor and

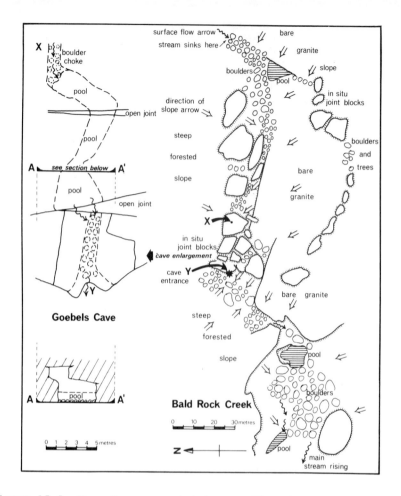

Figure 17.5　Map of an open joint cave (Type II), River Cave, Girraween National Park, Southeast Queensland, Australia (After Pound *et al.*, 1975)

roof of the cave are the sides of the excavated joint, though where it intersects the ground surface it is clogged with boulders. While all flow is now accommodated underground at this site, the former surface stream course can still be followed. The interior of this cave is shown in Figure 17.6. The rounded cobbles in the lower left corner of the photo are in the present stream course.

It is possible that caves of Type Ib may develop into caves of Type II if the stream becomes well incised into bedrock joints. Similarly it is possible that Type Ib caves could have been initiated as Type II with the development taking place in the

Figure 17.6   Interior of an open joint cave (Type II), River
Cave, Girraween National Park

Figure 17.7   Map of a closed joint cave (Type III), Goebel's
Cave, Girraween National Park (After Finlayson, 1982)

Figure 17.8   Interior of a closed joint cave (Type III), Goebel's
Cave, Girraween National Park (Photo by Ken Harris)

manner described above for the 'post' theory.

Type III   Closed joint caves

In this type the cave is formed along a joint but the cave
is completely roofed over by granite *in situ*. So far only one
example of this type is known: Goebel's Cave at Girraween
National Park, southern Queensland (Figure 17.7; Finlayson,
1982). Here the granite has a pronounced set of horizontal joints
which can be seen in the cross section shown in Figures 17.7 and
17.8, and the cave has developed along these joints. Other
streams near by flow underground along horizontal joints in
otherwise solid granite, though in these cases no accessible
passages have been found (see Finlayson, 1982). In this cave
type, it is not clear how the underground flow path is opened up
initially. A sufficiently large channel has been developed to
allow entry of sand and the polished walls of the cave indicate
that it has been enlarged by abrasion (Figure 17.8). Possible
mechanisms for the initial opening are pressure release, subsurface piping in weathered grus in the joints, or removal of
part of the rock in solution (though this seems unlikely).

The joint slab which forms the roof of Goebel's Cave has
been broken up into individual boulders both upstream and downstream of the cave site thus forming caves of Type Ib. The
possibility therefore exists that other Type Ib caves have developed from Type III caves.

CONCLUSIONS

Descriptions of granite caves in the literature and caves visited by the author have been used to develop a classification of caves in granite. Three major types are proposed: boulder caves, open joint caves, and closed joint caves. The first type has been subdivided into boulder-pile caves and boulder-filled stream channels. To date, very few detailed descriptions of caves in granite have been published but experience in the field and discussions with speleologists suggests that they may be far more common than is generally believed.

The recognition of the ability of caves to develop in granite has a number of important practical implications. For engineering geologists the presence of caves places severe restrictions on the siting of structures and on activities such as tunnelling. The work of Morris (1971) and Green and Maver (1959) illustrates the problems which can arise. Morris' work has been described earlier, and Green and Maver have reported massive flowages of granite grus filling an aqueduct tunnel being put through a granite hill. Labertouche granite cave is close to this site on the same bedrock and one possible explanation for its formation is subsurface eluviation of grus.

Granite is generally considered to be 'watertight' and therefore an ideal bedrock for catchment hydrological experiments. The experience in Victoria has been that this is not so and the problems have been discussed by Finlayson (1981).

The work so far reported on granite caves throws very little light on possible ages and rates of development. This could well prove to be a fruitful area of research which could help to produce estimates of long term denudation rates in granite landscapes.

Acknowledgements

For their generous hospitality and introductions to the granite caves of the Western USA, the author wishes to thank Ray Hardcastle, Los Angeles; Kevin Plaxco, Hemet; Rich and Susan Breisch, San Diego; and Tom Strong and Louise Hose, Boulder. Thanks are due also to John Webb, Geology Department, University of Melbourne, for helpful discussions and a critical review of the first draft.

REFERENCES

Allured, D. 1980. Lost Creek pseudokarst, Pike National Forest, Colorado. *Bull. Natn. Speleol. Soc.,* **42(2)**, p. 27.

Arnold, J. 1980. Death in the Rockies. *NSS News,* **38(9)**, 209-215.

Breisch, R. 1980. Greenhorn Caves, Kern County, California - America's deepest granite caves? *Bull. Natn. Speleol. Soc.,* **42(2)**, p. 27.

Breisch, R. 1981. Recent exploration of the Greenhorn Caves. *Speleo Digest,* **24**, 9-15.

Carroll, R.W. 1978. TSOD: Adirondack anorthosite talus monster. *NSS News,* **36(6)**, 119-121.

Chabert, C. 1980. Les grandes cavites en roches pseudo-karstiques ou non-karstiques. *Spelunca,* **35**, 109-115.

Finlayson, B.L. 1981. Underground streams in acid igneous rocks in Victoria. *Helictite,* **19(1)**, 5-14.

Finlayson, B.L. 1982. Granite caves in Girraween National Park, southeast Queensland. *Helictite,* **20(2)**, 53-59.

Green, K.D. and Maver, J.L. 1959. The Tarago River Aqueduct. *J. Inst. Engrs. Aust.,* **31**, 1-19.

Gurnee, R.H. and Gurnee, J. 1980. *Gurnee Guide to American Caves. A Comprehensive Guide to the Caves in the United States open to the public,* (Teaneck, NJ: Zephyrus Press) 252pp.

Halliday, W.R. 1963. Caves of Washington. *Inf. Circ. Wash. St. Div. Mines Min.,* **40**.

Halliday, W.R. 1974. *American Caves and Caving,* (New York: Harper and Row), 348pp.

Hedges, J. 1978. Karst caves in silicate rocks: North Carolina and Virginia. *Speleo Digest 1978,* **23**, 182-184A.

Kastning, E.H. 1976. Granitic karst and pseudokarst, Llano County, Texas, with special reference to Enchanted Rock Cave. *Proc. Natn. Speleol. Soc. A. Conv.,* 43-45.

Kastning, E.H. 1977. *Karst landforms and speleogenesis in Precambrian Granite, Llano County, Texas (USA).* Proc. 7th Congr. Int. Speleol., Sheffield, England, 253-255.

Matthews, P.G. 1979. *Check-list of Australian Caves.* (Australian Speleological Federation, Broadway), 73pp.

Morris, B.J. 1971. *River Murray Bridge Crossing.* Department of Mines. South Australia, Report Book No. 71/99.

Ollier, C.D. 1965. Some features of granite weathering in Australia. *Z. Geomorph.,* **9**, 285-304.

Pound, M.D., Gillieson, D.S., Shannon, C.H.C. and Riley, B. 1975. Granite Underground River, Wyberba, Qld (map). *Down Under,* **14(5)**, p.124.

Quick, D. 1972. Cahuilla Creek Cave. *The Explorer,* April issue, 45-56.

Shannon, C.H.C. 1975. *Pseudokarst caves in duricrust/granite terrain, Banana Range, Central Queensland.* Proc. 10th bienn. Conf. Aust. Speleol. Fed. Brisbane, December 1974, 20-24.

Shaw, P. 1980. Cave development on a granite inselberg, South Rupununi Savannas. *Z. Geomorph.,* 24, 68-76.

Smith, A.R. 1974. Enchanted Rock Cave, Llano County, Texas. *Texas Caver,* 19(5), p.78.

Streckeisen, A. 1976. To each plutonic rock its proper name. *Earth Sciences Review,* 12, 1-33.

Twidale, C.R. 1982. *Granite Landforms.* (Amsterdam: Elsevier), 372pp.

Wojcik, Z. 1961a. Karst phenomena and caves in the Karkonosze granites (abstract). *Die Höhle,* 12(1), p.76.

Wojcik, Z. 1961b. Caves in granites in the Tatra Mountains (abstract). *Akten des Dritten Internationalen Kongresses für Speläologie. Wien. Vol A.* p.43.

18

Queen of Spains Valley,
Maroon Town, Jamaica:
a cross-section of different types of tropical karst

K.H. Pfeffer

SUMMARY

This paper describes a detailed morphological study of the Queen
of Spains Valley, Maroon area. Examples of all types of karst
relief occur: karren, dolines, cockpit karst and poljes. Their
distribution in relation to the geology has been noted and
plotted on the accompanying maps. Certain of the landforms are
controlled by geological circumstances (for instance cockpit
karst requires the occurrence of 'pure' limestones). There are
also different landforms in the same type of rock for which no
petrographical or geological reason is apparent; such landforms
are explained as a result of successive relief generations caused
by phases of tectonic uplift. The generations of landforms could
be initiated by different original landforms or by different
climatic conditions or by a combination of both these reasons.
Further work is needed to resolve this problem.

RÉSUMÉ

On discute dans cet article d'une étude morphologique détaillée de
la Queen of Spains Valley, Maroon Town, Jamaique. Des examples de
tous les types de relief karstique apparaissent: des lapiés, des
dolines, des cockpits et des poljes. Leur distribution vis à vis
de la géologie est marquée sur les cartes. Certaines formes morphologiques sont contrôlées par la géologie (par example, il faut du
calcaire 'pur' pour que le cockpit karst se développe). Il y a
également des formes karstiques différentes dans la même variété de
roche. Donc l'évolution de ces formes ne s'explique pas par des
différences pétrographiques ou géologiques. On les explique plutôt
comme des éléments morphologiques d'âges différents initié successive-
ment par des phases de soulèvement. L'origine de ces formes d'âges
différents pourrait être attribuée soit aux variétés de formes
originales du relief ou aux conditions climatiques lors de leur développement ou peut-être à une combinaison des deux explications. Il
faut continuer les recherches pour résoudre ce problème.

INTRODUCTION

The landforms of the West Indian limestone areas can be divided into two groups.

(i) Karst margin plains

Parts of this relief are extensive plains on limestone with a cover of soil or alluvium and a - sometimes seasonally - surface drainage. 'Karstrandebenen', karst margin plains (Lehmann, 1954), are developed at Vorfluter level at the margin of karst areas or adjoining to the sea, through the interaction of surface drainage and soluble rock. Here and there Inselbergs are sitting in these plains, often falsely described as parts of cockpit karst landforms (Pfeffer, 1981).

A well developed plain can be observed north of Point-à-Pitre in the island of Guadeloupe (Blume, 1968; Lasserre, 1954; Pfeffer, 1981); a plain *in statu nascendi* exists north of Saint Louis 1-5 m above sea level in the area of the lower course of a Quaternary (now drowned and alluvial-filled), valley (Blume, 1970; Lasserre, 1950; Pfeffer, 1981). Karst margin plains develop on limestone in the Vorfluter level in the ecological conditions of a tropic and even a Mediterranean climate (Pfeffer, 1979).

Therefore, in a climatic geomorphological view, the climate boundary lines are wider for the karst margin plains than for planation processes in non-karstic rocks. Karst margin plains underlie karstification if they are uplifted over Vorfluter level.

(ii) Karst Areas

The essential literature (enumerated by Pfeffer, 1981) reports that karren, dolines, poljes and cockpit karst are developed at different drainages above Vorfluter level. A region that shows excellent examples of all these landforms lies in the northwest of Jamaica and was first pointed out by Marjorie Sweeting (1958).

KARST AREAS IN NORTHWEST JAMAICA

Reported by: Birot, Corbel and Muxart, 1968: Lehmann, 1954: Pfeffer, 1981; Sweeting, 1958: Versey, 1959, 1972.

Topographic maps: Topographic map of Jamaica 1:12 500 Sheets 41A, 41B, 41C, 41D, 42A, 42B, 42C, 42D, 51C, 52A, 52C.

Geological maps: Geological map of Jamaica 1:50 000 Sheets 5, 6, 8, 9.

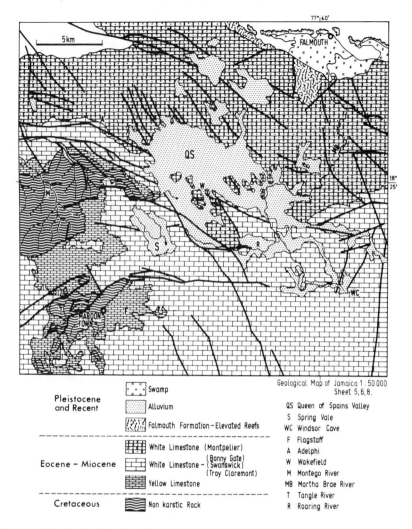

Figure 18.1 Geological map

If we go from Falmouth, (which lies 30 km eastward of Montego Bay), towards the south, across Quaternary coast terraces and two small ridges with intermediated basins filled with alluvium, we reach the Queen of Spains Valley. The Queen of Spains Valley is a polje with an extensive plain on a level of 300 ft, universally surrounded by higher relief - in the north and east 500 ft, in the west 500-1000 ft, in the south 500-700 ft. At the northern frame of the polje there are limestone hills with inclinations of 15°-40° and dolines between the hills (Figure 18.3). West of Adelphi in the influence of the deep cut of the Montego River system are even periodically flooded valleys.

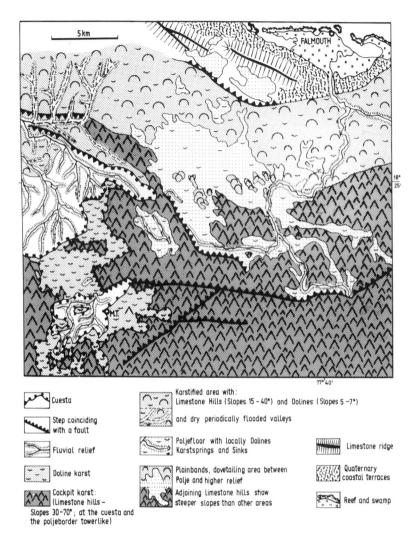

Figure 18.2   Geomorphological map

352

Figure 18.3   Limestone hills and dolines northwest Queen of
             Spains Valley polje near Adelphi; White Limestone
             - Montpelier Formation

At the southern frame of the Queen of Spains Valley polje
there are steep limestone hills which rise above the polje floor,
and there is a transition to cockpit karst. The soil which
covers the floor of the basin consists of weathering loams. The
upper part of the soil is red-brown, then yellow-red flame
colour. Grey-brown pisolith - containing sandy loams dominate
towards a depth to 60 cm and then change into grey-yellowish reduced bleached weathering loams and clays. Thin sections demonstrate these facts, we see clouds of clay minerals, iron hydro-
xids and flint and even quartz.

Further studies point out that the bottom of the basin is
dissected into many dolines, and some of them contain shallow
lakes (Figure 18.4). Towards the south the polje is bordered

Figure 18.4   Poljefloor with waterfilled doline and isolated
             limestone hill; Queen of Spains Valley polje near
             Wakefield

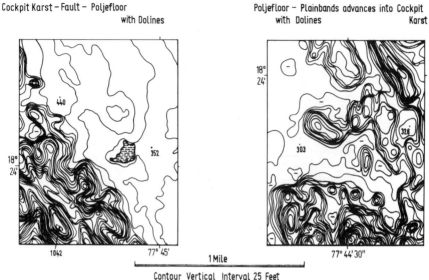

Cockpit Karst – Fault – Poljefloor
with Dolines

Poljefloor – Plainbands advances into Cockpit
with Dolines   Karst

Contour Vertical Interval 25 Feet
Top. Map of Jamaica 1:12 500 Sheet 42 B

Figure 18.5 Poljeborder - Queen of Spains Valley

by cockpit karst. The transition is in a part very abrupt and
linear; to some extent, however, the polje advances in bays and
longstretched plainbands into the higher relief (Figure 18.5).
The southern plainbands lie along an east-west running line which
forms an ascent to an adjoining cockpit karst area in the south
and is more than 1000 ft high (Figures 18.6 and 18.7). At the
border of this ascent, as well as at the southwestern border of
the polje, karst springs rise flowing northward as Roaring River

Figure 18.6   Queen of Spains Valley; view to the south

354

Figure 18.7   Queen of Spains Valley, aerial photograph (Survey Department, Kingston). Poljefloor with dolines, isolated limestone hill, plainbands and cockpit karst; east-west running step

Figure 18.8   Spring Vale polje: poljefloor with dolines, surrounded by cockpit karst

and Martha Brae River. In a canyon they break through the frame of the polje flowing to Falmouth where they reach the sea. Along the plainbands and in the direction of the plain, through which flows the Roaring River, the limestone hills are often towerlike with footcaves and stalagmite-curtains.

Amidst the cockpit karst area we find another polje, Spring Vale. At first sight one can make out a level of the basin consisting of alluvium. Further inspections show that it is dissected into many dolines. The slope inclination of these is 5-7° - one can recognize basic limestone here and there. Thus there is a direct coexistence of dolines and cone shaped mountains (Figure 18.8). The alluvium in the polje is visible up to a depth of about 3 m. The lower parts are flame coloured, yellow-red loams. Above them are found more sandy areas with a loamy reddish layer, covered by sandy loams of a lighter colour. At the southern and western borders, a cave-river emerges and also karst springs, but they disappear after a short distance of surface flow into the underground of a waterfilled doline.

The adjoining cockpit karst area (Figure 18.9) shows more kuppen with the following shape: next to the star shaped or long stretched cockpits concave slopes of 30° inclination are dominant and are followed by steeper slopes of 50-70°, whereas the tops of the kuppen are convex presenting gentler slopes of about 30°. The kuppen are often 'directed' and indicate the outcrop of the solid rock, and in combination with that a yellow-brown weathering loam occurs. At many places the bare rock with algae and lichens shows signs of solution - which in most cases are kavernöse, spongelike, karren. Thin sections indicate this as well as a permanent re-elimination of calcite. A most striking fact is that single kuppen are connected through flat, narrow saddles, often of the same level. The cockpits drop down into the level of theses 'saddles'. The 'saddles' are covered with weathering residues that differ from the reddish weathering loam one can find washed into the cockpits. The weathering residues covering the 'saddles' are yellow-brown loams and red clays and show a different chemical composition from the sediments in the cockpits.

In the area of Maroon Town there is an abrupt change of cockpit karst to doline karst. The doline karst subdivides the area into flat hills with highest inclinations of 10°. The bottoms of the dolines are flat with inclinations of 2-3°. Their soil consists of yellow-red spotted loams; open ponors at the

Figure 18.9   Doline karst (yellow limestone); cuesta of white limestone - cockpit karst with towerlike forms. Northwest of Maroon Town

Figure 18.10 Cockpit karst between Spring Vale and Maroon Town (white limestone)

Figure 18.11 Cuesta landscape northwest of Maroon Town; aerial photograph (Survey Department, Kingston) (see Figure 18.12). Fluvial relief-doline karst-cockpit karst cretaceous shales-yellow limestone-white limestone

deepest parts of the dolines, indicating basic limestone, point out the karsthydrography. Between Maroon Town and Flagstaff there exists a combination of dolines and steep limestone kuppen. On the one hand the area is a doline karst region, but on the other hand there are steep cones sitting on single flat hills. Towards the south cockpit karst follows again. In the transition zone steep, towerlike forms with broken rock at the foot of the kuppen are dominant (Figures 18.9 and 18.11). Towards the southwest of Maroon Town we finally find an area of non-karstic cretaceous rock which is unfit for karstification and is locally drained on the surface. The Tangle River system disappears entering the adjoining limestone areas.

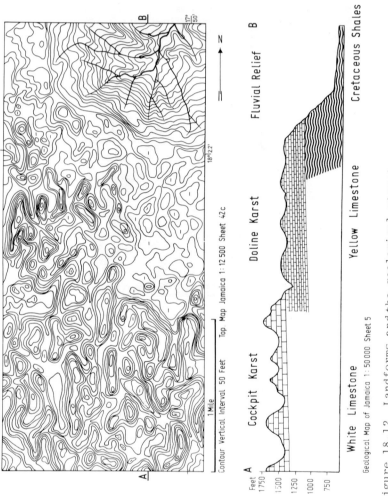

Contour Vertical Interval 50 Feet   Top Map Jamaica 1:12 500 Sheet 42c

Geological Map of Jamaica 1:50 000 Sheet 5

Figure 18.12 Landforms and the geological structure

REASONS FOR THE LANDFORMS

The combination of the described surface forms with the geological and petrographical circumstances results in the following facts:

A. Cockpit karst requires the occurrence of 'pure' limestone. In purest limestone the forms are steeper (50-70°), whereas limestone with marl layers develops only hills and dolines with inclinations of 10-40°. Steeper hills are at the border of the polje floors, accompanying the plainbands. Real tower forms are conditioned through their position in the relief, at the border of the cockpit karst region with the plainbands and polje floors and cuestas.

B. Impure limestone develops doline karst (Figure 18.12).

C. Poljes occur to some extent depending on dislocation lines and different rocks in the frame areas; but they need not always be so located as the Spring Vale demonstrates. The Spring Vale is obviously a form more of corrosion, a polje developed in one type of rock. Maybe this is the reason for the smaller extension of this polje.

D. There are different landforms in the same type of rock, and no petrographical or geological reason is visible.

GENERATIONS OF RELIEF

The development of dolines (Figure 18.13) in the Spring Vale, surrounded by cockpit karst - both developed in the same rock - just as dolines in the poljefloor and the plainbands in the Queen of Spains Valley area and even the Martha Brae River cutting through all karstlandforms require another explanation. It turns out that the originally developed landform community -polje-plainbands-cockpit karst was formed as different landforms in the course of a further karstification. These are time-sequences and therefore they can be addressed as generations of relief within the meaning of Büdel (1982). It might be possible that these generations of relief trace back to phases of tectonic uplift. And it might be possible that karstification of a rock covered with thick weathering residues shows many different morphodynamic behaviours, as does the original rock. The older generation of relief with its distribution of the landforms might therefore be able to shape the younger morphodynamic processes.   But we have to notice that the polje and the surrounding cockpit karst are Tertiary landforms and we should discuss whether the sinking sealevel - the Quaternary uplift - caused other landforms under the influence of different climates during the Quaternary.

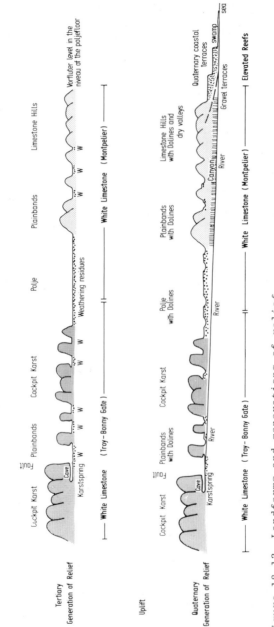

Figure 18.13 Landforms and generations of relief

The recent soils on the limestone, their different chemical composition from the cockpit fillings and even the different weathering residues on the saddles are hints. Even the Martha Brae River points to this fact because it was able to build a canyon, even in a limestone region, during the Quaternary period. Other marks are Quaternary gravels near Falmouth. Different type of sediments in the poljes point to this fact too.

DISCUSSION

In the tropical Island of Jamaica there exist different karst landforms. Cockpit karst and doline karst are spread side by side or are even dovetailed. Some differences in karst landforms are absolutely caused by petrography. But within the karst areas in the tropics there exist differences in landform that do not depend on petrography. It is a fact of time-sequences in the developing of landforms, that there are existing relief generations. The generations of karst landforms can be caused by different original landforms, by different climatic conditions or by the coincidence of both; these are problems to be cleared up by further investigations.

Acknowledgement

The field work was supported by Deutsche Forschungsgemeinschaft.

REFERENCES

Birot, P., Corbel, J. and Muxart, R. 1968. Morphologie des régiones calcaires à la Jamaique et à Puerto Rico. *CNRS 1967, Nouvelle Série,* 4, 335-392.

Blume, H. 1968. *Die Westindischen Inseln.* (Braunschweig: Westermann).

Blume, H. 1970. Karstmorphologische Beobachtungen auf den Inseln über dem Winde. *Tübinger Geogr. Studien, Bd.,* 34, 33-42.

Büdel, J. 1982. *Climatic Geomorphology.* (Princeton, NJ: Princeton University Press).

Lasserre, G. 1950. Marie-Galante. *Cahiers d'Outre-Mer,* 3, 123-152.

Lasserre, G. 1954. Notes sur la Karst de la Guadeloupe. *Erdkunde,* 8, 115-118.

Lehmann, H. 1954. Der tropische Kegelkarst auf den Großen Antillen. *Erdkunde,* 8, 130-139.

Pfeffer, K.-H. 1979. *Morphodynamiques en terrains calcaires et karstiques.* Actes du Symposium International sur l'érosion karstique, Aix-en-Provence - Marseille - Nîmes, Mémoire no. 1 de l'AFK, 215-224.

Pfeffer, K.-H. 1981. *Tropical Karst - Problems of the genesis and some new results of fieldwork.* (BGRG Tagung Manchester 1981), in press.

Sweeting, M. 1958. The Karstlands of Jamaica. *Geographical Journal,* **124**, 184-199.

Versey, H.R. 1959. *The hydrological character of the White Limestone formation of Jamaica.* Transactions of the 2nd Caribbean Congress, Kingston, 59-68.

Versey, H.R. 1972. Karst of Jamaica. In: *Important Karst Regions of the Northern Hemisphere,* eds. Herak and Stringfield, (New York: Elsevier), 445-466.

19

Slope form and process in cockpit karst in Belize

M. Day

SUMMARY

If karst landform development is to be fully understood there is a great need for detailed study of slope form and process. Detailed surveys of twenty-five slope profiles, five in each of five cockpits in Belize, reveal that the slopes are composed of essentially four identifiable units: staircases, broken cliffs, inclined bedrock slopes, and talus slopes. The occurrence of these slope units is associated with position on the slope. Staircases decrease in occurrence downslope; broken cliffs are most common in midslope sections; inclined bedrock slopes occur mostly at slope bases; talus slopes increase in occurrence downslope. Process studies show that, although there appears to be no consistent downslope variation in either soil pCO_2 or water hardness, over a six year period emplaced weight loss tablets suffer increased weight loss with increasing downslope position, regardless of slope unit type. Minimum weight losses occur on midslope cliff sections.

RÉSUMÉ

Pour mieux comprendre le développement du relief karstique on a besoin
d'études précises sur les processus d'évolution et la forme des
versants. Les levés topographiques détaillés de vingt cinq profils
de versant (cinq profils sur chacun des cinq cockpits) en Belize
montrent que les pentes se décomposent essentiellement en quatre
éléments: des escaliers, des corniches escarpées des pentes rocheuses
inclinées et des éboulis. Ces différents éléments se situent dans
des endroits bien déterminés du versant. Les escaliers deviennent
moins importants vers le bas; les corniches escarpées se trouvent
surtout au milieu des profils; les pentes rocheuses inclinées
apparaissent presque toujours à la base du versant; les éboulis
sont plus fréquents en bas des pentes, les études de processus ont
montré qu'en l'absence de variation notable de la pCO_2 des sols ou
de la dureté des eaux, des plaquettes de calcaire, en place depuis
six ans, ont subi des pertes croissantes du haut vers le bas des
versants, et cela quelque soit l'unité morphologique concernée.
Les pertes minimales intéressent la partie médiane des corniches.

INTRODUCTION

Although the slope has long been recognized as a fundamental
landscape unit, and despite the dividends that slope studies
have paid in terms of the understanding of process-form relationships, karst geomorphologists have paid scant attention to slope
morphology or to spatial process variations over those slopes.
Indeed, with the exception of those few studies which have
treated closed depressions as integrated units (Day, 1977; 1979;
Gunn, 1977, Gunn & Turnpenny, this volume) there have been few
attempts to address karst landform studies in any systematic manner
with regard to form-process relationships. While cave studies have
progressed considerably along these lines, surface studies are
little further forward in unravelling the threads binding together near-surface water behaviour, distribution of erosion,
and development of recognizable features.

Although studies with a 'working unit' approach have much
promise, it is easy to see why karst slopes have been afforded
little attention. They are often seemingly complex, with little
apparent continuity either in terms of form or systematic downslope transfer of superficial material. Moreover, in many
situations any water reaching the slope surface percolates
downward too rapidly to be involved in downslope transfers or
to be monitored by near-surface investigations. One must consider, then, whether surface form is really a product of surface
processes, of whether the near-surface is actually a rather
inactive zone masking a far more active 'subcutaneous' zone,
the significance of which has been pointed out in recent studies
of enclosed depressions (Gunn, 1977; Williams, 1983 and in press).

Where, as in many shallow dolines, the efficiency of vertical percolation and residue removal is less, and where a surface sediment cover remains, preliminary studies in Jamaica

364

suggest that slope processes are very similar to those of non-karst areas (Day, unpublished). There is much downslope movement of water and sediment, either at or close to the surface, with the result that both accumulate in depression bases producting a relatively thick regolith cover and frequent ponding. A *priori* one would suggest that a similar situation once prevailed in enclosed depressions where secondary permeability has now developed to the point that there is minimal superficial centrepital movement of water or regolith; and where surface slopes are left effectively as relict isolated units, separated by solutionally-enlarged fissures. The most significant function of such fissures in the overall continuing development of the landscape is the supply of surface runoff from small slope segment 'catchments', to the active subcutaneous zone.

Whatever the case in specific locations, slopes in karst terrains, and particularly those within enclosed depressions, demand attention both as component parts of the observed surface form and as the suppliers of water and material to other portions of the karst system.

Slopes in tropical karst terrain have received some attention although studies have been sporadic and little synthesis is possible yet. Of particular note are the studies of footslopes surrounding karst towers which are set in enclosing non-karstic plains. These footslopes are significant in particular because they mark the junction between the remnant tower and the 'active zone' bordering it, and because they function as the foci of water movement between the tower base and the surrounding plain. Such studies date from the work of Lehmann and co-workers (Lehmann, 1953a; 1953b; 1954; Lehmann *et al.*, 1956) on the origin of tower karst; more recently they have focussed on fluvial activity and the diversity of form (McDonald, 1975; 1976; 1979; Jennings, 1976; Day, 1978a; 1978b; Ireland, 1982).

In the context of more general investigation of slopes within tropical karst landscapes several of the tower karst studies are of immediate relevance. For example, McDonald's studies of tower margins provide valuable data on slope type occurrence. Footcaves around Batu Leattjakbuk, in Sulawesi (McDonald, 1976b), occupy 31% of the perimeter; bedrock inclines, often colluvium-mantled, occupy 27%; alluvial footslopes account for a further 32%; talus slopes, 6%; and perpendicular hillbases, 4%. While these figures may not be representative of other tower karst bases, particularly where cliff-foot river action is of less importance (Sweeting, 1968; Day, 1978a), they provide a useful basis for comparison with other tropical karst areas.

Slope studies within enclosed depressions in tropical karst have been undertaken sporadically, but there has been little attempt to systematize these studies and even less attempt to examine the role that the slopes play in overall landscape development. That such an approach has potential value is revealed by parallel studies of tower karst slopes (Crowther, 1980; and this volume).

In a recent study, Ireland (1982) paid considerable attention to slope forms within the cockpit and other karst of Belize, Jamaica and Puerto Rico. Although concerned primarily with the development and geomorphological role of case-hardening (Ireland, 1979) this study recognized four major slope categories with respect to position in the landscape: inter-hill slopes, hill bases, main slopes, and hill summits. These were further classified on the basis of overall form (straight, convex or concave); of overall gradient; and as to their composition (bedrock, talus etc.).

The most detailed studies of slopes within tropical enclosed depressions are those done in Jamaica by Aub (1964; 1969). Commenting on the steepness and variability of the slopes, Aub recognizes six basic slope unit types:

1. Staircase slopes, consisting of alternate ledges and risers. The ledges frequently correspond with bedding planes and are often mantled with debris. The dimensions of the ledges and risers are variable, steps averaging 2-3 m in height on 50° slopes.

2. Broken cliffs, similar to the above but with higher steps and more variable ledges. Such slopes are often honeycombed and the steps are dissected by widened joints.

3. Steep, even slopes, frequently honeycombed and partially covered with debris.

4. Major cliffs, undercut up to 3 m by horizontal notches and often associated with springs and sinkholes at the slope base.

5. Cliffs without undercutting and often rising from benches.

6. Scree slopes, difficult to distinguish from solid rock slopes particularly where the latter are mantled with soil.

Tjia (1969) has suggested that the development of staircase slopes on karst cones in the Gunung Sewu is controlled by the spacing of lineaments and the relative rates of vertical and lateral corrosion. The Gunung Sewu risers seldom exceed 2 m in height and decrease in magnitude with increasing proximity to the hill summits. Tjia suggests that a convex slope profile will develop where the vertical solution rate is less than the lateral rate, a straight profile will develop where the two rates are equal, and a concave profile will be produced where the vertical rate exceeds the lateral.

Monroe (1977) comments that in the Puerto Rican karst 'Nearly all deep depressions have concave slopes, which in the upper parts approach the vertical. This is the result of the tendency of the depressions to deepen by solution at the bottom, whereas there is little if any solution at the sides. Consequently the sides get steeper and eventually there is a sloughing off in small landslides, leaving vertical slopes.' (p.172).

In perhaps one of the most enterprising exercises concerned with slopes in tropical karst depressions, Smith, Drew and Atkinson (1972) have attempted to model depression development via consideration of erosion rates on internal slopes. Assuming slopes to stabilize at about 30°, when the majority of soil cover has been lost, they model a hypothetical conical cockpit depression, with or without a central shaft, developing in 0.6 million years. Such an approach to tropical karst is only ultimately profitable with acceptably accurate data on process rates and with more precise information on slope morphology.

It would thus serve karst geomorphology well were more studies devoted to the investigation of slopes and, to this end, a program of detailed study of enclosed depression slopes in the tropical karst of Belize has been started. This examination, which focusses upon a small number of cockpit-like depressions in the karst southeast of Belmopan (Figure 19.1), commenced in 1975 with the emplacement of pre-weighed limestone tablets which were to be used as indicators of weathering rates. The study, now augmented by data on slope morphology, soil carbon dioxide concentrations and slope water chemistry forms the basis for this paper.

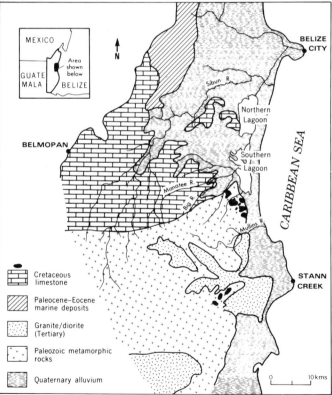

Figure 19.1   Generalised geology and drainage, east-central Belize

THE AREA STUDIED

Selected for study were five cockpits approximately 1 km east of the Hummingbird Highway and 6.5 km south of Belmopan in central Belize. This area was selected on the grounds that it appears not to differ in any significant way from other cockpit karst areas in central Belize. It is accessible by foot tracks, meteorological records are available for Belmopan and vegetation studies have been conducted in the vicinity.

The limestones and dolomites of Belize are Cretaceous in age and occur as flanking facies predominantly north, south and west of the non-karstic, igneous and metamorphic Maya Mountains (Figure 19.1). The carbonates are often massively-bedded, although individual beds vary between 0.5 and 10 m in thickness, and they dip away from the Maya Mountains at angles between 1 and 10° (McDonald, 1976; 1979; Day, 1978). Many of the limestones and dolomites are recrystallized or altered (McDonald, 1979; Day, 1978a; Ireland, 1982). There is evidence of dolomitisation and de-dolomitisation. The limestones are variable petrographically, running from dense micrites, through biomicrites and biosparites to coarse-grained sparites. Their purities, porosities, water absorption capacities and mechanical strengths appear also to be highly variable (Day, 1978; Ireland, 1982).

The dominant landforms developed on the carbonates are enclosed depressions, widely known as cockpits, and intervening residual hills. Towards the edges of the karst belt this terrain grades into tower karst in which groups or individual residual hills are surrounded by alluvium (McDonald, 1975; 1976; 1979). In the vicinity of the Maya Mountains there are also locations, such as at the Rio Frio cave, where carbonate hills sit on granitic bases (Sweeting, 1968). By comparison with similar karst areas in Jamaica and Puerto Rico, the cockpit karst retains many vestiges of an integrated surface drainage network. Although the majority of drainage is now subterranean, and exposed only in such features as the karst window, locally known as 'Blue Hole', southeast of Belmopan, there are several active, part-surface, part-underground rivers, such as Caves Branch (Miller, 1977, 1981, 1983) and Indian Creek.

In general, however, the terrain is pocket-marked by enclosed depressions or cockpits. Over a 21 km² area studied by the author (Day, 1978a) mean depression density is 9.7 km²; the mean surrounding summit density is 29.2/km²; and the resultant summit to depression density ratio is 3.01. Depressions are surrounded by a mean of 6 residual hills and are dispersed near-uniformly with a mean spacing of 0.192 km. Within the 21 km² study area, 50 depressions selected randomly indicated a preferred north-south orientation, although the explanation for this is unclear. Detailed measurements of depths and diameters of 7 cockpits (Day, 1978a) shows that they are smaller than those of other cockpit areas; mean depth is 38 m (standard deviation 11.0 m) and mean diameter is 139 m (s=51.5 m).

Soils developed within the depressions are variously greyish or reddish-brown rendzinas and vertisols of the Yaxa suite (Jenkin, 1972: Jenkin and Birchall, 1976: Furley and Newey, 1979). These have developed through weathering of the underlying limestone but are patchy in distribution and are deepest in 'pockets' which are often located over vertical joints. The soils are often rubbly clay loams with a blocky structure; their drainage is of high variability, and upper slopes present a xeric habitat. Furley and Newey (1979) provide detailed information on several soil profiles in a variety of slope locations. Although soil depth exceeds 50 cm locally, average depths are less than 30 cm; soil cover is absent on many of the steeper slope segments. Soil depth and moisture content increase typically downhill and other soil properties are influenced likewise by topographic position.

Vegetation of the area is a mixed, broadleaved, deciduous seasonal forest with palmetto and secondary thickets (Jenkin et al., 1976; Furley and Newey, 1979). It differs from true rainforest in being particularly rich in calcicole species, being shorter and having less clear stratification. Topographic position and associated soil conditions play a major role in determining species distribution (Furley and Newey, 1979). Locally vegetation shows the effects of disturbance by tropical storms, fires, insects and human activities (Furley and Newey, 1979) although the selected cockpits appear not to have been used for any cultivation within recent years.

Mean annual rainfall totals in the study area are between 2000 and 2400 mm (Walker, 1973; Furley and Newey, 1979; National Hydrometeorological Service, 1983). Long term summaries indicate that Caves Branch, 10 km southeast of the study area, has a mean of around 2400 mm per annum with a dry period of less than about 127 mm per month in February, March and April. Roaring River Estate, 5 km west of the study site, averages 2110 mm with a longer dry period from January to May (Walker, 1973: Furley and Newey, 1979). Belmopan, 6.5 km north of the study site, appears intermediate between the other two nearby stations; between 1976 and 1982 it had a mean annual total of 2211 mm and shows a marked dry period in March, April and May (National Hydrometeorological Service, 1983). For the same period mean annual temperature at Belmopan was 30.6°C.

The hypotheses being tested by the field research reported herein are as follows: first, on the basis of the literature survey, that different types of slope unit are recognizable within the karstic depressions; second, that these slope units are organized with respect to position, particularly in terms of proximity to slope bases and depression margins; third, that slope type and position are associated with variations in weathering rates particularly as a consequence of differing soil covers and moisture conditions.

PROCEDURE

Five enclosed depressions were selected for study on the basis of preliminary reconnaisance in 1975. The depressions were selected as being essentially representative of the larger depression population since they showed no obvious morphological differences from others in Belize (Day, 1978a). The depressions were selected also because of their proximity to the Hummingbird Highway and because they were accessible by short foot trails. Four main experiments were conducted.

Firstly, during November 1975 an initial investigation of 25 slope profiles, five within each depression, was carried out. Each profile began at what was identified as the lowest point in the depression base and trended upslope towards the summit of one of the surrounding residual hills. Five profiles were examined in each depression since each was surrounded by at least five residual hills. Measurement elsewhere in the Belize cockpit karst indicated that depressions have an average of six surrounding summits (Day, 1978a).

Each five-metre slope segment was classified subjectively in terms of general morphologic character. Cursary examination suggested that four of the slope types recognized in Jamaica by Aub (1969) dominated the scene: staircases, broken cliffs, inclined bedrock slopes (with occasional soil cover), and talus slopes. Accordingly, each five-metre slope segment was allocated to one of those four categories. Each profile was extended for 15 five-metre segments, each terminating 75 m from the starting point in the depression base. Profiles were terminated at 75 m since in most instances this brought the survey close to the depression margin. Considerations of time and effort also dictated that profiles be limited to 75 m lengths. The slope surveys were completed for each of the five depressions in July 1980.

Secondly, during 1975 125 pre-weighed limestone tablets were emplaced at 25 different sites on the surface of depression slopes; five tablets were emplaced at each site. Each of the tablet sites was located along one of the slope profiles, one profile being selected from each of the five depressions. Tablets were located at the surface, regardless of any soil cover so as to provide an approximately even coverage of the four slope segment types; seven tablet sites were on staircases (on the near-horizontal step surfaces), seven were on broken cliffs (suspended against the cliff face), six were on inclined bedrock or soil veneered slopes (anchored to the slope surface), and five were on talus slopes (lying on the surface). All tablets were of 1.5 cm diameter and 0.5 cm thickness, having a surface area of 5.89 cm^2. Tablets were all constructed of Jamaican White Limestone (Browns Town member) and were as homogeneous as possible. They were enclosed in nylon bags of 2 mm diameter mesh and thus were susceptible both to solution and to mechanical erosion processes.

370

Of the 125 tablets emplaced in 1975, 101 were recovered during January 1981, a recovery rate of just over 80%. Recovered tablets were reweighed to an accuracy of four decimal places, and the weight loss over the emplacement period, 2195 days was calculated. In most respects the weight loss measurement technique conforms to the guidelines suggested by Trudgill (1975) and employed elsewhere (Day, 1978a). Since the limestone used is not the same as the native bedrock, results indicate only relative weight losses suffered by the alien material and are not measures of actual rates of erosion being experienced by the Belizean limestone.

Thirdly, soil carbon dioxide concentrations were measured, using a portable Draeger gas analyzer with a soil probe, on two occasions - during a wet period in July 1980 and during a dry period in January 1981. (At Belmopan total rainfall for July 1980 was 191.26 mm; for January 1981 the total was 7.87 mm.) Concentrations were measured at points along the examined slope profiles in the immediate vicinity of the weight-loss tablets; they give thus some indication of soil carbon dioxide concentrations under different soil moisture conditions in the locations where surface erosion rates were measured. Soil carbon dioxide concentrations have been identified as indicators of potential solutional activity and have been measured in several areas of tropical karst terrain (see, for example Nicholson and Nicholson, 1969; Miotke, 1974; Trudgill, 1976, 1977; Day, 1978a). These studies point to the increase in concentrations with depth and moisture content. Measurements reported here were all made at the apparent soil-bedrock boundary, between 5 and 25 cm depth; they were made under two different sets of soil moisture conditions (although soil moisture contents were not quantified).

Lastly, during the wet period in July 1980 samples were collected of surface water occurring on the slope profiles. This was the only time that surface runoff has been observed on the slopes; as one might expect where the surface is irregular and cleft by enlarged fractures, surface flow is poorly organized and of very short duration. Such water samples as could be collected were measured for total hardness by standard EDTA titration (Douglas, 1968).

RESULTS

Slope segment types and their distribution

The distribution of the 375 categorized slope segments on the 5 slope profiles is shown in Table 19.1. 108 (28.8%) of the slope segments are staircases; 107 (28.5%) are broken cliffs; 82 (21.9%) are inclined bedrock or soil-veneered slopes; 78 (20.8%) are talus slopes.

Although the incidence of the four slope segment types shows that the slope profiles are not dominated by any one type, there is clear variation between near-base, midslope and near-summit locations. Segments within 25 m of the depression base

Table 19.1   Occurrence of slope segment types

Segment Type	Number Occurring		
	1-25 m from base	26-50 m from base	51-75 m from base
Staircase	14	21	73
Broken cliff	5	68	34
Inclined bedrock slope	61	7	14
Talus	45	29	4

Total number of staircase segments = 108

Total number of broken cliff segments = 107

Total number of inclined bedrock segments = 82

Total number of talus segments = 78

are dominated by inclined bedrock, or soil-veneered slopes (48.8%) and by talus slopes (36%); in the lower portions of the profiles staircases (11.2%) and broken cliffs (4%) are relatively uncommon. The midslope segments are composed predominantly of broken cliffs (54.4%); talus slopes (23.2%) and staircases (16.8%) are of similar, but lower frequency, and inclined bedrock or soil-mantled slopes are relatively rare (5.6%). Staircases are the most common slopes in the upper, near-summit portions of the profiles (58.4%); here broken cliffs (27.2%), inclined slopes (11.2%), and talus slopes (3.2%) are all of secondary importance in terms of frequency. Of the 108 staircase segments, 73 (67.6%) occur in the upper portions of profiles, more than 50 m from the depression base. Staircases decrease in occurrence downslope, only 14 (12.9%) of them occur within 25 m of depression bases. By contrast, broken cliffs are most common in the midslope sections of profiles; 68 (63.6%) of cliff segments occur between 26 m and 50 m from slope bases. In the upper portions of profiles occur 34 (31.7%) of the broken cliff segments, but they are rare (5, 4.7%) near depression bases. Of the 82 inclined bedrock, or soil-veneered slopes, the vast majority, 61 (74.4%) occur within 25 m of the lowest point in depressions. 14 inclined slopes (17.1%) occur more than 50 m distant from bases; they are least common in midslope sections (7, 8.5%). Talus slopes are most common near depression bases, where 45 occur out of the observed 78 (57.7%). They decrease in occurrence upslope, and only 4 (5.1%) were recorded further than 50 m from depression bases.

Soil carbon dioxide concentrations

Table 19.2 shows the soil carbon dioxide concentrations measured during July 1980 and January 1981. At both times there was apparently no clear variation with respect either to position on the slope profiles relative to depression bases, nor with respect to specific slope segment types (Table 19.3). Concentrations within 25 m of depression bases ranged from 0.5 to

Table 19.2   Soil carbon dioxide concentrations, July 1980
              and January 1981

Profile Number	Slope segment number ($\longrightarrow$ Upslope)											
	1	3	4	5	6	7	8	9	10	12	13	14
5			0.5		0.7			0.9		1.6		
			0.6		0.5			0.5		0.8		
9	1.4	0.7					1.5			0.9	2.2	
	1.1	0.6					1.0			0.8	0.5	
14	0.9		0.9					1.4		0.8		0.7
	0.7		0.9					1.2		0.1		0.3
20	0.8	1.5				0.8				0.6		
	0.3	1.2				0.6				0.9		
24	1.2			0.9	2.7	1.5		0.8	1.6		1.1	
	0.7			0.2	0.8	0.2		0.4	0.9		0.6	

First row of figures shows % soil pCO_2 in July 1980
Second row of figures shows % soil pCO_2 in January 1981
All values obtained at apparent soil/rock interface, 5-25 cm depth
All values are the mean of two readings at each site

Table 19.3   Soil carbon dioxide concentrations by slope
              segment type and location

Segment type	1-25 m from base		26-50 m from base		51-75 m from base	
	July	January	July	Janaury	July	January
Staircase	0.9	0.2	0.7	0.5	0.9	0.8
			2.7	0.8	2.2	0.5
					0.6	0.9
					1.1	0.6
Broken cliff	0.5	0.6	0.8	0.6	1.6	0.8
			1.5	1.0	0.8	0.1
			0.9	0.5		
			1.4	1.2		
Inclined	1.4	1.1	1.6	0.9	0.8	0.1
	0.9	0.7				
	0.8	0.3				
	1.2	0.7				
Talus	0.7	0.6	1.5	0.2		
	1.5	1.2	0.8	0.4		
	0.9	0.9				

All values % pCO_2, determined as indicated in Table 19.2

Table 19.4   Summary of water hardness measurements, July 1980

Profile Number	Slope segment number (——> Upslope)											
	1	3	4	5	6	7	8	9	10	12	13	14
5			52(1)		72(2)				-	52(2)		
9	45(2)	-					58(2)			50(1)		
14	69(3)		-					28(3)		-		
20	80(2)	82(2)				36(2)				-		
24	42(2)			106(3)	-	-		-	-		80(1)	

Figures show mean total hardness as mg.l^{-1}CaCO$_3$

Figures in parentheses indicate number of samples tested.

1.5% in July 1980 and from 0.2 to 1.2% in January 1981. Between 26 and 50 m from depression bases carbon dioxide concentration ranged from 0.7 to 2.7% in July 1980, and between 0.2 and 1.2% in January 1981. Upper slope portion ranges were from 0.6 to 2.2% in July 1980, and from 0.1 to 0.9% in January of the following year. With respect to slope type, ranges were similar. Concentrations over staircase slopes varied from 0.6 to 2.7% in July, and from 0.2 to 0.9% in January. Broken cliff readings fell between 0.5 and 1.6% in July, and between 0.1 to 1.2% in January. From 0.8 to 1.6% in July, and from 0.1 to 1.1% in January describes concentrations over inclined slopes; and over talus slopes values were from 0.7 to 1.5% in July and from 0.2 to 1.2% in January.

Although concentrations showed no clear relationship with slope segment type or position, in the majority of cases values were higher during July 1980 than in the following January when conditions were much drier.

Water hardness measurements

Table 19.4 shows the results of total hardness determinations for the samples that could be obtained during the rains of July 1980. Since this was the only time that sufficient water was present at the surface to facilitate sampling, and since the number of samples was low (only 28 total samples at 13 of the 25 weight-loss sites) no great significance can be attached to these results. Given the limited evidence however, two observations seem justified: first, hardness values are all relatively low (range 28-106 mg/l, mean 62 mg/l), second, there is no consistent variation with respect either to slope segment type or position on the slope.

Erosional weight losses

Table 19.5 shows the erosional weight losses experienced
by the tablets of Jamaican Browns Town Limestone between
November 1975 and January 1981 at each of the 25 sites on the
slope profiles. The breakdown of results by reference to slope
segment type and position is depicted in Table 19.6.

Within 25 m of depression bases the highest rates of erosional weight loss were demonstrated by tablets on inclined
bedrock or soil-veneered slopes which are the most common of
the segment types there, (0.0527 g/yr), and tablets on the much
less common staircase slope (0.0521 g/yr). Tablets on talus
slopes (0.0303 g/yr) and those on the single broken cliff segment
monitored (0.0215 g/yr) showed lower rates of weight loss.
Taken as a group regardless of slope segment type, tablets located on the 9 weight-loss sites within 25 m of depression bases
experienced a mean weight loss of 0.0417 g/yr. This mean loss
was considerably higher than that experienced by tablets on
midslope and upper slope segments.

On the midslope sites, between 26 m and 50 m from depression
bases, weight losses were comparable on the inclined bedrock
segment (0.0217 g/yr), on staircases (0.0213 g/yr) and on talus
slopes (0.0201 g/yr). Weight losses on broken cliff sites,
averaging 0.0110 g/yr were only about 50% of those recorded on
the other slope types. Taken as a whole, the tablets on the 9
midslope segments, regardless of segment type, suffered the
lowest mean weight losses (0.0166 g/yr).

Between 51 m and 75 m from depression bases the largest
weight losses were experienced by tablets on the sole inclined
bedrock site at this range (0.0305 g/yr). Weight losses on the
other two segment types monitored, staircases and broken cliffs
were similar (0.0216 g/yr and 0.0260 g/yr respectively). Taken
as a whole, mean weight losses on the upslope segment sites were
0.0241 g/yr, intermediate between those on basal and midslope
segments.

Of the four slope segment types on which tablets were emplaced, regardless of position on the slope profiles, the largest
weight losses were experienced by tablets on inclined bedrock
slopes (mean loss 0.0438 g/yr). Tablets on staircase segments
and on talus slope segments experienced the same mean weight
losses (0.0260 g/yr), although where both types were monitored,
up to 50 m away from depression bases, higher loss rates were
demonstrated by the tablets on staircases (Table 19.6). In all
cases, regardless of position on the slope profiles, the lowest
weight losses were suffered by tablets on broken cliffs (mean
loss 0.0168 g/yr). Taking all tablet weight losses, regardless
of slope segment type or position, mean weight losses over the
2195 day period were 0.0277 g/yr.

Table 19.5 Limestone tablet weight loss results, November 1975 to January 1981

Profile Number	Slope segment number (⟶ Upslope)									
	1	3	4	5	6	7	8	9	10	12
5			0.0215		0.0110 (3)			0.0107		0.0212
9	0.0680	0.0418							0.0113 (4)	0.0417
14	0.0812 (3)		0.0110 (3)				0.0125 (2)		0.0307 (4)	0.0305
20	0.0400	0.0382				0.0127 (2)		0.0081 (4)		0.0181
24	0.0215 (4)			0.0521	0.0325 (4)	0.0198 (4)		0.0203 (2)	0.0217 (4)	0.0152 (3)

All tablets of Jamaican Browns Town Limestone

Losses calculated as g/yr

All figures are means of five tablets' weight loss, unless shown otherwise by figures in parentheses

Table 19.6   Tablet weight losses by slope segment type
              and location

| Segment Type | Mean weight loss occurring | | | |
	1-25 m from base	26-50 m from base	51-75 m from base	All
Staircase	0.0521(1)	0.0213(2)	0.0216(4)	0.0260(7)
Broken cliff	0.0215(1)	0.0110(4)	0.0260(2)	0.0168(7)
Inclined bedrock	0.0527(4)	0.0217(1)	0.0305(1)	0.0438(6)
Talus	0.0303(3)	0.0201(2)	- (0)	0.0260(5)
All	0.0417(9)	0.0166(9)	0.0241(7)	0.0277(25)

Losses calculated as g/yr

Figures in parentheses indicate number of tablet sites on that slope
segment type for each location category

DISCUSSION

The four major slope segment types recognized in this study
appear to occur widely throughout tropical karst terrain.   They
have been identified within other cockpits (Aub, 1964; 1969;
Day, 1978a and unpublished) and at tower bases (McDonald, 1976;
Jennings, 1976); they may be a useful basis for overall slope
comparisons and may also prove worthy of greater study in their
own right, especially since they act as microcatchments leading
water to the subcutaneous zone.   One immediate comparison is
possible between the results of this study and those of a previously unpublished study by the author of slope units within
Jamaican cockpits.   As shown in Table 19.7 broken cliffs and
inclined bedrock slopes are more common in Belize, whereas staircases and talus slopes are more numerous in Jamaica.   Reasons
for these differences are not clear.   One immediate possibility
is that the differences, and also the locations of specific slope
segements within each group of cockpits, are geologically controlled.   In other words, as suggested by Tjia (1969), the

Table 19.7   Occurrence of slope segment types, Belize and Jamaica

| Segment Type | % of all slope segments | |
	Belize	Jamaica
Staircase	28.8	34
Broken cliff	28.5	17
Inclined bedrock slope	21.9	12
Talus	20.8	37

occurrence of certain slope types may result from differences in the relative frequency of bedding planes and vertical fissures. Staircases may occur where both have similar spacing; broken cliffs may dominate where beds are thick and vertical fissures numerous; inclines may dominate where there are no dominant vertical fissures and where lateral development cuts across one or more beds. This question requires further study, although geological structure is very much obscured in tropical karst by the vegetation cover. Geological control is not evident in the study area of Belize, where the slope segment distribution seems to bear no relation to bed thicknesses, but it may be important elsewhere.

Apart from geological control, the distribution of slope segments may be a reflection of process variations, as yet unclear, or of age differences. Monroe (1977) has suggested that cockpits deepen through time and that cliffs may break down to produce talus. The fewer cliffs and greater amounts of talus in the Jamican depressions may indicate that they are older than those in Belize. Along the same lines one could argue that in Jamaica bedrock inclines have been disrupted by development of vertical fissures; Jamaican cockpits are deeper than those in Belize (Day, 1978a).

The domination of cockpit bases by talus and inclined soil-mantled bedrock slopes is consistent with previous observations of slope breakdown (Monroe, 1977; Sweeting, 1968; Day, 1978a) and sediment accumulation (Smith, Drew and Atkinson, 1972; Day, 1978a). The bedrock inclines may also have played an important role in supplying water to central shafts, although no channels or shafts are evident now.

Midslope sections, where broken cliffs dominate, are the source areas for much of the basal talus. Soil is scanty here, there are few lateral segments and uninterrupted bedrock inclines are rare. Near-summit slopes resemble those of the cones described by Tjia (1969). Staircases dominate, and the overall profile is convex with shallow soils.

Soil carbon dioxide concentrations are difficult to interpret and show no clear relation to either slope segment type or position within the depressions. Concentrations are consistently higher under conditions of high soil moisture but how this relates to actual temporal variation in erosion rates is unclear. Overall concentrations are within the ranges reported by previous studies (Nicholson and Nicholson, 1969; Miotke, 1974; Trudgill, 1976; Day, 1978a; Crowther, 1983).

Water hardness measurements, although representing only one specific time period, suggest that water moving across the surface is doing so too rapidly to play a major role in limestone erosion. Surfaces at ground level act essentially as collecting areas for runoff which is still aggressive when it is directed underground down vertical fissures. Surface erosion seems unlikely to be keeping pace with that underground, and in a sense the surface is becoming increasingly isolated form the process foci and increasingly relict.

Erosional weight loss results are particularly interesting in light of the above findings. Overall weight losses are similar to those recorded previously in Belize and other tropical karst areas (Day, 1978a). Regardless of slope segment type, erosional weight losses appear to differ with slope position. Mean losses apparently are greatest in depression bases, least in midslope sections and intermediate near hill summits. Analysis of variance does not allow, however, statistical rejection of the null hypothesis that the samples represent chance variations within the same population. In light of this statistical insignificance no firm conclusions can be drawn from the data and further measurements clearly are called for. A priori one might expect greater weight losses with increasing downslope position because of the downslope water funnelling effect of the vegetation canopy which results in at least 14% more rainfall reaching the ground in depression bases than on surrounding hill summits (Aub, 1964).

Weight losses on the different slope segment types also show some evidence of systematic variation, although again statistically one cannot support the hypotheses that the samples represent different populations. One might expect different weight loss results since water behaves differently on the different types of slope segment, for example sinking rapidly into talus piles, lying on staircase 'steps', and moving gradually downslope across inclined slopes, especially where these are soil-mantled. Intuitively one would also expect that near-vertical broken cliffs would receive little rainfall and weight losses on those slopes would be minimal. Although one cannot support these hypotheses by statistical testing, it is interesting to note that the greatest weight losses are experienced by tablets located on inclined slopes near depression bases, which is to be expected a priori, and minimum weight losses were recorded on broken cliffs in midslope reaches.

The results of this study indicate that there is clear reason to pursue investigations of slopes within enclosed depressions in tropical karst terrain. It is evident that within cockpits there exists organization of form and process. This suggests that, even if their surfaces are essentially relict, they still behave as functional units and they may be regarded usefully as systems in which slope processes play a major role.

Acknowledgements

This study was initiated while the author was in receipt of a research studentship from the Natural Environment Research Council (UK). Later phases were funded in part by The Centre for Latin America, The Graduate School, University of Wisconsin-Milwaukee. Illustrations were prepared by Donna Schenstrom and Don Temple of the UWM Cartographic Service. Field assistance was rendered by R. North, M. Stein, C. Cleary, D. Schapiro, M. Simonds, B. Adetiba, A. Queenen and K. Queenen.

REFERENCES

Aub, C.F.T. 1964. *Limestone Scenery in Jamaica*. Unpublished Research Paper, Cambridge University.

Aub, C.F.T. 1969. Some observations on the karst morphology of Jamaica. *International Speleological Congress,* 5th, Stuttgart, Paper M16, 77 pp.

Crowther, J. 1980. *Karst Water Studies and Environment in West Malaysia*. Unpublished PhD Thesis, University of Hull.

Crowther, J. 1983. Carbon dioxide concentrations in some tropical karst soils, West Malaysia. *Catena,* 10, 27-39.

Crowther, J. 1985. Chemical erosion in tower karst terrain, Kinta Valley, Peninsular Malaysia.

Day, M.J. 1977. Surface hydrology within polygonal karst depressions in northern Jamaica. *International Speleological Congress,* 7th, Sheffield, 139-143.

Day, M.J. 1978a. The morphology of tropical humid karst with particular reference to the Caribbean and Central America. D. Phil. Thesis, Oxford University, 611pp.

Day, M.J. 1978b. Morphology and distribution of residual Limestone hills (mogotes) in the karst of northern Puerto Rico. *Bulletin of the Geological Society of America,* 89, 426-432.

Day, M.J. 1979. The hydrology of polygonal karst depressions in northern Jamaica. *Zeit Geomorph. N.F. Suppl. -Bd,* 32, 25-34.

Douglas, I. 1968. Field methods of water hardness determination. *British Geomorphological Research Group Technical Bulletin,* 1, 35pp.

Furley, P.A. and Newey, W.W. 1979. Variations in plant communities with topography over tropical limestone soils. *Journal of Biogeography,* 6, 1-15.

Gunn, J. 1977a. A model of the drainage system of a polygonal karst depression in the Waitomo area, North Island, New Zealand. *International Speleological Congress,* 7th, Sheffield, 225-229.

Gunn, J. 1977b. The hydrology of polygonal karst in the Waitomo area North Island, New Zealand. *International Speleological Congress,* 7th, Sheffield, 229-232.

Gunn, J., and Turnpenny, B. 1985. Storm hydrograph characteristics of three small limestone drainage basins in North Island, New Zealand.

Ireland, P.A.R. 1979. Geomorphological variations of 'case-hardening' in Puerto Rico. *Zeit. Geomorph. N.F., Suppl-Bd,* 32, 9-20.

Ireland, P.A.R. 1982. *Case-hardening and Karst Geomorphology in the Tropics with Particular Reference to the Caribbean and Belize*. D. Phil. Thesis, Oxford University, 394pp.

Jenkin, R.N. 1972. *The Belize Valley development study, British Honduras: Outline Report*. Unpublished Report, Land Resources Division, (Ministry of Overseas Development)

Jenkin, R.N. and Birchall, C.J. 1976. *The Soils of the Belize Valley, Belize. Supplementary Report*. Land Resources Division (Ministry of Overseas Development) 15.

Jenkin, R.N., Innes, R.R., Dunsmore, J.R., Walker, S.H., Birchall, C.J., and Briggs, J.S. 1976. *The Agricultural Development Potential of the Belize Valley*. Land Resources Division, (Ministry of Overseas Surveys), Land Resource Study, 24.

Jennings, J.N. 1976. A test of the importance of cliff-foot caves in tower karst development. *Zeit Geomorph. N.F. Suppl.-Bd, 26*, 92-97.

Lehmann, H. 1953a. Darstentwicklung in den Tropen. *Die Umschau in Wissenschaft und Technik, 18*, 559-562.

Lehmann, H. 1953b. Der tropische Kegelkarst in Westindien. *Tagungsber. u. wissensch. Abh., Dt. Geographentag Essen, 29*, 126-131.

Lehmann, H. 1954. Der tropische Kegelkarst auf den grossen Antillen. *Erdkunde, 8*, 130-139.

Lehmann, H., Krömmelbein, K. and Lötschert, W. 1956. Karstmorphologische geologische und botanische Studien in der Sierra de los Organos auf cuba. *Erdkunde, 10*, 185-204.

McDonald, R.C. 1975. Observations on hillslope erosion in tower karst topography of Belize. *Bulletin of the Geological Society of America, 86*, 255-256.

McDonald, R.C. 1976a. Hillslope base depressions in tower karst topography of Belize. *Zeit. Geormorph. N.F., Suppl.-Bd, 26*, 98-103.

McDonald, R.C. 1976b. Limestone morphology in South Sulawesi, Indonesia. *Zeit. Geomorph. N.F. Suppl.-Bd, 26*, 79-91.

McDonald, R.C. 1979. Tower karst geomorphology in Belize. *Zeit. Geomorph. Suppl.-Bd, 32*, 35-45.

Miller, T.E. 1977. Karst of the Caves Branch, Belize. *International Speleological Congress,* 7th, Sheffield, p. 314.

Miller, T.E. 1981. Hydrochemistry, hydrology and morphology of the Caves Branch Karst, Belize. Ph.D. Theses, McMaster Universtiy, 280p

Miller, T.E. 1983. Hydrology and hydrochemistry of the Caves Branch Karst, Belize. *Journal of Hydrology, 61*, 83-88.

Miotke, F.D. 1974. Carbon dioxide and the soil atmosphere. *Abhand. zur Karst - Und Höhlenkunde,* **A9**, 49pp.

Monroe, W.H. 1977. Origin of karst depressions in northern Puerto Rico. In: *Karst Hydrogeology,* ed. J.S. Tolson and F.L. Doyle, (Huntsville: University of Alabama), 169-175.

Nicholson, F.H. and Nicholson, H.M. 1969. A new method for measuring soil carbon dioxide for limestone solution studies. *Tournal of the British Speleological Association,* **6**, 136-148.

Smith, D.I., Drew, D.P. and Atkinson, T.C. 1972. Hypotheses of karst landform development in Jamaica. *Transactions of the Cave Research Group, Great Britain,* **14**, 159-173.

Sweeting, M.M. 1968. Karstic morphology of the Yucatan. In: *The University of Edinburgh Expedition to British Honduras - Yucatan, 1966.* General Report, Section **4**, 37-40.

Tjia, H.D. 1969. Slope development in tropical karst. *Zeit. Geomorph. N.F.,* **13**, 260-266.

Trudgill, S.T. 1975. Measurement of erosional weight loss of rock tablets. *British Geomorphological Research Group Technical Bulletin,* **17**, 13-19.

Trudgill, S.T. 1976. Rock weathering and climate. In: *Geomorphology and Climate,* ed. E. Derbyshire, 59-99.

Trudgill, S.T. 1977. The role of a soil cover in limestone weathering, Cockpit Country, Jamaica. *International Speleological Congress,* 7th, Sheffield, 401-404.

Walker, S.H. 1973. *Summary of Climatic Records for Belize.* Land Resources Division, (Overseas Development Administration, London), Supplementary Report, 3.

Williams, P.W. 1983. The role of the subcutaneous zone in Karst hydrology. *Journal of Hydrology,* **61**, 45-67.

Williams, P.W. in press. Subcutaneous hydrology and the development of dolines. *Zeit. für Geomorph.*

20

Aspects morphologiques du karst du Kelifely (Madagascar)

G. Rossi

RÉSUMÉ

Cette première reconnaissance du plateau karstique du Kelifely (Ouest de Madagascar) met en évidence l'existence d'une grande variété de paysages karstiques allant du simple causse au cockpit-karst.

La présence de diverses manifestations volcaniques se traduit par l'existence de formes volcano-karstiques souvent originales. Après un essai de typologie, l'auteur essaie de dégager les rapports entre la structure et les familles de formes.

SUMMARY

This first survey of the karstic plateau of the Kelifely (Western region of Madagascar) brings out the existence of a large variety of landscapes ranging from the plain limestone plateau to the cockpit-karst.

The presence of various volcanic manifestations is evidenced by the existence of volcano-karstic forms and often original ones at that. After discussing the typology of the forms, the author tries to pinpoint the relations existing between the structure and the families of forms.

INTRODUCTION

Le plateau du Kelifely est le plus vaste des karsts de Madagascar (Figure 20.1), Situé au Sud-Ouest de Majunga entre 16°30 et 17°20 de latitude Sud, il couvre une superficie d'environ 8000 km². De forme massive, 75 km du Nord au Sud, autant de l'Est à l'Ouest, il est limité au Sud et à l'Ouest par une puissante cuesta de 300 à 500 m de commandement qui domine une dépression évidée dans les grès triasiques de l'Isalo. Au Nord, les calcaires du Jurassique s'ennoient sous les séries marneuses et gréseuses du Crétacé.

C'est sur sa bordure nord-ouest que se trouve le karst du Namoroka (Rossi, 1977). Il est traversé de part en part suivant un axe Nord-Sud par la Mahavavy du Sud. Le plateau porte le nom d'Ankara à l'Est du fleuve et de Kelifely à l'Ouest.

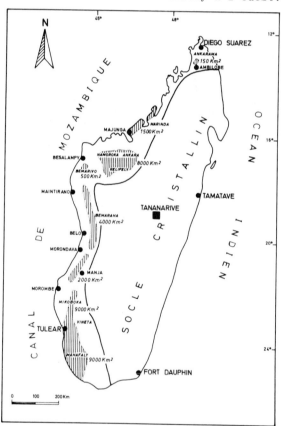

Figure 20.1   Croquis de situation des karsts malgaches

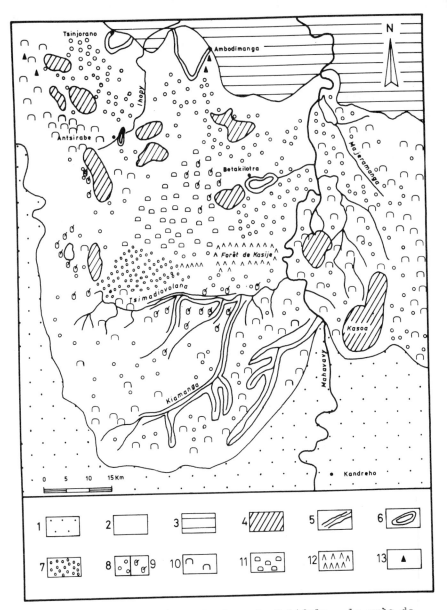

Figure 20.2 Croquis morphologique du Kelifely. 1: grès de
l'Isalo. 2: calcaires. 3: grès et argiles. 4: basaltes
et roches associées. 5: canyons. 6: poljés. 7: karst
dendritique. 8: zone de dolines. 9: kuppens.
10: cockpit. 11: tsingy. 12: édifices volcaniques
récents.

Ce karst est très peu connu; on ne dispose sur cette région que de quelques notes d'Abadie (1947). Cela s'explique par les difficultés d'accès et de circulation de ce vaste plateau pratiquement vide d'hommes à l'exception de quelques bandes de pillards.

La végétation est constituée d'une savane plus ou moins dense persemée d'arbres pyrophiles, *(Poupartia Caffra et Acridocarpus excelsus)* tandis que quelques îlots de forêt subsistent sur les versants du canyon de la Mahavavy et sur les calcaires massifs disséqués en tsingy de la forêt de Kasijy. Les dépressions sont colonisées par une végétation hygrophile à base de *Mimosa pudica* et de *Ficus sakalavarum*.

LES PRINCIPAUX ASPECTS DU MODELE KARSTIQUE

Dans leur ensemble, le Kelifely et l'Ankara sont un causse, c'est-à-dire un plateau sur lequel l'essentiel des formes karstiques est constitué par des dolines. Mais en fonction de la densité parfois extraordinaire de celles-ci et de leurs formes d'une diversité déconcertante on peut mettre en évidence plusieurs types de paysages. En outre, le Kelifely a été le théâtre d'importantes manifestations éruptives et on y observe de nombreuses formes volcano-karstiques originales. On peut ainsi définir trois grandes régions: l'Ankara, le Nord du Kelifely, le Sud du plateau et le réseau de la Mahavavy (Figure 20.2).

(i) Le causse de l'Ankara

Ce plateau fortement vallonné offre un relief typique de causse. De nombreux vallons secs se réunissent pour donner des vallées à écoulement intermittent, et isolent ainsi des lanières ou de petits massifs de taille kilométrique, découpés en coupoles qui rappellent beaucoup celles de karst du Bemaraha (G. Rossi, 1983).

Les buttes montrent le calcaire, fragmenté, affleurant sous une maigre végétation de pseudo-steppe. Tandis que les vallons, au profil transversal en berceau, sont remblayés par des argiles de dissolution colluvionnées à partir des versants, et en saison des pluies, le contraste est vif entre les fonds humides et verdoyants et les coupôles grisâtres.

Les calcaires sont disposés en bancs d'épaisseur métrique, ou décamétrique, de composition et de porosité variée. Localement, à la faveur d'un banc plus imperméable, apparaissent les traces d'un écoulement aérien. Les dolines en 'verre de montre' sont nombreuses sur les lanières de plateau et dans les fonds. Leur densité augmente en direction du Nord avec la fréquence des niveaux imperméables. Les vallées s'élargissent alors souvent en dépressions marécageuses de forme amiboide, aux contours imprécis (vallée de la Majeramanga).

(ii) Le Sud du Kelifely

A l'aspect général d'un plateau entaillé par de profondes vallées en V ou en canyon, qui isolent des lanières ou des fragments de plateau sur lesquels le drainage aérien est très réduit. Tous

Photo 1   Les buttes l'Ouest de l'Ankara.   Exemple d'évolution
     mixte fluviokarstique liée à l'affleurement de bancs
     métriques de roches carbonatées de porosité et de perméa-
     bilité différentes (cliché aérien vertical; 1/40 000ème).

ces cours d'eau prennent naissance au niveau de la cuesta qui
domine la dépression gréseuse et coulent vers le Nord-Est, en
direction de la Mahavavy.

Le relief des lanières de plateau   Dans le Sud on a un paysage
assez comparable à celui de l'Ankara, avec de rares dolines
généralement de grande taille. Mais peu à peu le nombre des
dolines augmente, les formes se diversifient et aux classiques
dolines en 'verre de montre', s'ajoutent de profondes dolines
en entonnoir ou même quelques dolines-puits, la plupart du temps
alignées et localisées à proximité des canyons, parallèlement
à ceux-ci.   On peut penser qu'il s'agit là de formes d'effondrement au-dessus d'importants conduits souterrains.

     Ce qui est remarquable également, c'est le grand développe-
ment des réseaux de drainage embryonnaires.   Une série de sources
situées au pied d'un interfluve à dolines forment un ruisseau,
parfois à écoulement permanent, lequel reçoit quelques affluents
provenant d'autres sources ou de dolines, puis après un parcours
de quelques kilomètres ou de quelques centaines de mètres, se
perd dans une dépression marécageuse subcirculaire ou amiboide,
les plus grandes ayant jusqu'à 2 à 3 km de grand axe.   Parfois,
à quelques centaines de mètres de là, et à une altitude plus
basse, une nouvelle ligne de sources donne naissance à un nouveau
réseau embryonnaire qui forme relais en direction de la vallée
ou du canyon à écoulement permanent.   Directement ou indirecte-
ment ces ébauches de réseau communiquent donc avec les drains
majeurs soit par l'intermédiaire de lignes de sources situées
sur le versant de la vallée principale ou au fond d'une reculée,
soit par de petits affluents à écoulement permanent dont
l'encaissement augmente progressivement vers l'aval (Figure 20.3).

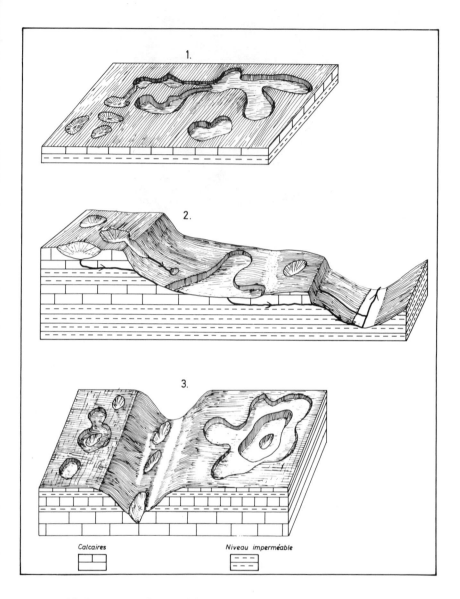

Figure 20.3 Types de reliefs de plateau. 1: dépression amiboide
sur série calcaire peu épaisse. 2: exemple de drainage sur
série de niveaux calcaires et de niveaux imperméables
alternés. 3: formes emboitées sur série de niveaux calcaires
et de niveaux imperméables alternés.

C'est aussi dans ce secteur que l'on observe des dolines étoilées. Il s'agit de profondes dolines en entonnoir dont les bords sont échancrés par des vallons secs suspendus au-dessus du fond. Parfois, ces vallons communiquent avec une large dépression, peu encaissée, à fond plat, elle-même défoncée par une ou plusieurs dolines en entonnoir. Les cas d'emboîtement de formes sont fréquents, dolines emboîtées dans des ouvalas ou doline-entonnoir dans une doline en 'verre de montre' (Figure 20.3).

Plus curieuses sont des formes en vallons alluviaux largement évasés dont les versants conservent un écoulement à partir de sources situées sous la corniche sommitale, mais dont le fond est sec et crevé de dolines dans lesquelles viennent se perdre ces ruisseaux. Ces vallons sont perchés au-dessus de la vallée principale ou forment un petit bassin plus ou moins fermé soutiré ou vidangé par un ruisseau à écoulement permanent.

Une dernière curiosité de cette partie du Kelifely est constituée par ce que nous baptiserons le 'karst dendritique' faute de lui avoir trouvé un équivalent dans la littérature. Ce relief très particulier s'observe dans l'Est entre les rivières Tsimadiavolana au Nord et Madiromageny au Sud et couvre une superficie d'environ 150 km^2 (Figure 20.4).

Il se présente comme une succession de petites dolines-entonnoir de diamètre presque toujours inférieur à 50 m, disposées en chapelets et dessinant exactement un tracé de réseau hydrographique dendritique très ramifié et très dense, parfois reliées entre elles par de petits vallons, elles communiquent souvent avec un ruisseau aérien. Dans certains cas, ces chapelets de dépressions forment un réseau anastomosé sans écoulement apparent vers l'extérieur. Il s'agit là de dolines d'effondrement situées au-dessus d'un véritable réseau hydrographique souterrain. On observe d'ailleurs, localement en bordure des drains majeurs

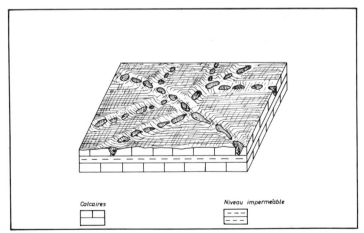

Calcaires   Niveau imperméable

Figure 20.4   Croquis schématique du karst dendritique

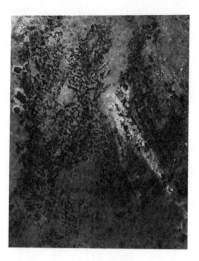

Photo 2 Exemple de karst dendritique. Réseau de dépressions
de petit diamètre, souvent allongées ou coalescents,
reproduisant en surface l'organisation d'un réseau de
drainage hypodermique (cliché vertical; 1/40 000ème).

un réseau aérien de dessin comparable, visiblement lié au dé-
blaiement complet de la couche karstifiable le long de ces
conduits souterrains; le profil en long de la vallée, constitué
d'une série de petites dépressions en forme de poire séparées
par de courts goulets, montre bien son origine. Dans le détail,
on remarque ainsi la présence de toutes les formes de transition
depuis les alignements de dolines-entonnoir jusqu'à une sorte
de vallée-chapelet.

Le réseau de la Mahavavy Dans l'extrême Sud-Est, les affluents
de la Mahavavy ont complètement disséqué la surface initiale du
plateau; il ne subsiste plus que de longues et étroites serres
ramifiées dont les sommets plats équi-altitudinaux correspondent
à un niveau calcaire résistant. Les vallées sont largement évasées, sans dissymétrie marquée, avec des pentes de l'ordre de
30%. L'encaissement de ces vallées est de 300 à 350 m et leur
fond plat est creusé dans les séries marneuses du Lias, ou
atteignent même l'Isalo gréseux.

Du fait de la faible surface des affleurements calcaires
sur les interfluves, les formes karstiques se limitent à quelques
dolines. Plus au Nord, la Kiamanga et la Tsimadiavolana coulent
dans la partie moyenne et supérieure de leurs cours au fond
d'impressionnants canyons, étroits, dont la profondeur varie de
50 m à l'aval jusqu'à près de 300 m à l'amont, leur fond est
bloqué sur les marnes liasiques. Les vallées secondaires se
terminent en reculées et se poursuivent, après un ressaut que le
ruisseau franchit en gorges, par des vallons évasés ou par des
petits canyons à méandres encaissés de 30 à 50 m. Tous ces cours

d'eau sont à écoulement permanent du fait de l'existence de niveaux imperméables sur lesquels ils sont bloqués.

(iii) Le Nord du Kelifely

La partie Nord du plateau du Kelifely est sans doute la plus intéressante de par la variété des formes que l'on y observe sur une surface finalement assez réduite, puisque de l'ordre de 1500 km² et par l'imbrication des phénomènes karstiques et volcaniques. Malheureusement, c'est aussi la région la plus difficilement accessible, sur laquelle nous ne disposons même pas de travaux géologiques précis.

Dans l'ensemble, il s'agit d'un plateau crevé d'une multitude de dépressions fermées. En fonction de la densité, de l'extension et de la forme de ces dépressions, on peut distinguer différents types de paysages.

Le plateau à dolines et à buttes La partie Ouest, en bordure de la cuesta, montre le relief le plus banal. Il s'agit d'un plateau parsemé de dépressions en 'verre de montre', peu nombreuses mais vastes (jusqu'à 1 km de grand axe), beaucoup conservent de l'eau durant toute l'année. Par contre, on remarque de nombreuses buttes à allure générale de coupoles qui ne sont pas sans rappeler le Kuppenkarst de Mariarano (Rossi, 1975). Ces buttes sont parfois isolées, plus souvent groupées en essaims, et, dans ce cas, il arrive que leur individualisation soit incomplète et des cols plus ou moins marqués les séparent les unes des autres (Photo 3). Cependant ce type de relief n'est pas exclusif, souvent les buttes n'apparaissent pas et le plateau se réduit à une surface pierreuse crevée de dolines de soutirage généralement peu profondes, parfois dissymétriques.

La plancher à dolines correspond à un calcaire franc (90 à 93% $CaCO_3$), compact, sans trace de dolomie, mais avec un résidu argileux de 6 à 10%. Sa porosité est de 3 à 4%. Le sommet plat ou légèrement bombé des buttes, portant de grands lapiés ou des tsingy, est lié à des calcaires francs (97-98% $CaCO_3$), très légèrement dolomitiques (1 à 2% $MgCO_3$), très purs (toujours moins de 1% de résidu), et très peu poreux (1 à 2%).

Les versants des buttes correspondent à des calcaires dolomitiques (80% $CaCO_3$ + 19% $MgCO_3$) ou à des dolomies (53-70% $CaCO_3$ + 30-37% $MgCO_3$), plus ou moins argileuses (1-10% residu), de porosité assez élevé (20 à 15%). Certaines buttes, en forme de coupoles aux versants surbaissés, assez comparables à celles de Mariarano, correspondant entièrement à des dolomies (57% CaCO + 2,8% résidu argileux), très poreuses (36%). La raideur du versant et son modelé de détail est en rapport avec le type de roche et sa porosité. Ainsi, les petites corniches ou les versants raides sont dus à des calcaires compacts, peu dolomitiques et peu poreux ou à des dolomies calcaires massives et peu poreuses. Inversement, les talus en pente douce sont taillés dans des dolomies ou calcaires dolomitiques plus ou moins pulvérulentes, très poreux.

Photo 3   Les Kuppen du nord du Kelifely.   Le plancher des buttes
    correspond à des calcaires compacts de faible porosité; la
    partie inférieure des versants à des calcaires dolomitiques
    ou des dolomies très poreuses.   La partie supérieure à des
    calcaires très purs et peu poreux.   (photo de l'auteur).-

Le cockpit-karst   Le centre et l'Est de cette région, jusqu'à
la Mahavavy, montrent un relief de 'cockpit karst' comparable
à celui qui a été décrit par de nombreux auteurs à la Jamaïque.
Mais, toujours en fonction de la forme et de la densité des dépressions, on peut mettre en évidence plusieurs types de paysages.

    En plusieurs points, le plateau apparaît comme taraudé par
de profondes dolines-puits, cylindriques, de taille variable:
la plus grande que nous ayons observé à 400 m de diamètre, les
plus petites moins de 20 m.   Leur densité maximale observée est
de 34 au km², mais il peut n'en exister que 5 ou 6 sur la même
surface.   L'aspect général évoque une surface dans laquelle on
aurait découpé, au hasard, à l'emporte-pièce, des centaines de
trous.   Dans le cas général, leur disposition ne paraît pas se
faire suivent des directions préférentielles, mais parfois des
alignements particulièrement spectaculaires sont visiblement
liés à des fractures et même, dans un cas, une série de ces
dolines, alignées, coalescentes, donnent une curieuse dépression
à allure de canyon à contours lobés.   Là où elles sont très
denses, elles tendent à isoler entre elles des fragments de
plateau ou des buttes à sommet plat, à versants subverticaux et
de dessin contourné qui finnesent ainsi par former, autour
des dépressions, un système anastomosé.

392

Photo 4   Deux types de cockpit-karst du Kelifely. Sur la moitié gauche
dolinespuits cylindriques parfois coalescentes. A partir
du coin inférieur droit et remotant transversalement dyke
basaltique. Dans le coin supérieur gauche cockpit à larges
dépressions amiboïdes (cliché vertical; 1/40 000ème).

Dans le second type, les dépressions sont nettement plus
larges que hautes, les versants sont en pente plus douce. Là
aussi, elles sont à fond plat, souvent coalescentes et isolent
entre elles des lanières de plateau également à dessin irrégulier.
Mais ces lanières ont un profil transversal arrondi, en dôme ou
en coupole. Localement, les dépressions, jointives, créent une
vallée amiboïde, marécageuse, à écoulement intermittent. Ces
vallées rejoignent rarement un cours d'eau permanent et forment
dans le cas général une ébauche de réseau sans écoulement aérien
vers l'extérieur (Photo 4).

Un troisième type de paysage est formé par des champs très
denses de dolines en 'verre de montre' assez profondes, isolant
entre elles un réseau de crêtes étroites. L'aspect évoque un
nid d'abeilles irrégulier. Ce paysage est remarquablement
développé au Nord-Ouest du Kelifely entre Adranomavo et Antsirabe.
Le fond de ces dolines est colmaté par des argiles hydromorphes,
tandis que les interfluves sont couverts par des argiles de dé-
calcification rouge-brique qui paraissent épaisses car le calcaire n'affleure qu'épisodiquement (Photo 5).

Enfin, un dernier type est caractérisé par des dolines-
entonnoirs qui isolent entre elles des interfluves à versants
convexo-concaves. Ces dolines s'organisent souvent en groupe
de quelques unités coalescentes donnant des dépressions de formes
diverses parfois reliées entre elles par de courtes, étroites, et
profondes gorges. Il faut noter que ce type est assez proche
du karst dendritique; ce qui le différencie, c'est, d'une part,
la taille plus grande des dolines et, d'autre part, le fait que
l'on n'a pas l'impression de réseau organisé mais d'une disposition plus anarchique.

Photo 5   Chaup de dolines en 'verre de montre' donnant un
paysage de nid d'abeilles. Drainage aérien intermittent
(cliché vertical: 1/40 000ème).

En résumé, il est possible de mettre en évidence quatre
types principaux de cockpit-karst:

- un type à dolines-puits à fond plat et à versants abrupts;
- un type à larges dépressions à fond plat et reliefs
  résiduels à versants convexes;
- un type à dolines en 'verre de montre' denses et interfluves étroits;
- un type à dolines-entonnoir et reliefs résiduels à
  versants convexo-concaves.

Ces différents paysages correspondent à des conditions
structurales déterminées et les groupes de formes ne sont que
rarement mêlés. Les dolines-puits sont des formes d'effondrement affectant une série de calcaires massifs (71-84% $CaCo_3$;
porosité 5-8%) assez épaisse (20-50 m), reposant sur un niveau
imperméable (48-55% $CaCo_3$ + résidu argileux; porosité 3%),
ayant entraîné le développement d'importants conduits souterrains
aboutissant aux ébauches de canyons formés par la coalescence
de dolines-puits.

Le second type apparaît sur des calcaires dolomitiques
d'épaisseur médiocre (10-20 m) mais de porosité beaucoup plus
élevée (15-22%), passant vers le bas à une série non dolomitique,
argileuse, compacte et peu poreuse (<5%).

Les secteurs de cockpit en 'nids d'abeilles' sont liés à
des dolomies (52-58% $CaCO_3$ + 30-35% $MgCO_3$ + 1-10% résidu
argileux), de forte porosité (17-37%), d'épaisseur assez faible
(10-15 m) reposant sur des dolomies (58% $CaCO_3$ + 41% $MgCO_3$) très
peu poreuses (2%).

Enfin, les dolines-entonnoir à l'origine des buttes convexo-
concaves sont typiquement des formes de soutirage et correspondent à l'affleurement d'épais calcaires hétérogènes plus ou moins

dolomitiques mais toujours assez poreux (11-18%).

Les tsingy (= Mega - Spitzkarren) Lorsque à la faveur de variations de faciés affleurent des calcaires cristallisés très purs,
très durs, peu poreux, ils sont disséqués en tsingy (Rossi,
1973). C'est le cas des petits massifs qui font suite vers
l'Est au karst du Namoroka. Mais on rencontre aussi de tels
entablements de quelques dizaines à quelques centaines de mètres
carrés un peu partout sur le plateau. Cependant dans le sud,
la forêt de Kasijy et celle de l'Analabe sont entièrement constituées de tables calcaires démantelées couvertes de tsingy.
Il s'agit d'une succession de chaos de blocs très difficilement
pénétrables.

(iv) Les poljés

Les poljés de bordure Au Nord du Kelifely, au contact avec les
séries argileuses du Crétacé, se sont développés, sur les calcaires, une série de poljés: Andranomatavy, Andranomavo, Tsinjorano et surtout Ambodimanga, le plus grand (30 km² environ)
et le plus intéressant (Figure 5).

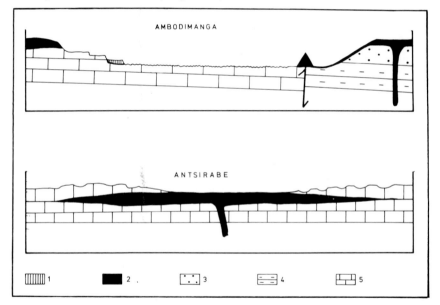

Figure 20.5 Coupe schématique des poljés d'Ambodimanga et
           d'Antsirabe.

    Entièrement dans le calcaire il est dominé au Nord par des
hauteurs gréseuses, le contact étant marqué par le lit d'une
petite rivière, l'Ankoba, qui draine le poljé vers le Nord. A
l'Ouest et au Sud les affleurement calcaires sont masqués par
d'épaisses séries basaltiques et c'est sur sa limite Est que se
dressent une série d'édifices volcaniques récents, pointements
et cônes stromboliens.

Parfaitement plat, son fond, marécageux, est recouvert d'argiles hydromorphes noires dont l'épaisseur d'ordre métrique est très variable. Au-dessous, le calcaire, massif, compact, légèrement argileux (80-85% $CaCO_3$), forme une surface corrodée irrégulière (à Rundkarren). Il est littéralement pourri sur plusieurs dizaines de centimètres, et sur 2 à 3 cm transformé en une pâte crayeuse qui se gratte facilement au couteau, ce qui montre à l'évidence le rôle de la corrosion dans l'évolution du poljé.

Si, aujourd'hui, le poljé est drainé vers l'extérieur il semble que cela n'ait pas toujours été le cas. En effet, sur son rebord ouest, près d'Ambalavary existent les traces de trois anciens niveaux. Les deux niveaux supérieurs situés à 50 et 30 m au-dessus du niveau actuel sont des replats d'érosion taillées dans le calcaire et recouverts, par place, de tufs calcaires. Le troisième niveau à 3/5 m est entièrement formé de tufs vacuolaires contenant des coquilles de gastéropodes. Ces éléments permettent d'envisager la présence d'un ancien lac qui se serait progressivement vidangé.

L'origine du poljé d'Ambodimanga est, en partie au moins, tectonique, la présence d'édifices volcaniques sur son rebord Est le démontre, il n'en reste pas moins qu'il s'agit d'une véritable dépression karstique, évidée entièrement dans le calcaire et liée, probablement, au blocage du drainage karstique au contact de séries non calcaires.

A l'inverse, on ne retrouve dans les poljés de Tsinjorano d'Andranomatavy et d'Andranomavo dont les caractères sont très voisins, ni niveaux anciens, ni indices d'une origine tectonique. Drainés vers l'extérieur leur évolution paraît être de type fluvio-karstique.

Les poljés de l'intérieur Sur le plateau on rencontre plusieurs poljé de taille très différente. Dans tous les cas il s'agit de dépressions crées par blocage de la dissolution sur un niveau imperméable. Le plus grand est celui de Betakilotra-Tondraka, une dizaine de kilomètres au Nord de la forêt de Kasijy.

Etiré sur 10 km dans la direction Nord-Sud, il couvre une superficie d'environ 35 km^2 et est limité au Nord et à l'Ouest par des coulées basaltiques très altérées. Le fond, marécageux, correspond à l'affleurement de calcaires compacts et très argileux.

Son drainage s'effectue de deux façons différentes. Le Nord est drainé à l'air libre par une petite rivière, la Tondraka, qui disparaît dans une perte à la sortie du poljé. Les eaux du Sud sont collectées dans une dépression amiboide située au contact des argiles du poljé et des calcaires du plateau. Cette dépression est soutirée en direction du canyon de la Mahavavy par un ruiseau à écoulement aérien intermittent: l'Andranovorombazaha.

Signalons encore un cas particulier, celui du poljé d'Antsirabe, Figure 5. De taille plus réduite (15 km^2), également drainé à l'air libre, son fond correspond au toit d'un sill basaltique. Ce sont les basaltes qui, dégagés des calcaires sus-jacents, puis altérés, servent de couche imperméable. A ce titre il s'agit là d'une forme mixte de type volcano karstique.

LE KARST ET LA STRUCTURE

La morphologie karstique du Kelifely-Ankara, la variété des formes sont à mettre en relation avec la structure dont nous allons préciser les grands traits.

(i) Les aspects généraux

La reconnaissance géologique a été mené par les géologues de la Société des Pétroles de Madagascar et du BRGM : Bauer et Rerat (1962), Razafimbelo (1964), Vendegies (1966), Guenot (1964), Donnot (1965), Donnot et Fournie (1965). L'ensemble de ces travaux a été synthétisé par Besairie (1966), Figure 6.

A la base, au-dessus des grès de l'Isalo, vient une série liasique complexe avec de fréquentes variations latérales de faciès et d'épaisseur. Elle est composée essentiellement de schistes, de grès, d'argiles et de marnes qui constituent le soubassement imperméable du karst. Celui-ci est développé dans le Bajocien-Bathonien qui débute par des marnes et se poursuit par une épaisse série de calcaires divers parfois dolomitiques, à intercalations argileuses. La série devient plus nettement calcaire vers le sommet avec des calcaires francs, compacts, sublithographiques et oolithiques, mais des bancs plus argileux demeurent.

L'épaisseur observée de la série varie de 420 m (Bajocien du Mont Kasoa plus Bathonien de l'Ambetatra) à 340 (sondage SPM d'Ihopy), et les pendages, faibles,(3° à 6°), sont sensiblement convergents vers le centre, donnant, ainsi, une allure de bassin au plateau du Kelifely-Ankara. Le caractère dominant de la lithologie est donc l'alternance de nombreux niveaux de calcaires variés de marnes ou d'argiles d'épaisseur relative variable. C'est là la cause fondamentale de l'aspect morphologique général du Kelifely et de Ankara.

En fonction du type de calcaire rencontré: franc, dolomitique, argileux, compact ou crayeux, de sa porosité, de l'épaisseur de la couche karstifiable au-dessus de l'imperméable relatif, on voit apparaître l'un ou l'autre des paysages que nous avons décrits. Cela permet de comprendre le grand développement de la karstification superficielle mais aussi l'existence, ça et là, de réseaux hydrographiques aériens embryonnaires coulant sur un banc relativement imperméable et peu épais, puis disparaissant dans une dépression fermée qui, elle, a déjà défoncé ce niveau et va évoluer par dissolution latérale pour donner les 'dépressions amiboides'.

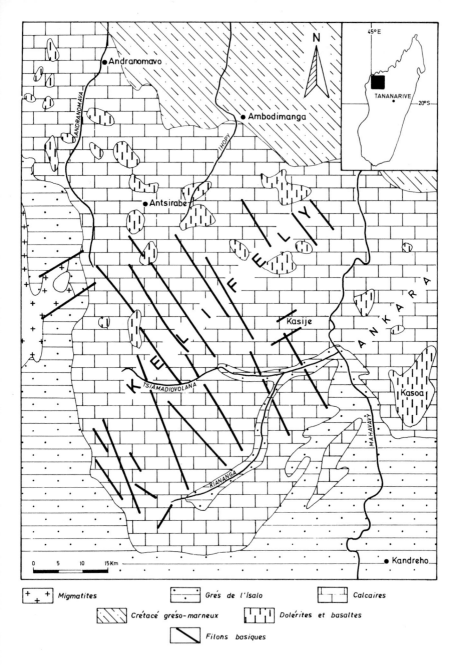

Figure 20.6   Croquis Géologique

398

De la même façon, le 'karst dendritique' paraît lié à l'existence d'un banc de calcaire compact relativement peu épais reposant sur un niveau imperméable sur lequel sont bloqués les écoulements souterrains. Ceux-ci ont creusé un réseau ramifié de galeries de petit diamètre au-dessus desquelles se produisent les séries d'effondrements qui donnent en surface ce paysage particulier.

L'ensemble de ce drainage karstique s'effectue en direction et en fonction des canyons du réseau de la Mahavavy, plus ou moins bloqués sur la série schisto-argileuse liasique, véritable niveau de base de ces karsts. Les reculées, les vallées sèches perchées actuellement défoncées par des dolines, nous paraissent dues, pour l'essentiel, à l'érosion régressive et au creusement au sein de cette succession de calcaires et de niveaux imperméables. C'est ce dernier point que traduit, en particulier, l'abondance des emboitements de formes. Tant que le niveau marneux sur lequel est bloqué l'écoulement n'est pas érodé, le vallon évolue comme n'importe quel autre cours d'eau. Lorsque le niveau calcaire sous-jacent est atteint, il y a infiltration et formation de dolines de dissolution qui vont s'encaisser dans le fond. Les ruisseaux adjacents vont conserver un écoulement aérien sur les marnes qui affleurent sur le versant, puis s'infiltrer dans les calcaires.

La forme des dolines, leur densité, sont à mettre en rapport avec les mêmes facteurs et les modifications de paysage que nous avons observées sur le plateau s'expliquent par les rapides et importantes variations verticales et latérales de faciès au sein de cette série néritique.

La tectonique cassante ne se manifeste dans la topographie que par l'importance des manifestations volcaniques. L'absence d'escarpements et de fractures ouvertes s'explique par le fait que les rejeux des failles du socle s'amortissent dans l'épaisse série sédimentaire plastique.

Au niveau de la karstification, l'influence de la tectonique se fait sentir essentiellement dans les alignements de dépressions fermées. Mais, malgré la densité de la fracturation attestée par la fréquence des dykes, ces alignements sont loin d'être le cas général. Ils ne se voient nettement que dans le paysage de dolines-puits où ils créent même des ébauches de canyons lorsque ces dolines sont coalescentes.

(ii) Les rapports lithologie - formes karstiques

Si la disposition structurale à l'échelle régionale rend compte de l'aspect général du plateau, les variations lithologiques locales contribuent à expliquer les changements souvent rapides de paysage karstique. A la lumière des observations et des analyses, deux facteurs nous paraissent jouer un rôle déterminant dans la typologie des formes: l'épaisseur de la couche karstifiable au-dessus de l'imperméable relatif et la porosité de la roche.

L'épaisseur de la couche karstifiable influe sur la vigueur des formes: hauteur des buttes, profondeur des dépressions. La porosité détermine l'aspect de la forme. Globalement, plus la porosité est grande, plus les formes sont douces, cette remarque que nous avons déjà faite à propos du karst du Bemaraha, est également vraie pour le Kelifely.

Ainsi, les formes en 'nid d'abeille', le cockpit à larges dépressions et longs versants convexes correspondent à des calcaires, calcaires dolomitiques ou dolomies dont la porosité est toujours élevée (de 15 à 37%). Une telle porosité entraîne une imbibition complète de la roche et une dissolution dans la masse. A l'inverse les roches carbonatées peu poreuses donnent des formes plus raides, plus aigues car la dissolution s'exerce essentiellement le long des zones de perméabilité en grand (fissures, broyages..), et, sur la forme elle-même, la dissolution est essentiellement pelliculaire. Enfin, les calcaires peu poreux, généralement compacts et massifs, même lorsqu'ils sont très purs, localisent les formes d'effondrement. L'eau, qui a pénétré à la faveur des cassures auxquelles ils sont sensibles, se concentre en conduits au niveau d'un imperméable relatif et crée un réseau souterrain dont les cavités finissent par se répercuter en surface.

Au total, si la nature chimique de la roche influe directement sur l'intensité de la karstification, c'est la porosité qui contrôle fondamentalement le type de modelé; l'épaisseur de la série karstifiable influaut sur le développement des formes. C'est l'extrême variabilité des faciès, des épaisseurs, des dispositions structurales dans le Kelifely qui explique la diversité des formes.

LES RELIEFS VOLCANIQUES ET VOLCANO-KARSTIQUES

Outre l'extraordinaire variété de son relief karstique, l'originalité majeure du Kelifely réside dans le grand développement des phénomènes volcaniques, et dans l'imbrication du volcanisme et de la karstification qui se traduit par l'apparition de formes particulières.

(i) Le volcanisme du Kelifely

On peut distinguer essentiellement quatre types de manifestations éruptives. La plus ancienne est constituée dans le Nord et l'Ouest du plateau par de vastes affleurements de roches de composition basaltique. Très altérés, ces épanchements donnent en surface des argiles ferrallitiques rouge vif.

Les épaisseurs apparentes sont très variables, allant de quelques mètres à plusieurs dizaines de mètres. Le type de gisement est difficile à préciser. Dans certains cas il semble que l'on ait à faire à des sills ayant bavé en surface sur plusieurs kilomètres de distance. Cela est suggéré par la topographie des affleurements presque toujours dissymétriques lorsq'on les recoupe perpendiculairement à la direction de l'affleurement. L'un des cas les plus nets étant celui du sill traversé par la piste de Vilanandro à Andranomavo. Mais la plupart du temps il n'est pas possible de déterminer s'il s'agit de sill ou de coulées d'origine fissurale. Aucan élément ne permet de juger de l'âge de ces basaltes. Les altérations nous sont apparues très semblables à celles des basaltes fini-crétacés connus dans tout l'Ouest malgache.

Un second type est constitué par de gros appareils parfois accompagnés par d'épaisses coulées. Le mont Kasoa, l'Ampetsapetsa, l'Antsohimajera au Sud, l'Antsosa, l'Ambetratra, l'Ambohimibaboka au Nord, en sont des exemples. Ces édifices au relief vigoureux dominent de 100 à 300 m la surface ondulée du causse. Il s'agit pour nous d'extrusions car, outre leur forme pyramidale ou conique caractéristique, les coulées sont constituées de basaltes passant parfois progressivement vers le centre des émissions à des dolérites ou même des gabbros (Kasoa). Là aussi, nous ignorons leur âge, mais en fonction des altérations on peut penser qu'ils sont nettement plus récents que les éruptions du type précédent, il pourrait peut-être s'agir de manifestations contemporaines du volcanisme oligo-miocène que nous avons mis en évidence au Nord de Majunga (datation à 35 ± 3 M.A.).

Au sud du poljé d'Ambodimanga il existe une série de pointements basaltiques et de cônes stromboliens. Les plus anciens sont très altérés et, bien que ces formes soient parfaitement identifiables, le ruissellement et le colluvionnement ont largement retouché les versants. En fonction de ce que nous avons observé dans le Nord et l'Ouest de l'île, nous sommes tenté de leur attribuer un âge quaternaire ancien. Certains pointements, tels l'Ambohitralika (Photo 6), sont par contre extrêmement frais et leur altération est pratiquement nulle. Il semble donc qu'il existe plusieurs générations d'édifices éruptifs. Notons que c'est le seul secteur du Kelifely où nous ayons reconnu des cônes stromboliens, (Figure 20.6).

Enfin, le plateau est parcouru par de nombreux dykes d'épaisseur, de longueur, de composition et d'âge variables. Les plus petits ont quelques dizaines de mètres de long et une épaisseur d'ordre métrique. Les plus grands dépassent 10 km et atteignent 300 m de large, s'élargissant parfois en dômes ou en véritables petits massifs (Ambatojoby, au sud d'Andranomavo). Les orientations sont variées avec une grande fréquence de la direction N 6° W. Il s'agit en grande majorité de filons basaltiques passant à des dolérites au centre des plus épais, mais au sud d'Ambodimanga nous avons observé une série de dykes trachytiques et rhyolitiques tous très altérés et recoupés par les émissions basiques. Celles-ci paraissent appartenir à plusieurs générations. Les plus anciennes, entièrement altérées, sont en creux au milieu des calcaires. D'autres, moins alterees, forment des lignes de colline aux versants fuyants. Les plus récentes donnent des reliefs particulièrement vigoureux, parfois de véritables murs pouvant atteindre 20 à 30 m de haut.

Photo 6 L' Ambohitralika, pointement basaltique sur la bordure Est du polje d'Ambohimanga. (photo de l'auteur).

(ii) <u>Les formes volcano-karstiques</u>

L'imbrication des phénomènes volcaniques et karstiques a donné naissance à une série de formes dont certaines sont originales, (Figure 20.7).

Les crypto-dolines Lorsque les coulés (ou les sills) sont venus recouvrir les calcaires, la poursuite de la dissolution sous les basaltes a provoqué, à leur surface, la formation de dolines de soutirage dont l'aspect dépend directement de leur épaisseur.

Sur basaltes peu épais (de l'ordre du décamètre) et entièrement altérés, le paysage est celui d'une multitude de dépressions en 'verre de montre', largement évasées. Les interfluves, étroits et arrondis sont dans les basaltes mais il n'est pas rare que le calcaire affleure sur les versants et au fond de la doline. Cette disposition est extremement courante au centre et à l'Ouest du Kelifely. Les argiles sont progressivement soutirées et parfois il ne reste qu'une mince bande de basaltes altérés au sommet de l'interfluve.

Si l'épaisseur des basaltes augmente les dolines tendent vers une forme en entonnoir. Les plus profondes que nous ayons observées atteignent une trentaine de mètres. Le calcaire n'affleure pas et il n'est pas rare qu'une nappe d'eau permanente occupe le fond de la dépression. L'un des plus beaux exemples est celui de l'Amboalando au nord du poljé de Betakilotra, où la surface est tellement taraudée que les interfluves se limitent à d'étroites crêtes aiguës.

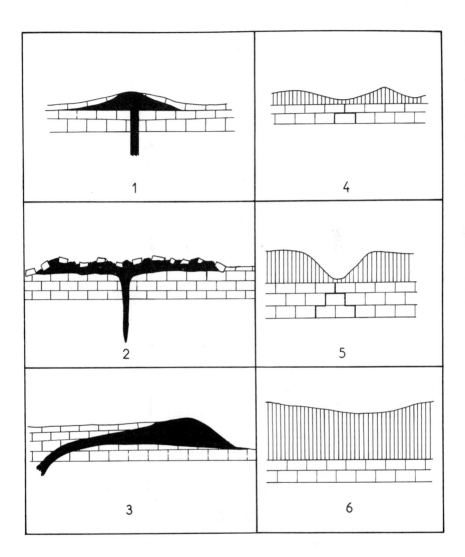

Figure 20.7 Principales formes volcano-karstiques:
1: dôme volcanique. 2: soulèvement par boursouflures
irrégulières. 3: sill passant à un dôme. 4: doline en
'verre de montre' sur basaltes peu épais. 5: doline-entonnoir
sur basaltes plus épais. 6: dépression peu marquée sur
basaltes très épais.

Les caractères crypto-karstiques s'atténuent si l'épaisseur des basaltes devient trop importante. On peut fixer le seuil autour de 50 à 60 m. La coulée n'est alors affectée que de rares dépressions peu marquées et de formes variées, rondes, ovoides, allongées, amiboides. Le plateau de Betsemboka, à l'Ouest d'Ambodimanga est l'illustration de ce cas.

Les dômes Les basaltes ont parfois soulevé les entablements calcaires donnant deux catégories principales de formes. La plus courante se présente comme une succession de boursouflures irrégulières formant de petites collines arrondies d'une dizaine de mètres de hauteur. Les versants et le sommet sont tapissés par le calcaire fragmenté en plaques et en blocs irréguliers disposés en tous sens. Les basaltes, apparaissent entre les calcaires, particulièrement au sommet essentiellement sous forme: de cailloutis emballés dans des argiles d'alteration.

Moins fréquemment, ils se sont insinués entre les fissures des calcaires et les ont soulevés sans en bouleverser la structure. Le dôme se présente alors comme une colline convexe circulaire ou ovoide dont le sommet est formé par un chapeau basaltique tandis que sur les versants les bancs calcaires affleurent sous une pellicule d'éboulis de basalte (Photo 7).

Dans un cas comme dans l'autre les altérations sont très médiocres et nous pensons que ces formes appartiennent au Quaternaire récent. Elles représentent probablement, avec les pointements d'Ambodimanga, la phase terminale du volcanisme du Kelifely.

Photo 7 Dôme résultant du soulèvement des calcaires par des basaltes. Le versant est pavé de blocs calcaires, le sommet est formé de basaltes altérés. (photo de l'auteur).

Les dépressions liées à des dykes C'est au Sud du plateau que les dykes les plus épais, altérés, ont localisé des dépressions fermées. Celles-ci ont toutes en commun d'être profondes, à fond plat et à versants subverticaux correspondant au contact calcaire/basalte. En fait, on constate que ce dernier caractère est dû à la cuisson des calcaires aux épontes ce qui a donné de part et d'autre du dyke une bande de cornéennes d'épaisseur décimétrique. Ceci étant, les dépressions sont de plusieurs types. Le plus souvent il s'agit de chapelets de dolines-puits plus ou moins coalescentes pouvant même aller jusqu'à la formation d'un petit canyon. Mais parfois l'évidement des argiles d'altération des basaltes donne une cuvette rectiligne, étroite et allongee, avec ou sans écoulement vers l'extérieur.

Signalons encore un cas très curieux. A l'Est du poljé de Betakilotra on observe un lac en forme de croissant très régulier d'environ 400 m de diamètre. A l'examen il s'avère qu'il est localisé sur un ring-dyke mis en creux au milieu de l'encaissant calcaire. Enfin on peut remarquer que lorsque l'altération des filons est moins poussée et qu'ils sont encore en relief par rapport aux calcaires, il arrive qu'ils donnent naissance à des étangs temporaires plus ou moins marécageux par barrage des écoulements hypodermiques.

Les microformes de cuisson et de karst couvert Les habituelles microformes de karst couvert en obus, en dalles, en coussins, en lames, sont très nombreuses dans les puissantes argiles ferrallitiques de décomposition des basaltes. Les blocs calcaires emballées dans ces argiles ou en cours d'exhumation ont un aspect émoussé caractéristique. Leur surface est grossièrement lisse, granuleuse au toucher, et les encoches basales de dissolution plus ou moins marquées sont fréquentes donnant parfois des 'rochers-champignons'.

En de nombreux points du plateau les argiles de dissolution des calcaires ont été cuites au contact des basaltes. On a lors une mosaique de dalles calcaires cimentées par une pâte argileuse qui a la consistance de la brique. Les calcaires s'avèrent cependant plus résistants, et lorsque les argiles ont été partiellement déblayées on obtient, parfois, de curieuses formes ayant l'aspect de pavés plus ou moins dechaussés (photo 8).

Photo 8 Dallage résultant du dégagement des argiles de décalci-
fication cuites au contact des basaltes. (photo de l'auteur).

CONCLUSION

Le plateau du Kelifely est donc un remarquable exemple de karst
tropical dans lequel les composantes structurales conditionnent
la forme et la densité des dépressions fermées qui sont à
l'origine de la déconcertante variété de paysages allant du
simple causse aux cockpit-karsts. La présentation et l'essai
de typologie des formes que nous venons de tenter met en évidence
la très grande richesse de ce karst que l'on considérait comme
l'un des plus banals des karst malgaches.

Bien des problèmes demeurent en suspens. En premier lieu
le karst profond dont on ne sait pratiquement rien, sauf que les
circulations doivent être importantes et complexes du fait des
caractères structuraux de la série sédimentaire et de l'inter-
férence du volcanisme. Les phénomènes volcano-karstiques méritent
des études détaillées pour préciser leurs rapports, en particulier
l'influence des éruptions sur la karstification et du drainage
karstique sur l'altération des basaltes. Le volcanisme lui-même
doit retenir l'attention car le vaste entablement calcaire du
Kelifely-Ankara, a vraissemblablement enregistré tous les
épisodes volcaniques qui marquent l'histoire de l'évolution du
graben du Mozambique depuis le Crétacé supérieur. Enfin, il est
certainement possible de mieux préciser les liens entre les
formes et la lithologie, car la dépendance est, de toute évidence, étroite.

Il est encore trop tôt pour essayer de définir les principaux traits de l'évolution morphologique du Kelifely mais il est certain que par l'extraordinaire variété des formes, des conditions structurales, par l'importance et la diversité du volcanisme, le Kelifely constitue un champ d'études unique à Madagascar.

REFERENCES

Abadie, Ch. 1947. Note sur la région du Kelifely. *Bull. Acad. Malg.*, **27**, Tananarive.

Bauer, J., et Rerat, J.C. 1962. Etude d'ensemble du bassin de Majunga au Sud de la presqu'île d'Ampasindava. *Arch. SPM*, **509(3)**, Tananarive.

Besairie, H. 1966. Carte géologique de 1/500 000 ème. *Feuille Maintirano. Service géologique.* Tananarive.

Donnot, M. 1965. Minéralisations stratiformes dans les causes du Kelifely et de l'Ankara. *C.R. Sem. Géol. Tananarive.*

Donnot, M., et Fournié, L. 1965. Contribution à l'étude de l'Isalo-Lias-Dogger dans les régions de Bekodoka et de Kandreho. *C.R. Sem. Géol. Tananarive.*

Fabre, G., et Nicod, J. 1982. Modalités et Rôle de la corrosion crypto-karstique dans les karsts mediterranées et tropicaux. *Zeit. Geomorph. N.F. Suppl. Bd.*, **26**, 35-54.

Guenot, B. 1964. Bordure ouest et sud du bassin de Majunga. Isalo et formations marines du Lias et du Dogger. *Arch. SPM.*, **580**, Tananarive.

Razafinbelo, E. 1964. Les variations du Lias et du Dogger dans la région de la Betsiboka. *Arch. SPM.*, **594**, Tananarive.

Rossi, G. 1973. Problèmes morphologiques du Karst de l'Ankarana. *Mad. Rev. Géogr.*, **23**, Tananarive.

Rossi, G. 1975. Aspects morphologiques du Karst de Narinda. *Mad. Rev. Géogr.*, **27**, Tananarive.

Rossi, G. 1976. Karst et dissolution des calcaires en milieu tropical. *Zeit. Geomorph. N.F. Suppl. Bd.*, **26**, (Berlin - Stuttgart), 124-152.

Rossi, G. 1977. Le Karst du Namoroka. *Rev. Géom. Dyn.*, **3**, Paris.

Rossi, G. 1977. L'Extrême Nord de Madagascar. *EDISUD-Aix-en-Provence*, 1980.

Rossi, G. 1983. Le karst du Bemaraha. *Mém. et Doc. du CNRs. Phénomènes karstiques III*, Paris, 45-64.

21

Aspects morphologiques des karsts Eocènes du sud-ouest Malgache

J. Salomon

RÉSUMÉ

L'auteur présente un tableau des karsts Éocènes du sud-ouest malgache dont l'intérêt principal vient de leur structure géographique. A la jointure de deux domaines climatiques, ces karsts offrent une très grande varietée de formes héritées d'influences climatiques différentes mais superposées. Les principaux aspects du modelé sont présentés tandis que les familles de formes sont également mises en relation avec la structure, notamment la tectonique et la lithologie, cette dernière étant elle-même la conséquence d'une sédimentation irrégulière.

SUMMARY

Presents a view of the south-west Eocene limestone areas of Malagasy, the main interest of which lies in their geographical position. These karsts, located at the interface of two climatic zones, provide a wide diversity of forms derived from the varying climatic influences. The key outlines of relief are presented. The families of forms present are connected with structure and, more particularly, with tectonics and lithology, the latter factor itself being the consequence of irregular sedimentation.

INTRODUCTION

Les karsts du Sud-Ouest malgache correspondent à l'extrêmité méridionale de la vaste auréole sédimentaire de l'ouest de la Grande Ile. Les sédimentations crétacée et éocène ont permis le dépôt d'épaisses séries de calcaires marins et de marno-calcaires se prêtant à la karstification. De véritables causses se sont ainsi constitués, donnant lieu à des karsts originaux, développés en milieu semi-aride, mais dont l'essentiel a dû se faire sous des paleo-climats plus humides que le climat actuel.

LE CADRE GEOGRAPHIQUE ET LES DIFFERENTES UNITES

(i) Climat et végétation

Les plateaux karstiques du Sud-Ouest malgache se situent de part et d'autre du Tropique du Capricorne. Du nord au sud, ils s'étirent sur près de 400 km, avec une largeur moyenne oscillant autour de 50 km, l'ensemble couvrant près de 13 000 km², (figure 1).

Ces plateaux connaissent un régime pluviométrique marqué par la rareté des précipitations (7 à 9 mois secs) mais plus encore par l'extrême variabilité interannuelle de celles-ci. Le total pluviométrique oscille en moyenne entre 400mm (Mahafaly) et 900mm (Mikoboka), mais les pluies sont concentrées sur une courte période de quelques mois (de novembre à février). La plus grande partie des pluies tombe sous forme d'averses violentes à la suite d'orages ou du passage de cyclones. Pour l'ensemble les plateaux, la moyenne mensuelle des températures est élevée puisqu'elle est comprise entre 21°C et 25°C. L'évapotranspiration théorique est estimée à 400mm (J. Aurouze, 1959), ce qui limite fortement le volume susceptible de s'infiltrer. L'évolution actuelle apparaît donc comme très ralentie.

La végétation climatique dominante est la forêt dense sèche caducifoliée ou le fourré xérophile à épineux avec une forte proportion d'espèces endémiques. (J.N. Salomon, 1978). Cependant ces formations ont énormément régressé face à la multiplicité des défrichements. Dans de nombreux secteurs elles ont été à peu près éliminées au profit de la savane.

(ii) Le Mikoboka

Le karst du Mikoboka couvre environ 2500 km². Il s'étire du Mangoky au nord jusqu'au Fiherenana au sud, (soit 170 km), avec des largeurs variables: 50 km sur le Fiherenana et quelques kilomètres seulement sur le Mangoky.

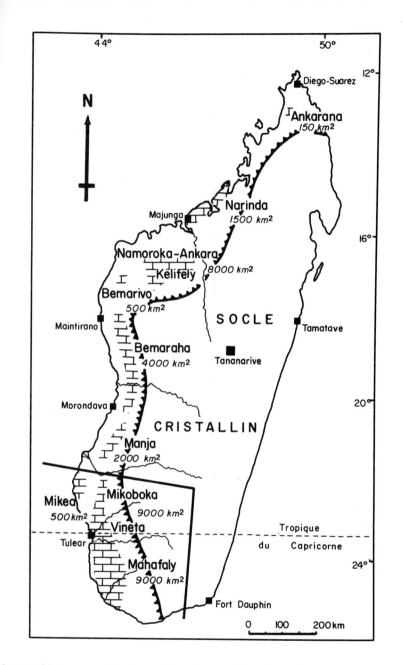

Figure 21.1   Les karsts malgaches et localisation des karsts
du Sud-Ouest

411

Les limites orientales et occidentales du plateau sont bien définies:

- à l'ouest, le causse domine la plaine côtière par un rempart vigoureux de falaises et d'escarpements dans la genèse desquels il faut souligner le rôle de la tectonique, ce qu'attestent de multiples facettes de faille.

- à l'est, les assises de l'Eocène forment une grande cuesta (200 à 400m de hauteur relative) sur le Crétacé, trouée d'entonnoirs de percées conséquentes.

Sur tout le causse il faut souligner la grande importance d'une tectonique cassante responsable de nombreux rejets et d'escarpements brutaux portant les sommets de la corniche à des altitudes élevées: Ianadabo, 820m; Ambolatany, 1081m. Les séries de fractures (direction principale: N 10° à N 15°; directions secondaires plus ou moins orthogonales) ont engendré un quadrillage tectonique qui explique l'essentiel de la topographie: horsts, grabens, directions des canyons, alignements de buttes ou de dolines etc...

Le Mikoboka est une région où dominent des paysages aux contours brutaux, hachés de ravins arides et taillés de gorges étroites. C'est un pays sec où l'eau s'infiltre, couvert de maigres savanes désertées par l'homme. D'un point de vue karstique, les lapiés, les dolines et les poljés tectoniques sont les formes les plus remarquables du causse. Les formes souterraines sont encore mal connues en dépit de quelques explorations (J. Duflos, 1966-1968).

(iii) <u>Les plateaux de Belomotra et de Vineta</u>

L'ensemble des plateaux de Vineta et de Belomotra est également bien individualisé. En forme de quadrilatère il est limité au nord-ouest et au nord par le canyon du Fiherenana, à l'est par la grande cuesta de la Sakondry, au sud par la vallée de l'Onilahy, enfin à l'ouest par le grand escarpement de faille qui domine la plaine de Tuléar.

Le plateau de Vineta est incliné en direction du sud-sud-est selon une pente d'environ 0,6% qui correspond à une surface d'érosion meso-tertiaire. Dans le détail celle-ci est gauchie du fait de quelques failles et reprises d'érosion. Les calcaires, massifs, de couleur claire et jaunâtre sont de type micro-cristallin ou micro-granulaire. Très fossilifères (e.g. Alvéolines, Nummulites ou Milioles) ils sont également très purs, contenant seulement 1 a 3% de résidus argileux. Ils se prêtent très bien à la karstification (nombreux lapiés) cependant des formes telles que les dolines sont assez rares.

Le plateau de Belomotra est un vaste monoclinal à faible pendage sud-ouest, qui est affecté de petites fractures de direction SSE-NNE et à faibles rejets. Deux faciés voisinent côte à côte, opposant calcaires purs et impurs, massifs ou lités. Le premier est un faciés sub-littoral représenté par des calcaires détritiques et récifaux (Eocène moyen) donnant des roches moins pures, souvent marneuses, qui n'engendrent qu'une très médiocre karstification mais favorisent les encroûtements. Le second faciès est composé de calcaires à Alvéolines, fins et clairs, compacts, très durs et purs (98% de $CaCO_3$) qui se prêtent très bien à la karstification et donnent de beaux lapiés dès qu'ils sont en surface. En effet des secteurs importants du plateau ont été recouverts par des épandages sableux venus de l'intérieur. De ce fait les formes crypto-karstiques sont fréquentes et constituent une des originalités de ce karst.

(iv) Le plateau Mahafaly

Au sud de l'Onilahy le grand plateau Mahafaly façonné dans les terrains éocènes, calcaires et marno-calcaires couvre près de 9000 km². Il est limité à l'ouest par un grand talus rectiligne, prolongement vers le sud de l'escarpement de Tulear qui domine la plaine côtière. A l'est il forme une cuesta ayant de 50 à 150m de hauteur relative avec des rentrants correspondant aux entonnoirs de percée conséquente de la Menarandra et de la Linta. Vers le sud les calcaires disparaissent progressivement dans l'Androy recouverts de formations néogènes et quaternaires.

Le plateau Mahafaly est découpé transversalement en trois parties par la gorge de la Linta et par le couloir d'Itomboina qui correspond à un axe géographique fossile néogène (R. Battistini, 1964).

La partie septentrionale entre Onilahy et couloir d'Itomboina inclut une vaste dépression intérieure, la plaine d'Ankazomanga. La partie centrale (6000 km²) entre la Linta et le couloir d'Itomboina est un vaste quadrilatère de 100 km du nord au sud, et de 50 km d'est en ouest. Malheureusement très mal connue car peu pénétrable en raison de la présence d'un bush épineux très dense, cette région est la plus intéressante au point de vue morphologie karstique; elle est littéralement truffée d'avens et de dolines. Le secteur au sud de la Linta, bien qu'assez étendu (entre 20 et 45 km), n'offre qu'un intérêt secondaire pour le karst.

Une circulation souterraine dans le Mahafaly est attestée par l'existence de résurgences dans la basse vallée de l'Onilahy et sur la plaine côtière mahafaly (et parfois même en mer) qui prouvent l'existence d'une circulation des eaux de la nappe générale sous la partie principale du plateau, dans des conduits karstiques où elles se trouvant probablement en charge. Ceci est confirmé par l'affleurement fréquent de la nappe générale dans le fond de nombreux avens.

LES PRINCIPAUX ASPECTS DU MODELÉ

Un grand nombre de formes karstiques sont représentées dans les plateaux du Sud-Ouest malgache. Ceci s'explique par l'étendue de la région considérée et surtout par la situation de celle-ci qui lui a permis de subir tant dans le passé que dans le présent l'influence des climats alternativement semi-arides et sub-humides. Nous présentons ici les types de formes qui caractérisent le mieux ces karsts peu connus.

(i) Les dolines et les dépressions fermées

Ce sont les formes les plus remarquables notamment dans le Mikoboka et dans certains secteurs du Mahafaly où elles criblent littéralement le plateau (densité souvent supérieure à 1/km²). Deux grands types de dolines sont particulièrement intéressants; les dolines en 'soucoupe' et les dolines d'effondrement ou 'avens en chaudrons', (Figures 2 et 3).

Dans le Mikoboka et secondairement dans le plateau de Vineta, le premier type se présente sous forme de dépressions fermées peu profondes aux versants peu inclinés (10°) avec un fond plat argileux, parfois marécageux en saison des pluies. Elles se localisent tantôt sur les parties des anciennes surfaces où le drainage a toujours été peu concentré, tantôt dans la partie supérieure des vallées sèches. Dans le premier cas les champs de dolines sont particulièrement fréquents dans les secteurs où les dépôts artificiels peu épais sont étendus. Dans le second cas il semble que la lenteur de l'écoulement (ruptures de pentes et seuils) soit un facteur favorable à l'apparition des dolines.

Dans le Mahafaly la morphologie des dépressions s'explique par le peu d'homogénéité et par la nature marno-calcaire des assises sédimentaires du sommet de l'Eocène. Vers l'Ouest où le calcaire est plus franc le modelé karstique devient plus vigoureux et les rebords des dolines plus nets, (Figures 4 et 5).

Dans tous les cas les fonds des dépressions sont colmatés par des argiles résiduelles dans lesquelles on retrouve de nombreux quartz. Par ailleurs il est certain que la disposition du piquetage et les alignements de dolines obéissent aux directions de fracturation; failles et fractures jouent le rôle de drains.

Les 'avens en chaudrons' ont été décrits pour première fois par R. Battistini (1964) sur le plateau Mahafaly. Moins représentée que le cas précédent (plus d'une centaine cependant), cette forme est très spectaculaire du fait même de ses dimensions et de l'aspect tranché des avens. Ces avens correspondant pour l'ensemble des plateaux à des calcaires compacts de l'Eocène moyen.

La forme de ces avens se rapproche du cercle. Les avens ont souvent une très grande profondeur, celle-ci équivalant de nombreuses fois au diamètre. Les dimensions sont très variables; elles vont de quelques dizaines de mètres a plus de 250m pour le diamètre, et de 40 à une centaine de mètres pour la profondeur (105m pour l'aven de Manamby dans le Mikoboka). Les plus caractéristiques ont des rebords et des parois abruptes donnant brutalement sur un fond de masses d'éboulis calcaires plus ou moins pris dans une gangue argileuse. Certains ont une embouchure plus étroite que le fond ce qui s' explique par l'existence d'un encorbellement dans la partie inférieure des parois verticales.

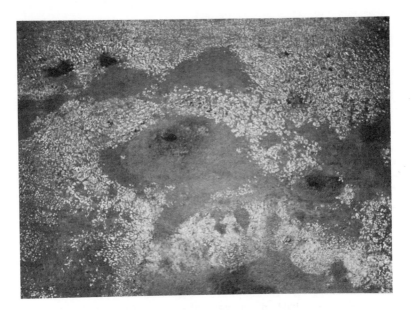

Figure 21.2   Dolines en soucoupes et champs de lapiès sur le
causse du Mikoboka. Les zones d'absorption sont
soulignées par les arbres.

Figure 21.3   L'aven en chandron de Tolikisy sur le Plateau de
Belomotra.   A pic de 105m.

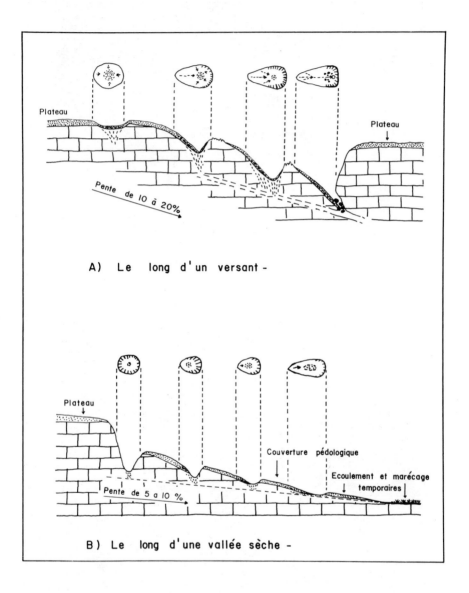

Figure 21.4   Evolution des formes des dolines dans le Mikoboka en fonction de la pente.

416

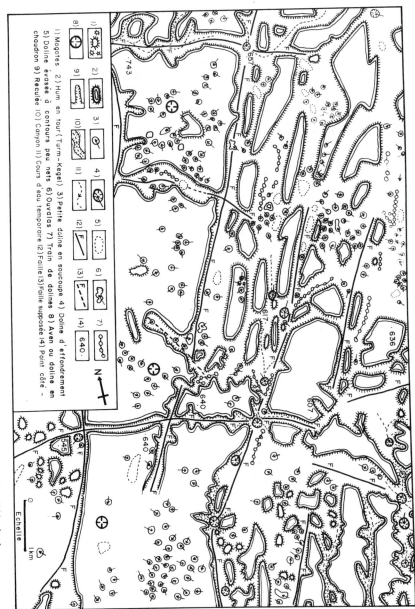

Figure 21.5 Mise en evidence du rôle de la tectonique dans le karst du Mikoboka

1) Mogotes, 2) Hum en tour (Turm-Kegel) 3) Petite doline en soucoupe 4) Doline d'effondrement
5) Doline évasée à contours peu nets 6) Ouvalas 7) Train de dolines 8) Aven ou doline en
chaudron 9) Reculée 10) Canyon 11) Cours d'eau temporaire 12) Faille 13) Faille supposée 14) Point coté -

1)
2)
3)
4)
5)
6)
7)
8)
9)
10)
11)
12)
13)
14) 640.

N

-743

65

617

636

640

607

645

640

Echelle

0

1km

Ces 'avens en chaudrons' semblent se produire à la suite de l'effondrement du toit d'une salle ou d'un conduit vertical lorsque ceux-ci sont relativement proches de la surface. Le Sud-Ouest malgache est une région où la pluviométrie connaît de forts contrastes saisonniers, aussi les variations de la zone noyée qui en résultent signifient-elles que les plafonds des salles sont soumis à d'énormes différences de pression hydraulique. C'est pourquoi les effondrements sont fréquents. L'aven d'effondrement en chaudron serait par conséquent une forme caractéristique des karsts tabulaires des régions tropicales à fort contraste saisonnier et à longue saison sèche. De fait, des formes similaires sont également fréquentes dans les karsts de Nullarbor en Australie ou elles sont héritées (JN. Jennings & D.C. Lowry, 1974) et dans les karsts du Yucatan (cenotes) au Mexique (J. Corbel, 1959).

(ii) Les lapiés

Ces micro-formes classiques sont rares dans les zones où se développent les vallées sèches et les dolines actuelles; au contraire, leur emplacement paraît concentré sur les pentes. En fait ils ne sont bien développés que dans les calcaires purs dont l'affleurement est net. Presque tous les types de lapiés se rencontrent dans le Sud-Ouest malgache. Nous mettrons cependant en exergue certaines formes caractéristiques ou assez fréquentes.

Le secteur de Nosy-Ambositra au nord du Mikoboka développe par exemple de beaux entablements à tsingy caractérisés par des lames acérées et des dentelles de calcaires ainsi que par de grandes kamenitsas et des trous de dissolution. Cette forme, remarquablement analysée par G. Rossi (1974, 1980) dans l'Extrême-Nord de Madagascar, peut atteindre ici jusqu'à 5 à 6 mètres sur les lèvres des fractures ou les rebords des plateaux. La fracturation et le diaclasage assez serrés des calcaires guide la formation de ces dents acérées d'autant plus que les deux directions principales du diaclasage dessinent par recoupement des losanges. Notons au passage que les secteurs à tsingy correspondent à la fois aux secteurs les plus arrosés du plateau et aux calcaires les plus purs. Cette forme atteint ici, à Madagascar, sa limite méridionale (Figure 6).

La plateau de Vineta présente pour sa part des lapiés endogés et des formes de corrosion exhumés de sables rouges ferrallitiques. Ce sont des blocs et chicots arrondis à formes amiboïdes ainsi que des champs de pseudo-galets. Les calcaires travaillés par la corrosion crypto-karstique ont des surfaces lisses, douces au toucher au moment de leur dégagement de la couverture pédologique. Ce sont souvent des roches perforées dont les trous sont dûs pour un bon nombre aux racines des plantes (rôle de l'acide humique). L'observation fréquente d'une altération pelliculaire des calcaires au sein de ces sols rouges indique que la décarbonatation se poursuit encore de nos jours (M. Sourdat, 1973; JN. Salomon, 1980). L'analyse de quelques fentes et poches karstiques permettrait de mieux préciser l'évolution, mais il est déjà certain que le rôle des processus de caractères biochimique et géochimique est fondamental (Figs 7 & 8)

Figure 21.6   Le karst a 'tsingy' de Nosy Ambositra, Mikoboka

Figure 21.7   Emergence du karst couvert de Vineta.
Lapiés arrondis (Rundkaren) et formes lisses

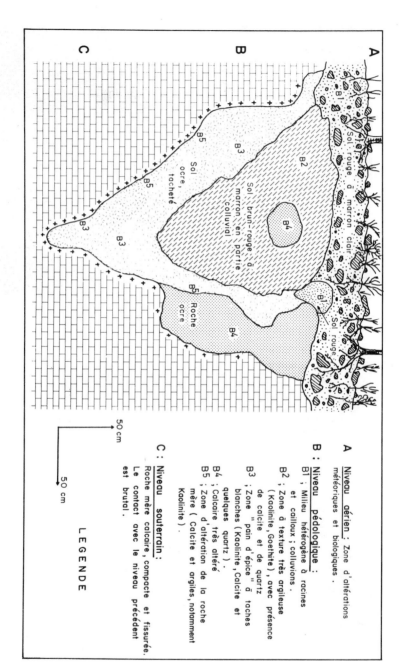

Figure 21.8 Schéma d'une poche karstique du plateau de Vineta montrant l'ancienneté relative du karst

A : Niveau aérien : Zone d'altérations météoriques et biologiques.

B : Niveau pédologique :
B1 ; Milieu hétérogène à racines et cailloux ; colluvions.
B2 ; Zone à texture très argileuse (Kaolinite, Goethite) , avec présence de calcite et de quartz.
B3 ; Zone " pain d'épice " à taches blanches (Kaolinite , Calcite et quelques quartz) .
B4 ; Calcaire très altéré.
B5 ; Zone d'altération de la roche mère (Calcite et argiles, notamment Kaolinite).

C : Niveau souterrain :
Roche mère calcaire, compacte et fissurée.
Le contact avec le niveau précédent est brutal.

50 cm

50 cm

L E G E N D E

(iii) Les buttes

Ces formes résiduelles ne se rencontrent que sur le causse
du Mikoboka. Ces reliefs sont de tailles et de dimensions
extrêmement variées mais d'altitudes peu différenciées (moins
d'une centaine de mètres de hauteur relative). Le type le plus
courant est celui de grosses coupoles surbaissées (kuppen) disposées en petits groupes dont les unités sont séparées par des
couloirs et des seuils plus ou moins marqués. A partir de quelques analyses effectuées il semble que les buttes en coupoles
correspondent à des calcaires épais, homogènes, crayeux et assez
poreux (environ 20%). Aussi peut-on supposer que dans bien des
cas la butte a pu être préformée au moment de la sédimentation.
Au contraire les buttes aux formes irrégulières et à versants
très raides paraissent liées à des calcaires compacts plus
résistants. L'importance des conditions lithologiques et tectoniques dans la différenciation apparaît ici fondamentale.

En fait la multiplicité des formes est grande et complexe
et beaucoup échappent aux classifications traditionnelles. Il
semble que cette complexité des formes vienne du fait que la
région est un domaine de transition entre un milieu tropical
humide et un milieu sub-aride. Le Mikoboka a subi autrefois les
effets de climats plus humides que l'actuel, ce qui a sans doute
permis le développement de formes karstiques correspondantes.
Mais ces climats ont opéré en alternance avec des climats plus
secs, proches du climat actuel, aussi les formes que nous rencon-
trons aujourd'hui relèvent-elles d'une origine fort composite.

(iv) Les canyons et les vallées karstiques

La surface des plateaux calcaires du Sud-Ouest malgache
constitue un immense impluvium (13 000 km²) susceptible
d'alimenter de nombreux cours d'eau. Cependant la nature calcaire du substrat et les conditions climatiques actuelles
n'autorisent le parcours aérien qu'à un petit nombre de rivières,
en majorité allogènes.

Les vallées, dont la direction générale est presque toujours
est-ouest sont formées par des cours d'eau qui naissent sur les
roches plus ou moins imperméables du Crétacé ou du socle ancien,
dans des régions plus arrosées (P 600mm). Ces cours d'eau ont
creusé d'importants canyons (Manombo, Fiherenana, Linta) étroits
et enfoncés (de 200 à 500m) qui semblent directement commandés
par la structure; les parois verticales ou subverticales sont
liées à la massiveté des calcaires, tandis que les aspects de
détail reflètent les variations de faciès. Dans de nombreux
cas (canyon de la Manombo notamment) les eaux se perdent plus
ou moins dans les talwegs et réapparaissent plus en aval en une
ou plusieurs résurgences alignées dans le lit même du cours
d'eau.

Mais ce sont des vallées sèches qui sont les formes de
vallées les plus nombreuses. Les réseaux denses et hiérarchisés
qu'elles dessinent entre les canyons sont surtout orientés vers
l'ouest, conformément au pendage de la série sédimentaire et à
la topographie. Cependant la fracturation guide souvent les

tracés qui sont fréquemment coudés. D'ailleurs sur le Mikoboka nombre de vallées sont en fait de véritables poljés structuraux liés à des grabens longiformes, longs de plusieurs kilomètres mais très étroits (200 à 300m) et se recoupant parfois à angle droit.

Le creusement épigénétique des canyons (qui a souvent entraîné l'inhibition de l'évolution des formes superficielles) est probablement responsable du développement des karsts souterrains qui restent à découvrir en dépit de quelques explorations de reconnaissance (A. Kiener, 1964; J. Duflos, 1966, 1968).

Aujourd'hui le modelé des canyons et vallées karstiques apparaît comme largement hérité des anciennes phases pluviales; la période actuelle n'apporte plus que des retouches de détail.

(v) Les croûtes et les tufs

Un dernier trait fondamental des karsts du Sud-Ouest malgache est l'importance et la fréquence des encroûtements. Le plateau de Belomotra est représentatif d'un type d'évolution conduisant à des encroûtements généralisés. Ses calcaires lités sont généralement gréseux et affleurent sous forme de strates partiellement altérées. Ils se désagrègent en libérant des résidus limono-calcaires qui, en s'interposant entre le sol et la roche freinent le drainage et l'évacuation en solution des bicarbonates de telle sorte que les sols associés restent neutres. De ce fait ils s'opposent à l'évolution d'un modelé karstique élaboré. Par ailleurs, ces sols rouges, hérités de périodes où l'altération prédominait, s'érodent et font appaître des horizons limono-calcaires. Ces derniers, à mesure qu'ils se rapprochent de la surface, s'enrichissent en carbonates et une nouvelle structure crypto-cristalline remplace la structure originelle (Sourdat *et al.*, 1973). Il se produit des encroûtements épais (jusqu'à 3m) car il y a actuellement recarbonation systématique. Ces croûtes semblent êtres liées à un climat tel que les remontées capillaires (où le rôle de pompage des racines est à souligner) puissent succéder à un régime lixiviant. Il faut également mettre en valeur le rôle du ruissellement dans la formation des croûtes. En effet, on retrouve ces dernières sur les formations superficielles de faible pente où l'eau de ruissellement s'évapore et dépose sous forme de calcaire pulvérulent dissous.

Un autre cas de dépôt carbonaté est celui des tufs dont les amas parfois considérables empâtent les versants de certaines vallées telle que celle de l'Onilahy. Ces tufs récents pour la plupart correspondent à d'anciennes sources pétrifiantes aujourd-'hui taries (JN. Salomon, 1981). Ces tufs se présentent sous forme d'amas volumineux de roche renfermant de nombreux moulages de débris végétaux fossilisés. En surface la roche est poreuse, légère, caverneuse et friable. Dessous, le tuf est un peu plus induré et présente parfois de petites croûtes subhorizontales de 1 à 2mm d'épaisseur formant litage. Ce dernier est a correler avec les alternances de ruissellement saisonnières. Un cas intéressant est la 'vallée des Sept Lacs' composée d'une série de vasques karstiques engendrées par des micro-barrages de tufs,

le long d'un ruisseau affluent de l'Onilahy. Entre deux 'Lacs'
l'écoulement du ruisseau de fait par des petits chenaux méan-
driformes entre lesquels s'est développé un 'mondmilch' léger
et pulvérulent sur lequel les pas crissent et laissent des
empreintes.

L'ensemble de ces tufs est lié à la forte minéralisation
atteinte par les eaux, sans doute en raison de circulations
lentes de type phréatique.

LES FACTEURS STRUCTURAUX ET LA GENESE DES FORMES

Plusieurs travaux du Service Géologique et les études faites pour
le compte de la S.P.M ont permis de connaitre l'essentiel de la
structure des plateaux (E. Basse, 1935; JP. Karche, 1961;
A. Pachoud, 1954). L'ensemble de ces travaux ont été synthétisés
par H. Besairie (1972).

(i) Stratigraphie

Celle-ci a été complétée et fait apparaître trois
subdivisions avec très schématiquement:

- un Eocène inférieur, le plus important et comprenant
essentiellement des calcaires compacts.

- un Eocène moyen, avec une base formée de calcaires
détritiques et récifaux et un sommet de calcaires
marneux.

- un Eocène supérieur, d'épaisseur et d'extension
réduites (plateau de Belomotra) sous forme de marno-
calcaires.

La puissance de la série Eocène augmente du sud vers le
nord jusqu'au niveau de l'Onilahy où elle atteint 400m.   Cette
épaisseur se maintient jusqu'au Fiherenana puis diminue progressivement vers le Mangoky où elle n'atteint plus que 150m.

D'une façon générale les calcaires éocènes sont compacts et
très durs ce qui explique en grande partie la constitution de
reliefs aux formes lourdes, massives et arrondies, mais souvent
aptes à la karstification.

(ii) Tectonique

La fréquence et l'intensité des failles est variable;
relativement modestes pour le Mahafaly, elles atteignent leur
maximum d'intensité au centre du Mikoboka.   Un réseau principal,
composé de fractures de direction N10° à N15°, correspond à une
partie du faisceau dit du Sikily dont la direction dite 'Côte
Est' correspond à une direction majeure à Madagascar.   Des
réseaux secondaires de direction moyenne est-ouest (Mikoboka,
Belomotra), ou NW-SE (Mahafaly) permettent un quadrillage tectonique qui apparaît parfaitement dans la topographie de certains
secteurs.   Ces cassures déterminent une série de gradins et de
panneaux affaissés dont certains ont pu, en recueillant les eaux

d'écoulement, évoluer en poljés.

Cette tectonique cassante, qui se manifeste de façon directe par des escarpements brutaux, s'explique par la nature essentiellement rigide des formations calcaires et par la présence proche ou locale d'anciens centres éruptifs (Analavelona, Mikoboka).

Au niveau de la karstification l'influence de la tectonique est très importante: elle se fait sentir essentiellement dans les tracés des vallées et canyons, la formation des poljés structuraux et les alignements de dépressions fermées ou de buttes.

(iii) Lithologie

Les variations lithologiques locales et l'épaisseur de la couche karstifiable contribuent pour une large part à expliquer les différences de paysages karstiques.

L'épaisseur influe sur la vigueur des formes; hauteur des buttes, profondeur des canyons et des dépressions, développement du réseau souterrain. Ce n'est sans doute pas par hasard si c'est dans le sud du Mikoboka où l'épaisseur de l'Eocène atteint 400m que les formes karstiques sont les plus exacerbées (e.g. canyons, dolines puits, poljés). Mais c'est surtout la nature chimique et la porosité de la roche qui déterminent l'aspect des formes. Plusieurs auteurs ont déjà signalé l'influence de la porosité des roches calcaires particulièrement M. Sweeting (1955) et J. Nicod (1971). En règle générale, dans le Sud-Ouest malgache, plus la porosité est grande, plus les formes sont douces; inversement, moins elle est élevée, plus la dissolution est réduite, pelliculaire, s'exerçant surtout le long des surfaces verticales et obliques, ainsi que le long des fissures.

Dans le Mahafaly, les calcaires marneux, peu homogènes, à porosité élevée (15 à 40%) engendrent des dépressions fermées, peu encaissées, liées à une imbibition d'importance de la roche puis une dissolution dans la masse. Ils favorisent la venue de croûtes épaisses (Belomotra, Mahafaly). Par contre il y a peu de lapiés.

Dans le Mikoboka, c'est dans les secteurs où la porosité du calcaire est la plus forte (plus de 15%) que la densité des dolines est la plus grande et que les secteurs de kuppen se développent. Dans le détail, la dissolution, plus diffuse, génère des formes assez émoussées (lapiés médiocres).

Par contre lorsque la porosité est faible (moins de 10%), des formes brutales apparaissent favorisées par des calcaires francs et massifs. Ce sont les lapiés aigüs (Tsingy) du secteur de Nosy-Ambositra ou d'Analafanja, les formes d'effondrement (dolines-puits profondes de 20 à 30m). Enfin le développement d'un réseau souterrain est possible, surtout si les fractures facilitent la pénétration de l'eau (plateau Mahafaly). Par contre les croûtes sont peu fréquentes et peu épaisses.

Dans le plateau de Vineta les calcaires compacts, micro-cristallins, très purs (98% de $CaCO_3$) et très poreux sont très favorables à une corrosion de type crypto-karstique, remarquablement illustrée par de nombreuses formes lisses et arrondies.

CONCLUSION

Les karsts éocènes du Sud-Ouest malgache constituent un domaine d'étude exceptionnel dans le monde tropical en ce sens que leur situation géographique leur a permis de cumuler les empreintes successives de paleoclimats alternatifs fort contrastés, tantôt sub-humides, tantôt semi-arides. L'ancienneté de l'évolution morphologique de ces karsts ne fait guère de doute et commence probablement bien avant le Pliocène, comme l'indiquent les multiples formes douces (parfois exhumées à la surface), les nombreux matériaux détritiques plioquaternaires qui ont rempli certaines cavités et comblé une partie des dépressions. L'essentiel du développement s'est effectué à la faveur des périodes humides, mais les périodes sèches ont permis des re-touches importantes du paysage qui aujourd'hui s'apparente davantage à un karst méditerranéen qu'à un karst tropical clas-sique. Si au cours du Quaternaire les actions érosive se sont poursuivies, avec notamment l'enfoncement remarquable du réseau hydrographique permettant le développement de formes souterraines et transformant l'ensemble en un holokarst, aujourd'hui l'évolution est en grande partie bloquée du fait de l'indigence des précipitations.

Les premières reconnaissances ont mis en évidence le rôle fondamental de la structure qui semble déterminer la plupart des formes, notamment la tectonique et la porosité. Mais l'infinité des possibilités de combinaisons structurales à l'échelle locale explique pour une grande part la grande variété des modelés karstiques observés.

Enfin, il convient d'attirer l'attention sur les aquifères karstiques de ces plateaux. Leur importance, en amont de vastes plaines alluviales, ne saurait être mésestimée. Leur étude devrait être entreprise dans la perspective d'un mise en valeur par irrigation de ces terrains fertiles.

REFERENCES

Aurouze, J. 1959. Hydrogéologie du Sud de Madagascar. *Thèse Sc. Paris.*

Basse, E. 1935. Etude géologique du Sud-Ouest de Madagascar. *Mém. Société Geol. Fr.*, 10(4), No 24.

Battistini, R. 1964. L'Extrême Sud de Madagascar. *Thèse Lettres, Ed. Cujas,* Paris.

Besairie, H. 1972. Géologie de Madagascar. Les terrains sédimentaires. *Ann. Geol. Mad.*, **35**.

Corbel, J. 1959. Karsts du Yucatan et de la Floride. *Bull. Assoc. Geogr. Françaises,* **283**.

Duflos, J. 1966. Bilan des explorations biospéléologiques pour l'année 1963. *Mad. Rev. Géog.,* 9.

Duflos, J. 1968. Bilan des explorations biospéléologiques pour l'année 1966. *Mad. Rev. Géog.,* 10/11.

Jenning, J.N. and Lowry, D.C. 1974. The karst of Nullarbor (Australia). *Zeit. Geomorph.,* NF, 18-1-35-81, Berlin-Stuttgart.

Karche, J.P. 1961. Contribution à l'étude géologique et hydrogéologique du plateau calcaire Mahafaly. *Thèse 3ème cycle,* Paris, ronéo.

Karche, J.P. 1963. Stratigraphie du plateau Mahafaly à Madagascar. *CR Sem Géol., Ann. Géol. Mad.,* 33, 75-79.

Kiener, A. 1964. De la présence de certaines populations ichtyologiques dans les eaux souterraines des formations karstiques de la côte ouest de Madagascar. *Thèse Sc.,* Paris.

Nicod, J. 1971. Quelques remarques sur la dissolution des dolomies. *Bull. Assoc. Géogr. Françaises,* **389/390**.

Pachoud, A. 1954. Etude du plateau éocène de la côte Sud-Ouest entre Onilahy et Mangoky. *Archives SPM.*

Rossi, G. 1977. L'Extrême-Nord de Madagascar. *Thèse, Lettres, Edisud,* Aix-en-Provence.

Salomon, J.N. 1978. Fourrés et forêts sèches du Sud-Ouest malgache. *Rev. Géog. Madag.,* **32**.

Salomon, J.N. 1979. Corrosion et évolution karstique dans les plateaux de Belomotra et de Vineta (Sud-Ouest de Madagascar). *Actes Symposium Erosion karstique,* Aix-Marseille, Nîmes.

Salomon, J.N. 1981. Les tufs de la vallée de l'Onilahy et les Sept Lacs (Sud-Ouest de Madagascar). *Actes Colloque A.G.F., Formations carbonatées externes. Tufs et travertins,* Paris.

Sourdat, M., *et al.* 1973. Phénomènes de pédogénèse et de karstification le Sud-Ouest de Madagascar. *Rev. Geog. Madag.,* **18**.

Sweeting, M.M. 1955. Denudation in Limestone Regions Symposium. *Geogr. Journ.,* **132**, Londres.

22

Chemical erosion in tower karst terrain, Kinta valley, Peninsular Malaysia

J. Crowther

SUMMARY

Chemical weathering rates in the tower karst terrain of the Kinta
valley are estimated from two independent data sets: the solutional
potential of soil waters, calculated from soil carbon dioxide data;
and the total hardness of 148 karst waters, including surface streams,
soil throughflow, cave seepages and groundwaters from the alluvium
and underlying aquifer of the valley plain. The results reveal marked
variations in weathering conditions on the limestone towers, with
open system carbonate weathering potentials ranging from 82 ppm on
rocky hilltops to 210 and 243 ppm, respectively, in hilltop depressions
and on the moderate footslopes. This pattern of weathering accentuates
the steepness and ruggedness of the relief. Total hardness varies
between 50 ppm for rivers draining the alluvial karst plain and 257
ppm (including measured aggressiveness) for groundwaters sampled at
the alluvium/bedrock interface in tin mine workings. Chemical
denudation is appreciably slower on the tower karst hills
(85 mm/1000 yr) than beneath the adjacent plains (155 mm/1000 yr).

RÉSUMÉ

La vitesse d'érosion chimique dans le karst à tourelles de la vallée
de Kinta est estimée à partir de deux séries de données indépendantes:
le potentiel de dissolution des eaux du sol, calculée à partir de
leurs teneurs en CO_2; et la dureté totale de 148 échantillons d'eaux
karstiques, provenant de cours d'eau de surface, d'écoulements dans
les sols, d'eaux d'infiltration dans des grottes et de nappes
phréatiques dans les alluvions ou sous la plaine fluviatile. Les
résultats montrent des variations importantes de dissolution sur les
tourelles calcaires. Le potentiel de dissolution varie de 82 ppm
sur les sommets rocheux à 210 ppm dans les dépressions sommitals et
243 ppm au bas de pentes assez douces. Ces variations dans les
conditions de l'érosion accentuent la raideur et l'énergie du relief.
La dureté totale varie de 50 ppm pour les rivières drainant la plaine
alluviale karstique à 257 ppm (en incluant l'agressivité mesurée)
pour des eaux phréatiques prélevées à la jonction des alluvions et
de la roche dans des mines d'étain. L'érosion chimique est beaucoup
plus lente au sommet des tourelles calcaires (72 mm/1000 an) que
dans la plaine en contrebas (131 mm/1000 an).

INTRODUCTION

Tower karst terrain, characteristically comprising isolated
limestone hills separated by alluvium or detrital sands, occurs
widely throughout the humid tropics. Because of its unique form
and its particular significance in the morphoclimatic debate
(Smith and Atkinson, 1976; Brook and Ford, 1978), tower karst
has long provided an important research focus. Previous studies
suggest that the towers may develop from residual cone karst
hills by lateral undercutting at the base level of erosion
(Sweeting, 1958; Gerstenhauer, 1960; Verstappen, 1960). Alternatively, where the structural and lithological properties of the
host limestone favour deep vertical dissection (e.g. Subis,
Sarawak - Wilford and Wall, 1965; Emia valley, New Guinea -
Williams, 1972) they may form directly from labyrinth karst
(Brook and Ford, 1978), with basal undercutting being a secondary
process. The importance of other geological controls, including
rock hardness (Day, 1982) and regional setting, especially in
relation to adjacent non-carbonate lithologies (McDonald, 1976a),
has also been demonstrated. However, except for recent investi-
gatons of basal undercutting (McDonald, 1975; 1976b; Jennings,
1976) and case-hardening (Ireland, 1979) geomorphic processes
have been little studied in such terrain. The present paper
reports on the spatial distribution and rate of chemical
weathering in the classic karst tract of the Kinta valley,
Peninsular Malaysia. Two independent sets of data are presented:
1) the solutional potential of groundwater recharge waters,
calculated from soil carbon dioxide measurements; and 2) a
summary of water hardness figures from 148 sites, including soil
throughflow waters, cave seepages, seepages at the sub-alluvial
karst surface, deep groundwaters and surface streams. Implications of the findings for karst landform development are
discussed.

FIELD AREA

The Kinta valley (101°E, 4°N) lies to the west of the Main Range
(Figure 22.1). On the lowland karst plains of the valley the
mean annual temperature is 26°C and annual rainfall ranges from
2514-3663 mm (mean 2847 mm), the wettest area being in the
southeast. The Kinta Limestones, of Silurian to Permian age, are
confined to the central axis of the valley and pre-date the
granites of the flanking Main and Kledang Ranges. They include
several relatively thin argillaceous beds, and exceed 3000 m in

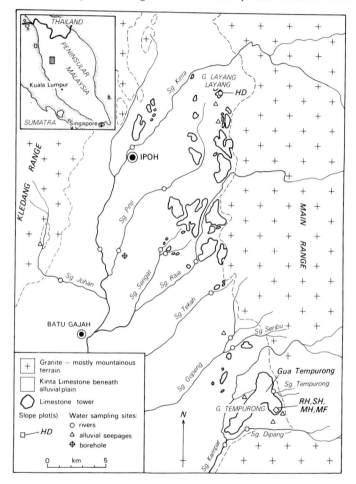

Figure 22.1   Field area and location of sampling sites; two of
the tin mines in which alluvial seepages were
sampled lie outside the area shown, 3 and 5 km
south of Batu Gajah.

429

stratigraphic thickness (Ingham and Bradford, 1960; Suntharalingham, 1968) and were folded and recrystallized by regional metamorphism in the late Triassic. The resultant marble is fine grained, very pure and mechanically strong, with vertical and subvertical joints and faults providing the main lines of weakness. The valley has been above sea level since the Jurassic and, except for minor Cretaceous-Oligocene earth movements (Gobbett, 1971; Stauffer, 1973) and Quaternary sea level changes, the Cainozoic has been a period of uninterrupted erosion under relatively stable climatic (Morgan, 1976) and tectonic conditions (Stauffer, 1973).

The limestones outcrop as residual towers, ranging from several ha to 10 km^2 in area and reaching a maximum height of 612 m a.s.l. The hills comprise six principal topographic units: rock cliffs, rocky hilltops, hilltop depressions, steep hill-slopes (45-60°), moderate hillslopes (30-45°) and moderate footslopes (30-45°). The distinction between the last two units is based largely on pedological differences. The moderate hill-slopes generally occur above about 130 m and, as in the other hillslope and hilltop units, the soils are derived from the underlying limestone. Typically, they are very porous, dark reddish brown (2.5 YR 3/4) clays, containing lateritic gravels. In contrast, the moderate footslopes are mantled by thin alluvial or colluvial deposits and their soils are relatively dense, dark yellowish brown (10 YR 4/4) clays or sandy clays, with a dis-tinctive quartz-rich gravel fraction. Evidence from field reconnaissance and air photographs indicates that the hilltop depressions and moderate footslopes are less widespread than the other topographic units, though the exact area occupied by each remains to be established. Further details of the meso-topography, soils and vegetation of these units are presented in Crowther (1982a). The catchment areas afforded by the lime-stone outcrops are too small to maintain autogenic underground streams, and the large cave passages which permeate the towers are mostly relict features, now infilling with speleothems.

The surrounding plain comprises an extensive, early or mid-Pleistocene alluvial deposit, the 'Old Alluvium', varying from 30-70 m a.s.l. (Walker, 1956; Stauffer, 1973). The alluvium is mostly 3-20 m deep, though isolated pockets in the limestone contain thicker deposits (Ingham and Bradford, 1960). The sub-alluvial karst surface, exposed in tin mine workings, is mostly irregular and pinnacled, but smoother surfaces do occur, especially around the margins of the hills. Little is known of the underlying aquifer since it has not been widely exploited. However, the frequent occurrence of land subsidence in the valley (F.S. Chong, Geological Survey of Malaysia, pers. comm.) and the high, sustained yields from existing bore holes indicate sizeable water-filled passages in the limestone.

EXPERIMENTAL DESIGN AND METHODS

Two separate but related studies were undertaken. The first was designed to assess spatial variations in weathering rates on the limestone hills from soil carbon dioxide data. In this context the rock cliffs are unimportant since they receive little direct rainfall and are devoid of soil. Five plots representative of the remaining topographic units were established, the hilltop depression being on the summit of G. Layang Layang (G., Gunong = hill) and the rest being located on the southeastern spur of G. Tempurong (Figure 22.1). In each, one soil profile was examined in detail, and slope pantometer and soil depth surveys were made along two or three 30 m transects running down the local slope. Groundwater recharge points and their micro-catchment areas were estimated (procedures given in Crowther, 1984) in order to determine the relative proportions of water passing through different depths of soil before entering the limestone. Additionally, the moderate hillslope and footslope plots formed part of a larger network of soil carbon dioxide monitoring sites in the west coast karst regions of the peninsula, and regular measurements were made over a one year period. Previous studies suggest that the peak carbon dioxide concentration ($MAXCO_2$) recorded during long-term observations is most representative of conditions during groundwater recharge events (Crowther, 1982b). Also, soil depth (cm) and bulk density (g/cm^3) account for 86% of the observed spatial variation in $MAXCO_2$ (per cent by volume) according to the equation (Crowther, 1983a; 1984):

$$\log_{10} (MAXCO_2) = 1.146 \text{ (BDEN)} + 0.00698 \text{ (DEPTH)} - 1.227$$

This equation is used to predict $MAXCO_2$ in the three Kinta valley sites which were not monitored. These data, combined with the estimated patterns of water movement on the slopes, were then used to determine the carbon dioxide content of the air with which waters ultimately equilibriate before entering the limestone. Since limestone solution in the peninsula occurs predominantly under open system conditions (Crowther, 1984), open system carbonate weathering potentials have been calculated using equilibrium equations from Picknett (1973) and Picknett et al., (1976) for a temperature of 25°C.

The second study focussed on variations in water hardness within the valley. In all, 148 sites were investigated, with 43 being sampled regularly over a one year period. 84 were underground seepages in Gua Tempurong (Gua = cave), a large cave which passes through G. Tempurong (Crowther, 1978). Soil throughflow was collected from the soil-rock interface in the moderate footslope plot at a depth of 60 cm. 48 alluvial seepages were sampled, 37 being from the sub-alluvial karst surface and the rest being confined within the alluvium at various heights above the underlying bedrock. All the major rivers were included, and deep karst groundwater from a depth of approximately 20 m beneath the base of the alluvium was obtained from the only known borehole. Total hardness was determined by standard titration methods using EDTA. The chemical aggressiveness of

431

the water was assessed by measuring the total hardness of samples
before and after saturation with Analar calcium carbonate, the
latter being added to a duplicate sample at the time of collection (Stenner, 1969).

RESULTS AND DISCUSSION

(i) Weathering potentials

The results, summarized in Table 22.1, show marked differences in weathering environment between the five topographic
units. The lowest carbonate weathering potential (mean, 82 ppm)
occurs in the deeply dissected, pinnacle-like terrain of the
rocky hilltops. Here the soils are confined to rock crevices
and the base of larger solution runnels, and occupy only about
5-35% of the surface. Thus, more than half the groundwater recharge in the study plot is runoff from completely bare catchments, with an estimated weathering potential of 50 ppm (Figure
22.2), and a further 27% encounters only organic-rich soils,
less than 10 cm deep. The steep hillslopes typically have thin
and patchy mineral soils with a well-developed crumb structure
and a low bulk density (0.70 g/cm^3 at 20 cm). Localized depressions in the bedrock surface contain soils deeper than 60 cm,

Table 22.1   Summary of soil data and estimates of soil carbon
dioxide concentrations and open system weathering
potentials for the five plots.

Plot (see Figure 22.1)	Mean soil depth* (cm)	Bulk density at 20 cm (g/cm^3)	Mean $MAXCO_2$ (% by vol)	Mean weathering potential ($CaCO_3$, ppm)
RH	7.8	0.70	0.20	82
HD	95.8	0.75	2.71	243
SH	24.4	0.70	0.50	119
MH	49.9	0.68	0.86	148
MF	40.0	1.13	2.47	210
Overall	43.6	0.79	1.35	160

*Depth through which waters percolate before entering limestone.

with $MAXCO_2$ values around 1.2%. Therefore, whilst the average
weathering potential in the steep hillslope plot is only 119 ppm,
levels locally exceed 175 ppm. On the moderate hillslopes the
soil cover is deeper and more continuous, with recharge waters
passing on average through 49.9 cm of soil before entering the
limestone (cf. 24.4 cm in steep hillslope plot). Because of the
low bulk density of these soils $MAXCO_2$ is limited to about 1.4%
(weathering potential, c. 190 ppm) even in deeper soil pockets
on the bedrock or talus slopes. Nevertheless, the moderate
hillslope plot is clearly distinguished by half its waters having
a weathering potential in the 160-200 ppm range. Notably higher

432

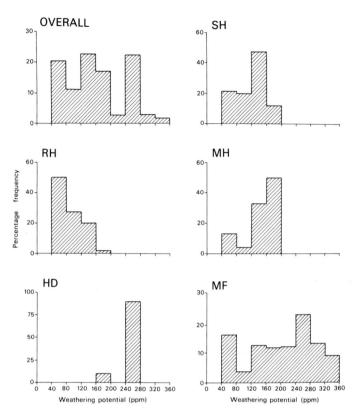

Figure 22.2   Open system carbonate weathering potentials
(CaCO$_3$, ppm) in the study plots. For location
of plots see Figure 22.1

weathering potentials were recorded in the hilltop depression
and moderate footslope plots.   In the former this principally
reflects the considerable depth of residual mineral soils on the
depression floor.   Thus, the average depth through which waters
percolate before entering the bedrock is 95.8 cm (maximum,
240 cm), and the mean MAXCO$_2$ is 2.71%.   The high weathering
potential of 210 ppm on the moderate footslope is mostly attributable to gaseous diffusion being relatively impeded in the
denser alluvial/colluvial soil.   Isolated pockets in the bedrock
or talus, containing soils deeper than 80 cm, have estimated
MAXCO$_2$ concentrations in excess of 5.0% (maximum, 6.75%) and
more than half the waters draining the plot have solutional
capacities well over 200 ppm (maximum, 351 ppm).   However, the
presence of some completely bare or thinly covered catchments
on the footslopes markedly reduces their weathering potential.
Since hilltop depressions and moderate footslopes are less extensive in the valley than the other topographic units, the un-
weighted mean figures given for soil depth (43.6 cm), MAXCO$_2$

(1.35%) and weathering potential (160 ppm) probably slightly
overestimate the overall conditions on the limestone towers.

(ii)   Water hardness

   The observed total hardness concentrations exhibit wide
variations, both between the six systematic groupings of sites
and within the four groupings from which more than one site was
investigated (Table 22.2).   Throughflow waters, sampled regularly at the soil/rock interface in the moderate footslope plot,
have an average hardness of 147 ppm.   This lies within the
136-199 ppm range recorded at similar sites elsewhere in the
peninsula (Crowther, 1980) and, in view of the low carbonate
content of the soil (<0.05%), indicates the rapid rate of solution at the sub-soil weathering front.   Nearby seepages in Gua
Tempurong have a lower mean hardness of 124 ppm.   This compares
with figures of 111 and 153 ppm for Gua Anak Takun and Gua Batu,
two tower karst caves near Kuala Lumpur (Crowther, 1980), and
with a mean value of about 95 ppm reported from similar terrain
in the Mulu National Park, Sarawak (Friedrich, 1980; Laverty,
1980).   When plotted against equilibrium curves for the pH of
saturated calcite solutions in the presence of 0-30% magnesium
at 25°C (Picknett, 1972), the majority of the 84 sites sampled
are saturated or supersaturated with respect to calcite.   This,
combined with the uniformly high temperature of 24°C in the cave,
favours rapid deposition, and much of the inter-site variability
is attributable to differences in the opportunity for deposition
once the waters emerge in the cave.   Thus the higher total
hardness values are generally found in those waters dripping
from small stalactites less than 1.5 m long (mean, 141 ppm);
whereas the lower concentrations tend to occur where waters seep
through or trickle over larger speleothems before collection
(mean, 112 ppm).

Table 22.2   Total hardness ($CaCO_3$, ppm) of karst waters

	n	Mean*	Minimum	Maximum	Standard deviation
Throughflow	1	147	-	-	-
Cave seepages	84	124	68	231	35
Seepages within alluvium	11	84 (73)	4	213	74
Seepages at sub-alluvial karst surface	37	225 (32)	109	374	66
Rivers	14	50	16	128	40
Aquifer beneath plain	1	217	-	-	-

*Chemical aggressiveness given in parentheses.

   The alluvial sediments of the plains are extremely variable
in composition.   The bulk is free of carbonate material, and
most waters sampled within the alluvium have less than 55 ppm
total hardness and a measured chemical aggressiveness in excess
of 60 ppm.   Locally, however, boulders and smaller fragments of
limestone are incorporated in the matrix and groundwaters

encountering these have notably higher hardness values, typically in the 150-200 ppm range. Waters at the sub-alluvial karst surface generally have much higher total hardness values (mean, 225 ppm), though the majority are undersaturated, the mean aggressiveness being 32 ppm (range, 0-130 ppm). Waters seeping through the alluvium therefore have a mean solutional potential of 257 ppm, which is higher than the other types of karst water. Comparable total hardness figures from beneath the blanket sands in Puerto Rico range from about 20 ppm for shallow groundwaters in carbonate-free sands to 150 ppm for well water from deeper deposits, closer to the underlying limestone (Miotke, 1973). Non-alkaline hardness accounts on average for only 6% of the total hardness of the alluvial seepages. The high weathering potential seems therefore to be derived mostly from biogenic carbon dioxide in the deep and quite dense alluvial soils and sediments. Carbon dioxide was not measured in the alluvial soils of the Kinta valley, but in the Mulu National Park (Laverty, 1980) and Sulawesi (McDonald, 1976a) the soils of the alluvial terraces and plains were found to contain appreciably higher concentrations than those of the adjacent karst outcrops.

The total hardness of rivers draining the karst alluvial plain varies between 16 and 128 ppm (mean, 50 ppm), which corresponds closely with the 30-90 ppm range recorded under similar conditions in Sarawak (Sweeting, 1979). The catchments of the rivers studied differ markedly in size (2-650 km^2) and lithological composition. The highest hardness concentrations (105-128 ppm) were found in three small streams, the Sg. Tempurong (Sg., Sungai = river), the Sg. Sengat and the east-bank tributary of the Sengat. In all three catchments the alluvial cover is very thin and consequently some stream waters derived from the alluvium will have been in direct contact with limestone. Elsewhere on the plain the rivers have characteristically low hardness concentrations. In part this is attributable to many of the drainage basins comprising a high proportion of granitic terrain (control sites on two rivers in the granite foothills had hardness concentrations of 9 and 26 ppm). Thus the Sg. Kinta, Sg. Johan, Sg. Raia, Sg. Gopeng, Sg. Kampar and Sg. Dipang, with 85-96% non-carbonate lithologies in their catchments, have 16-57 ppm total hardness. Other results suggest that there is very little input of carbonate-rich water to the major rivers of the valley even where sizeable limestone outcrops and expanses of karst alluvial plain are present. Thus 20-48 ppm total hardness was recorded at two sites on the Sg. Pinji and one on the Sg. Tekah, despite their catchments including 9-16% limestone towers and 65-84% karst plain. The implication is that virtually all the groundwater in the hills and alluvium directly feeds the karst aquifer beneath the plain, with groundwater contributions to surface runoff in the valley being negligible.

The total hardness of the borehole water (217 ppm) lies within the 130-339 ppm range recorded for deep artesian wells in Puerto Rico (Giusti, 1978). Besides the two sources mentioned above, the water in the Kinta valley aquifer may be derived from channel leakage from surface streams. Of these three sources, water seeping through the alluvium generally has the highest hardness, with a mean of 257 ppm (including measured aggressiveness). Corresponding figures are 124 and 50 ppm, respectively, for groundwaters in the towers and surface streams. It seems therefore that much of the groundwater in the karst aquifer originates as percolation through the alluvium, with the minor contributions from other sources causing relatively little dilution.

(iii) Chemical denudation rates

Rates of chemical erosion on the limestone towers may be estimated from both data sets. The mean open system weathering potential predicted from the soil carbon dioxide results is 160 ppm, though this figure is probably an overestimate for two reasons. First, each topographic unit is weighted equally, whereas the two units with the highest weathering potentials occur less frequently than the others. Secondly, the model assumes that weathering occurs under open system conditions, with all water achieving equilibrium with the soil atmosphere. However, in reality, much groundwater recharge may not quite fully equilibriate with carbon dioxide in the soil before entering the limestone. The total hardness of underground seepages in Gua Tempurong, when weighted according to the discharge of each site, averages 121 ppm. Since appreciable carbonate deposition occurs once groundwaters emerge into vadose passages, this figure probably underestimates the solutional potential of groundwaters close to the surface of the outcrop. Thus, 121 and 160 ppm may be regarded as extreme values, with a figure of 140 ppm perhaps providing the best estimate. The mean total hardness of seepages at the sub-alluvial karst surface (257 ppm, including aggressiveness of 32 ppm) is used in estimating denudation on the adjacent plains.

Studies in forested granite catchments elsewhere in the peninsular have shown evapotranspiration rates to be about 17% less than evaporation pan measurements (Low and Goh, 1972). Applying this correction to available evaporation data (Nieuwolt, 1965) gives an annual evapotranspiration of 1244 mm and an average effective rainfall of 1603 mm (range, 1270-2419 mm). In the absence of specific water balance data for the limestone hills effective rainfall provides the best estimate of annual soil percolation and groundwater flow. It should be noted, however, that periodic moisture deficits are likely in the thinner soils of the steep hillslopes and rocky hilltops, and that the overall evapotranspirational loss from the towers will be slightly less than the calculated figure. Rainfall in the field area has a mean total hardness of only 1 ppm. Inputs from this source have therefore been ignored in calculating denudation rates.

Chemical erosion on the tower karst hills averages 85 mm/1000 yr, with rates varying from 67 mm/1000 yr in the drier northern and western parts of the valley to 128 mm/1000 yr in the wetter southeast. This compares with reported figures of 80 and 150 mm/1000 yr, respectively, for tower karst terrain in the Mulu National Park (Laverty, 1980) and in Maros, Sulawesi (Balázs, 1973). The denudation rate on the plains of the Kinta valley is estimated to be 155 mm/1000 yr, with a corresponding range of 123-235 mm/1000 yr. An estimate of 30-300 mm/1000 yr, based on morphological evidence, has been made for solutional erosion beneath detrital sands in Puerto Rico (Monroe, 1969).

(iv)   Tower karst development in the Kinta valley

On theoretical grounds Paton (1964) attributes tower karst formation in Peninsular Malaysia to chemical denudation being much more rapid along river channels and in low-lying swamp areas than on the hills, where the thinness of the soil cover is held to be the limiting factor. Deep linear dissection, facilitated by the pronounced vertical and subvertical jointing of the Kinta Limestones (Crowther, 1983b), is thus regarded as the primary mechanism, with the tower hills evolving from a labyrinth type karst (Brook and Ford, 1978). The secondary process of lateral planation is now far advanced and downcutting by rivers is minimal. The overall form and detailed meso and micro-relief of the sub-alluvial karst surface are clearly of solutional origin (Ingham and Bradford, 1960; Jennings, 1972), though the effectiveness of contemporary weathering processes at the alluvium/bedrock interface has been in doubt. In some places, for example, the alluvial sediments dip steeply as they have accommodated themselves to cavities which have developed in the limestone surface since initial sedimentation (Mohammed Ayob, 1970). Elsewhere, however, the basal sediments of the Old Alluvium are horizontally bedded, even within solution-widened crevices (Stauffer, 1973), suggesting that the weathered karst surface developed sub-aerially prior to alluviation and that there has been little subsequent modification. The present results demonstrate that solution is active beneath the alluvium, with the rate of surface lowering exceeding that on the hills. Because of differential groundwater movement within the alluvium, guided by sedimentary structures and the topography of the under-lying bedrock, solution is probably distributed very unevenly. At some locations the surface will be lowered rapidly, whereas at others the rate will be very slow. Such variations are consistent with the above stratigraphic evidence and with the marked irregularity of the sub-alluvial karst surface (Ingham and Bradford, 1960).

Previous studies have attributed the steepness of the tower karst relief to basal undercutting by streams, swamps and soil waters (Paton, 1964; Jennings, 1976) and to structural control (Crowther, 1983b). The present results suggest that the spatial pattern of weathering on the hills may also be important. Thus the uncliffed margins of the towers mostly comprise moderate footslopes which, because of their relatively dense alluvial/colluvial soils, have a greater solutional potential than the higher hillslopes. As a consequence, the basal slopes tend to be lowered preferentially, thereby steepening the towers. Additionally, weathering is generally more rapid on the flanking slopes of the hills than on the predominantly rocky summits. There is a marked contrast on the hilltops between the sporadic soil-filled depressions, which are foci of accelerated weathering and adjacent, bare and thinly covered rock surfaces. These variations further serve to accentuate the relief of the towers and perpetuate the ruggedness of the terrain.

CONCLUSIONS

There are marked differences in weathering environment between the five topographic units studied on the limestone towers, with the highest carbonate weathering potentials being recorded for hilltop depressions (243 ppm) and moderate footslopes (210 ppm), and the lowest for rocky hilltops (82 ppm). This pattern of weathering on the hills serves to accentuate the steepness and ruggedness of the terrain.

Karst waters in the Kinta valley differ widely in total hardness, ranging from a mean of 50 ppm for rivers draining the alluvial karst plain to 257 ppm (including aggressiveness) and 217 ppm, respectively, for groundwaters from the sub-alluvial karst surface and from the karst aquifer beneath the plain. Cave seepages average 124 ppm (range, 68-231 ppm), with much of their variability being attributable to differences in the opportunity for carbonate deposition once the groundwaters emerge into vadose passages.

Chemical denudation on the tower karst hills, based on a representative water hardness of 140 ppm, averages 85 mm/1000 yr, whereas a higher rate of 155 mm/1000 yr is recorded for the alluvial karst plain.

Acknowledgements

The fieldwork was funded by a NERC studentship, under the supervision of Dr A.F. Pitty, and by a grant from the University of Hull. Laboratory facilities were provided by the Departments of Geography and Geology, University Malaya, Kuala Lumpur.

REFERENCES

Balázs, D. 1973. Comparative morphogenetical study of karst regions in tropical and temperate areas with examples from Celebes and Hungary. *Transactions of the Cave Research Group of Great Britain,* **15**, 1-7.

Brook, G.A. and Ford, D.C. 1978. The origin of labyrinth and tower karst and the climatic conditions necessary for their development. *Nature,* **275**, 493-96.

Crowther, J. 1978. Karst regions and caves of the Malay Peninsula, west of the Main Range. *Transactions of the British Cave Research Association,* **5**, 188-214.

Crowther, J. 1980. *Karst water studies and environment in West Malaysia.* (Unpublished Ph.D. Thesis, University of Hull).

Crowther, J. 1982a. Ecological observations in a tropical karst terrain, West Malaysia. I. Variations in topography, soils and vegetation. *Journal of Biogeography,* **9**, 65-78.

Crowther, J. 1982b. A technique for sampling soil air: some results and methodological implications. *Transactions of the British Cave Research Association,* **9**, 47-54.

Crowther, J. 1983a. Carbon dioxide concentrations in some tropical karst soils, West Malaysia. *Catena,* **10**, 27-39.

Crowther, J. 1983b. Hydrology of autogenic percolation systems in some tropical karst outcrops, West Malaysia. *Journal of Hydrology,* **60**, 227-42.

Crowther, J. 1984. Soil carbon dioxide and weathering potentials in tropical karst terrain, Peninsula Malaysia: a preliminary model. *Earth Surface Processes and Landforms,* **9**, 397-407.

Day, M.J. 1982. The influence of some material properties on the development of tropical karst terrain. *Transactions of the British Cave Research Association,* **9**, 27-37.

Friedrich, H. 1980. Symposium on the geomorphology of the Mulu Hills: VII. The water chemistry of the unsaturated zone in the Melinau Limestone. *Geographical Journal,* **146**, 246-58.

Gerstenhauer, A. 1960. Der tropische Kegelkarst in Tabasco (Mexico). *Zeitschrift für Geomorphologie, Supplement Band,* **2**, 22-48.

Giusti, E.V. 1978. Hydrogeology of the karst of Puerto Rico. *Professional Paper of the United States Geological Survey,* **1012**, p 68.

Gobbett, D.J. 1971. Joint pattern and faulting in the Kinta Valley, West Malaysia. *Bulletin of the Geological Society of Malaysia,* **4**, 39-48.

Ingham, F.T. and Bradford, E.F. 1960. The geology and mineral resources of the Kinta Valley, Perak. *District Memoir, Federation of Malaya Geological Survey,* **9**, p 347.

Ireland, P. 1979. Geomorphological variations of 'case-hardening' in Puerto Rico. *Zeitschrift für Geomorphologie, Supplement Band,* **32**, 9-20.

Jennings, J.N. 1972. The character of tropical humid karst. *Zeitscrift für Geomorphologie, N.F.,* **16**, 336-41.

Jennings, J.N. 1976. A test of the importance of cliff-foot caves in tower karst development. *Zeitschrift für Geomorphologie Supplement Band,* **26**, 92-97.

Laverty, M. 1980. Symposium on the geomorphology of the Mulu Hills: VI. Water chemistry in the Gunung Mulu National Park including problems of interpretation and use. *Geographical Journal,* **146**, 232-57.

McDonald, R.C. 1975. Observations on hillslope erosion in tower karst topography of Belize. *Bulletin of the Geological Society of America,* **86**, 255-56.

McDonald, R.C. 1976a. Limestone morphology in South Sulawesi, Indonesia. *Zeitschrift für Geomorphologie, Supplement Band,* **26**, 79-91.

McDonald, R.C. 1976b. Hillslope base depressions in tower karst topography of Belize. *Zeitschrift für Geomorphologie, Supplement Band,* **26**, 98-103.

Miotke, F.D. 1973. The subsidence of the surface between mogotes in Puerto Rico. *Caves and Karst,* **15**, 1-12.

Mohammed Ayob 1970. Quaternary sediments at Sungei Besi, West Malaysia. *Bulletin of the Geological Society of Malaysia,* **3**, 53-61.

Monroe, W.H. 1969. Evidence of subterranean sheet solution under weathered detrital cover in Puerto Rico. In: *Problems of the Karst Denudation, Proceedings of the Symposium on Karst Denudation, Brno,* ed. O. Stelcl, 111-21.

Morgan, R.P.C. 1976. The role of climate in the denudation system: a case study from West Malaysia. In: *Geomorphology and Climate,* ed. E. Derbyshire, (London: John Wiley and Sons), 317-43.

Nieuwolt, S. 1965. Evaporation and water balances in Malaya. *Journal of Tropical Geography,* **20**, 34-53.

Paton, J.R. 1964. The origin of the limestone hills of Malaya. *Journal of Tropical Geography,* **18**, 138-47.

Picknett, R.G. 1972. The pH of calcite solutions with and without magnesium present, and the implications concerning rejuvenated aggressiveness. *Transactions of the British Cave Research Group of Great Britain,* **14**, 141-50.

Picknett, R.G. 1973. Saturated calcite solutions from 10 to 40°C: a theoretical study evaluating the solubility product and other constants. *Transactions of the British Cave Research Group of Great Britain,* **15**, 67-80.

Picknett, R.G., Bray, L.G. and Stenner, R.D. 1976. The chemistry of cave waters. In: *The Science of Speleology,* eds. T.D. Ford and C.H.D. Cullingford, (London: Academic Press), 213-66.

Smith, D.I. and Atkinson, T.C. 1976. Process, landforms and climate in limestone regions. In: *Geomorphology and Climate,* ed. E. Derbyshire, (London: John Wiley and Sons), 367-409.

Stauffer, P.H. 1973. Cenozoic. In: *Geology of the Malay Peninsula: West Malaysia and Singapore,* eds. D.J. Gobbett and C.S. Hutchison, (New York: John Wiley and Sons), 143-76.

Stenner, R.D. 1969. The measurement of the aggressiveness of water towards calcium carbonate. *Transactions of the British Cave Research Group of Great Britain,* **11**, 175-200.

Suntharalingham, T. 1968. Upper Palaeozoic stratigraphy of the area west of Kampar, Perak. *Bulletin of the Geological Society of Malaysia,* **1**, 1-15.

Sweeting, M.M. 1958. The karstlands of Jamaica. *Geographical Journal,* **124**, 184-99.

Sweeting, M.M. 1979. Weathering and solution of the Melinau Limestones in the Gunong Mulu National Park, Sarawak, Malaysia. *Annales de la Société Géologique de Belgique,* **102**, 53–57.

Verstappen, H.Th. 1960. Some observations on karst development in the Malay Archipelago. *Journal of Tropical Geography,* **14**, 1–10.

Walker, D. 1956. Studies in the Quaternary of the Malay Peninsula: 1. Alluvial deposits of Perak and changes in the relative levels of land and sea. *Journal of the federated Malay States Museums,* **1/2**, 19–34.

Wilford, G.E. and Wall, J.R.D. 1965. Karst topography in Sarawak. *Journal of Tropical Geography,* **21**, 44–70.

Williams, P.W. 1972. Morphometric analysis of polygonal karst in New Guinea. *Bulletin of the Geological Society of America,* **83**, 761–96.

Additional reference:

Low, K.S. and Goh, K.C. 1972. The water balance of five catchments in Salangor. *Journal of Tropical Geography,* **35**, 60–66.

23

The hydrological development
of tropical tower karst:
an example from Peninsular Malaysia

S.J. Gale

SUMMARY

Studies of the morphology and sedimentary infill of abandoned drainage
networks in tropical karst towers in Selangor, Peninsular Malaysia
have enabled four major phases of hydrological development to be
recognised. These have allowed a partial reconstruction of the sequence
of landform and drainage development in the area. The available
evidence suggests that this development began during or prior to the
Lower Quaternary, indicating a considerable age for tower karst
formation in the region. The fossil drainage networks therefore
provide an indication of environmental conditions during a period
within which little is known of environmental history in Peninsular
Malaysia, confirming the value of karst features for palaeoenvironmental reconstruction in areas which have experienced long histories
of erosion.

RÉSUMÉ

Les études de la morphologie et du remplissage sédimentaire des réseaux
de drainage abandonnés dans les karsts tropicaux à tourelles de
Selangor (Malaisie) ont révélé quatre phases majeures de développement
hydrologique. Ces recherches ont permis de proposer une reconstruction
partielle de la genèse du paysage et du drainage de cette région.
Celle-ci aurait commencé pendant ou avant le Quaternaire ancien.
Ceci indique l'ancienneté des tourelles karstiques. Les réseaux de
drainage fossiles fournissent des indications sur l'environnement
d'une région pour laquelle on a par ailleurs très peu de renseignements
pendant cette période ancienne. Cela confirme l'intérêt des formes
karstiques comme indicateur des paléoenvironnements.

INTRODUCTION

Despite the significance of tower karst in tropical karst regions, few efforts have been made to study the extensive abandoned hydrological networks frequently preserved in karst towers. It seems likely that these networks are but the dissected remnants of once extensive drainage systems and, as such, they may provide the answers to many questions of drainage and landscape evolution in tropical karst areas.

This proposition was tested by investigating the tower karst of the central Selangor region of peninsular Malaysia (Figure 23.1). This region constitutes the southernmost component of the mainland southeast Asian karst, which itself forms the most extensive belt of tower karst in the world. More importantly, the tower karst of central Selangor exhibits similar topographic relationships to those found elsewhere in peninsular southeast Asia, with the towers rising from alluvial plains and the limestone fringing topographically-higher impermeable rocks whose rivers drain directly into the karst.

The central Selangor area possesses several advantages for a study of landscape and drainage development. First, the lowland areas of equatorial southeast Asia are amongst the few areas of the world where possibly little or no climatic change has taken place during the Quaternary (Ashton, 1972, p. 51, 54-55; CLIMAP, 1976; Prell et al., 1980). Secondly, central Selangor experiences a true tropical wet (Af) climate with uniformly high temperatures (minimum mean-monthly temperature = 25.8°C, maximum mean-monthly temperature = 26.8°C (Dale, 1963)) and uniformly high precipitation (mean daily rainfall in driest month = 9.4 mm, mean daily rainfall in wettest month = 14.0 mm (Dale, 1960)). Thirdly, there is no evidence of significant tectonic activity in peninsular Malaysia since the Tertiary (Gobbett and Tjia, 1973, 317-328; Stauffer, 1973a, p. 143; Tjia, 1981). As a consequence, hydrological and geomorphological development in the area during the Quaternary can be regarded as having taken place against a background of environmental near-stability.

On the other hand, peninsular Malaysia has been a topographically positive area since at least the start of the Cenozoic (Stauffer, 1973a, p.143). Consequently, it has experienced a long period of denudation with the result that only in a few areas is there a depositional record of environmental conditions during that period (Stauffer, 1973a). It is in this context that studies of karst may be most useful, for limestone landscapes exhibit two particular advantages for investigations of environmental history. First, they are able to preserve the fine detail of former drainage systems in the form of caves eroded in the bedrock. By contrast, surface streams continually rework their channels so that only fragments of earlier systems remain to enable inferences to be made about past hydrological conditions. Secondly, once formed, these caves may function as sediment traps, preserving depositional evidence of underground and surface events away from the erosive effects of subaerial processes.

444

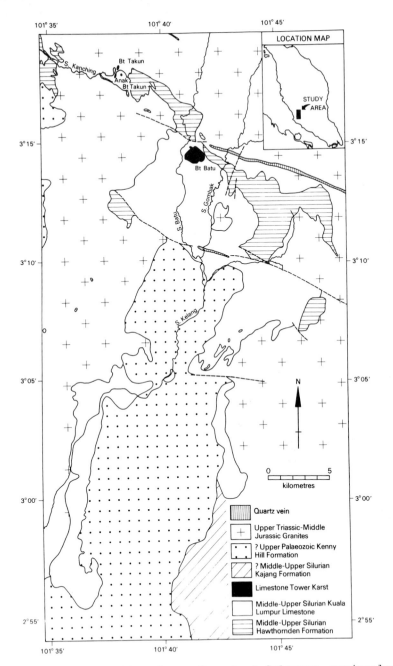

Figure 23.1   The solid geology of central Selangor, peninsular
Malaysia (after Roe, 1953 and Yin, 1976).

445

It was hoped that these advantages could be capitalised on to provide not only evidence of the character and sequence of environmental change in peninsular Malaysia during the Upper Cenozoic, but also information on the nature of drainage and landscape development in tropical karst areas as a whole.

THE CENTRAL SELANGOR KARST

The central Selangor karst consists of a discontinuous series of outcrops of Middle to Upper Silurian Kuala Lumpur Limestone which fringe the western side of the granitic Main Range of peninsular Malaysia (Figure 23.1). Other limestones exist further north in the state, mainly as lens-shaped bands interbedded with argillaceous rocks, but these are of limited extent and have no surface expression (Roe, 1951, 15-18; 1953, 20-23). The relationship of these limestones to the Kuala Lumpur Limestone is unclear, although Jones (1968) has assigned them a Lower Palaeozoic age.

The karst of central Selangor is in an advanced state of denudation. It consists largely of a buried landscape, hidden beneath accumulations of alluvial material. Only at three locations does the limestone outcrop at the surface to form karst towers (Figure 23.1). Nevertheless, the buried karst can be seen in numerous alluvial tin workings throughout the area, where it is exposed at depths varying from a few metres to a few decametres.

The date of burial of the karst has been partly elucidated by studies of the chronology of deposition of the overlying alluvium. ^{14}C and fission-track dates on material from the upper parts of the depositional sequences have given ages of up to >41 500 bp (Haile and Ayob, 1968; Stauffer, 1973b; Stauffer *et al.,* 1980, 157-58; Nishimura and Stauffer, 1981); whilst reversely-magnetised sediments at the base of the sequences may be cautiously interpreted as indicating that deposition began at least 0.7 Ma bp, during the Matuyama magnetic-polarity epoch (Haile and Watkins, 1972).

The deposition of these sediments appears to have been fundamental to the development of the karst in the area, for the landscape seems to have evolved in a fashion similar to that suggested by McDonald (1976; 1979) for other areas of tower karst, where calcareous and topographically-higher non-calcareous rocks are juxtaposed. In such areas, allogenic rivers, rising on the impermeable non-calcareous beds, either sink upon reaching the limestone or, given the intensity of monsoon rainstorms, flow in a torrential fashion across the limestone. The resultant incision of the karst by the rivers tends to give rise to a deeply-dissected topography characterised by narrow corridors separating steep-sided limestone hills. The absence of surface flows and slope processes on the permeable limestone acts to maintain the steep-sided form of the valleys. Elsewhere it has been shown that these corridors may also develop partly as a result of either cavern collapse (McDonald, 1976, 83-84) or subaerial solution (Lehmann, 1953).

446

The surrounding hills, composed of highly-weathered granites, would have provided an easily-erodible source of sediment for the allogenic rivers flowing across the limestone. Consequently, as the karst corridors developed, alluviation would have taken place within them, encouraged by a loss of stream competence associated either with a reduction in stream gradient at the foot of the granite hills, or with a reduction in stream flow as water sank at the limestone margin. The deposition of alluvial sediments in the corridors would have resulted in the formation of an impermeable surface in the corridors, and this would have initiated a change from largely-vertical to largely-horizontal erosion processes in the valleys. Previous workers have suggested a range of processes that might contribute to lateral erosion. These include solutional undercutting by swamp waters, by ephemeral lakes at the tower bases, or by soil moisture; solutional surface wash; lateral fluvial solution and corrasion; and spring-sapping at the limestone-alluvium contact. As a result, the steep-sided limestone hills would have been undercut and would have retreated. The sub-alluvial surface may have continued to be deepened, although fluvial incision would no longer have been localised within a narrow corridor, whilst the rare occurrence of alluvial dolines and slumped alluvial sequences in central Selangor suggests that sub-alluvial solution would have been a relatively localised phenomenon.

With the retreat of the limestone hills, the landscape would have begun to correspond to that found in the area at present, with occasional towers separated by alluvial plains, beneath which are found buried limestone surfaces. Across these plains continue to flow allogenic rivers which carry sediment from the surrounding impermeable uplands and continue to build up the level of the alluvial surface.

ANAK BUKIT TAKUN AND THE UPPER KANCHING VALLEY

The karst tower of Anak Bukit Takun in the Upper Kanching Valley was chosen as the most suitable part of the central Selangor karst for the investigation of hydrological and landscape development (Figures 23.1 and 23.2). The tower is sufficiently small for it to be believed that almost all the caves that exist within it are known; whilst the Upper Kanching Valley constitutes a discrete drainage and landscape unit which is small enough to be studied in its entirety, and yet which mirrors the topography and structure of tower karst areas elsewhere in peninsular southeast Asia. Anak Bukit Takun has also been the subject of recent studies of contemporary hydrological and geochemical processes (Crowther, 1979; 1981; 1982; 1983), thus enabling comparison to be made with those processes regarded as having occurred in the past.

The overall form of the Upper Kanching Valley is that of a flat-floored basin at an altitude of c. 90 m above Land Survey Datum (LSD), encircled by steep slopes which reach heights in excess of 300 m LSD. To the north, south and west, the sides of the basin are composed of granites of probable Upper Triassic

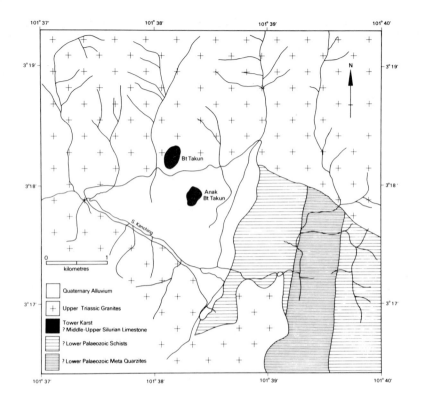

Figure 23.2   The geology of the Upper Kanching Valley,
               Selangor   (after Loganathan, 1970   and Ismail,
               1979, with some modifications by Gale)

age (Bignell and Snelling, 1977, 31-34), whilst to the east, the
side of the basin is composed of a westerly-dipping succession
of (?)Lower Palaeozoic metasedimentary rocks (Loganathan, 1970)
(Figure 23.2). The bedrock floor of the basin consists of limestone underlain, at depths of c. 25 m (Roe, 1953, 22, 117), by
granite, although in many places the limestone has been totally
removed, leaving the granite exposed. This is particularly the
case in the northern part of the basin, where the two remaining
limestone towers are both perched on granite pedestals (Figure
23.2). The limestones, which are only exposed within the basin,
consist of crystalline, grey to cream, pure calcitic marbles
(Loganathan, 1970, p.33; Ismail, 1979, 22-22a). No fossils have
yet been found in the limestone, although Jones (1973, 39-40)
has suggested that the beds are the same age as the Middle to
Upper Silurian Kuala Lumpur Limestone found 4.4 km to the
southwest. The limestones dip steeply at angles of c. 60-90°
to the east, and on the basis of this and the amount of limestone
exposed in the karst towers, the thickness of the limestone unit
may be calculated as at least 280 m.

Both at present and during the past, the basin has acted as a locus of deposition for the alluvium carried by the steep, actively-eroding streams which drain the surrounding uplands. The present outlet to the basin is provided by the westerly-draining Sungai Kanching, which has incised a valley through the lip of the basin. However, it is possible that at some stage in the past the main drainage of the basin may have been to the east.

The alluvium forms a complicated depositional sequence varying in thickness between 10 and 30 m (Scrivenor and Jones, 1919, p.104; Roe, 1953, p.22). It surrounds the tower of Anak Bukit Takun and overlies a complex eroded surface cut across both the limestone and the granite. Where it has been exposed from beneath the alluvial cover, the limestone can be seen to be deeply solutionally-dissected and to exhibit pinnacle-like forms (Loganathan, 1970, 7, 30; Ismail, 1979, p.7).

The alluvial deposits have been investigated by Loganathan (1970) and Gale (in preparation). It is thought that they represent an initial episode of very coarse alluvial deposition during which boulders of granite and quartz were carried by streams draining the uplands to the north and west of the area. This was followed by a more complex episode of finer alluvial sedimentation, during which smaller, laterally-migrating streams deposited c. 10 m of gravels, sands and silts, representing channel, overbank and floodplain deposits.

GUA ANAK TAKUN

The majority of the caves found within Anak Bukit Takun form part of a single system, Gua Anak Takun, almost entirely filling the tower. Several vertical shafts have also been found on the tower summit, as well as some examples of foot caves at the tower base, but none of these appears to be very extensive.

Gua Anak Takun forms a complex multi-level system extending over a vertical range of 65 m (Figures 23.3 and 23.4). Owing to the metamorphosed nature of the limestone in which it is developed, bedding planes are almost non-existent, so most passages are aligned along joints. However, other structural controls on passage location can also be recognised, of which the shale units exposed between the Pipe Corridor and the Bench Corridor are of particular importance (Figure 23.5). Along shale units 1 and 3, cave development appears to have been encouraged and the passage roofs extend high up along the vertically-bedded shale bands. By contrast, unit 2 has acted to inhibit cave development and the shale has prevented further solutional development along the east side of the Bench Corridor.

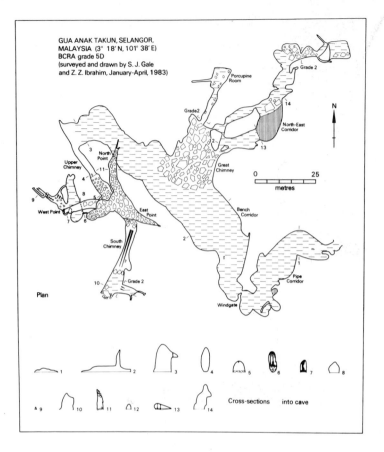

Figure 23.3   Gua Anak Takun, Upper Kanching Valley, Selangor;
plan view

HYDROLOGICAL DEVELOPMENT OF GUA ANAK TAKUN

Stages 1 and 2

Solutional flow markings (scallops) on the walls of the
Upper Chimney and South Chimney of the cave show that these passages formed a phreatic loop within which water flowed up the
Upper Chimney and down the South Chimney (Figures 23.3 and 23.4).
Since both the South Chimney and the Upper Chimney are developed
along near-vertical joints, there is likely to have been no con-
straint on the height of their development other than a hydraulic
one. The maximum height of the phreatic loop should correspond
to the height at which, neglecting frictional effects, hydrostatic pressure equals zero. If this is the case, then the local

450

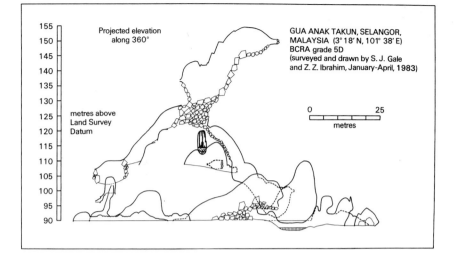

Figure 23.4   Gua Anak Takun, Upper Kanching Valley, Selangor;
projected elevation along 360°

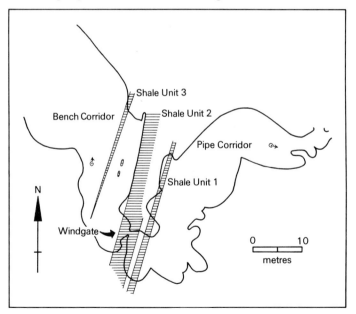

Figure 23.5   The location of the shale units in Gua Anak Takun

Table 23.1   Stages in the development of Gua Anak Takun and
              the Upper Kanching Valley

Stage	Internal events	External events
1	Formation of high-level caves under phreatic conditions. Local phreatic level at >152 m LSD.	Continuous limestone mass at altitude of >152 m LSD, contiguous with adjacent impermeable rocks.
2	Formation of mid and low-level caves under phreatic conditions (Q_{max} = 0.85 m^3 s^{-1}). Local phreatic level at c. 130 m LSD.	Entrenchment of limestone mass by >22 m.
3a	Vadose trenching of mid-level caves. Local phreatic level at ≤100 m LSD.	Entrenchment of limestone mass by ≥30 m.
3b	Collapse of high-level caves.	
3c	Speleothem deposition in mid-level caves.	
?4a	Fluvial deposition in low-level caves.	
4b	Collapse of low-level caves.	
4c-4e	Speleothem deposition in low-level caves. Local phreatic level at <87 m LSD.	Entrenchment of limestone mass to <87 m LSD. Separation of tower from adjacent impermeable rocks.
4d	Infill and solutional notching of low-level caves by static-water body.	?Static-water body outside tower. Alluviation of inter-tower surface.
4e	Speleothem deposition and collapse in low-level caves.	Retreat of tower walls.

height of the phreatic surface at the time of development of the
phreatic loop would have been c. 130 m LSD. By the time of the
development of the phreatic loop, therefore, the upper-level
passages in the cave can no longer have been phreatically active.
Thus, the North Point and the East Point form part of the earliest
phase of drainage development for which there is evidence
(Stage 1) (Figures 23.3 and 23.4). Although these passages have
experienced large-scale cavern collapse, it is clear that they
must have formed beneath a local phreatic level of at least
152 m LSD (Figure 23.4).

During Stage 1, the landscape outside the cave must have
been very different to that existing today. Since the height
of the phreatic surface within the limestone is ultimately
governed by the height of the resurgence levels where the water
leaves the aquifer, and since these resurgence levels are controlled by local base-level (probably the level of the rivers
crossing the limestone), then a number of inferences can be made.
First, river levels must have been at least 60 m above those
of the present. Secondly, and as a consequence of this, the
limestone must have been laterally more extensive than at present. Thirdly, the limestone must have been contiguous with the

adjacent impermeable rocks, for without concentrated-flow recharge to the aquifer, as would have occurred with streams
flowing off the adjacent impermeable rocks, cave development
could not have occurred.

By the time of the next stage of hydrological development
represented in the cave, that associated with the formation of
the phreatic loop (Stage 2), local phreatic levels must have
fallen by at least 22 m to c. 130 m LSD. The lowering of resurgence levels necessary for this to have occurred suggests
that the two stages were separated by a phase of considerable
fluvial incision outside the cave.

Measurements of dissolution bedforms (scallops) on the walls
of the Upper Chimney have enabled the estimation of former flow
conditions in the phreatic loop. Using the methods of Gale
(1984), a mean flow velocity of 0.03 m s^{-1} and a discharge of
0.85 m^{3}s^{-1} have been calculated. It has been suggested
that scallop assemblages tend to reflect conditions of
relatively long return-period flows in caves. If this is the
case, the cave was probably not a major conduit at the time of
its development, although it is likely to have been of more than
local significance.

At the lowest level in the cave occur the horizontal passages
of the Pipe Corridor, Bench Corridor and the North-East Corridor
(Figures 23.3 and 23.4). Although these appear at first sight
to be indicative of a phase of hydrological development distinct
from that of Stage 2, there is evidence that this was not the
case. In particular, the existence of avens and shafts of clear
phreatic form in the Bench and North-East Corridors indicate the
development of these passages at a local phreatic level of at
least 110 m LSD. Since such roof features can only conclusively
indicate a minimum altitude for the old phreatic level, the low-
level passages are most easily explained as having developed
contemporaneously with the phreatic loop of the Upper Chimney-
South Chimney. This interpretation is supported by the evidence
of flow markings in the Bench Corridor, indicating flow to the
northwest, in the direction of the Upper Chimney, and by the
absence of major vadose-trenching in either limb of the phreatic
loop, as might have been expected given a long period of vadose
flow down to a local phreatic level of c. 110 m LSD.

Although the low-level passages might be best interpreted
as having developed contemporaneously with those of the Upper
and South Chimneys, it is clear from the evidence of the flow
markings in the cave that these passages did not form a simple,
single system. Scallops in the roof of the Pipe Corridor indicate flow to the northeast, out of the cave; whereas flow
markings in the roof of the Bench Corridor, although not generally
demonstrating any asymmetry, appear to indicate flow to the
northwest, into the cave (Figure 23.3). These two passages
are connected by the Windgate, a short crawl formed by mechanical
collapse of the shale bed dividing them (Figure 23.5). Because
elsewhere this shale unit has acted to prevent cave development
and the Windgate shows no evidence of flow; and since the
scallops indicate that flow in each passage was in opposite

453

directions, it is concluded that the Bench and Pipe Corridors developed as hydrologically-distinct systems. It is suggested that the Pipe Corridor may have formerly extended further south, adjacent to shale unit 2 and aligned along shale unit 1. The extension could easily be buried where the present roof dips below the thick sequences of clastic deposits which constitute the present floor of the cave. In a similar fashion, the Bench Corridor may have formerly extended further south, adjacent to shale unit 2 and aligned along shale unit 3. Alternatively, the Bench Corridor may have been fed by flow down the major shaft found in the cave roof at the southern end of the passage (Figure 23.4).

Stage 3

Beyond Stage 2, events in the cave are difficult to relate to episodes of landform development outside. It is clear that at some time, the local phreatic level must have fallen to near present heights to leave the passages abandoned; presumably this was associated with continued fluvial incision and dissection of the landscape outside the cave. Inside the cave, however, a number of minor events can be placed in a simple time-sequence. First, with the draining of the phreatic loop, phreatic conditions in the Upper and South Chimneys were replaced by vadose, giving rise to a phase of vadose incision (Stage 3a). That this phase was relatively short-lived is indicated by the poorly-developed nature of the vadose trenching. Secondly, at some time after the abandonment of the phreatic loop, there occurred the collapse of the highest-level passages, breaking down the roof of the phreatic loop and infilling it with a choke of massive blocks (Stage 3b)(Figure 23.4). The resultant breakdown cone extended part-way down each of the limbs of the loop, in some cases infilling the vadose trenches of the previous phase. The episode of breakdown may have been associated with a rapid regional lowering of groundwater levels, causing a fall in pressure and the collapse of the unsupported conduits. This explanation has been proposed by Sweeting (1950, p.75) for northwest Yorkshire, and by Brink and Partridge (1965, 25-33) for South Africa. Subsequently, percolation waters deposited thick sequences of calcite on top of the breakdown in the West Point (Stage 3c)(Figure 23.4).

Stage 4

At some stage during the development of the lower passages, an episode of fluvial sedimentation occurred (Stage ?4a). This is represented by micaceous fluvial sands found beneath stalagmite in the North-East Corridor (Figure 23.3). These deposits are likely to have been laid down under vadose conditions after the lowering of resurgence levels during Stage 3. Unfortunately a vadose origin cannot be easily established on sedimentological grounds, and nor can a study of passage morphology provide any evidence of vadose conditions in the lower passages, since all but the passage roofs are hidden beneath thick accumulations of sediment. The fluvial deposits may therefore also be interpreted as having been deposited under phreatic conditions during Stage 2.

After Stage ?4a, there is no further evidence of active flow in the cave. This may have been the result either of the continued lowering of external resurgence levels, or of the final separation of the tower from the concentrated surface flow draining off the surrounding impermeable rocks. The former explanation seems the less likely given that, adjacent to Anak Bukit Takun, the impermeable granite basement is found only c. 10 m below the level of the lower passages, and given that, throughout the area, the granite is found at depths only c. 25 m below the limestone surface (Roe, 1953, 22, 117). Under these circumstances, it is probable that the existing lower-level passages formed the lowest levels of cave development in the area.

The abandonment of the caves meant that the deposition of secondary calcite, which overlies the fluvial deposits in the North-East Corridor, could commence (Stages 4c-4e). In many parts of the lower passages, this phase of deposition is still active. In the Great Chimney the stalagmite overlies breakdown deposits (Figures 23.3 and 23.4). Although this suggests that an episode of collapse (Stage 4b) preceded that of stalagmite precipitation, it is likely that stalagmite deposition also occurred prior to the episode of breakdown.

The final episode for which there is evidence in the cave, is that of a phase of static-water erosion and deposition (Stage 4d). The evidence for this comes from three sources. First , in the North-East Corridor, a horizontal water-mark around the cave walls indicates the existence of a standing-water body c. 1 m above present levels. Secondly, infilling the lower-level passages to a depth of at least 2 m is a sequence of pale brown, finely-laminated (c. 1 mm) silts. These appear to represent deposition under static-water conditions, possibly of material washed in from outside the cave. Thirdly, throughout the Pipe and Bench Corridors is a distinctive notch in the passage walls c. 0.1-0.2 m high and up to 3 m deep, just above the level of the present infill. Such notches can only have been formed by solution under static-water conditions.

All these features imply some form of external water-level control, rather than just the localised effect of ponding inside the cave. The simplest explanation is to regard this as the result of the presence of lacustrine conditions outside the cave. There is some evidence for the existence of such conditions in the alluvial sedimentary record in the area, although it is unclear whether the height of the lacustrine deposits corresponds to the height of the features found in the cave.

The present cave is still experiencing minor modification in the form of continuing secondary precipitation of calcite and passage collapse due to tower-wall retreat (Stage 4e).

CONCLUSIONS

This study has provided evidence of a simple sequence of drainage and landscape development in the Upper Kanching Valley (Table 23.1). During the earliest part of this sequence, a landscape very different from that of the present must have existed in the area, and the basin of the Upper Kanching Valley must have formed a continuous karst surface over 60 m above the present level of the basin floor. Rivers flowing off the surrounding, and possibly overlying, impermeable rocks would have either sunk upon reaching the limestone or would have incised narrow valleys across it. Evidence in the caves shows that, as this incision continued, a sequence of drainage systems, each related to a lower resurgence level, developed in the limestone, until the remaining karst hills were finally cut off from concentrated-flow recharge from the surrounding impermeable areas.

The chronology of this development cannot be easily established at present, although isotopic and magnetostratigraphic studies of the two phases of speleothem development in the cave (Stages 3c and 4c-4e) are in progress. In other parts of the central Selangor karst, the deposition of alluvium between the towers may have begun over 0.7 Ma bp. This might indicate a similar age for Stage 3a in the development of Gua Anak Takun, the earliest stage by which the valleys could have cut down to levels close to those of the present. If this is the case, then Stages 1 and 2 of cave development might have occurred during the Lower Quaternary, or even the Tertiary. The evidence of environmental change provided by Gua Anak Takun is therefore significant, since this is a period which is represented by a major gap in most conventional geological sequences in peninsular Malaysia. Such chronologies are highly speculative, however, and further discussion must await the results of work now in progress.

These results may also be of significance with regard to the question of tower karst development in the rest of southeast Asia. These areas of tower karst appear to have experienced near-continuous histories of erosion, with the result that, outside the caves, little evidence of the chronology of their development has been preserved. This study has shown that valuable clues to the sequence and nature of that development may be obtained from a study of the abandoned drainage networks found within the towers. Moreover, it has also offered an indication of the possible age of karstification in the region and has shown that the landscapes may be of considerable age.

Acknowledgements

I acknowledge the award of a Research Fellowship by Jesus College, Oxford which allowed me to complete this work; and the assistance provided by Jabatan Sains Alam Sekitar, Universiti Pertanian Malaysia and the Department of Geology, University of Malaya. An earlier draft of this paper was critically read by Miss Z.Z. Ibrahim, whose help with fieldwork is also gratefully acknowledged.

REFERENCES

Ashton, P.S. 1972. The Quaternary geomorphological history of western Malesia and lowland forest phytogeography. *University of Hull Department of Geography Miscellaneous Series,* **13**, 35-62.

Bignell, J.D. and Snelling, N.J. 1977. Geochronology of Malayan granites. *Overseas Geology and Mineral Resources,* **47**, 73pp.

Brink, A.B.A. and Partridge, T.C. 1965. Transvaal karst: some considerations of development and morphology with special reference to sinkholes and subsidence on the Far West Rand. *South African Geographical Journal,* **47**, 11-34.

CLIMAP 1976. The surface of the ice-age Earth. *Science,* **191**, 1131-1137.

Crowther, J. 1979. Limestone solution on exposed rock outcrops in West Malaysia. In: *Geographical Approaches to Fluvial Processes,* ed. A.F. Pitty, (Norwich: Geo Abstracts), 31-50.

Crowther, J. 1981. Small-scale spatial variations in the chemistry of diffuse-flow seepages in Gua Anak Takun, West Malaysia. *Transactions of the British Cave Research Association,* **8**, 168-177.

Crowther, J. 1982. Temperature characteristics of seepages in four West Malaysian caves. *Transactions of the British Cave Research Association,* **9**, 38-46.

Crowther, J. 1983. Hydrology of autogenic percolation systems in some tropical karst outcrops, West Malaysia. *Journal of Hydrology,* **60**, 227-242.

Dale, W.L. 1960. The rainfall of Malaya, part II. *Journal of Tropical Geography,* **14**, 11-28.

Dale, W.L. 1963. Surface temperatures in Malaya. *Journal of Tropical Geography,* **17**, 57-71.

Gale, S.J. 1984. The hydraulics of conduit flow in carbonate aquifers. *Journal of Hydrology,* **70**, 309-327.

Gale, S.J. and Hunt, C.O. in prep. The alluvial sediments of the Ulu Kanching basin, Malysia: a gravel-dominated facies assemblage in a humid-tropical environment.

Gobbett, D.J. and Tjia, H.D. 1973. Tectonic history. In: *Geology of the Malay Peninsula,* eds D.J. Gobbett and C.S. Hutchison, (New York: Wiley-Interscience), 305-334.

Haile, N.S. and Ayob, M. 1968. Note on radiometric age determination of samples of peat and wood from tin-bearing Quaternary deposits at Sungei Besi Tin Mines, Selangor. Malaysia. *Geological Magazine,* **105**, 519-520.

Haile, N.S. and Watkins, N.D. 1972. The use of paleomagnetic reversals in Pleistocene geochronology in southeast Asia. *Geological Society of Malaysia Newsletter,* **34** (Annex), 17-18.

Ismail, J. 1979. *Geology of Templer Park Area, Selangor.* Unpublished B.Sc. thesis, University of Malaya, 58 pp.

Jones, C.R. 1968. Lower Paleozoic rocks of Malay Peninsula. *Bulletin of the American Association of Petroleum Geologists,* **52**, 1259-1278.

Jones, C.R. 1973. Lower Paleozoic. In: *Geology of the Malay Peninsula,* eds D.J. Gobbett and C.S. Hutchison, (New York: Wiley-Interscience), 25-60.

Lehmann, H. 1953. Der tropische Kegelkarst in Westindien. *Deutscher geographentag Verhandlungen,* **29**, 126-131.

Loganathan, P. 1970. *Geology and Geochemical Study of the Templer Park Area, Selangor, West Malaysia.* Unpublished B.Sc. thesis, University of Malaya, 93pp.

McDonald, R.C. 1976. Limestone morphology in South Sulawesi, Indonesia. *Zeitschrift für Geomorphologie N.F. Supplementband,* **26**, 79-91.

McDonald, R.C. 1979. Tower karst geomorphology in Belize. *Zeitschrift für Geomorphologie N.F. Supplementband,* **32**, 35-45.

Nishimura, S. and Stauffer, P.H. 1981. Fission-track ages of zircons from the Serdang volcanic ash, peninsular Malaysia. *Warta Geologi,* **7**, 39-41.

Prell, W.L., Hutson, W.H., Williams, D.F., Bé, A.W.H., Geitzenauer, K. and Molfino, B. 1980. Surface circulation of the Indian Ocean during the last glacial maximum, approximately 18,000 yr B.P. *Quaternary Research,* **14**, 309-336.

Roe, F.W. 1951. The geology and mineral resources of the Fraser's Hill Area, Selangor, Perak and Pahang, Federation of Malaya. *Geological Survey of Malaya Memoir,* **5**, (New Series), 138pp.

Roe, F.W. 1953. The geology and mineral resources of the neighbourhood of Kuala Selangor and Rasa, Selangor, Federation of Malaya, with an account of the geology of Batu Arang coal-field. *Geological Survey of Malaya Memoir,* **7**, (New Series), 163pp.

Scrivenor, J.B. and Jones, W.R. 1919. The geology of South Perak, North Selangor and The Dindings. *Geology Department of the Federated Malay States,* (Kuala Lumpur: Malay States Govt Press), 196pp.

Stauffer, P.H. 1973a. Cenozoic. In: *Geology of the Malay Peninsula,* eds D.J. Gobbett and C.S. Hutchison, (New York: Wiley-Interscience), 143-176.

Stauffer, P.H. 1973b. Late Pleistocene age indicated for volcanic ash in West Malaysia. *Geological Society of Malaysia Newsletter,* **40**, 1-4.

Stauffer, P.H., Nishimura, S. and Batchelor, B.C. 1980. Volcanic ash in Malaya from a catastrophic eruption of Toba, Sumatra, 30,000 years ago. In: *Physical Geography of Indonesia Island Arcs,* ed. S. Nishimura, (Kyoto: Kyoto University Press), 156-164.

Sweeting, M.M. 1950. Erosion cycles and limestone caverns in the Ingleborough district. *Geographical Journal,* **115**, 63-78.

Tjia, H.D. 1981. A Quaternary fault in peninsular Malaysia: a nontectonic interpretation. *Warta Geologi,* **7**, 115-117.

Yin E.H. 1976. Kuala Lumpur. *Geological Survey of Malaysia New Series Peninsular Malaysia,* 1:63,360 Sheet 94.

24

Limestone weathering under a soil cover and the evolution of limestone pavements, Malham district, north Yorkshire, U K

S.T. Trudgill

SUMMARY

Micro-erosion meter data derived from a subaerial surface site indicate current rates of erosion of the order of 0.01 - 0.05 mm a year. Sub-soil erosion rates, derived from observations of weight loss of limestone fragments, indicate rates both higher and lower than this under acid and alkaline soils respectively. Under acid soils, the soil may subside progressively as bedrock dissolution proceeds, exposing upstanding portions of limestone pavement without the erosional loss of soil. Small scale bedrock landforms of the order of 5 - 40 cm are thought to have been produced in post glacial times.

RÉSUMÉ

La mesure de la micro-érosion dans un site superficiel à l'air libre indique des vitesses d'érosion de l'ordre de 0.01 - 0.05 mm par an. La vitesse d'érosion dans les sols, évaluée par la perte de poids de plaquettes de calcaire révèle des taux plus élevés dans le cas de sols acides et moins élevés dans le cas de sols alcalins. Sous des sols acides, le sol peut s'affaisser au fur et à mesure que la roche calcaire sous-jacente est dissoute, ce qui a pour effet de mettre en relief des dalles calcaires là où ces mêmes sols acides n'existent pas. A petite échelle, on pense que des formes sculptées dans la roche en place dont la taille est de l'ordre de 5 a 40 cm ont pu être créees depuis la fin de la dernière période glaciaire.

INTRODUCTION

Limestone surfaces in North Yorkshire show both strong evidence
of glacial planation and also of subsequent modification by sub-
soil and subaerial weathering. Of these latter modifications,
the solutional dissection under acid soil covers is the most
marked. Studies of present day weathering processes have involved the measurement of rates of erosion under soils and subaerially, together with observations of hydrochemical processes
and of the local role of organic acids in weathering. The evolution of limestone pavements in the area is discussed in the
light of the data derived.

THE FIELD AREA

The Carboniferous Limestone outcrops extensively in the area,
bounded to the north by the Millstone Grit which lies stratigraphically above the limestone. Stratigraphically below the
limestone are the Silurian slates which outcrop locally to form
the floor of Malham Tarn. The geomorphology and geology of the
area are described by Clayton (1981). The elevation of the area
is some 400 m above sea level and it has a high rainfall of
1483 mm annually. These conditions have encouraged the leaching
of soils, even where carbonate is present in the soil parent
material. Some parent materials consist of glacial drift derived from the Millstone Grit and these readily give rise to
acid podsolised soils. On carbonate rich drift derived from
the Carboniferous Limestone, calcareous brown earths occur, but
often with an acid upper few centimetres. On limestone surfaces
bare of glacial drift, or where there is a very shallow calcareous drift, carbonate rich rendzina soils have developed.
Where fragments of limestone are absent and the rock surface is
coherent, acid organic matter may develop under high rainfall,
giving rise to a ranker soil. In the case of the rendzina,
organic matter tends to accumulate through the formation of
stable calcium humates while, in the case of the ranker, organic
matter tends to accumulate because of acidity and wetness. The
most calcareous soils are found on steep slopes covered with
carbonate rich glacial drift; here carbonate rich throughflow
and mechanical movement of soil combine to offset the effects
of leaching, helping to bring carbonate material back towards
the soil surface. Elsewhere, extensive areas of soil free limestone pavement occur, though the surfaces are usually covered
with a lichen flora to a greater or lesser extent.

SUBAERIAL RATES OF EROSION

From the evidence of glacial erratic pedestals, where bedrock is locally protected under the erratic but eroded away from the erratic (Trudgill, 1983), Clayton (1981) suggests that 40 - 50 cm of erosion has occurred in 10 000 - 12 000 years of postglacial time. This is approximately equivalent to a rate of 40 - 50 mm/1000 years or 0.04 - 0.05 mm annually. Locally, features greater than 40 - 50 cm in depth can be produced where acid water is funnelled from peat areas or otherwise concentrated in runnels.

In order to measure present day rates of erosion, a micro-erosion meter technique has been used (High and Hanna, 1970; Trudgill, High and Hanna, 1981; Trudgill, 1983). Reference studs have been inserted into the rock surface at a subaerial site north of the Field Centre at Malham Tarn. Micrometer readings of the height of the rock surface are taken in successive years. On subaerial surfaces, lichen growth often occurs. Such growth can yield positive increments relative to the studs and thus only long term data can give reliable results. At this location Trudgill (1981) reported data for 2000 days (5.48 years) for 2 sites and for 630 days (1.73 years) for 4 sites. The data are presented in Table 24.1. Increments are still visible for the shorter term data, with the highest rate of 0.04 mm a year being coincident with the rate suggested by Clayton's data.

Table 24.1   Rates of surface lowering on a lichen covered subaerial limestone surface, Malham Tarn Field Centre, N. Yorkshire, U.K. (mm yr^{-1})

SITE	Annual rate calculated for day 1 - 630	Annual rate calculated for day 1 - 2000
1	0.014	Site lost by stud deterioration
2	+ 0.027	"
3	0.016	"
4	0.041	"
5	0.024	0.0135
6	0.012	0.0037

The longer term data show a lower rate. These data suggest that features could be formed in postglacial time of the order of 3.5 - 40 cm in depth. The validity of such extrapolations through time is unknown, but the use of two independent methods, glacial erratic pedestals and micro-erosion meters, yields data of comparable orders of magnitude.

Rates of erosion under soil were calculated for the Burren district of Co. Clare, Eire, by Trudgill (1976a) using the weight loss of limestone tablets. Weight loss data were converted to a volume loss (volume = weight/density), and volume loss was distributed over the surface area in order to estimate a rate in mm per year (Trudgill, 1975). Tablets were placed throughout the soil profile, but taking the data for the presumed site of active solutional processes (the soil — bedrock interface for acid soils and the acid soil — carbonate rich interface for calcareous soils) the data show a wide range (Table 24.2). Acid soils show a range around 1 - 2 mm a year, while circumneutral and weakly acid soils show rates comparable to, or lower than, those quoted for subaerial rates above. For calcareous soils, the rates were lower than for subaerial sites. Extrapolating these rates over postglacial time yields amounts of loss of around 1.4 cm under calcareous soils, 5 cm under weakly acid soils and up to 20 m under the most acid, wet peat soils. The latter figure pertains to areas where acid runoff from peat is concentrated, and indicates the potential for cave entrance formation where such situations occur. Under soil covers, loss is liable to be limited by the facility of percolation water to transport weathering products away from the site of dissolution. Given the low permeability of most peat covers, this figure is almost certainly an overestimate and would not apply to rock under peat where free flow of water was limited. To this extent, the placing of rock tablets under highly acid covers represent an artifical situation since the tablets are liable to be placed in contact with acid peat slightly above the accumulation of weathering products at the irregularly shaped peat — bedrock interface.

In the Malham district, both cut rock tablets and naturally occurring stones were used to study weight losses. They were placed on sloping sites, one set under calcareous soils and one under acid soils. Both were developed from glacial drift. The data are shown in Table 24.3. It is again evident that rates under calcareous soils are lower than those for subaerial conditions, while the highest rates are under acid soils.

It is evident that soil pH measurements can, to a certain extent, be used as a surrogate measurement and as a predictor for erosion rates under soil. However, as discussed above for peat soils, hydrological conditions are also important. The placing of a rock tablet in an acid soil does represent an artificial situation in some cases. The rock will dissolve by diffusion processes into the acid medium surrounding it. The situation does not simulate the conditions of weathering which may be transport dependent. The tablet is too small to simulate the build up of weathering products which can occur, and limit the dissolution of a larger rock mass. Thus, the study of water movement is also an important aspect of the investigation. This is difficult to study directly, but a method is suggested by Trudgill (1975) of using gypsum tablets to study water flow within soils. The dissolution of gypsum is independent of pH

Table 24.2 Soil type and sub-soil erosion rate (mm yr^{-1})

		Limestone erosion rate
1.	Acid brown earth, pH 6	0.0084 - 0.0253
2.	Humus rendzina, pH 7	0.0047 - 0.0050
3.	Humus rendzina, pH 6.5	0.0027 - 0.0056
4.	Calcareous brown earth, pH 7.9	0.0001 - 0.0014
5.	Peat bog, pH 4.5	1.8372 - 5.2976
6.	Limestone ranker, pH 7.5	2.9327 - 5.3268

Table 24.3 Weight loss of limestone fragments under acid and calcareous soils, Malham area, Yorkshire, U.K.

(% Weight loss per year)

Acid soils (pH 4-6, 0-0.1 % CaCO$_3$)	Alkaline soils (pH 7-8, 1-10 % CaCO$_3$)
.04	.004
.05	.002
.04	.007
.05	.004
.02	.002
.04	.002
.03	.005
.11	.004
.06	.002
.04	.002
.08	.002
.36	.003
	.003
	.009
	.005

at the normal range of soil pH (down to pH 3.9), but is dependent on water flow (Crabtree and Trudgill, 1984 a, b). Thus, solutional weight loss can be used to indicate whether or not water flow is occurring within the soil profile at the position of relevance to bedrock dissolution. Weight loss data for gypsum tablets in calcareous and acid soils are presented in Table 24.4. It is clear that the zones of greatest gypsum weight loss may coincide with the zones of greatest limestone tablet weight loss, but that the two features interact. In the calcareous soils, a looser matrix at 30 - 40 cm in the soil permits

Table 24.4   Weight loss of gypsum tablets, calcareous soils,
              Malham Tarn Field Centre, Yorkshire, U.K.

Soil depth (cm)	Weight loss (%)
5	5
15	7
25	8
35	18
45	2

the rapid flow of water. However, this water is carbonate rich
water, and thus the location of the greatest limestone solutional
erosion is at a position above this where contact with less
calcareous soils occurs. Under acid soils, weight loss was
maximal at 50 - 60 cm, a subsoil position above the soil parent
material of glacial drift.

SOIL LOSS FROM LIMESTONE PAVEMENTS

The evidence for soil loss in the Burren district of Co. Clare,
Eire, has been reviewed by Bell and Limbrey (1982) and by Drew
(1983). Principally, they cite the presence of brown earth soil
covers under archaeological remains, while these soils are absent
away from the remains. The inference is that soil has been lost
from around the archaeological sites. They also point to soil
infills in depressions and other cavities as possible soil deposition sites. It is, however, also arguable that the
archaeological sites were constructed on patches of soil. In
opposition to this point is the presence of brown soil under
some older walls, where the argument is that linear patches of
soil were unlikely to exist before wall building. The general
conclusion of the authors is that soil loss has occurred to a
greater or lesser extent following clearances by man. If this
is the case, and if the erosion rates of limestone surfaces
depend upon the presence and nature of any soil cover, then
modification of the limestone weathering environment is liable
to have occurred.

In the Malham area, Pigott (1959) followed a similar line
of argument. However, the suggestion was that if widespread
soil loss had occurred, then depositional sites whould also be
evident. Thus, evidence was sought in the form of sediments in
the obvious collection basin of Malham Tarn. Although there
were deglacial silts, such deposits were not, however, found:
'the deposits show no evidence of Post-glacial erosion of
mineral soils' (p.101). The question thus arises as to whether
losses have in fact occurred, and if so, of what type of soil
and what the location of this soil material is at the present
time.

There are two kinds of soil to consider. Firstly, the
thinner organic soils, which would be relatively easy to lose
without much depositional evidence, and secondly the mineral
soils. In the case of the organic soils, any clearances would
have resulted in the drying out of the surface, encouraging the
oxidation of the soil and the loss of moss covers. This is
paralleled by untouched forest soils visible today in parts of
New Zealand, where thick moss covers and organic accumulations
carpet the floors of limestone woodlands. On woodland clearance,
these are rapidly lost as the surface dries out. Mineral soils,
however, will not be so readily lost.

It can be argued that mineral soils are able to disappear
from the surface without erosional loss, transport and deposition.
They may simply be lowered *in situ* by subsidence as sub-soil rock
dissolution occurs. Here the loss is of bedrock, with transport
of dissolved rock material in solution down small fissures and
joints. Provided this solutional loss is in some way uneven,
some parts of the rock - and therefore the soil cover above it
- will sink faster than others, leading to the eventual break-
through of previously sub-soil bedrock to the surface. (Figure
24.1). In this way, pockets of soil will be found, let down into
the landscape by the subsurface loss of bedrock, surrounded by
upstanding portions of the rock mass which have been exposed by
soil lowering. The important aspect is, then, one of soil subsidence, rather than of retreat or erosion. In parallel, there
would clearly be little in the way of deposited, eroded soils,
except where surface fissures connect locally to near surface
caves. Here, soil material may be visible washing down cave
walls, but this would be a local, rather than a widespread phenomena.

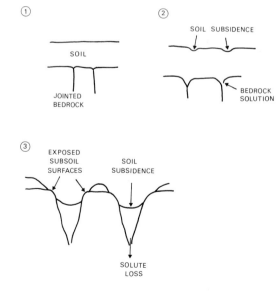

Figure 24.1 Progression envisaged for the subsidence of soil
   during the solution of limestone bedrock under soil

That soils have been lost from limestone surfaces is evident
from two lines of argument. Firstly, from observations of
lichens, and secondly from the observations of small scale landforms thought to be characteristic of sub-soil origin but now
found in subaerial situations. Lichenometry was used by Trudgill
et al. (1979), and lichen growth was also studied by Jones (1965)
to show that lichen size often decreases near to soil edges.
The inference is that near to soil edges, there is a younger
limestone surface, more recently exposed and colonised by younger,
smaller lichens. On the morphological line of argument, Trudgill
(1976a, b) excavated several limestone surfaces under a variety
of soil types. Cuspate, arcuate, and runnelled or otherwise
dissected surfaces were only found under acid soils (Figure 24.2).
The argument then is that if these forms are observed to be present subaerially then soil loss has occurred. In particular,
the presence of the arcuate or cuspate forms is thought to be
diagnostic of soil loss, since these forms are particularly
characteristic forms found under acid soils. Tabular forms are
characteristic subaerial forms. Thus, it can be argued that
tabular forms are evidence that there has been no soil presence
and no soil loss; arcuate or cuspate forms which are present subaerially give evidence of soil loss (Figure 24.3).

SUBAERIAL

SUBSOIL   INCREASING SOIL ACIDITY

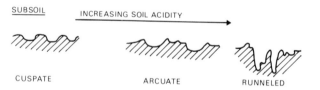

CUSPATE   ARCUATE   RUNNELED

Figure 24.2   Subaerial and subsoil bedrock forms; subsoil forms
              with increasing acidity, assuming a permeable soil

This view can be supported by the presence of such forms
at the edges of areas of acid soil where soil subsidence is
likely to have occurred (Jones, 1965). Specifically, at Malham
there are some old field boundaries in the area above Malham
cove, thought to be associated with medieval times. The area
now has a very partial cover of soil and it is often inferred
that soil erosion has occurred since it is argued that it is
unlikely that bare areas of rock would have been enclosed. While,
of course, bare areas could have been enclosed for such things
as winter stock protection or boundary assertion, it can be
argued that, on morphological grounds, the area once had a more
extensive soil cover. Here, arcuate and cuspate forms can be
seen and taken as evidence of a former acid soil cover
(Figure 24.4). Again, this is easier to understand if simple

Figure 24.3   Arcuate and runnelled forms of limestone exposed
by the subsidence of acid, peaty soils.   Scar
close, N. Yorkshire

Figure 24.4   Old wall on a limestone area above Malham cove,
N. Yorkshire

in situ soil subsidence has occurred. Taking the erosion rates for limestone bedrock under acid soils quoted above, it would only take 5 - 20 cm bedrock lowering in places for the soil to sink from the surface, exposing the joint blocks as upstanding parts of the surface. This would appear to be feasible from the time scales available and the rates involved because several cm of rock could be dissolved down runnels and joints in the centuries since medieval times.

CONCLUSIONS

It can be inferred that a glacially planed surface existed from glacial times, which has subsequently been modified by up to the order of 20 - 40 cm of erosion on a widespread scale. Local dissection due to lithological weakness and/or focussing of acid waters could have given rise to dissection of an order of magnitude deeper than this, more in places where cave development has occurred. Under calcareous soils, the glacial surface is protected, showing either a plane surface with little joint opening, or possibly relict or subglacial joint opening. Under acid soils, joint opening was more rapid than under subaerial conditions, provided that the soil was both acid and well drained. On poorly drained peat, the contribution to erosional processes is one where acid runoff from the peat is funneled onto the limestone. Under acid, well drained soils, bedrock erosion can proceed so that soil can subside gently down opened joints, leaving relict subsoil landforms exposed subaerially. Other minor solutional modifications may be superimposed on bare surfaces where water and algae collect in rock pools or where acid water drips from tree bark; the water is not only acid but will also have chelates present in it, acting further to weather the limestone. Thus, the form of limestone surfaces may be able to act as a clue to their past history; further observations will be able to qualify, refute or confirm the possible scheme suggested above.

Acknowledgements

To Richard Smith of Leeds University for discussion and to present and former staff of Malham Tarn Field Centre, especially Maggie Calloway.

REFERENCES

Bell, M. and Limbrey 1982. Environmental archaeology of karstic terrains: the example of the Burren, Co. Clare, Ireland. In: *Archaeological Aspects of Woodland Ecology,* Symposia of the Association for Environmental Archaeology, No. 2; B.A.R., International Series, 146, 115-127.

Clayton, K. 1981. Explanatory description of the landforms of the Malham area. *Field Studies,* 5, 389-423.

Crabtree, R.W. and Trudgill, S.T. 1984. a. Two microweight loss techniques for use in hillslope solute studies. *British Geomorphological Research Group, Technical Bulletin.* **32**.

Crabtree, R.W. and Trudgill, S.T. 1984. b. The use of gypsum spheres for identifying water flow routes in soils. *Earth Surface Processes and Landforms.* **9**, 25-34.

Drew, D.P. 1983. Accelerated soil erosion in a karst area: The Burren, Western Ireland. *Journal of Hydrology,* **61**, 113-124.

High, C.J. and Hanna, F.K. 1970. A method for the direct measurement of erosion on rock surfaces. *British Geomorphological Research Group, Technical Bulletin,* **5**.

Jones, R.J. 1965. Aspects of the biological weathering of limestone pavement. *Proceedings of the Geologists' Association,* **76**, 421-434.

Pigott, M.E. and Pigott, C.D. 1959. Stratigraphy and pollen analysis of Malham Tarn and Tarn Moss. *Field Studies,* **1**, 84-101.

Trudgill, S.T. 1975. Measurement of erosional weight loss of rock tablets. *British Geomorphological Research Group, Technical Bulletin,* **17**, 13-19.

Trudgill, S.T. 1976a. Limestone erosion under soil. *Proceedings of the International Congress of Speleology,* Academia, Prague, II, Ba 044, 409-422.

Trudgill, S.T. 1976b. The erosion of limestones under soil and the long term stability of soil-vegetation systems on limestone. *Earth Surface Processes,* **1**, 31-41.

Trudgill, S.T. 1983. *Weathering and Erosion,* (Butterworths).

Trudgill, S.T., Crabtree, R.W. and Walker, P.J.C. 1979. The age of exposure of limestone pavements - a pilot lichenometric study in Co. Clare, Eire. *Transactions of the British Cave Research Association,* **6**, 10-14.

Trudgill, S.T., High, C.J. and Hanna, F.K. 1981. Improvements to the micro-erosion meter. *British Geomorphological Research Group, Technical Bulletin,* **29**, 3-17.

25

The kamenitzas of Gait Barrows National Nature Reserve, north Lancashire, England

L. Rose and P. Vincent

SUMMARY

Gait Barrows National Nature Reserve has some of the best developed low-altitude limestone pavements in the British Isles. A characteristic feature of these pavements is the presence of both active and fossil kamenitzas. To gain some insight into the karstic processes involved in the development of kamenitzas a sample of eleven solution pits was chosen for detailed study. Weekly water samples have been analysed for calcium, magnesium, pH and conductivity. Variations in the water chemistry between kamenitzas is attributable to such variables as biological activity and catchment area. The location of kamenitzas appears to be strongly controlled by the presence of calcite veins which traverse the pavements. Veins which stand proud on the pavement become grooves within the kamenitza. Dissolution and fracture of the calcite veins within the bases of a kamenitza eventually leads to water leakage and the termination of kamenitza development.

RÉSUMÉ

Les tables de lapiés de la National Nature Reserve de Gait Barrows sont parmi les plus belles des Iles Britanniques. Un phénomène caractéristique de ces affleurements est la présence de kamenitzas, certains actifs, d'autres fossils. Afin de discerner les processus karstiques impliqués dans leur développement on a choisi onze kamenitzas pour des études détaillées. Une fois par semaine des échantillons d'eau ont été prélevés en vue d'analyser le calcium, le magnésium, le pH et la conductivité. Les variations observées dans la chimie des eaux, d'une kamenitza à l'autre, sont attribuées à des paramètres tels que l'activité biologique et l'étendue de la zone drainée. L'emplacement des kamenitzas semble être étroitement guidé par les filons de calcite. Des filons qui se trouvent en relief par rapport au calcaire encaissant des dalles apparaissent au contraire en creux dans les kamenitzas. La dissolution et la fracturation des veines de calcite au fond d'une kamenitza peuvent éventuellement aboutir à l'infiltration de l'eau et interrompre le développement de cette kamenitza.

INTRODUCTION

One of the most interesting features of the limestone pavements of the Gait Barrows National Nature Reserve in north-west England is the presence of a large number of small, often saucer-shaped water-filled depressions caused by localised corrosion of the bare limestone. Such features are usually known by their Serbian name, kamenitza but other terms are also found in the literature (Table 1).

Table 25.1   Alternative terminology in the literature

Term	Author
clint pool	Sweeting (1966)
rock pool	Williams (1966)
solution basin	Sweeting (1973)
solution cup	Zotov (1941)
solution pan	Frye and Swineford (1947)
solution pit	Wentworth (1944)
Tinajitas	Udden (1925)

Kamenitzas have not attracted much detailed attention by Karstologists and there is a dearth of published material on their morphogenesis and water chemistry. Sweeting (1966) provides a brief account of kamenitzas in northern England and examined the water chemistry for a small sample. Williams (1966) in a more extensive study in western Ireland measured the calcium carbonate and pH of 118 rain-fed pools and plotted his results on a Trombe graph.

The present account describes the kamenitzas at Gait Barrows and reports on a recent water chemistry monitoring programme which attempted to elucidate the many factors controlling inter and intra-kamenitza variability.

STUDY AREA

Gait Barrows NNR (SD 481 769) is an exceptionally important area of limestone pavement and woodland located some 15 km north of Lancaster (Figure 25.1). Open pavements are developed on thickly bedded sparitic limestones which have been extensively scoured by Devensian ice from the Lake District (Figure 25.2).

In contrast to many pavements in northern England the pavements at Gait Barrows are poorly griked and rundkarren, indicative of a former soil cover, are uncommon.

Present-day climate is mild and oceanic with an annual rainfall at Gait Barrows of about 1100 mm.

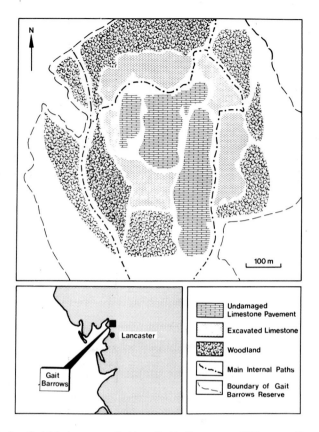

Figure 25.1   Outline map of the Gait Barrows NNR, north
Lancashire

THE SITING OF KAMENITZAS

The siting of kamenitzas at Gait Barrows is far from random and
almost without exception they are associated with mineral veins
that traverse the pavements.   The chemical composition of these
veins is as follows:

Calcite	85%
Dolomite	5-7%
Quartz	4-5%
Magnesite	3-4%
Rhodocrosite	trace

On the open pavements the mineral veins are readily observed as
raised brown ridges.   When the mineral veins are traced into a
kamenitza the ridge is almost always replaced by a groove where
the vein material has been destroyed (Figure 25.3).

Figure 25.2   Gait Barrows NNR – central, poorly griked
pavement

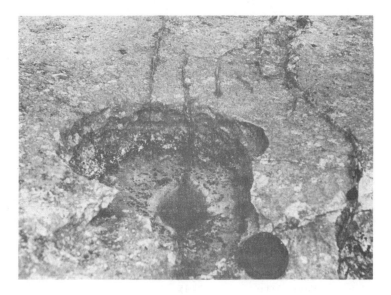

Figure 25.3   Raised mineral veins shown here become slots on
the floor of the kamenitza

Kamenitzas are, by definition, water collecting regions, whereas the raised mineral veins on the open pavement are water shedding regions and herein lies one of the fundamental problems of the kamenitzas at Gait Barrows. Evidently, on the pavement, the veins are more resistant to corrosion but this being the case it is difficult to see how a kamenitza might develop. In many cases, vein material does not just pass into the kamenitza in a haphazard manner but can be seen to bisect its plan geometry, which strongly suggests a centre of origin about the vein.

It might be supposed that the present relative vein-pavement relief was reversed when (and if) the Gait Barrows pavements were covered by post-glacial peat and/or soil. Subsequent soil erosion then exposed the veins as grooves which might collect water and so develop into kamenitzas. This supposition assumes that the vein material is less resistant to acid attack than the adjacent limestone but this is known not to be the case. A simple experiment, whereby a 3 litre ebonite cylinder was placed over a vein and glued down on to the limestone pavement, demonstrated this. It was half filled with 1M HCl which was drained and replaced every other day during the 36 days of the experiment (Figure 25.4). At the end of the experiment the cylinder was removed and it was observed that the limestone surface had been lowered by 13 mm. and the vein remained proud of the lowered surface.

Figure 25.4   Ebonite cylinder placed on vein and filled with HCl. The vein remained proud of the limestone surface

If the vein material is not less chemically resistant then perhaps it is mechanically weaker? A semi-quantitative assessment of the relative hardness of vein material as compared with the country rock was obtained by a Schmidt Rebound Hammer Type N (Day and Goudie, 1977). Notwithstanding the various site problems associated with the use of this instrument (Ireland, 1979) the results shown in Table 2 confirm the mechanical weakness of the veins as compared with the limestone.

Table 25.2   Schmidt Hammer rebound values for vein and pavement rock

	Rebound Value	R
	Vein	limestone
Mean	27.9	47.8
Standard Deviation (n = 30)	6.5	4.4

In the context of the north of England environment and recent geomorphological history only two processes seem capable of exploiting the mechanical weakness of the veins, namely, frost and glacial processes. Both frost damage and glacial scour might produce the necessary water collecting sites but to accept this view one would also have to accept that the pavements have remained essentially soil and vegetation free throughout the post-glacial period. Frost damage alone might be responsible after the erosion of the assumed soil cover (a point discussed later).

KAMENITZA MORPHOLOGY

Plan Form

The kamenitzas at Gait Barrows exhibit a wide variety of plan form but four broad categories may be distinguished:

i) circular: almost perfectly circular kamenitza exist but it is usual to find the wall breached by an overflow karren (Figure 25.5)

ii) linear: these are very common on the clints of the eastern pavement. They nearly always lie over a mineral vein. It is quite evident that these linear forms are the forerunners of some grikes (Figure 25.6)

iii) T-shaped: these have developed from a linear kamenitza whose veins run across the slope. The overflow waters have drained down the slope to complete the shape (Figure 25.7)

iv) irregular: where many mineral veins traverse the kamenitza irregular embayments develop positioned along the veins (Figure 25.8).

Figure 25.5   Almost circular pool filled with algae and sedges

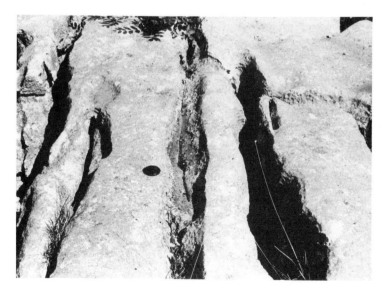

Figure 25.6   Dry linear kamenitza with central vein now
knotched

Figure 25.7   T-shaped kamenitza on the eastern pavement

Figure 25.8   Irregular kamenitza on the central pavement

Figure 25.9   Abandoned stepped kamenitzas on the central
               pavement

Although most kamenitzas at Gait Barrows are single forms there
are several examples of stepped kamenitzas (Figure 25.9).
Analogous forms have been described in granite by Dzulynski and
Kotarba (1979).

    Kamenitzas vary considerably in size. The largest, currently
active, forms at Gait Barrows are approximately 1 metre in diameter and there are abandoned kamenitzas which are twice this
size. Sweeting (1973) indicates the average diameters of
kamenitzas to be from a few centimetres to over three metres.
However, there must be a genuine difficulty in defining the
lower limit in exactly the same way that there is a difficulty
in delimiting the width of the smallest grike.

Floors and Walls

    The great majority of active kamenitzas have vertical, or
overhanging walls, which terminate in an angular junction with
the surrounding pavement. The walls are often roughly pitted
but there are few signs of the linear flutes as observed on the
walls of tinajitas by Frye and Swineford (1947).

    At Gait Barrows the floors of the kamenitzas are smooth
but not horizontal. Typically, the floors dip gently down to
a deep central pit or groove which is usually hidden by a fill
of organic debris which is easily excavated. Some representative
cross-profiles of kamenitzas are shown in Figure 25.10. It is
of interest to note that the cockling of the walls is a feature
of water filled kamenitzas and evidently obliterated once the
pool has drained.

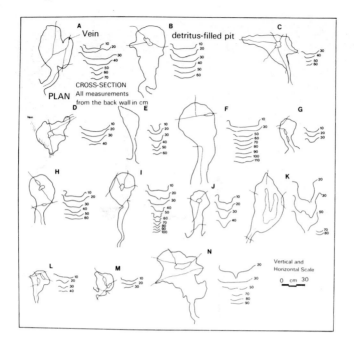

Figure 25.10   Typical cross-profiles and plan forms of
kamenitzas. All distances are from the backwall
of the kamenitza

Several abandoned kamenitzas have a gutter-like depression
at the base of the wall; it is not yet known how this feature
develops (Figure 25.11).

WATER CHEMISTRY: METHODS

In order to discover more about the corrosional activity in the
pool waters of the kamenitzas at Gait Barrows, a water sampling
programme was undertaken between 24th October, 1982 and 18th
July, 1983 when all the kamenitza pools dried up during a prolonged drought.

Eleven kamenitzas were chosen for detailed study (Figure
25.12). The pools investigated varied considerably in their
morphology and flora and are thought to represent the range of
kamenitza environments at Gait Barrows.

A plant list for the eleven kamenitzas was made on the 13th
July, 1983 and is shown in Table 3.

Figure 25.11   Abandoned kamenitza with well developed lateral
                gutter

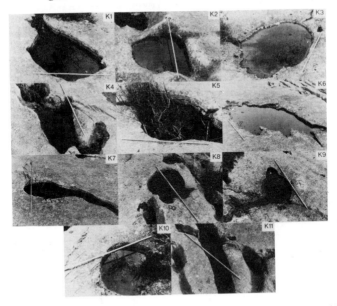

Figure 25.12   Photomosaic of kamenitzas chosen for detailed
                study. (scale = 1m)

Table 25.3   Plant list for K1-K11 (July 1983)

K1)   Small amount of dried algal mat.

K2)   Fine humic sediment.

K3   *Spirogyra* sp. *Juncus acutiflorus, Poa trivialis.*

K4   *Spirogyra* sp. *Juncus articulatus, Salix cinerea.*

K5   *Typha latifolia, Sorbus aucuparia, Succisa pratensis
        Juncus articulatus, Teucreum scorodonium Festuca ovina,
        Betula pubescens, Molinia caerulea* moss species -
        Hygrohypnum sp.

K6   Algal mat.

K7   *Epilobium parviflorum, Salix cinerea,* moss species -
        Hygrohypnum sp.

K8   -

K9   Algal mat.

K10   *Spirogyra* sp.

K11   *Juncus articulalus, Epilobium adenocaulon,* moss species
        - *Fissidens adianthoides.*

Approximately every week during the sampling period 180 ml.
samples were collected from the eleven pools (K1-K11) by
immersing a small glass beaker just below the surface of the
water.   Samples were stored in polythene bottles for transport
to a nearby laboratory at Leighton Moss Bird Sanctuary where
they were filtered through Whatman filter paper No. 541.
Filtered samples were analysed for pH and conductivity on research quality instruments within two hours of being sampled in
the field.   In addition, rain water samples were collected from
a glass funnel and jar placed on the central limestone pavement.

All water samples were subsequently examined in the laboratory at the Geography Department, Lancaster University.   Calcium plus magnesium were estimated with EDTA using Eriochrome
Black T as an indicator at pH 9.5 using Betz and Noll's buffer;
calcium alone was estimated with EDTA at pH 12.5 using Patton
and Reeder's indicator.

No attempt was made to take water samples at different
levels within a kamenitza pool.   Whilst this would have been
interesting it was felt that surface sampling would provide the
most consistent method given the great fluctuations in water
levels.   Likewise we have avoided any diurnal variability in
water properties due to plant activity by taking all samples
at mid-day.

WATER CHEMISTRY: MEASURES OF SATURATION

Because of the very limited amount of water sample available
from each kamenitza and the consequent lack of alkalinity measurements it was not possible to employ one of the usual methods
for the assessment of saturation with respect to $CaCO_3$ (Ford,
1971; Stenner, 1969). Instead, we have obtained approximate,
but nevertheless useful, measures of saturation based on the
pure calcite/CO_2/H_2O equilibrium system (Stenner, *op. cit.,*
Picknett *et. al.,* 1976). Impurities in natural waters such as
magnesium and sulphate are known to interfere with this system
but it is now thought by one of us (L.R.) that their individual
effects probably cancel each other out.

Two relationships have been established:

pH* - the equilibrium pH

Picknett (1973) has published concentrations for the
calcite/CO_2/H_2O system and these data, together with some additional measurements kindly made available by Picknett (pers.
comm.) have allowed us to compute the following regression equation relating pH to Total calcium (mM) and temperature (°C):

$$pH^* = 8.159 - 0.8115 \ \ln \text{calcium} - 0.01622 \ \text{temperature} \qquad (1)$$
$$ (0.013) \ (0.006) \qquad\qquad (0.0007)$$

where the figures in brackets are standard errors. R^2 for
equation (1) is 0.997 and is extremely satisfactory. We have
not used predictions from (1) in any rigorous way but the sign
and magnitude of pH-pH* are, in themselves, useful insights into
the activity of the kamenitza pools.

Ca* - the equilibrium calcium levels

In (1) the pH levels are dependent on both biological and
atmospheric sources of CO_2 and we can gain a little more insight
if we now calculate the equilibrium calcium levels where the
sole source of CO_2 is from the atmosphere.

We calculated Ca* as follows:

i) Picknett (1973) also published the concentrations
    of free CO_2 in the calcite/CO_2/H_2O system and these
    data together with additional figures supplied by
    Picknett (pers. comm.) have allowed us to calculate
    the equilibrium concentrations of free CO_2 in the
    pool waters relative to that in the atmosphere.
    This relative concentration (RC) is obtained as
    follows:

$$\text{Equilibrium } pCO_2 \text{ (water sample)} = \frac{\text{free } CO_2}{K_H}$$

where K_H is the Henry constant

and,

$$RC = \frac{\text{Equilibrium } pCO_2 \text{ (water sample)}}{\text{Atmospheric } pCO_2}$$

A small grid of RC values is shown in Table 4.

ii) When calcium levels are in equilibrium with the
     atmosphere RC = 1 and we can use the data in
     Table 4 to interpolate values of Ca* for this
     condition at any given temperature. Inter-
     polation was achieved by fitting a regression
     model to the data in Table 4. The best fit
     model was:

$$\ln(Ca*) = 4.470 + 0.3236 \ln RC - 0.02049T \qquad (2)$$
$$ (0.025) \quad (0.012) \quad (0.001)$$

where the figures in brackets are standard errors.
R^2 for equation (2) was 0.998. Since the
logarithm of 1 is zero, equation (2) simplifies
to:

$$\ln(Ca*) = 4.470 - 0.02049T \qquad (3)$$

Table 25.4 RC values for the calcite/CO_2/H_2O system

			Temperature (°C) (T)		
Ca*(10^{-5}M)	0	10	16	20	25
180	9.322	–	–	–	–
100	1.285	3.147	4.713	6.830	14.980
80	0.554	1.750	2.471	3.615	7.934
60	0.163	0.720	1.056	1.570	3.467
40	0.017	0.191	0.306	0.462	1.039

WATER CHEMISTRY: RESULTS

Table 5 shows pH and calcium level summaries for K1-K11 during
the sampling period. Both the mean and range of calcium levels
are broadly in accord with the findings of Williams (1966). He
reported an average calcium carbonate concentration of
66 x 10^{-5}M and an average pH of 7.8 although there is no information given by Williams as to the sampling date. None of our
calcium levels reach the 278 x 10^{-5}M measured by Sweeting (1966)
on the nearby Hutton Roof Crags. This figure would require a
dissolved CO_2 concentration of more than 70 times atmospheric
pCO_2 which seems rather high unless her water samples were obtained from the biologically active sludge at the base of a
pool.

Table 5 brings out well the floristic differences in the eleven samples. K5, with *Typha latifolia* and by far the greatest biomass is clearly distinguishable from K3, K4 and K10, all rich in *Spirogyra*. This alga is known to raise the pH of waters by its absorption of HCO_3^- ions and the excretion of OH^- ions. On the other hand, K5 with *Typha* has by far the largest biomass subject to seasonal decay and *Typha* itself has a not inconsiderable summer root stock which presumably loses CO_2 through respiration. We might also take note of the high calcium levels in K2 and K7 both of which have been observed to have tufaceous material adhering to the plants from time to time. Magnesium levels and the calcium/magnesium ratios for all pools were examined but were not revealing and will not be further described.

Table 25.5 Calcium and pH summary statistics for K1-11

	Calcium ($10^{-5}M$)			pH			
	min.	max.	mean	min.	max.	mean	sample size
K1	32.40	130.20	68.27	7.20	9.05	7.73	30
K2	44.60	179.00	75.17	7.35	9.63	8.17	31
K3	37.40	173.20	68.42	7.48	9.98	8.46	33
K4	24.00	130.40	56.26	7.25	10.30	8.78	34
K5	56.40	132.00	84.78	6.95	8.03	7.34	29
K6	37.60	145.60	78.24	7.26	9.73	8.15	33
K7	33.60	189.20	75.03	7.30	9.55	8.36	32
K8	49.40	163.00	85.23	7.42	10.02	8.31	30
K9	34.80	152.60	80.33	7.05	9.43	7.95	33
K10	37.60	144.00	65.96	7.19	9.60	8.44	33
K11	39.60	156.80	78.97	6.79	10.13	8.19	31
		grand mean =	74.24		grand mean =	8.17	

Seasonal drift in calcium and pH

Figures 13 and 14 show the seasonal drift in calcium and pH levels and they immediately reveal the complexities of the kamenitza system, although the trends in pH clearly mimic the general rise in pool temperature and reduction in rainfall (Figure 25.15).

An examination of Figure 25.13 suggests three groups of kamenitza with respect to calcium trends:

group 1: K1 - discernable drift. A kamenitza with small biomass.

group 2: K2, K3, K4, K7, K10 - no discernable seasonal drift and low variability. This group includes the spirogyra pools and

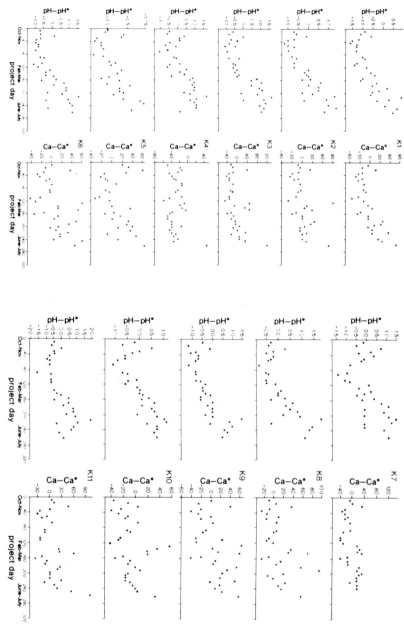

Figure 25.16 pH-pH* and Ca-Ca* trends for K1-K11

pools with large moss biomass. The occasional very high calcium levels are due to evaporation and freezing.

group 3: K5, K6, K8, K9, K11 - no seasonal drift and highly variable calcium levels.

Seasonal drift in pH is well marked in all eleven kamenitzas. Winter values are low reflecting biomass decomposition and regular flooding of the pools by rain, whilst summer values are higher reflecting evaporation, biomass growth and the selective activity of some plants.

Season drift in saturation levels

Figure 6 shows pairs of plots for the kamenitzas illustrating the trends in Ca-Ca* and pH-pH*. Before describing the results it is relevant to note what kinds of factors influence these relationships:

pH > pH*   plant activity using HCO_3^-

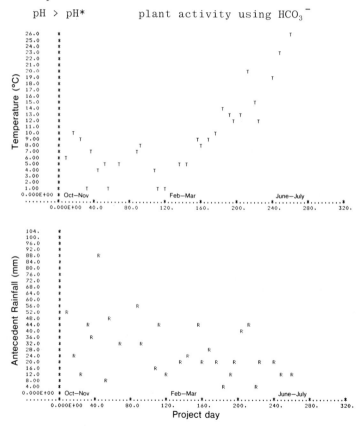

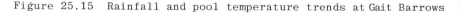

Figure 25.15   Rainfall and pool temperature trends at Gait Barrows

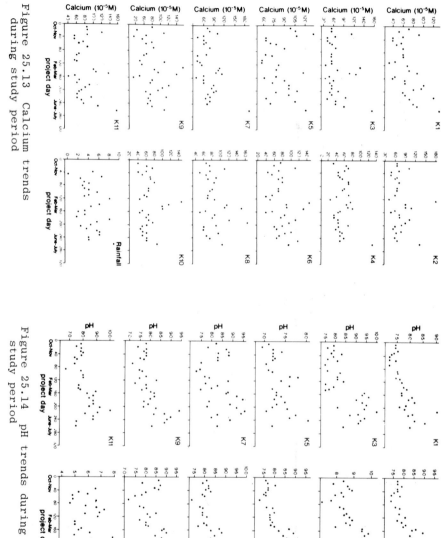

Figure 25.13 Calcium trends during study period

Figure 25.14 pH trends during study period

pH < pH*	plant decay, recent flooding lack of time to come to equilibrium
Ca > Ca*	evaporation; ice formation
Ca < Ca*	CO_2 removal, slow return to equilibrium when cold.

The correspondence, or otherwise, of these pairs of data serves to distinguish those pools where biological activity is of some importance from pools with little or no biomass. This is seen clearly in Figure 25.16 for K4 where the pH-pH* levels become positive from about project day 130 whilst its corresponding Ca-Ca* levels remain negative throughout, apart from day 261 when all pools underwent severe evaporation. In K4 the growth of *Spirogyra* effectively increases the pH above equilibrium and at the same time the removal of CO_2 effectively depresses the calcium levels. The same general picture holds for K3 and K10, the other pools containing *Spirogyra* (Figure 25.16).

Several pools exhibit very high values for Ca-Ca* on or shortly after project day 120 (12th February, 1983) and these reflect the concentration of liquor as a consequence of the development of a raft of ice over the pools. Indeed, several samples on day 128 could only be obtained by drilling a hole with a brace and bit through the ice and sampling the water with a 100 ml pipette.

K5 shows a particularly distinctive pair of plots (Figure 25.16). It is the only pool in the sample in which pH-pH* remains negative throughout the sampling period. This pool, as we have already indicated, has easily the greatest biomass of those sampled and the low pH values probably reflect the plant decay in what is in effect a thin peat accumulating in this the deepest pool of our sample.

Most kamenitzas show a winter dip in the pH-pH* observations which clearly reflects the seasonality of decay. This is well shown in K7 whose floor is carpeted with moss and algae.

THE DEVELOPMENT OF KAMENITZAS

Relatively little is known about the rates of kamenitza development. Sweeting (1966) on an experimental site in northern England observed the development of solution pits up to 3-5 cm deep in less than ten years. It should be noted however that these rates are exceptional and probably reflect the special nature of the site where peaty waters drained into a newly cleared limestone pavement from the adjacent moor.

Zotov (1941) speculated that solution cups developed on boulders one metre high in New Zealand would completely destroy the host rock in a few thousand years.

Some simple calculations allow an estimate to be made of the age of the kamenitzas at Gait Barrows:

i) Dimensions of kamenitza   radius   20 cm
                                         depth   10 cm
                                         volume = 12566cc

ii) Rainfall - present day estimate   = 1100 mm $yr.^{-1}$

iii) Average $CaCO_3$ content of pools   = 74 x 10^{-5}M

iv) Assumed specific gravity of rock   = 2.65

v) Volume of rock x specific gravity = 33300 gr to be dissolved.

vi) Volume of rainfall needed to dissolve (e) = 33300/0.074   = 450000 litres

vii) Annual volume of rain entering pool Π r^2 x 110 cm   = 138.23 litres

viii) Age = $\dfrac{450000}{138}$ = approx. <u>3260</u> years.

In the above calculations several simplistic assumptions were made. For example it is known that the country rock is not pure $CaCO_3$ and that occasionally carbonate sediment is blown from the kamenitzas. But these errors are more than balanced by the fact that in the above calculations we have assumed that all the rainfall leaves the kamenitza carrying its share of $CaCO_3$. This is clearly not the case; kamenitzas do flood during prolonged heavy rainfall but for much of the time they act as evaporating pans. If the denominator in (h) is reduced by half, thus allowing for some evaporation, the estimated age doubles to some 6000 years: very probably this reduction should be more.

It is self-evident that a kamenitza will only enlarge if the dissolved limestone is removed, either by flooding, leakage or by wind during dry periods. However, it seems not unreasonable to suppose that, should the kamenitza pool dry out, some of the carbonate will be precipitated into the pores and surface irregularities on the floor of the pool. This simple supposition has the following important consequence. Whereas corrosion of the walls of a kamenitza attacks fresh limestone, basal corrosion will, for at least part of the time, attack the precipitated $CaCO_3$. As a result kamenitzas will widen more quickly than they deepen.

In effect, the repeated precipitation of carbonate on the floor of the kamenitza might case-harden the limestone. For conservation reasons it has not yet been possible to make a thin-section of the floor rock at Gait Barrows but it was possible during the July 1983 drought to use the Schmidt hammer to see if the floors are harder than the surrounding pavements (Ireland, 1979). The results are shown in Table 6. Both R values are significantly higher than the R value for the limestone pavement (Table 2). For example, using the worst case, K3, a difference of means t-test gave t_{calc}=2.507 with 58 degrees

Table 25.6 Schmidt Hammer rebound values for the floors
of K3 and K4 measured during the July 1983 drought

	Rebound Value R	
	K3 (floor)	K7 (floor)
Mean	50.40	52.13
Standard Deviation (n = 30)	2.54	2.28

of freedom. These preliminary findings not only point to an explanation for the basic geometry of kamenitzas but also to the
important fact that, to some extent, $CaCO_3$ is recycled, which
itself would slow down the rate of kamenitza growth and thus
adding weight to the notion that they are 'old' features.

It would be wrong, however, to think that kamenitzas only
develop by corrosion involving standing water in the pools.
Figure 25.17 shows the angular debris collected from K9. This
debris was produced by frost and ice action but we do not know
yet what the annual production is. There is also some field
evidence that kamenitzas are modified by overland flow.
Figure 25.18 shows an abandoned kamenitza whose walls are fluted
by trittkarren-like recesses. The form of these recesses is
almost indistinguishable from those recently described by Vincent
in northern Norway (Vincent, 1983).

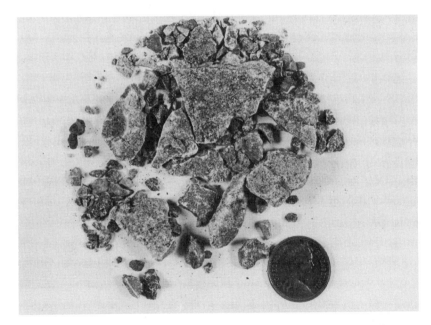

Figure 25.17 Angular debris in K9 resulting from frost/ice damage

Figure 25.18   Trittkarren-like flutings on wall of abandoned
               kamenitza

At Gait Barrows the development of kamenitzas is abruptly
terminated when the vein material at their bases is destroyed
and standing water no longer collects. As the basal slot widens,
organic accumulations are washed away and the kamenitzas often
take on a characteristic key-hole form (Figure 25.19).

In our earlier discussion on the siting of kamenitzas we
suggested that vein material was mechanically much weaker than
the country rock but chemically more resistant, and it might be
wondered why the vein is knotched within the confines of the
kamenitza. There are no certain answers to this question. There
is no doubt that the development of ice during the winter is an
effective agency within the kamenitza and it seems reasonable to
suppose that the weaker vein material will be more effectively
comminuted than the limestone. Comminution of the vein will
lead to a topographical low which will cause water to lie longest
over the vein. Organic debris decaying in this water will enhance and prolong solution activity in this zone. Thus once the
hollow is created the whole cycle of events is one of positive
feedback.

An alternative explanation for the grooved vein zone within
the kamenitzas relies on the presence of a weak junction between
the vein and the country rock which might be exploited. There
is no evidence for such a weakness when the junction is examined
in thin section. Furthermore, the whole width of a vein entering
a kamenitza becomes a groove which tends to suggest that the
answer to the problem lies in the vein material itself and not
its junctions. Interestingly enough a similar situation appears
to occur in the Nahanni Plateau Karst, Canada where Brook and

Figure 25.19   Abandoned kamenitza with classic key-hole shape

Ford (1977, Figure 1) illustrate elliptical solution pits developed in microfractures filled with secondary calcite; the
fractures are slightly raised above the general surface level.
Brook and Ford go on to suggest that in this area, grikes are
formed by the coalescence of strings of solution pits.   There
is no doubt that many grikes at Gait Barrows have been formed
in a similar manner.

CONCLUSIONS

Having examined the kamenitzas at Gait Barrows for several years
our overriding impression is that these seemingly simple karst
features are, in fact, extremely complex.

It has been argued that the kamenitzas at Gait Barrows are
relatively old and may have been initiated soon after the
Devensian ice wasted from the area some 12 000 years ago.   And,
indeed, that their siting and initiation might have been due
to the scouring of vein material by ice thus giving rise to the
initial hollow sited over a vein.

Measurements of the water chemistry of eleven kamenitzas
over a ten month period show a complex environment influenced
by plant growth, type of plant, evaporation, ice formation and
other factors.   It would seem that regular monitoring of individual kamenitzas is the only way to reveal their fascinating
story.

REFERENCES

Brook, G.A. and Ford, D.C. 1977. The sequential development of karst landforms in the Nahanni region of northern Canada and a remarkable size hierarchy. *Proc. 7th Intern. Speleol. Congress,* Sheffield, 77-81.

Day, M.J., and Goudie, A.S. 1977. Field assessment of rock hardness using the Schmidt Test Hammer. *Brit. Geomorph. Res. Grp., Techn. Bull.,* **18**, 19-29.

Dzulynski, S.T., and Kotarba, A. 1979. Solution pans and their bearing on the development of pediments and tors in granite. *Z. Geomorph.,* **23**, 172-191.

Ford, D.C. 1971. Characteristics of limestone solution in the Southern Rock Mountains and Selkirk Mountains, Alberta and British Columbia. *Can. Journ. of Earth Sci.,* **8**, 585-609.

Frye, J.C., and Swineford, A. 1947. Solution features on Cretaceous sandstone in central Kansas. *Amer. J. Sci.,* **245**, 366-379.

Ireland, P. 1979. Geomorphological variations of 'case-hardening' in Puerto Rico. *Z. Geomorph. Suppl.-Bd.,* **32**, 9-20.

Picknett, R.G. 1973. Saturated calcite solutions from 10 to 40°C: a theoretical study evaluating the solubility product and other constants. *Trans. Cave Res. Grp. G.B.,* **15**, 67-80.

Picknett, R.G., Bray, L.G. and Stenner, R.D. 1976. The Chemistry of cave waters. Ch. 7 In: *The Science of Speleology,* eds Ford, T.D. & Cullingford, C.H.D. (Academic Press, London), 593pp.

Stenner, R.D. 1969. The measurement of the aggressiveness of water towards calcium carbonate. *Trans. Cave Res. Grp., G.B.,* **11**, 175-200.

Sweeting, M.M. 1966. The weathering of limestones. Ch. 6 In: *Essays in Geomorphology,* ed Dury, G.H. (Heineman, London), 404pp.

Sweeting, M.M. 1973. *Karst landforms.* (Columbia, New York), 362pp.

Udden, J.A. 1925. Etched potholes. *Univ. of Texas, Bull.,* **52**, 61-78.

Vincent, P.J. 1983. The morphology and morphometry of some arctic trittkarren. *Z. Geomorph.,* **27**, 205-222.

Wentworth, C.K. 1944. Potholes, pits and pans: subaerial and marine. *J. Geol.,* **52**, 117-130.

Williams, P.W. 1966. Limestone pavements with special reference to western Ireland. *Inst. Brit. Geogr. Trans.,* **40**, 155-172.

Zotov, V.D. 1941. Pot-holing of limestone by development of solution cups. *J. Geomorph.,* **4**, 71-73.

26

Some aspects of the morphometry of grikes: a mixture model approach

L. Rose and P. Vincent

SUMMARY

Morphometric studies of karst landforms have rarely paid attention
to the fact that the landforms may comprise a mixture of populations.
Such populations arise quite naturally when landform development
occurs in pulses. In the case of grikes it is hypothesised that
glacial truncation of the pre-glacial surfaces was imperfect. Where
truncation was partial, an older set of grikes was preserved and
have widened in post-glacial times. Where truncation was complete,
grike initiation took place entirely during the post-glacial period.
On any one stretch of pavement the two populations of grikes may be
detected by the careful analysis of the morphometric data. In the
present study, histograms of grike width data from several pavements
in the Morecambe Bay karst area have been examined using a statistical algorithm which fits mixtures of Normal distributions to the
data. The applicability of this mixture modelling approach to
morphometric studies in general is briefly discussed and it is suggested that it be adopted when it is suspected that the karst landforms are the product of more than one phase of development.

RÉSUMÉ

Les études morphométriques appliquées au relief calcaire n'ont guère
prêté attention au fait que le modelé se compose d'un mélange de
données statistiques différentes. Ces données sont produites
naturellement quand le développement du relief a lieu en plusieurs
phases. En ce qui concerne les lapiés on pense que l'érosion
glaciaire des surfaces préglaciaires a été inégale. Lorsque les
surfaces étaient érodées partiellement on trouve d'anciens
lapiés qui ont été élargis dans la période post-glaciaire. Lorsque
les roches ont été complètement rabotées, les lapiés ont été en-
taillés au cours du post-glaciaire. Pour chaque endroit ces deux
types de lapiés peuvent être observés selon l'analyse des résultats
morphométriques. On a examiné des histogrammes de largeurs des
lapiés pour plusieurs tables calcaires de la région karstique de
Morecombe Bay. On a utilisé une formule statistique qui permet
de déterminer si ils ont des distributions statistiques normales.
L'application générale de cette méthode aux études morphométriques
est discutée. On suggère l'utilisation de cette méthode quand on
pense que le relief calcaire a été développé au cours de périodes
différentes.

INTRODUCTION

By far and away the best known, and, in many ways the most
spectacular, karst landforms in the north-west of England are
the limestone pavements. But in spite of having received a good
deal of attention over the last hundred years or so (Sweeting,
1973) many aspects of these roughly horizontal exposures of
limestone bedrock are still puzzling.

It is now a commonly held view that limestone pavements are
polygenetic and the term glaciokarstic has been aptly applied.
Extensive glacial scour paved the way for solutional processes
which have produced a variety of karren forms etched into the
once more or less planar surfaces. Precisely how effective
glacial erosion has been in the obliteration of pre-glacial
features is a matter of much speculation and a survey of the
available literature shows a wide range of opinion.

In this paper we shall examine one simple and, relatively
easily measured, aspect of pavement morphometry, grike width,
which we hope may shed some light on the problem of form inher-
itence for the pavement areas of north-west England. The morphometric methods we shall employ are generally applicable to
all karst morphometric problems.

MODELS OF PAVEMENT DEVELOPMENT

There is no commonly held view of the geomorphological development of the limestone pavements in north-west England. Without
doubt the major point of contention is the degree to which the
pavement areas were scoured by Devensian ice which inundated
the north of England from about 26 000 years B.P. to 14 000 B.P.

Clayton's views on the development of limestone pavements
(Clayton, 1981) are illustrated in Figure 26.1. In his paper
he states (p. 407):

> Their restriction to the most strongly (and most
> recently) glaciated parts of the British Isles
> suggests a glacial origin, although when writing
> in 1966 I was inclined to limit the work of ice
> to the clearing, or exhumation, of a surface
> created by pre-glacial subsurface weathering.
> This does not go far enough and there is now wide
> agreement that pavements represent quite deep
> stripping of weathered limestone layers down to
> relatively solid and little weathered bedding
> planes.

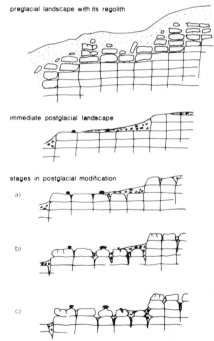

Figure 26.1 Development of limestone pavements in northern
England according to Clayton (1981)

In fact it is quite difficult to find much evidence of the wide agreement which Clayton alludes to. Sweeting (1973, p. 87) goes some way towards Clayton's views when she cites the fact that in Yorkshire and western Ireland the pavement, protected beneath glacial erratics, has unopened joints whereas away from such protection the joints are widened into grikes. The problem with this sort of evidence is that it is very selective. In many areas of the Morecambe Bay karst, north-west England we can equally observe erratics over widened joints which might, therefore, pre-date the glaciation. But there are other problems associated with Clayton's model.

In Figure 26.1 we observe that Clayton indicates a weathered regolith, presumably developed during the Ipswichian inter-glacial period. There is no geomorphological or pedological evidence for such a cover and it is purely speculative. Indeed, if we are permitted to invoke the Law of Uniformitarianism then it is difficult to see why the Ipswichian karst landscape should be so very different from the present Flandrian. Indeed, we know from the presence of thermophilous plant species that the Ipswichian interglacial was probably several degrees centigrade warmer than the present interglacial and it is difficult to see why Clayton's pre-glacial landscape is depicted with few grikes when one would expect grikes deeper than those we can currently observe. We do not know what Clayton intends by the use of the term regolith. He can't, presumably, mean material derived by *in situ* weathering alone. If this were the case there would have to have been an enormous amount of weathering given the relative purity of the limestones in northern England.

At the other extreme we have the views of Pigott (1965). His central thesis is that grikes developed during interglacial times under a deeply weathered mantle. In Devensian times glacial scour to different depths would produce pavements with characteristics dependent on the depth of scour (Figure 26.2). This thesis has much to commend it. On the one hand Pigott re-cognises the importance of variable glacial scour and on the other provides a strong argument why some grikes can be relic. But it is not actually clear whether or not Pigott supports the idea that some grikes can be post-glacial.

Goldie (1981) has modified the Pigott model so as to include both thickness of the pre-glacial regolith cover and the degree of scour, her point being that small amounts of scour might plane-smooth a pavement covered by little or no regolith but not a pavement covered by thick debris. Goldie's suggestion seems eminently reasonable at the conceptual level but it has little basis factually. It is not clear what she implies by 'debris' in her model (Figure 26.3) but any unconsolidated material must surely have been swept away by ice which was several thousand feet thick in the north of England during the Devensian glac-iation.

Goldie's model of pavement development shows no widening or production of grikes post-glacially which is puzzling. She states (Goldie, 1981, p. 209) 'but if 49 cm of solution can take place in 12 000 years then a grike could be as wide as 98 cm

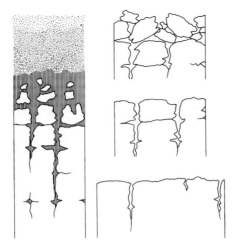

Figure 26.2   Three types of limestone pavement (right) which
would be derived from a deeply weathered limestone
profile (left) by planing down to three different
levels, according to Pigott (1965). Dots represent
a mixture of loess and solution residue, vertical
bars represent yellow clay

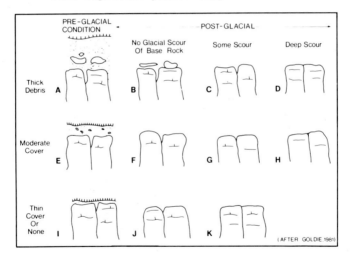

Figure 26.3   Pre-glacial and glacial factors influencing
pavements according to Goldie (1981)

without dating from before the Last Glaciation'. But if pavements can be affected this much post-glacially it is a wonder that one can supposedly deduce the nature of the pre-glacial environment! The 49 cm of solution Goldie refers to relates to the pedestal height of perched blocks which are found at many sites in northern England. It is doubtful whether we can apply estimates of surface lowering to grike width development; the two environments are very dissimilar. And, incidentally, there is no evidence, in the north of England that the Pennines were deglaciated some 12 000 years ago. Such estimates are based on extrapolation from areas such as the Lake District where ice certainly lingered longer.

We believe the most satisfactory model for the development of limestone pavements is that of Williams (1966). Unlike Clayton, he acknowledges the survival of pre-glacial grikes and states (p. 168): 'in the Ingleborough district where grikes are commonly deeper and wider than in western Ireland a high percentage may date from before the last glaciation'. Although his diagram of pavement development (Figure 26.4) doesn't really make clear the point that both relic and post-Devensian grikes are modified post-glacially it is clear, to us at least, that William's model is the only one to fit the observable field conditions in the north of England.

Figure 26.4
Suggested stages for the development of limestone pavements according to Williams (1966)

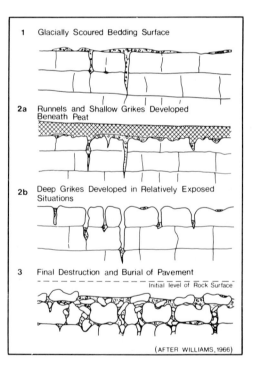

1   Glacially Scoured Bedding Surface

2a   Runnels and Shallow Grikes Developed Beneath Peat

2b   Deep Grikes Developed in Relatively Exposed Situations

3   Final Destruction and Burial of Pavement

Initial level of Rock Surface

(AFTER WILLIAMS, 1966)

At some sites in western Ireland Williams (1966) also noticed a strong spatial autocorrelation in grike widths, the grikes becoming deeper away from the marginal drift cover on the pavement. If the drift dates from the Last Glaciation then the modification must be post-glacial. His point here being that the drift cover in some way protects the glacially scoured pavement. However it is highly conjectural to depict the pavement surface under the retreating drift cover as ungriked. Indeed, Jones (1965) comes to precisely the opposite conclusion and states (p. 425), 'A traverse from the intermediate regions of a pavement towards drift cover reveals a different development. The grikes and channels grow wider and wider yet the rock surface is fresh and not decayed ... These observations provide some evidence that the most complete solution occurs near the drift-pavement boundary. It can be concluded that active channelling and grike formation have been taking place beneath the drift cover'.

Clearly, the antithetical conclusions reached by Williams and Jones are in large measure due to the nature of the drift cover and whether or not it is permeable to CO_2. But it is also true to say that neither author takes into account the possible variation in the pre-glacial condition of the land surface. Even receding drift covers of calcareous till would reveal grikes if they were not scoured away by the ice.

EVIDENCE FOR PRE-DEVENSIAN KARST LANDSCAPE IN NORTH-WEST ENGLAND

There is now a large body of evidence to support the view that there was not wholesale stripping of the karst landscape by Devensian ice. At several sites on the Silverdale Peninsula, Morecambe Bay, there are large dolines, some exceeding 100 m in diameter. Given present solution rates it is inconceivable that these features formed post-glacially. Excellent examples of large pre-glacial dolines are to be found on Warton Crag (SD 493730).

On the northern coast of Morecambe Bay Hodgson (1867) describes a quarry section near Ulverston (SD 295783) in which a griked limestone surface is capped with up to 5 m of till, the grikes themselves being filled with stone-free tenacious clay. It is difficult to imagine grikes forming under such a depth of till and the stone-free clay in contact with the limestone could well be the same type of weathering deposit as that described by Pigott in Derbyshire (Pigott, 1965).

Curiously enough, as far as we can tell nobody in the published literature has used the evidence for a pre-glacial karst provided by glacial erratics. At Underlaid Wood (SD 484785), some 25 km north of Lancaster, there are several hundred Silurian gritstone erratics practically all of which lie in the grikes. This is such a non-random pattern that one can only reasonably conclude that the erratics were deposited into, or onto, the already opened grikes as the Devensian ice wasted.

Figure 26.5 Silurian erratic resting in grike, Underlaid Wood

(Figure 26.5). The griked surface of the pavement would have
concentrated both sub-glacial and pro-glacial meltwaters which
would have drained into the pavement, thus concentrating erratics
in the grikes. There is no likelihood whatsoever that the
erratics could have been pushed into the grikes by man or animals;
the upper surfaces of the erratics are covered with lichen,
whilst the undersurfaces are lichen-free, supporting the view
that these stones have been undisturbed for a long time.

Waltham and Harmon (1977) have also shown from isotopically
dated stalagmites that many of the valleys in north-west England
were cut very nearly to their present thalweg by Anglian times
at the latest. This finding implies that Wolstonian and Devensian ice did little to modify valley form and, since glacial
erosion is concentrated in valleys rather than on watersheds,
there is every reason to believe that Devensian ice was much
less effective in stripping limestone pavements than is sometimes
thought.

GRIKE MORPHOMETRY: THE PRESENT STUDY

In order to decide whether or not there is any evidence for two grike sets, a relic and a post-glacial set, on the pavements of the Morecambe Bay area, we decided to concentrate on one aspect of the morphometry which can be reasonably objectively measured, namely, grike width.

Without care, measuring and indeed defining grike width can be an extremely arbitrary process and in order to remove as much subjectivity as possible from the measurement process a large pair of metal calipers was constructed (Figure 26.6). This instrument used as its reference plane the points of contact of the long arm of the calipers and the pavement surface. Grike width was recorded as the distance between the two short arms which extended 15 cm from their supporting arm. This procedure defines a grike width, but of course not *the* grike width which depends entirely on where one chooses to measure it. Our procedure overcomes the problems associated with defining grike width in those grikes whose junctions with the pavement surface are gently flared.

Three pavement areas were chosen for study and at each site a random sample of widths was obtained by a simple random walk procedure. Two of the pavements are located on the Silverdale Peninsula, Morecambe Bay, at Longtail Wood (SD 484798) and Underlaid Wood (SD 484785). The third, at Holme Park Fell, lies some 10 km to the east at a slightly higher altitude (136 m O.D.) at SD (529787). The Holme Park Fell pavement is described by Goldie (1981). General views of these three pavements are shown in Figures 26.7, 26.8 and 26.9.

Figure 26.6 Large calipers for grike width measurements

Figure 26.7   General view of Holme Park Fell Pavement, north-west England (Tony Aldridge)

Figure 26.8   General view of Underlaid Wood Pavement, north-west England

Figure 26.9   General view of Longtail Wood Pavement, north-west
England

GRIKE WIDTH MEASUREMENTS AND NORMAL MIXTURE MODELS

The notion that karst landforms may be a mixture of two or more
populations is not new. Drake and Ford (1972), for example,
examined the spatial pattern of two generations of sinkholes
and Kemmerly (1982) has described two lognormal populations of
dolines distinguished by their density. Both of these examples
have the two populations separated spatially but in the present
study we shall try and resolve the components when they are contained in one area, as on a pavement.

In order to separate grike widths into two populations we
first have to define some suitable probability distribution for
the populations. In the first instance it seems reasonable to
suppose that each is normally distributed. That is to say we
hypothesise that we might have an essentially relic population
of grikes whose widths are $\sim N(\mu, \sigma^2)$ and a post-glacial population
of grikes whose widths are also $\sim N(\mu, \sigma^2)$. It is not necessarily
true that two distributions overlap and indeed, it is for this
reason that we need to use statistical methods to differentiate
them.

There are several numerical algorithms available for the
estimation of the parameters of mixtures of Normal distributions
(Everitt and Hand, 1981) and we have used the procedure called
the EM algorithm (Aitkin and Tunnicliffe Wilson, 1980). This
algorithm provides maximum likelihood estimates of the populations

means and variances, $\hat{\mu}_i$ and $\hat{\sigma}_i^2$ and also the proportions in the mixture, $\hat{p}_i$. The essential nature of the algorithm is the alternation of Expectation and Maximization steps and the procedure converges rapidly. Mundry (1972) and Clark (1976) provide useful reviews of the statistics of multimodal distributions within an earth science framework.

Of course it is possible to fit Normal distributions to any sort of data and we need to know how good a fit we have achieved. Formal goodness-of-fit statistics remain a problem with mixture models. The usual likelihood ratio tests are generally invalid for mixture models but may be a rough and ready guide. In such tests differences in -2 log L (where L is the likelihood) between models are approximately χ^2 on the appropriate degrees of freedom depending on the numbers of parameters estimated. Two other useful approaches to the goodness-of-fit problem can be adopted. Having fitted, say, a two-component Normal mixture we can do a conventional χ^2 goodness-of-fit between the observed grike width frequencies and those predicted with a mixture model. For this test we have n-k-1 degrees of freedom where k is the number of estimated parameters, i.e. $\hat{\mu}_1$, $\hat{\mu}_2$, $\hat{\sigma}_1^2$, $\hat{\sigma}_2^2$ and $\hat{p}$. If the calculated χ^2 value is larger than the tabulated value we reject the model.

The second approach to the detection of mixtures is to employ some sort of graphical plot. Just as a cumulative Normal distribution plots as a straight line on arithmetic probability paper then plots have been devised that give characteristic output if a mixture is present. One such plot is that described by Fowlkes (1979). Fowlkes shows that if the standardized sample quantiles, Q_i, are plotted against the quantities $\Phi(z_i)-P_i$, Normal mixture distributions will plot as cyclical patterns with maximum departure from $\Phi(z_i)-P_i=0$ occurring for central values of Q. $\Phi(z_i)$ is the integral under the Standard Normal distribution,

$$\Phi(z) = \int_{-\infty}^{z} \frac{1}{\sqrt{2\pi}} \exp(-\tfrac{1}{2}u^2)\,du$$

and P_i defines the cumulative probability of the expected Normal Order Statistic and is,

$$P_i = (i-\tfrac{1}{2})/N$$

where N is the number of observations.

RESULTS

Histograms of the grike width measurements for the three pavements are shown in Figure 26.10 together with superimposed curves representing the predicted frequencies from a two-component Normal mixture analysis using the EM algorithm. Simple summary statistics and the parameter estimates from the two-component model are shown in Table 26.1 together with χ^2 goodness-of-fit values and estimates of -2 log L.

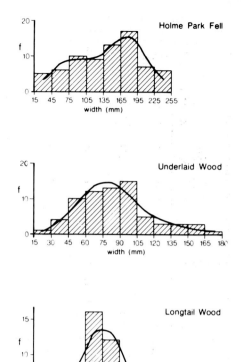

Figure 26.10 Histograms and fitted two-component Normal mixtures for three pavements in north-west England

Our single component mean estimate for Holme Park Fell broadly agrees with Goldie's findings ($\hat{\mu}$ = 130 mm) but our estimate of 3422 mm for σ^2 is more than twice as large as Goldie's measurement ($_{\hat{\sigma}}{}^2$ = 1600 mm).

A single Normal distribution does not fit any of the measured data well as is shown by the large χ^2 values. All three sets of data show a drop in -2 log L between the one and two component models which would be significant on 3 df if this test were appropriate. The Fowlkes plots for the three sets of data are shown in Figure 26.11 and there is clear evidence for two components for Holme Park Fell and Underlaid Wood but not Longtail Wood. A χ^2 goodness-of-fit test indicates that we should reject the two component Normal model for Longtail Wood ($\chi^2{}_{1,0.05}$ = 3.84) but accept it as a reasonable portrayal of the data for the Holme Park Fell and Underlaid Wood sites. All in all, there is clear evidence for a mixture of grike widths at two sites and it is tempting to ascribe the wide population to be relic (with post-glacial modification) and the narrower

509

Table 26.1 Statistical summaries for one and two component Normal mixture models for grike width data (mm)

	1 Component Normal				2 Component Normal Mixture								
	$\hat{\mu}$	$\hat{\sigma}^2$	-2 log L	χ^2	$\hat{\mu}_1$	$\hat{\mu}_2$	$\hat{\sigma}_1^2$	$\hat{\sigma}_2^2$	$\hat{p}_1$	$\hat{p}_2$	-2 log L	χ^2
HOLME PARK FELL n = 73	142.6	3422.0	20012	4.33 (df=1)	72.0	171.7	914.1	1559.0	0.29	0.71	19817	1.84 (df=1)
LONGTAIL WOOD n = 51	164.7	903.3	15924	9.23 (df=1)	152.4	180.1	885.8	500.3	0.55	0.44	15900	3.94 (df=1)
UNDERLAID WOOD n = 70	86.1	1028.0	8332	6.69 (df=2)	71.9	109.0	460.4	1098	0.62	0.38	8252	2.84 (df=1)

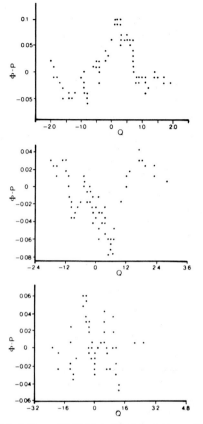

Figure 26.11 Fowlkes plots
for grike width data

population to be post-glacial in age. Clearly there are grikes
lying in a middle width range about which we can say very little;
they have an equal probability of belonging to either set.

Both Holme Park Fell and Underlaid Wood have a component
mean, $\hat{\mu}_1$, of about 72 mm which we might reasonably interpret as
the mean grike width of the post-glacial set. The means, $\hat{\mu}_2$,
of the second components are very different. Notwithstanding
all sorts of site differences one possible reason for the
narrower mean grike widths at Underlaid Wood ($\hat{\mu}_2$ = 109 mm) is
more extensive glacial scouring and, therefore, truncation to
a lower level. Even if the difference in altitude did not
significantly affect ice scour (Underlaid Wood is at 35 m O.D.
compared with 136 m O.D. for Holme Park Fell) then it might well
have had an effect on the length of time each site was scoured.

If our random samples of grike widths are representative
we can also make one or two interesting points about the estimated mixing proportions, $\hat{p}_i$. At Holme Park Fell we estimate
29 per cent of the grikes to belong to the post-glacial set
whilst at Underlaid Wood some 62 per cent belong to this

511

component. These data support the idea that there was less scouring by ice at Holme Park Fell, and, therefore, fewer grikes stripped away whose joint locations could have opened up again in the post-glacial period.

It is difficult to make much of the Longtail Wood data as we can't satisfy ourselves that there are two components in the data. We might recall the fact though that if a pavement has developed its complete complement of grikes, whatever that may be, and if it is partially stripped by ice, there will not be a second set of grikes developed post-glacially. In other words one population does not automatically imply a post-glacial set. This might be the case at Longtail Wood which has the largest grikes ($\hat{\mu}$ = 164 mm) of those measured.

CONCLUSIONS

In the above analyses we have shown that there is good evidence at two pavement sites in the Morecambe Bay karst for two components of grike widths. By analysing small individual pavements we have excluded the effects of lithology (Sweeting and Sweeting, 1969; Goldie, 1981) and it is reasonable to conclude that the two Normal components relate to two distinct phases of pavement development (Figure 26.12). In this respect our results confirm the model of pavement development suggested by Williams.

Pre-Glacial Grike System

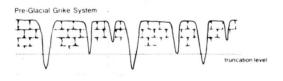

truncation level

Partial Truncation by Glacier

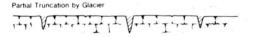

Post-Glacial Grike Systems

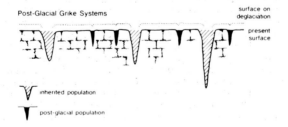

surface on deglaciation

present surface

inherited population

post-glacial population

Figure 26.12   Diagrammatic model to show the development of a two-component Normal mixture of grike widths

At Underlaid Wood, Silurian erratics in grikes are common
and in one small area we have logged 88 erratics in only 162
linear metres of grike. The average width of the grike at the
erratic is 126 mm which must be the very upper limit to grike
widening in the post-glacial. If the grikes were to have
opened much more than this all the erratics would have fallen
to the floors of the grikes. But in order to capture the
erratics in the first place some of the grikes at Underlaid
Wood, the erratic-containing grikes, must have been open to
some extent already. This argument supports our view that 72 mm
or so is a good approximation for the post-glacial opening of
grikes at Holme Park Fell and Underlaid Wood, and very probably
for most of the pavements of the Morecambe Bay karst.

REFERENCES

Aitkin, M. and Tunnicliffe Wilson, G. 1980. Mixture models,
outliers and the EM algorithm. *Techometrics,* **22**, 325-331.

Clayton, K. 1981. Explanatory description of the landforms of
the Malham area. *Field Studies,* **5**, 389-423.

Clark, M.W. 1976. Some methods for statistical analyses of
multimodal distributions and their application to grain-
size data. *Mathematical Geology,* **8**, 267-282.

Drake, J.J. and Ford, D.C. 1972. The analysis of growth patterns
of two-generation populations: the example of karst sinkholes. *Canadian Geographer,* **16**, 381-384.

Everitt, B.S. and Hand, D.J. 1981. *Finite Mixture Distributions.*
(Chapman & Hall, London).

Fowlkes, F.B. 1979. Some methods for studying the mixture of
two Normal (Lognormal) distributions. *J. American Statistical Assoc.,* **74**, 561-575.

Goldie, H.S. 1981. Morphometry of the limestone pavements of
Farleton Knott, (Cumbria, England). *Trans. Brit. Cave Research Assoc.,* **8**, 207-224.

Hodgson, E. 1867. The moulded limestones of Furness. *Geological
Magazine,* **4**, 401-406.

Jones, R.L. 1965. Aspects of the biological weathering of
limestone pavement. *Proc. Geol. Assoc.,* **76**, 421-433.

Kemmerly, P.R. 1982. Spatial analysis of a karst depression
population: clues to genesis. *Geol. Soc. American Bull.,*
93, 1078-1086.

Mundry, E. 1972. On the resolution of mixed frequency distributions into Normal components. *Mathematical Geology,* **4**,
55-60.

Pigott, C.D. 1965. The structure of limestone surfaces in
Derbyshire. *Geogr. J.,* 131, 41-44.

Sweeting, M.M. 1973. *Karst Landforms.* (Columbia Univ. Press,
New York).

Sweeting, M.M. and Sweeting, G.S. 1969. Some aspects of the Carboniferous limestone in relation to its landforms with special reference to N.W. Yorkshire and County Clare. *Études et Travaux de Mediterranée. Revue Géographique Des Pays Mediterranéens,* **7**, 201-209.

Waltham, A.C. and Harmon, R.S. 1977. Chronology of Cave development in the Yorkshire Dales, England. *Proc. 7th International Speleological Congress, Sheffield,* 423-425.

Williams, P.W. 1966. Limestone pavements with special reference to western Ireland. *Inst. Brit. Geogr. Trans.,* **40**, 155-171.

27

Human influence on landforms:
the case of limestone pavements

H.S. Goldie

SUMMARY

The limestone pavements of the British Isles provide an interesting
example of human activity as an agent of geomorphological change.
This paper looks at the history of human influences on limestone
pavements, especially in northwestern England, examines recent
damage, and discusses the actions being taken to protect these
fascinating and beautiful landforms. The activities which have
affected the pavements have been varied, and the importance of
any individual activity has changed over time. In recent decades
the pressures have increased and conservation bodies have become
concerned with the problem in order to protect pavement sites from
further damage. Very few pavement sites in the British Isles have
been unaffected by damage or alteration in the past 30 years, and
some have suffered very severely.

RÉSUMÉ

Les tables de lapiés des Iles Britanniques fournissent un exemple
intéressant de l'influence de l'homme sur des phénomènes geo-
morphologiques. Dans cet article on examine l'histoire des influences anthropiques sur les tables de lapiés (particulièrement
dans le nord-ouest de l'Angleterre), l'importance des dommages
récents qu'ils ont subis et les actions entreprises pour protéger
ces paysages à la fois beaux et d'un grand intérèt scientifique.
Diverses activités ont intéressé les tables de lapiés et
l'importance de ces activités a changé au cours des temps. Dans
les récentes décades la pression de l'homme s'est accrue et des
organismes de protection de la nature se sont inquietés de
sauvgarder certains sites de tables de lapiés menacés par des
degâts éventuels. Dans les Iles Britanniques, trés peu de tables
de lapiés n'ont pas subi de détérioration pendant les 30 dernières
années et certains sites ont été en grande partie détruits.

INTRODUCTION

The activities of man as a geomorphological agent have been discussed at various times, for example Thomas (1956) and Brown (1970). It is necessary to look beyond field evidence to historical documentation of economic activities in order to elucidate the development of some landforms and to explain the presence of others. This has been illustrated by work such as that of Prince (1964) on pit⌐ and ponds in Norfolk.

In the case of limestone pavements it is obvious from observation in the field that the blocks or clints which compose the pavements have in some areas been removed by man and used in various ways. Previous literature briefly mentions areas where damage has occurred, and types of evidence for this damage and its dating, (Sweeting, 1972; Goldie, 1973, 1976, 1981; Ward ard Evans, 1976). This paper stems from such earlier studies and reports on further work which is still in progress. The recent research has looked particularly at field evidence and at material made available by the Nature Conservancy Council, which is active in trying to protect limestone outcrops from clint removal.

This work comes at a time when there is increasing action to conserve features of geomorphological, geological and biological value in our environment, in the face of increasing pressure on that environment from a variety of sources. Other karst landforms, apart from limestone pavements, such as caves, have been vulnerable to damage, in some cases for decades (Black, 1969; Stanton, 1982).

The combination of evidence establishes that limestone pavements in the British Isles have been profoundly altered by human activities. Merely to observe the pavement outcrops and to conclude that their features are entirely the result of natural processes could result in erroneous ideas about their development. Problems of analysis arise in situations where proof of human interference is not available, but where the field situation seems similar to that of areas where there is proof of damage. Older damage is more difficult to recognize in the field than recent damage, therefore it can be difficult to infer human interference. Further problems arise when trying to establish what effect indirect, rather than direct, activities have had on these landforms. The direct effects have been so profound and extensive in some areas as to justify the legal protection of limestone pavements in Great Britain under the Wildlife and Countryside Act, 1981. No such protection exists in the Republic of Ireland, although the removal of clints is also very extensive there.

Man's influence on limestone pavements, particularly in Britain and Ireland stems from a number of factors, including the proximity of pavement sites to settlements and communications, the value of the pavement areas to agriculture in upland areas,

516

and in some areas the value of the limestone itself as a
marketable commodity of varying use. This raises problems of
land-use conflict in some of the less-spoiled areas of the
British Isles.

Economic activities have directly or indirectly affected
limestone pavement features and distribution over a considerable
period of time. The general areas within which pavements are
found have been influenced by grazing and cultivation since
prehistoric times and these activities will have had their effect
on the vegetation and soil, thereby indirectly influencing pavement distribution. There have also been activities which have
directly affected pavement outcrops.

Such activities include the removal of limestone for road,
wall and building construction, decoration, the burning of limestone for lime, the removal of limestone to improve pasture, and
the removal of the rock to supply garden rockery stone for the
horticultural trade. The last of these reached its greatest
intensity in recent years.

SOURCES AND METHODS

A variety of sources and methods has been used to obtain evidence for the effect of these activities on limestone pavements.
Field evidence has probably been the most important, especially
as it shows exactly how the ground surface can be altered. But
other sources are interesting and some can supply information
for sites which might not necessarily reveal evidence in the
field, even on close inspection. Some sources of evidence of
course can produce figures of quantities of stone involved.
Local contacts, literature sources, examination and comparison
of different map series, examination of aerial photographs,
Inclosure Acts, estate records, local newspapers and Nature
Conservancy Council files have all been used, in addition to
field evidence, to put together a picture of what has happened
to limestone pavements. The location map (Figure 27.1) indicates
the main areas of pavements examined in this work.

Local contacts have in general not been very informative.
There is great reticence in North West England because the question
of limestone pavement removal has been a bone of contention between some local farmers and landowners, and conservation bodies.
The problem in a sense typifies the clash in attitudes to the
land which can arise between different interests in a National
Park, Site of Special Scientific Interest or other partly protected area of natural beauty. This has been the case particularly in the Yorkshire Dales National Park, where many important
limestone pavement sites are found and where, in the past, much
damage has been done to them.

The Chartulary of Fountains Abbey, which in Mediaeval times
owned much of the land containing pavement in the Craven District
of Yorkshire, offered no specific information on use of limestone,
but the evidence it gave of the economic activities in the Dales

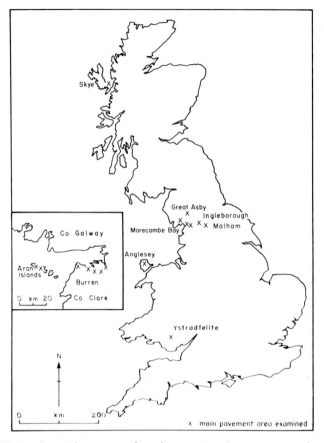

Figure 27.1   Location map of main pavement areas examined in
Britain and Western Ireland (Eire)

up to 1539 supports the idea of pressure on soil and vegetation
due to grazing, which might lead to soil erosion and exposure
of pavement outcrops.

Archaeological literature confirmed some of the field evidence of the use of clints in the building of old structures and
confirmed general pressure of settlement on the areas where
pavement occurs. Examination in the field of some of the sites
mentioned in this literature quite distinctly shows that limestone pavement was cleared and used in construction, for example
at the prehistoric standing stone circle at Knipe Scar (Lowther),
near Bampton, Cumbria (Noble, 1907).

Maps may reveal evidence of changes in the extent of pavement within the period of human occupation. An early edition
of the six inches to one mile Ordnance Survey maps of Craven from
the 1890s, was therefore compared with the most recent available.

Unfortunately, this source of evidence was not fruitful, due to the fact that the editions are inaccurate and differ in the way in which they represent pavement; indeed there are differences in the method of representing pavements within each edition. As a consequence, changes which appear from these comparisons to have taken place need not actually have done so. They may merely reflect changes in cartographic method or accuracy. Six inch Ordnance Survey maps were also used to ascertain pressure on limestone from usage in walling, lime kilns, sheepfolds and quarries (see below).

Evidence from the Inclosure Awards and Acts of the late 18th and early 19th centuries from Craven, shows that some pavement was used for walling. The Malham Inclosure Award map depicts limestone pavement outcrops with walls crossing them (Goldie, 1976). The pressure for walling was greatest in the dales rather than on the moors, but in both areas pavement patches were used where they provided the most available form of rock. It is difficult to calculate the quantities involved and to assess the exact effect on the pavement. Grassy areas on either side of walls which cross pavement indicate removal, for example on the west side of Wharfedale above Chapel House Wood, and on Gauber Pasture at the north end of Ingleborough (Figure 27.2). A map compiled by measuring the length of wall in each kilometre square on the six inch O.S. maps for the area gives an idea of quantities and regional variation in pressure (Figure 27.3). Densities as high as 8 km of wall per km^2 are found in Wharfedale and Ribblesdale. The majority of the walls involved are constructed of limestone.

Figure 27.2   A stone wall using pavement on Gauber Pasture, Ingleborough, Yorkshire

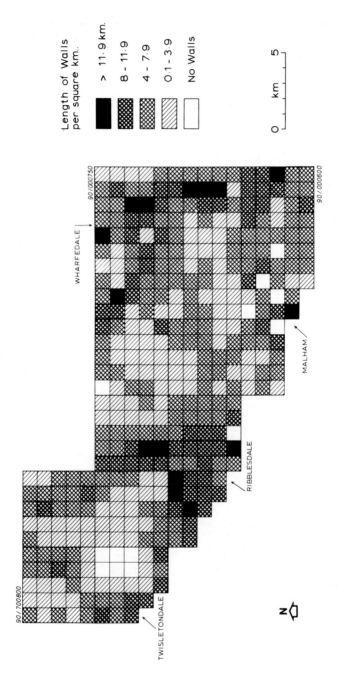

Figure 27.3 Density map of walling in the Craven district, Yorkshire, England

The cash books of the Ingleborough Estate give documentary evidence of the amount of stone used on the estate for walling and lime in the early 19th century. Wall construction peaked in 1842, 1855 and the early 1870s. The bulk of the stone involved in the walling was limestone, though some was grit. Use of limestone for lime showed a very large peak around 1842.

Air photographs show examples of direct pressure on pavement from old settlements. One photograph of Raven Scar, Yorkshire (UH 93, Committee for Aerial Photography, Cambridge) shows very clearly the way in which a space in pavement has been cleared for the construction of a sheepfold; another of Scales Moor, Yorkshire (UH 83, Cambridge) shows a further example of a sheep shelter or fold using pavement. Photographs showing old hut circles, settlements, small enclosures and field systems from the Iron Age, near pavement, indicate the possible pressure on pavement outcrops at this period, for example on Cowside Flask, Malham Moor (BAQ 47, Cambridge).

Local newspapers in Northwest England, such as the Craven Herald and Westmorland Gazette, have confirmed the activity of removal and have reported on Public Inquiries into the problems caused. Information has also come from the files and records of the Nature Conservancy Council (NCC) and from discussions with NCC officers. A comprehensive botanical survey of limestone pavements was carried out in the mid-1970s by Ward and Evans. This survey included assessments of pavement damage and is an important source of information for the NCC in its work to protect pavement sites. There is approximately 2150 ha of limestone pavement in Britain and this survey detected damage to 97 per cent of the sites and regarded only 13 per cent of pavement sites as being 95 per cent or more intact. (Ward and Evans 1976; Frankland, 1980). It was estimated that about half of the total pavement had been damaged to some degree.

Field evidence of damage to pavements includes the equipment used by contractors. Hydraulic shovels, heavy lorries and other heavy equipment have been seen by the author and by other observers at various times on a number of pavements which are known to have been damaged (Figure 27.4). Sweeting (1972) recorded an example on Gaythorne Plain, Cumbria. Equipment has been seen on the same area more recently, and at Andrew Scar nearby a corrugated iron chute, still in place in 1982, was the means by which clints were moved off the pavement above the scar. Further features associated with damage have a geomorphological expression, such as access tracks onto pavement, machinery marks in the rock and explosive boreholes. The construction of access tracks often involves the filling in of grikes with rubble, as at Gaitbarrows, Cumbria.

Figure 27.4   Machinery for removing clints on limestone
             pavement at Andrew Scar, near Great Asby, Cumbria

GEOMORPHOLOGICAL CHARACTERISTICS
OF LIMESTONE PAVEMENT DAMAGE

A number of geomorphological changes result from the removal of
clints from the surface of limestone pavement. Firstly, there
are obvious changes in the level of the limestone to the extent
of the thickness of the bed or beds removed. There are concomitant changes in the morphometry of the pavements; after damage
clints are in general longer and wider than before, and grikes
shallower (Figures 27.5 and 6). Secondly, the rock surface
beneath clints is rougher than the usual pavement surfaces which
have been scoured by glaciers and affected by solution, probably
under a soil and vegetation cover, for a lengthy period
(Figure 27.7). Thirdly, the removal process produces a considerable amount of small debris. This debris can be seen on the
damaged surfaces, filling what remains of small solution features,
and larger material can block up the grikes to varying degrees.
Fourthly, clints are not always removed from the damaged site.
Sometimes they can be found wedged in grikes, sometimes left in
heaps. The observation of clints in this way largely depends
upon the stage of the removal operation when the site was seen
by the author, though in some cases, as at Hampsfield Fell
(discussed later) removal operations were stopped by legal action
and clints remain on the site in piles. Fifthly, there is a
lack of lichen growth on freshly damaged limestone pavements.
Study of lichen growth on such damaged surfaces might well prove
to be a useful line of evidence for dating damage for areas
where no other precise information is available, in a similar
way to lichen studies used to date exposure as a result of soil
erosion (Trudgill, Crabtree and Walker, 1979).

522

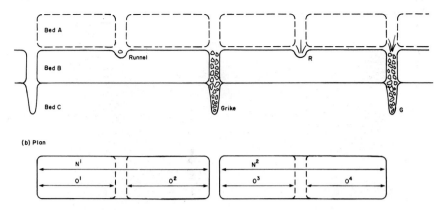

(a) Section

Bed A

Runnel

Bed B

Bed C

Grike

R

G

(b) Plan

N^1

O^1

O^2

N^2

O^3

O^4

Figure 27.5   Diagrams to illustrate the effects on clint length
of the removal of clint tops (bed A)

(a)

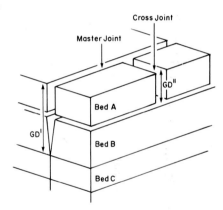

Cross Joint

Master Joint

GD''

Bed A

GD'

Bed B

Bed C

Figure 27.6   Diagram to
illustrate the effects
on grike depth of the
removal of clint tops.
GD' and GD'' are
measurements prior to
damage, GD''' is after
damage

(b)

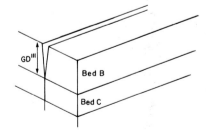

GD'''

Bed B

Bed C

GD = Grike Depth

Figure 27.7   Geomorphological characteristic of limestone
               pavement damage : lowered clint surfaces,
               roughened surface and small debris

Overall, a damaged limestone pavement has a very different appearance, both in general and detailed terms, compared with an undamaged pavement. The geomorphological effects at a freshly damaged site are clear, but problems arise when trying to interpret field evidence in areas where damage has occurred years ago and its effects obscured by the passage of time.

DESTINATIONS OF CLINTS REMOVED FROM LIMESTONE PAVEMENTS

One of the clearest types of evidence of the removal of extensive amounts of limestone pavement blocks comes from seeing the blocks at their destinations. Some uses totally destroy the limestone, for instance lime making. The location of lime kilns near pavement outcrops which have been damaged is evidence of this use of clints, for example near Conistone in Wharfedale. However, the use of clints for construction and decoration of buildings and gardens can clearly be seen.

Not all blocks of limestone used in limestone areas for constructions such as walls, roads and buildings will be clints. Some of the rock will be loose surface stones, or come from quarries. There are many occasions though when the state of a pavement, and its proximity to settlement strongly suggests that blocks from the pavement have been used in construction. This can be confirmed when the characteristic runnel markings of clints can be seen on stones in walls and buildings. Some buildings use trimmed clints in their construction, others contain whole clint blocks. Obvious instances of the latter are ancient structures such as the remains of hut walls in Oxenber Wood, Yorkshire and at the 4th century A.D. village at Din Lligwy on

Anglesey. At the latter site there is a clearing of about 0.2 ha for the village between two wooded areas of limestone pavement (Craster, 1953). The bases of the walls of the huts are clints *in situ*, and the remains of constructed walls and gateposts are identifiable clints which have been moved (Figure 27.8).

Other ancient structures clearly made from limestone pavement blocks include the burial chamber at Plas Lligwy on Anglesey: the dolmens of the Burren, Eire, for example Poulnabrone Dolmen (Figure 27.9); and other smaller burial chambers in the Burren. A defensive use at stone forts on Arainn is described later. Stone circles, sheep folds and walls have already been mentioned.

Figure 27.8 The 4th century A.D. village at Din Lligwy on Anglesey showing use of *in situ* clints and clints which have been moved

Figure 27.9 Poulnabrone Dolmen, Burren, Co. Clare, constructed with several large clints

There is also evidence of indirect effects on pavement distribution. Raistrick and Holmes (1962) drew attention to the presence of Iron Age field boundaries on Malham Moor. This indicates the settlement pressure on the environment at this period, since the fields would have originally had soil in them, where now they are bare rock. Drew (1983) discusses the evidence for deforestation and soil erosion in the Burren in the late Bronze Age. This evidence supports the idea that limestone pavement has been increased in extent by the indirect effects of man. It also confirms the likelihood that the rock was used to build structures in this period.

A frequent modern use of broken pieces of well-runnelled clints is as a bizarre decoration on the tops of garden walls. This is a common feature of villages and towns in and near the limestone areas of Northwest England, for example Horton-in-Ribblesdale, Tebay, Bowness-on-Windermere, Kendal, Little Urswick and Ingleton. (Figure 27.10). This usage is systematic along whole streets and in some cases is added to by the use of large intact clints of suitable dimension (approximately 1.5 m by 0.5 m) for gate posts. In one suburban road in Kendal 42 such clint posts have been counted (Figure 27.11). Neighbouring roads have the same feature, and in addition, many of the garden walls are topped by broken clint pieces. This housing development dates from the early 20th century and the gate posts were probably put in when the houses were built. At the very minimum these posts account for the damage of 30 m^2 of pavement, but this excludes allowance for grike widths, and of course the clints would have been selectively removed for this use as the size and shape of the pieces would be important. Thus a much larger pavement area would have been damaged in numerous places to obtain these posts.

Other examples of the decorative use of clints includes toppings for gateposts, for example near Grange-over-Sands (Cumbria); the porch framing around the entrance of an hotel in Bowness, which uses several very large well-runnelled clints; and in Miln thorpe clints have been used to shield the municipal waste bins (Figure 27.12).

On Arainn, Co. Galway, Eire, clints are used to make the water-troughs which are found in many of the very numerous small fields. These troughs and their catchment slopes are constructed from limestone pieces cemented together.

A more ignominious destination of clints is to be abandoned in heaps. This is common in the Burren of Co. Clare, Eire, and appears to have increased in frequency in recent years. Fields of pavement are cleared by bulldozer; the remaining soil grasses over quite quickly and the area becomes good grazing, while the clints are dumped in piles around the edge of the newly created fields. In cases where the bulldozing has occurred some years before, the runnels on the clints testify to their origin. The Irish do not seem to have developed a taste for decorating their gardens with water-worn limestone, hence the clints bulldozed aside are abandoned. In Ireland the stone from pavements has also been used for construction and many damaged pavement sites

Figure 27.10 Broken clints decorating a garden wall in
Horton-in-Ribblesdale, Yorkshire

Figure 27.11 Clints used
as gateposts, Kendal,
Cumbria

Figure 27.12   Clints used to hide waste bins, Milnthorpe, Cumbria

Figure 27.13   Pavement near Kinvarra, Burren, bulldozed into
                heaps in order to increase grazing area

can be seen near settlements to testify to this use, for example
near Ballyvaughan and Kinvarra on the north coast of the Burren
(Figure 27.13).

In England this practice of abandoning clints is fairly rare
as clints have a commercial value in the horticultural trade.
Nevertheless at Little Urswick, Cumbria, clints have been cleared
by a farmer, heaped up with cleared shrub vegetation, and burned,
thus increasing pasture.   Clint heaps are also found in England
on damaged pavement where the removal activity has been stopped
in mid-process by the efforts of conservation bodies such as the
Nature Conservancy Council.   An example is at Hampsfield Fell
near Grange-over-Sands (Figure 27.14).

Figure 27.14   Damaged clints
abandoned in a heap,
Hampsfield Fell, Cumbria

Finally, the use which has caused much of the damage to
pavements in the last twenty or thirty years, particularly of
Cumbrian and Yorkshire pavements, has been of so-called 'water-
worn' limestone for garden rockeries. 'Water-worn' limestone
means the solution runnelled clints. These attractive features
have been much sought after in the horticultural trade. The
efforts of the NCC and other bodies have stopped this activity
in some areas, for example, the Yorkshire Dales. But the figures
quoted earlier indicate that possibly over 1000 ha of pavement
may have been damaged, much of it by removal for garden rockery
stone. Figures of actual quantities are not easy to obtain as
removal was a casual industry in many cases, but Table 27.1 lists
figures quoted at the Public Inquiry in 1962 on removal from
Scales Moor, showing that much water-worn limestone had been removed from the pavements around Ingleborough.

British Rail estimated that between 1947 and 1955 a maximum
of 300 tons a year of rockery limestone was forwarded from
Ribblehead, Horton and Settle stations. This is a small amount,
consisting of odd loads picked up by farmers to enhance their
livelihood. However, removal was done more commercially on
Gauber Pasture and on Scales Moor. According to the Dalesman
(Anon, 1956), 8000 to 14 000 tons of clints were removed from
Ingleborough each year, transported by rail and lorry, clearly
for a number of years. Amount of removal was almost certainly
influenced by accessibility, hence the extensive removal from
Scales Moor.

Table 27.1   Estimates of quantities of clints removed from
limestone pavement, presented to the Scales Moor
Public Inquiry 1962

District	Approx. period	Approx. quantity removed (tons)
Gauber Pasture	1910 - 56	20 000 - 25 000
Ingman Lodge Hall & High & Low Pasture	1927 - 35	7 000 - 8 000
Ashes Shaw Pasture	1945 - 50	4 000 - 5 000
Philpin Sleights	1954 - 58	3 000

(source: Ward and Evans, 1976, vol. VI)

Many gardens, particularly in and near the limestone areas
of Northwest England, have rockeries made from limestone pavement blocks. Sometimes the blocks are well-runnelled, especially
in the older and larger gardens. In the early days of removal
of clints for rockeries it was done carefully, by crowbar, and
for a fairly discerning and specialized market. Such activity,
though causing a certain amount of damage did not produce the
devastation which has been seen more recently. The modern
mechanised methods of ripping out the clints, sometimes even
using explosives, can damage the clints and therefore the runnel
patterns are broken up. In other words, the very feature which
attracts people to use this particular type of rockery stone
is frequently damaged on extraction. Limestone blocks from an
ordinary quarry would therefore be just as satisfactory in many
of these modern gardens.

There are well-known gardens which contain water-worn limestone rockeries; some of these are open to the public, or are
featured in magazines, thus encouraging the modern demand
(Minney, 1983). One well-known example is Sizergh Castle, Cumbria,
a National Trust property open to the public. It contains a
large rock garden, made from clints with distinct runnel patterns,
across which a stream flows. This rockery was built at the turn
of the century before the present concern about damage to limestone pavements, and indeed would not have been built by the
castle's present owners. Limestone pavement rockeries were dis-
played at the 1863 and 1911 exhibitions at Crystal Palace, and
at the 1951 Festival of Britain. The limestone at Crystal Palace
was obtained from Gauber Pasture at the north end of Ingleborough.
Such rockeries were destroyed at the end of the exhibitions. The
use has continued at more recent exhibitions such as the 1981
Chelsea Flower Show (NCC NE 6/5/7/2). In the nineteenth century
runnelled limestone from the Ingleton area was even exported to
South America for garden rockeries on coffee plantations
(Anon, 1956).

Even local authorities have been known to purchase water-
worn limestone and blocks can be found in such strange places as
a traffic island in York and the garden of a York museum. On
private land examples such as the landscaped garden of a London
hotel, garden rockeries made of clints on the Calthorpe estate

in Birmingham, similar rockeries in Leeds, Grassington and other towns, and a rockery which decorates the steps of a factory at Netherton near Dudley, W. Midlands, illustrate the wide range of destinations of this material.

A further threat to limestone pavements is an incidental result of the commercial quarrying of limestone. In Britain an estimated 26 per cent of the aggregates used are crushed limestone (NCC file S601/5/1), hence limestone quarrying is an important economic activity. Large limestone quarries even in national parks, such as that at Horton-in-Ribblesdale in the Yorkshire Dales, testify to this. In some regions of Britain the proportion of aggregates coming from limestone is higher, in parts of Wales it is over 70 per cent. A number of these quarries are in limestone hillsides surmounted by pavements, which will be chewed into as the quarry expands. Table 2 lists quarries identified by the NCC as threatening limestone pavement sites. Some of them have already removed large amounts of pavement. For example Holmepark quarry, Cumbria has destroyed pavement which was regarded as showing unique geomorphological features. The quarry has expanded and now surrounds a pavement site (Clawthorpe Fell) which is protected from further inroads under a National Nature Reserve agreement with the owners. Indeed the very existence of the quarry surrounding the pavement actually means that Clawthorpe Fell should be protected in the future from haphazard clint removal. Some of the sites affected by quarries are of national importance, such as that at Middlebarrow, Cumbria. Other pavements affected are good and of regional importance for their botanical and geomorphological features, for example Kilnsey in Wharfedale and Blindcrake Clints, Cumbria. At other quarries, such as at Strath Suardal on Skye, the pavement has not yet been damaged by the quarry, but could eventually be, if not protected, due to proximity to the pavement outcrop.

Table 27.2 Location of limestone quarries adjacent to limestone pavement outcrops

Name	Location
Maeshafn	Clwyd
Haverbrack Bank	Cumbria
Middlebarrow	"
Holmepark	"
Blindcrake Clints	"
Crosby Ravensworth	"
Gaythorne Plain	"
Ribblehead	Yorkshire
Horton-in-Ribblesdale	"
Skythorns	"
Strath Suardal	Skye

(Source: NCC file S601/5/1 pt 3)

PROBLEMS IN INTERPRETING THE FIELD EVIDENCE

Virtually no pavement site in the British Isles visited by the author appears to be completely free of some signs of damage. However, there are cases where the field evidence is ambiguous, especially if the limestone is well-fractured and the clints therefore small and easily displaced by natural processes and grazing animals. There will be areas where the natural state of the pavement is very disturbed and where it is virtually impossible to assess damage if no independent evidence is present. For this reason the assessment of damage by Ward and Evans (1976) may be an overestimate for some areas. When there is independent evidence of damage, such as walls and cairns made of pavement material on fractured pavements, for example at Ystradfellte in South Wales (Figure 27.15) and Blue Scar, Littondale, Yorkshire, this is evidence of human involvement, though not complete proof that all the apparent 'damage' is artificial. The field evidence is more convincing on pavements with larger clints which would be fairly difficult for animals to dislodge and where natural processes are possibly the main cause of dislodgement, aided by some human interference. An example of this is on the west-facing scar edge of Hampsfield Fell where clints of approximately 1 m to 3 m in dimensions have been displaced downslope. Frost action, joint opening aided by pressure release, and gravity are all factors which could be involved here.

Figure 27.15 Cairn on fractured limestone pavement, Ystradfellte, South Wales

If blocks are obviously missing from such a site then human removal is highly likely to be involved also. This would need very careful checking in the field. Documentary evidence (NCC files) shows that human interference has affected much of this area, and so the scar edge displacement at Hampsfield Fell is probably due to a combination of human and natural processes.

Problems can arise in interpreting the older damage, for instance at Gauber Pasture, Ingleborough. The apparently older damage here fits the known usage of clints from this area in the nineteenth and early twentieth centuries. There is lichen regrowth on lowered clints, and solution features are reforming. Further evidence are the clints seen used in old walls and sheep shelters. In the western part of Gauber Pasture damage is extensive and appears to be fairly recent compared with further east. Removal in the whole area was facilitated by proximity to roads and a railway, there is a station very near the pavement. In other areas though, evidence similar to that described above may lack independent corroboration of human influence.

CASE STUDIES

Hampsfield Fell

Extensive areas of limestone pavement occur on Hampsfield Fell, which lies to the northwest of Grange-over-Sands on the west side of Morecambe Bay. The fell is a north-south ridge up to 242 m in height, which has a gentle dip to the northwest giving a west-facing scarp. There is pavement on the top and the eastern side of the fell. The area is a popular one with walkers, and has excellent views over Morecambe Bay and towards the Lake District. The pavement has been severely damaged, mainly on the eastern side, and is now the subject of the first limestone pavement protection order under the provisions of the 1981 Wildlife and Countryside Act. The pavement is good geomorphologically and though it has no unique features it displays a variety of massive and undamaged pavement and many runnel features.

Damage has occurred to the site over many years but increased in 1968 and it therefore became the concern of protection bodies. Efforts were made to safeguard the site and enforcement procedures were imposed which limited the damage to the removal of 10 to 20 tons of limestone pavement blocks per week (NCC file(c) SD 38/2 part 3). This early removal was by 'hand'. Operations in the 1970s involved the removal of blocks as large as 200 kg, about 0.5 m by 1 m, by a single operator and attempts were made to increase the scope of the removal, though these were unsuccessful. In 1982 a Public Inquiry confirmed a ban on the removal of limestone altogether, and this ban was upheld by the Environment Secretary. Thus there should be no further stripping of clint tops from this site.

The removal of clints from Hampsfield Fell has left some very clear geomorphological effects which were examined in 1982 and 1983. On the top of the fell there is a small area of damaged pavement and a pile of rubble, in addition to good intact pavement. On the damaged part there is grass growing where the grikes of the top clints would have been or where deep runnels had been dissolved through the top bed and begun to be etched into the bed below. One possible effect of clint removal is to leave larger clints beneath and this is illustrated by the measurements taken at Hampsfield Fell (Table 27.3).

Table 27.3   Clint sizes 'before' and 'after' damage, measured on Hampsfield Fell, Cumbria

	'Before'	'After' (in metres)
Clint 1	1.50	7.5
	0.90	N.B. 'Before' clints marked
	1.15	on this larger clint beneath
	1.55	by 4 areas of gravel and grass
	2.40	across its width
Clint 2	1.05	3
	1.95	N.B. 1 gravel and grass mark
Clint 3	1.30	2.5
	1.20	N.B. 1 gravel and grass mark

The marks on the damaged surface are not entirely conclusive about the exact pre-damage pattern of clints and various possibilities are suggested in Figure 27.16. Figure 27.16a illustrates what was found in the field. Figure 27.16b illustrates possible interpretations of this evidence. Measurements were made of undamaged pavement at Hampsfield Fell on the same stratum and very close to the damaged site. The clints at the undamaged site are well and deeply runnelled, which suggests that the clints at the damaged site could have been well-runnelled too. If this was the case the clints removed would have been arranged in the possible options of A, B or C (Figure 27.16b) rather than D.

Great Asby Scar

    Limestone pavement removal in the Great Asby Scar area of Cumbria took place 'on an organised basis for many years' (NCC file 81-AS2). The scale of the operation was small, but over a period of years the damage was widespread. Nothing remains of the original pavement surface in some areas, for example on Gaythorne Plain, and in other areas the pavement is partially damaged. NCC files on the Asby pavements show that planning permission for the removal of surface limestone was refused. However, in spite of the activity not being permitted, limestone was taken from these pavements. Action was therefore taken in 1970 and 1971 to prevent this. It was, as usual in these cases, difficult to control the removal of loose rock. There was a legal problem concerning ownership of the loose rock, which complicated matters.

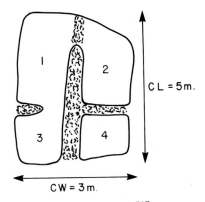

CL = 5m.

CW = 3m.

CW = Clint width   CL = Clint length   Gravel and grass

Figure 27.16a   Damaged clints observed on Hampsfield Fell,
Cumbria, England

A.

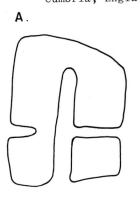

B.

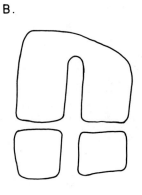

C.

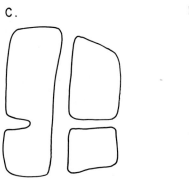

D.

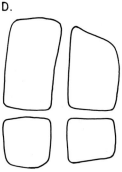

Figure 27.16b   Possible pre-damage arrangements of clint
(in Figure 27.5a)

In the early 1970s the area was described as possessing a
number of fine, almost, intact pavements with well-developed
clint and grike structures and an abundance of lime-loving plants.
At the same time however, tractor-mounted power shovels were to
be seen ripping up the pavements, that is, removing clints which
were not 'loose' in any sense of the word.   The surface left now
is typical of a damaged pavement: rough, lacking surface solution
features and with much small limestone gravel, like hardcore.
The area on Gaythorne Plain affected in this way is probably the
most extensively damaged pavement in North West England (Figure
27.17).

Figure 27.17   Extensive damaged limestone pavement,
                Gaythorne Plain, Cumbria.

The Nature Conservancy Council (NCC) has tackled the problem
at Great Asby Scar, firstly by pressing for the cessation of
limestone removal, and secondly in some areas by purchasing the
land concerned for Nature Reserves.   A Nature Reserve was thus
created at Asby Scar in 1976 and some of the areas of Great Asby
Scar not acquired by the Nature Conservancy Council have SSSI
status.

Gaitbarrows

Ratcliffe (1977) refers to this pavement in Cumbria as being
the most important single example of limestone pavement in
Britain.   Its botanical importance is very great; it is top of
Ward and Evan's floristic assessment of pavement sites in Great
Britain.   It is also very interesting geomorphologically, showing
an extremely varied range of surface solution features.   As an
example of the problems involved in trying to protect valuable
scientific sites from clint removal its history is sobering.

Concern for the site began in the 1960s when it became obvious
that pavement was being damaged by clint removal. Removal had
occurred as early as 1912. Being private, wooded land it was
extremely difficult for NCC officers to gather information about
illegal clint removal. The NCC and other bodies involved in
trying to protect the site were acutely conscious of the potential dangers of protection measures. For instance, a compulsory
purchase order for the site could be appealed against and damage
accelerated by the owner in the interim. The site was eventually
acquired and made into a National Nature Reserve and was opened
as such in 1977. Despite the fact that about 50% of the original
pavement at Gaitbarrows has been removed it is still extremely
important scientifically. About 5 ha of intact pavement remain.
The site shows very clearly the effects of clint removal, with
lowered clints, rubble strewn surfaces and access tracks across
pavement with grikes infilled with rubble. Heavy machinery and
explosives were used at Gaitbarrows, unlike in earlier days. An
important lesson learnt here was that even thickly-bedded and
large clints are not safe from such modern methods of extraction.

Eire

In the Burren, West Ireland, a number of pavement sites observed show evidence of damage. At Blackhead in the North West
Burren lowered clint surfaces next to intact clints indicate
damage. There are stone walls using clints in the area. At
Burrenwee further east the pavements are extremely messy, there
is much broken rock debris in the grikes and there are walls and
buildings adjacent to and on the pavement. In the Corker Pass,
south of Kinvarra, an area by the roadside has been bulldozed
and is now good grazing. A further area, of about 1 ha on the
west side of the pass had recently been bulldozed when seen by
the author in 1983. The clints were heaped around the cleared
area. Along the same road further south heaps of clints seen
in grazed fields indicate slightly older clearance. Near Corco-
more Abbey, in the same area, a new barn was seen adjacent to
about 0.5 ha of damaged pavement which had been manured. The
abbey itself contains some large clints in its structure as did
stone walls nearly, indicating old removal. At a measured pavement site near the abbey lowered clint surfaces, shallow grikes
and poorly developed solution features were further pointers to
damage. In addition there were fresh tractor tracks, fresh
rubble and displaced clints, suggesting some recent removal. On
the damaged parts of the pavement grikes averaged 0.68 m deep,
whilst on the undamaged parts they averaged 1.0 m deep.

The slope above Aillwee cave in the Burren has small pavement patches on narrow terraces. Some of these are very disturbed with walls across and near the pavement, and clints stuck
in grikes. Lichen growing on the damaged pavement indicates that
the damage here was not particularly recent. A newly made track
over the moor above Aillwee does however plough through pavement
outcrops causing much damage and displacement. On the lower
slopes of Slieve Carron there are cleared areas with clints
heaped around the fields by the road, whilst at higher sites
small walls across pavement were clearly constructed from pavement blocks. At the south end of Slieve Carron an excellent area

seen undamaged by the author in 1980 was, when seen again in 1983, threatened by newly built gravel and access tracks.

In the Carron depression, partially damaged pavement by the river showed differences in grike depths; grike depths in damaged pavements averaged 0.28 m, those in undamaged pavements averaged 0.6 m. At one location near a very smooth grikeless area, working of the pavement for what appeared to be tombstones was seen by the author.

At various other sites in the Burren similar signs of damage to those mentioned above were observed.

Limestone pavements on the main island of the Aran Islands, Arainn, also showed damage. This is not surprising as the large amount of bare limestone on the island makes life extremely difficult for farmers. The farmers on Arainn literally make fields by scraping together what soil they can from the pavement, adding sand and sea-weed to supplement the meagre soil. Many fields on Arainn have been cleared of limestone outcrops, including pavements, to produce fields, the rock being used for the very numerous walls. Arainn shows some interesting types of damage. There are several stone forts on the island, of Iron Age period (Robinson, 1980). These have involved huge quantities of limestone in their construction, for example Dun Dhubhcathaire and Dun Aonghasa. In addition to this pressure on pavement near the forts, jagged clint blocks were used to form defensive lines of 'chevaux de frises' beyond the walls. Pavement outcrops near these forts show the expected effect of lowered clint surfaces. On other pavements on Arainn farmers have attempted to fill grikes with stones, probably to prevent animals injuring themselves. Lastly, near Mainistir an area of several hectares of pavement is being destroyed for gravel, crushing machinery was seen on the site.

CONCLUSION

This paper has drawn attention to the effects of human activities on limestone pavements. It has shown that these activities have been extensive and, in some cases, very damaging to these landforms. There are areas where the effects have been the understandable result of a landscape having an overabundance of surface limestone, for instance on Arainn and in the Burren, Eire. Here the effects of man have largely been the consequence of farmers' attempts to increase their grazing area. But clints from limestone pavements have also been deliberately used in structures of many kinds both in Britain and Ireland. In many parts of Britain large areas of pavement have been exploited for the commercial value of the clints for garden rockeries and other decorative purposes. This has caused extensive and serious damage, sufficient to require legal protection for limestone pavements.

The evidence for these effects have been varied, including historical sources as well as field evidence. There are circumstances where it is necessary to look beyond field evidence to other material to elucidate what has happened in the field. The combination of evidence from a variety of sources is essential if a full picture of the effects of man on these landforms is to be obtained.

Acknowledgements

The author wishes to thank Dr. H. Frankland, Dr. S. Ward and Miss H. Robertson of the Nature Conservancy Council for their kind assistance. However, the opinions expressed in this article are those of the author. Durham University is thanked for contributing towards the cost of fieldwork.

REFERENCES

Anon, 1956. *Dalesman.* **18(7)**, p. 341.

Black, G.P. 1969. Conservation and access. *Manual of caving techniques,* 380-394, (Routledge Kegan Paul, London).

Brown, E.H. 1970. Man shapes the earth. *Geog. Journ.,* **136**, 74-85.

Craster, O.E. 1953. *Ancient Monuments in Anglesey.* (H.M.S.O. London).

Drew, D. 1983. Accelerated soil erosion in a karst area: the Burren, Western Ireland. *J. Hydrol.,* **61**, 113-124.

Frankland, H. 1980. Excursion to Gaitbarrows; background notes. *Inst. Brit. Geog. Annual Conference.*

Goldie, H.S. 1973. The limestone pavements of Craven. *Trans. Cave Res. G.B.,* **15(3)**, 175-190.

Goldie, H.S. 1976. *Limestone pavements: with special reference to North West England.* Unpublished D.Phil. thesis, Oxford University.

Goldie, H.S. 1981. Morphometry of the limestone pavements of Farleton Knott, (Cumbria, England). *Trans. Brit. Cave Res. Assoc.,* **8(4)**, 207-224.

Minney, P. 1983. Something Old, Something New. *Homes and Gardens,* **10(64)**, 50-55.

Noble (Miss) 1907. The stone circle at Knipe Scar. *Trans. Cumb. Westm. Antiq. & Arch. Soc.,* 211-214.

Prince, H.C. 1964. The origin of pits and depressions in Norfolk. *Geography,* **49**, 15-32.

Raistrick, A. and Holmes, P. 1962. Archaeology of Malham Moor. *Field Studies,* **1(4)**, 73-96.

Ratcliffe, A. 1977. *A Nature Conservation Review.* Vol. 2, (Cambridge University Press).

Robinson, T.D. 1980. *The Aran Islands, Co. Galway, Eire.* A map and guide. (Cill Ronain, Eire).

Stanton, W.I. 1982. Mendip-Pressures on its Caves and Karst. *Trans. Brit. Cave Res. Assoc.,* **9(3)**, 176-183.

Sweeting, M.M. 1972. Karst of Great Britain. Ch. 13 In: *Karst: Important karst regions of the Northern Hemisphere,* eds. M. Herak and V.T. Stringfield, (Elsevier, Amsterdam).

Thomas, T.M. 1970. The limestone pavements of the north crop of the South Wales coalfield. *Trans. Inst. Brit. Geog.,* **50**, 87-105.

Thomas, W.L. 1956. *Man's role in changing the face of the Earth.* (University of Chicago Press, Chicago).

Trudgill, S.T., Crabtree, R.W. and Walker, P.J.C. 1979. The age of exposure of limestone pavements - a pilot lichenometric study in Co. Clare, Eire. *Trans. Brit. Cave Res. Assoc.,* **6(1)**, 10-14.

Ward, S.D. and Evans, D.F. 1976. *Limestone pavements: A botanical survey and conservation assessment based on botanical criteria.* (Institute of Terrestrial Ecology).

Ward, S.D. and Evans, D.F. 1976. Conservation assessment of British limestone pavements based on floristic criteria. *Biol. Cons.,* **9**, 217-233.

28

Valley excavation in the Yorkshire Dales karst

A.C. Waltham

SUMMARY

The Yorkshire Dales region is one of spectacular glaciokarst
containing extensive cave systems. Uranium series determinations
of stalagmite ages allow estimates of the dates of cave passage
drainage when contemporary valley floors were at lower levels.
Tentative results for three valleys west of Ingleborough suggest
a mean rate of valley floor excavation of 0.12 m per 1000 years,
and a history of the Dales extending over at least a million
years.

RÉSUMÉ

La région des Yorkshire Dales présente un paysage glacio-karstique
spectaculaire avec de vastes systèmes de grottes. La détermination
en série de l'âge de stalagmites au moyen des isotopes de l'uranium
a permis de dater approximativement le moment où les galeries
souterraines se sont vidées vers des vallées dont le plancher se
trouvait à un niveau plus bas. Les résultats préliminaires pour
trois vallées qui se trouvent à l'ouest d'Ingleborough indiquent
une vitesse moyenne de 0.12 m/1000 ans pour le creusement des
fonds des vallées et une durée d'évolution des Dales d'au moins
un million d'années.

INTRODUCTION

Within the region generally known as the Yorkshire Dales, the Ingleborough-Malham area provides the finest and best-known glacial karst in Britain. Limestone dominates the landscape for more than 500 km² across the axis of the Northern Pennines, and practically all the karst is developed in a single unit of almost horizontal Carboniferous limestone, nearly 200 m thick. Impermeable slates lie below, and the dominantly shale sequence of the Yoredale Series lies above. To the south and south-west the limestone is truncated by the Craven Fault system, and to the west by the Dent Fault.

The area was glaciated repeatedly during the Pleistocene, including the Devensian period. The main Dales are fine glaciated U-shaped troughs breaching the full depth of the limestone and now carry the regional drainage to the south. Ice also covered large areas of the limestone plateaux and stripped them of their Yoredale cover; spectacular pavements now characterize the upland glaciokarst. Ingleborough and the other hills have summits of the Yoredale and later rocks; streams gather on the Yoredales and flow down to the Carboniferous Limestone where they nearly all sink underground. Most of the resurgences are on the floors of the Dales, at, or near, the base of the limestone.

Numerous caves are known within the karst. At present more than 260 km of passages have been mapped; they are mostly in large dendritic systems. There is a full range of active and fossil, phreatic and vadose cave passages. A typical cave system consists of young vadose canyons which intersect and invade older phreatic tunnels, before draining into active phreatic tubes (Waltham *et al.*, 1981). Few passages relate directly to the water table; the active phreas is locally more than 50 m deep, and fossil phreatic tunnels are known with a vertical range of over 70 m. There is an uneven altitudinal distribution of cave passages, and this was formerly related to past erosion levels (Sweeting, 1950). However, it can be shown that there is also a strict geological control of the caves (Waltham, 1970), and zones of shale beds within the limestone are responsible for the dominant levels of development.

The debate, over control by either geology or erosional history, extends also to the plateau surfaces, where the main limestone benches at about 420 m clearly have a complex origin. Sloping surfaces, mainly west of Ingleborough, follow the gentle dip of the top of the limestone and show a stratimorphic origin. In contrast benches cut across contrasting lithologies in the Malham area demonstrate the role of planation. Pleistocene ice moved from north to south over the whole karst; it both aided stripping of the plateau surfaces and also modified and partly excavated the main valleys.

The multi-phase origin of the caves is clearly demonstrated
by their morphologies, but the successive periods of glacial erosion removed most signs of earlier topographies. The inter-
related history of cave development and valley glaciation is
shown by both the modern karstic drainage into the Dales and also
the truncation of fossil phreatic caves by glaciated valley sides.
No absolute dating of surface landforms has yet been possible,
but age determinations of stalagmites, using the uranium series
disequilibrium method (Harmon *et al.*, 1975) has allowed construction of a chronology of cave development.

THE CAVE CHRONOLOGY

Stalagmite dates already obtained show that the caves span a
history longer than the 350 000 years which is the upper limit
of the uranium-series method (Atkinson *et al.*, 1978; Gascoyne,
1981a). Within this range most stalagmite deposition, and therefore solutional activity, took place during the warmer phases of
the Pleistocene, in a pattern now widely recognised (Hennig,
et al., 1983).

The cave stalagmite chronology offers the potential of
establishing a history of valley excavation by correlation of
cave and valley morphologies. The basic premise is that the old
valley floor levels were also the levels of the contemporary resurgences, and that these can be recognised by changes from
vadose to phreatic morphology in the relevant cave passages.
(The possibility of a perched phreas can be eliminated by detailed
mapping of cave morphologies.) The critical event is the draining
of the phreatic caves as a consequence of valley floor lowering;
the latest possible dates can then be ascribed by dating the
oldest subaerial stalagmites in the newly-drained caves.

Many stalagmite dates are now available from the Yorkshire
Dales, but most are of little value in determining valley histories. The dates are either too young to be relevant, or are
from old high-level interfluve caves now unrelatable to valley
incision. Furthermore, many cave systems are fragmented by collapse, inundation, sediment infilling or stalagmite blockage.
Only in the three valleys west of Ingleborough (Figure 28.1) is
there adequate understanding of the cave geomorphologies to
enable us to confidently relate the stalagmite deposition to past
resurgences. Old stalagmites in key locations are not easily
found; only 12 of the dates so far obtained are significant to
the direct correlation with valley excavation, and the implications of this thesis must, therefore, be regarded as tentative.

THE WESTERN YORKSHIRE DALES

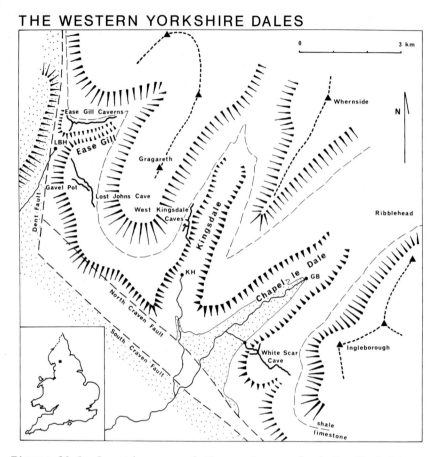

Figure 28.1   Location map of the western end of the Yorkshire
               Dales karst area (Key to resurgences: LBH - Leck
               Beck Head; KH - Keld Head; GB - God's Bridge)

VALLEY EXCAVATION

Chapel le Dale

Chapel le Dale is a deep glaciated trough which separates the
western slopes of Ingleborough from the rise to Whernside. It
descends steeply from the Ribblehead basin; it then has a gentle
gradient where floored by the slates beneath the limestone and
finally breaks through the line of the Craven Faults (Figure
28.2). The limestone south of the North Craven Fault is at a
lower level and almost isolated from that to the north by the
rising front of basement rock; it extends only to the South
Craven Fault. The present main resurgence in Chapel le Dale is

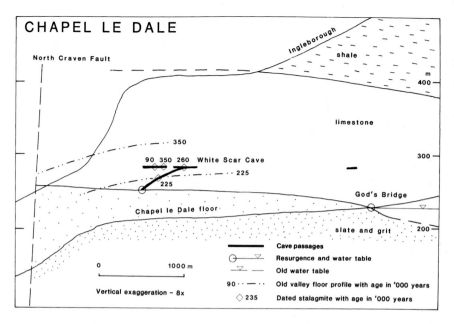

Figure 28.2 Projected elevation of Chapel le Dale, with
relevant caves, dated stalagmite locations and
approximate profiles of past valley floors showing
maximum altitudes at given times

at God's Bridge and is close to the base of the limestone; it
has an extensive cavernous phreas behind it.

    In White Scar Cave (Figures 28.1 and 28.2), the low-level
Main Streamway drains northwestwards from the tributary Crina
Bottom valley, to the modern cave entrance. The passage has
yielded *in situ* stalagmite up to 225 000 years old (Waltham,
1977). Being basement controlled, this passage cannot have
drained out much further down the valley, and the stalagmite
altitude and age, therefore, give the maximum elevation of the
contemporary valley floor roughly outside the cave. High-level
tunnels in the same cave once carried both the main Chapel le
Dale water and the Crina Bottom drainage. *In situ* stalagmite
here has been dated to 90 000 years. More significantly, loose
stalagmite up to 350 000 years old (Gascoyne, 1981b) almost certainly originates from these levels. As this cave passage drained
down valley, its resurgence may conservatively be placed as far
down as the North Craven Fault, with its emptying implying a
maximum altitude for the contemporary valley floor at that position. The two fossil valley floors reconstructed on Figure 28.2
have been given the same profiles as the present valley, with
levels related to the dated cave drainage points.

Kingsdale

Lying just west of Whernside, Kingsdale has an outlet close
to that of Chapel le Dale (Figure 28.1). It is another glaciated
trough, descending steadily through the limestone towards the
scarps of the North Craven Fault. Its floor supports a fine
terminal moraine behind which lacustrine and alluvial sediments
accumulated before the moraine was breached; preliminary geophysical results show the sediments to be about 20 m deep outside
Keld Head (Figure 28.3). The main cave passages are in the West
Kingsdale system, with modern drainage in the lowest passage
ponded by the valley fill at the Keld Head resurgence (Waltham
et al., 1981).

A major low-level fossil phreatic cave, truncated in the
valley wall, contains flowstone dated to 239 000 years. A greater
age for similar material, quoted in Atkinson *et al.*, 1978, is
regarded with suspicion due to contamination, and only the
younger, more conservative, age is considered here. If the drainage of this cave is related to valley floor lowering as far
downstream as the North Craven Fault, reconstruction of the fossil valley profile is as shown on Figure 28.3; the profile is
drawn conformable to the present rockhead. Fragments of high-
level fossil caves, within the same system, allow morphological
identification of their contemporary water table. This supports
the reconstruction of another valley profile keyed to a resurgence by the fault; the profile remains so far undated, and
relevant stalagmite may well be beyond the range of the uranium
series method.

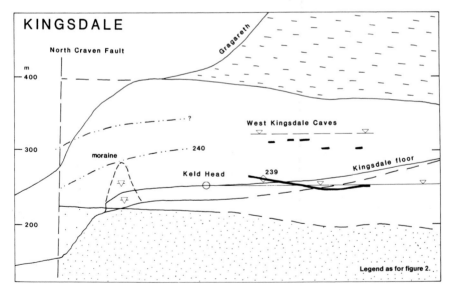

Figure 28.3   Projected elevation of Kingsdale; data and key
as in Figure 28.2

Ease Gill

West of Gragareth, a broad bowl is closed to the north and was, therefore, protected from major glacial erosion (Figure 28.1). It is floored with thick boulder clay now fluvially entrenched and drained by Ease Gill Beck. It has a steeper profile (Figure 28.4) than the adjacent more glaciated troughs, and downstream cuts obliquely through the Dent Fault on to noncarbonate rocks. Beneath the valley sides more than 70 km of cave passages have been mapped (Waltham and Brook, 1980), all draining to the Leck Beck Head resurgence and containing extensive, complex fossil levels.

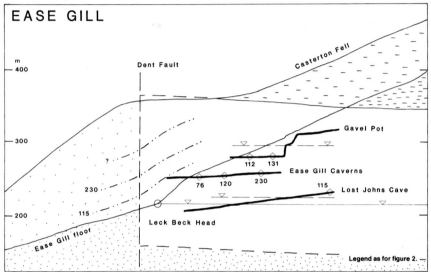

Figure 28.4   Projected elevation of Ease Gill; data and key
as in Figure 28.2

In the low-level conduit of Lost Johns Cave, the present water level is that of Leck Beck Head. Passage roof morphology clearly shows an older ponding level, probably also the contemporary valley floor resurgence level, just 7 m higher (Waltham, 1974). The age of this resurgence level is inferred from stalagmite upstream of the ponding in the same passage dated to 90 000-115 000 years (Gascoyne, 1979, 1981b). In Ease Gill Caverns, the main high-level trunk passage has yielded stalagmites of various ages, the oldest being 230 000 years (Gascoyne, 1979), which can, therefore, imply a maximum altitude for a valley floor resurgence upstream of the fault at that time. In Gavel Pot an old water table at 290 m is clearly recognisable from the cave morphology, but stalagmites dated from the fossil phreatic tunnels have so far yielded ages too young to be significant. The two upper valley floor profiles in Figure 28.4 may require upward adjustment if it can be shown that the fossil Gavel and Ease Gill passages resurged significantly downstream of Leck Beck Head.

This is possible because of the valley's oblique crossing of the Dent Fault (Figure 28.1), and remains unproven until more caves are explored and mapped.

DISCUSSION

Within these three valleys, erosion rates appear to be broadly comparable, though perhaps rather lower in the less intensely glaciated Ease Gill Valley. A correlation of stalagmite ages with their heights above the modern valley floor at their prob- ably contemporary resurgence points (Figure 28.5) gives a maximum mean rate for valley floor excavation of 0.12 m per 1000 years. This compares well with the figures proposed by Gascoyne (1981b) based on a slightly different approach with some common data. Conclusions can only be tentative due to the scarcity of signif- icantly old stalagmite age determinations, laboratory errors in

VALLEY FLOOR EXCAVATION
W. Yorkshire Dales

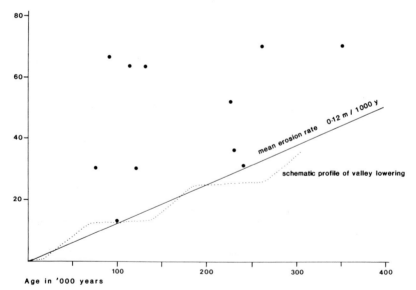

Figure 28.5 Graphical correlation of measured stalagmite ages with their heights above the modern valley floor at contemporary resurgence points. A line drawn below the lowest stalagmite plots indicates the maximum possible mean erosion rate; the stepped profile is probably more representative of valley lowering history in view of climatic variation

the age determination method (mostly around ± 10%) and the un-
certainty of some cave morphological correlations.

To suggest uniform erosion rate through the climatic variations of the Pleistocene is too simplistic. Erosion in the
Yorkshire Dales was probably faster under glacial conditions,
with less surface erosion under the karstic conditions during
interglacial phases. The stepped profile on Figure 28.5 is,
therefore, probably a more realistic history of valley excavation,
correlating the periods of stalagmite deposition with warmer
climates and with the erosion record. As the Yorkshire Dales
are typically around 150 m deep, their history appears to span
at least a million years, and a large part of their excavation
appears to pre-date the recognised glaciations of the Devensian,
Wolstonian and Anglian.

Acknowledgements

The author gratefully acknowledges R.S. Harmon, for his
laboratory work on the stalagmites, P.L. Smart and T.C. Atkinson
for valuable discussion, and numerous colleagues for assistance
during fieldwork.

REFERENCES

Atkinson, T.C., Harmon, R.S., Smart, P.L. and Waltham, A.C. 1978.
    Paleoclimatic and geomorphic implications of $^{230}Th/^{234}U$
    dates on speleothems from Britain. *Nature, 272*, 24-28.

Gascoyne, M. 1979. Pleistocene climates determined from stable
    isotope and geochronology studies of speleothem. Unpublished
    thesis, McMaster University.

Gascoyne, M. 1981a. A climate record of the Yorkshire Dales for
    the last 300 000 years. *Proceedings of 8th International
    Congress of Speleology* (Bowling Green, Ky), 96-98.

Gascoyne, M. 1981b. Rates of cave passage entrenchment and val-
    ley lowering determined from speleothem age measurements.
    Proceedings of 8th International Congress of Speleology
    (Bowling Green, Ky), 99-100.

Harmon, R.S., Thompson, P., Schwarcz, H.P. and Ford, D.C. 1975.
    Uranium series dating of speleothems. *Bulletin of National
    Speleological Society, 37*, 21-33.

Hennig, G.J., Grün, R. and Brunnacker, K. 1983. Speleothems,
    travertines and paleoclimates. *Quaternary Research, 20*,
    1-29.

Sweeting, M.M. 1950. Erosion cycles and limestone caverns in the
    Ingleborough district. *Geographical Journal, 115*, 63-78.

Waltham, A.C. 1970. Cave development in the limestone of the
    Ingleborough district. *Geographical Journal, 136*, 574-585.

Waltham, A.C. (ed.), 1974. *Limestones and caves of north-west
    England,* (David and Charles, Newton Abbot), 477pp.

Waltham, A.C. 1977. White Scar Cave, Ingleton. *Transactions of British Cave Research Association,* 4, 345-353.

Waltham, A.C. and Brook, D.B. 1980. The Three Counties Cave Systems. *Transactions of British Cave Research Association,* 7, 121.

Waltham, A.C., Brook, D.B., Statham, O.W. and Yeadon, T.G. 1981. Swinsto Hole, Kingsdale: a type example of cave development in the limestone of northern England. *Geographical Journal,* 147, 350-353.

29

Buried palaeokarstic features in South Wales: examples from Vaynor and Cwar Yr Ystrad quarries, near Merthyr Tydfil

Y. Battiau-Queney

SUMMARY

On the North Crop of the South Wales Coalfield, the Vaynor and Cwar yr Ystrad Carboniferous Limestone quarries exhibit remarkable fossilized karstic landforms. Their subaerial origin is proved by the good preservation of vertical grooves on some of their limestone walls. They were subsequently buried by a loose unsorted material. This material was deposited rapidly as a result of the destruction of deep tropical soils developed on nearby non-carbonate rocks. The exact age of burial is unknown but a lower Neogene age would be consistent with a post-burial pedogenesis evolution that implies a still relatively hot climate.

RÉSUMÉ

Les carrières de calcaire carbonifère de Vaynor et de Cwar yr Ystrad, situées sur le rebord nord du synclinorium houiller sud-gallois, présentent de magnifiques formes karstiques que l'exploitation a récemment exhumées. Ce sont de grandes poches à parois subverticales, profondes d'une dizaine de mètres. Sur les parois calcaires, des cannelures verticales, parfois très bien conservées, prouvent l'origine subaérienne de ces formes: il s'agit d'un karst à tourelles, pinacles ou mamelons, développé sous un climat chaud et humide, vraisemblablement en même temps qu'un vaste système de cavités souterraines aujourd'hui perché à plus de 200m au-dessus des rivières principales. Ce karst a été brutalement enfoui sous un matériel meuble, très mal trié, qui provenait de la liquidation de sols profonds, très évolués, formés sur les roches non calcaires affleurant dans la région (grès, siltstones, shales). La date de cette fossilisation n'est pas connue exactement. Cependant, les travaux en cours suggèrent qu'après le piégeage du matériel fossilisant, celui-ci aurait subi une pédogénèse sous un climat encore assez chaud. L'enfouissement pourrait donc remonter au Néogène inférieur.

Ce paléokarst est un témoignage, parmi d'autres, de l'importance des héritages tertiaires dans le relief actuel des Iles Britanniques.

INTRODUCTION

Eleven years ago, buried paleokarsts were described in the Trefil and Vaynor quarries (Battiau-Queney, 1973). They were interpreted as Tertiary landforms to take into account the presence of kaolinite and corroded quartz associated with goethite in the material filling up the limestone cavities. The proposed interpretation was also consistent with the general geomorphological preglacial evolution of Wales (Battiau-Queney, 1984).

Since 1973 new developments of quarrying at Cwar y Ystrad, Cwar yr Hendre and Vaynor have provided opportunities to observe new karstic features, which are described below.

REGIONAL GEOLOGICAL AND GEOMORPHOLOGICAL SETTING

The Cwar yr Ystrad and Vaynor quarries are situated on the North Crop of the Carboniferous Liemstone to the south of the Brecon Beacons scarp (Figure 29.1). The Carboniferous Limestone was deposited in Dinantian times on a carbonate shelf on the south edge of St George's Land, an area which covered most of the present mid Wales. The sequence thins rapidly northwards and in the Merthyr Tydfil area, the upper part is partially missing under the Millstone Grit, a siliclastic Namurian deltaic formation. Figure 29.2 shows that several disconformities exist within the Carboniferous Limestone sequence (Ramsbottom, 1973; Wright, 1982, 1983). Some of them are associated with paleokarsts (Wright, 1982a). It must be emphasized that the sequence is not entirely calcareous: the top of the Llanelly Formation, the so-called Gilwern Clay Member, consists of floodplain deposits with channel sandstones (the Garn Caws Sandstone), conglomerates and claystones with calcrete profiles (Wright, 1982b). These sandstones outcrop at the top of the Cwar yr Ystrad quarry (Wright, personal communication based on the work of W. Barclay) and do not differ greatly from the basal grits of the Namurian discussed below.

In that area, Lower Carboniferous rocks dip slightly to the south-southeast (Figure 29.3). The limestone which is exposed in the Vaynor and Cwar yr Ystrad quarries belongs to the previously called 'Seminula Main Limestone', that is the 'Oolite Group' and the 'Llanelly Formation' of the new classification. It is generally very hard, consisting almost exclusively of carbonate (up to 99%) and has a very low porosity (less than 1%) so that waters percolate exclusively through fissures and joints. Those properties are all favourable to the process of karstification, with formation of underground cavities and development of superficial solution features (karren, lapies and swallow-holes).

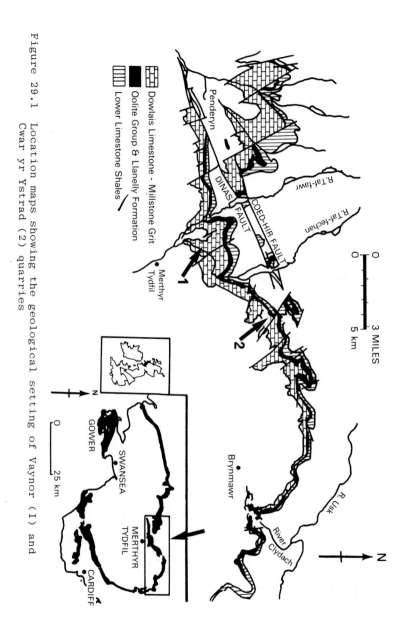

Figure 29.1   Location maps showing the geological setting of Vaynor (I) and Cwar yr Ystrad (2) quarries

Dowlais Limestone - Millstone Grit
Oolite Group & Llanelly Formation
Lower Limestone Shales

Penderyn
Merthyr Tydfil
DINAS FAULT
COED-HIR FAULT
R.Taf-fawr
R.Taf-fechan
Brynmawr
R. Usk
River Clydach

GOWER
SWANSEA
MERTHYR TYDFIL
CARDIFF

0   3 MILES
0   5 km

0   25 km

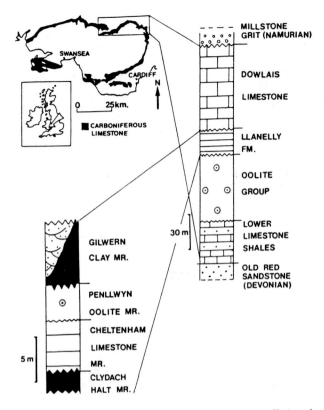

Figure 29.2   Geological setting of the Cwar yr Ystrad and Vaynor
              quarries.   The major stratigraphic units in that
              area and the subdivisions of the Llanelly Formation
              are shown.   Reproduced with permission from Wright,
              1983

The channel sandstone and conglomerates intrastratified in
the Llanelly Formation offer several facies: the most widespread
seems to be a fine quartzitic sandstone with some rare biotite
(Figure 29.4).   Limestone, chert and polycrystalline grains are
not infrequent.   There are also pebbly quartzose sandstones.
In the field it is often difficult to differentiate these
Dinantian rocks from Namurian sandstones.

This region has been a land area since upper Palaeozoic
times.   Perhaps it was submerged by lower and mid-Jurassic seas,
although nowhere on the North Crop of the South Wales Coalfield
have Mesozoic deposits been found in the numerous karstic Carboniferous Limestone cavities (1).   Nevertheless convergent arguments suggest a final emergence before Cenomanian (Battiau-
Queney, 1984).   It follows that Wales (and especially this area)

(1) On the contrary, such deposits are frequently observed in
the Vale of Glamorgan.

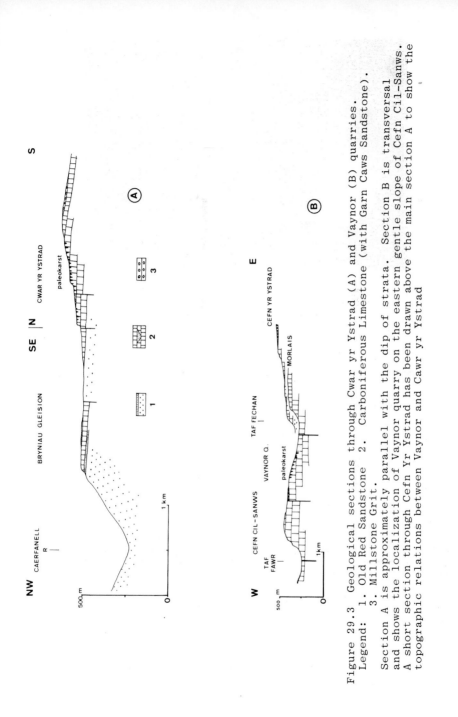

Figure 29.3   Geological sections through Cwar yr Ystrad (A) and Vaynor (B) quarries.
Legend: 1. Old Red Sandstone   2.   Carboniferous Limestone (with Garn Caws Sandstone).
         3. Millstone Grit.

Section A is approximately parallel with the dip of strata.   Section B is transversal
and shows the localization of Vaynor quarry on the eastern gentle slope of Cefn Cil-Sanws.
A short section through Cefn Yr Ystrad has been drawn above the main section A to show the
topographic relations between Vaynor and Cawr yr Ystrad

Figure 29.4   Thin section of a quartz arenite from the Llanelly
                Formation (Garn Caws Sandstone) outcropping at
                Cwar yr Ystrad

suffered a continental evolution for 100 million years at least.
During this long period with hot, and more or less wet climate,
intense karstification is assumed to have taken place on Carboniferous Limestone outcrops.   Evidence of that long sub-aerial
evolution should be present in the present landscape (as relict
landforms) or in the quarries (as buried or interstratal features), because there is good reason to believe that the thickness
of rocks which have been eroded away does not exceed a few tens
of metres (Battiau-Queney, 1984).

KARSTIC FEATURES IN THE VAYNOR
AND CWAR YR YSTRAD QUARRIES

The Vaynor quarry (NG: SO 037095) is situated on the east side
of Cefn Cil Sanws which reaches a height of 460 m and is partially
capped with Millstone Grit quartzitic sandstones.   The quarry is
open between 365 and 290 m.   Several huge pockets can be observed
where the local limestone is replaced by a reddish brown material.   They descend from the topographic surface to ten metres
below it.   It seems that the apparent floor of the pockets is
roughly parallel with the southeast dipping slope of Cefn Cil
Sanws.   Some pockets are very wide, more than 20 m (Figure 28.5),
others are pipe-shaped.

    The Cwar yr Ystrad quarries (NG: SO 090145) are situated
around 515-580 m along a frontal scarp controlled by a small NE
trending fault probably linked with the 'Neath Disturbance'.
(Figure 29.3) On aerial photographs this fault line appears pitted
with small swallow-holes but it was not drawn on the old geological map.

Figure 29.5   A large pocket in Vaynor quarry. It is filled with
a loose, unsorted material including large blocks
of weathered sandstone, probably coming from the
nearby outcrop of Millstone Grit

Figure 29.6   An aspect of Cwar yr Ystrad quarry. Several pockets
are seen on the left. Garn Caws Sandstone outcrops
at the top right

The quarrying has exposed numerous pockets filled up with brown
reddish material (Figure 29.6). The siliceous Garn Caws Sandstone outcrops at the top of the eastern front where it was
probably downfaulted along a NW trending fault. Pockets are
several metres deep and disappear with depth.

In both cases, it is clear that pockets have developed downwards from the present topographic surface or from a surface not
very different to it. The main questions arising from these
forms and deposits are: were these cavities created subaerially
or under a sedimentary cover? what is the material infilling
the cavities? what sort of geomorphological evolution can be
deduced from these forms?

Figure 29.7   Vaynor quarry: detail of the edge of a pocket.
The limestone surface is smooth and gently convex.
The burial material here is fine and contains more
than 40% clay particles

Figure 29.8   Cwar yr Ystrad quarry: a pocket side with well
preserved rillenkarren; vertical channels and
grooves prove the subaerial origin of the karstic
pinacles

Figure 29.9   Vaynor quarry: detail of a pocket wall carved with
               vertical grooving. In the middle of the photograph,
               the black lens cap gives the scale. The burial
               material appears on the right. It is rich in clay

Figure 29.10   Cwar yr Ystrad quarry: detail of a limestone wall
               at the edge of a karstic pocket. The bedding joints
               are seen and the remains of vertical channels are
               recognized

The inner sides of the pockets

Three main form-types have been observed in these quarries:

i) The limestone face displays multiconvex forms with smooth surfaces (Figure 29.7). This type occurs frequently at Vaynor.

ii) The pocket sides are nearly vertical and carved with rillenkarren, channels and grooves. Some of them are well preserved at Cwar yr Ystrad (Figure 29.8) and Vaynor (Figure 29.9).

iii) The pocket sides are vertical with traces of channelling and grooving but the limestone surface is rough and subhorizontal bedding joints disrupt the vertical continuity of karren (Figure 29.10). This type is widespread at Cwar yr Ystrad and frequent at Vaynor.

The second type of pocket sides obviously indicates subaerial evolution with solution of limestone by run-off waters. Two morphoclimatic systems seem particularly relevant to explaining these forms: a hot and wet climate or a cold climate with a thick snow cover. In the second case, the in-filling would have postdated the Pleistocene glacial periods. In fact, the nature of the material (discussed below) suggests that the first explanation is more appropriate.

The first type of pocket sides is not diagnostic of any specific climatic regime. Smooth convex shapes can be observed, for instance under a waterfall, and locally at Vaynor, multiconvex subvertical faces suggest such an origin (Figure 29.11). This hypothesis is consistent with the presence of a stratified deposit with graded bedding preserved in a small sheltered hollow at the base of a subvertical smooth face. Graded bedding could be the result of deposition in a sheltered place away from the main current. Yet, it cannot be excluded that smooth surfaces such as those in Figure 29.7 could have evolved also under a permeable cover.

The third type is more interesting because it suggests ancient subaerial solution features which were subsequently degraded after burial with a permeable material.

Interpretation

Vertical channelling and grooving prove the subaerial origin of at least several large cavities in the Vaynor and Cwar yr Ystrad quarries. They result from solution at the atmosphere-rock interface: they are true karstic surface features developed when limestone was uncovered.

In other cases, the same solution forms are much degraded and it is clear that degradation took place after burial of the karstic cavities by a sufficiently permeable material: in that way waters percolating through the overlying material could dissolve the limestone beneath. The more permeable the filling material is, the more degraded the rillenkarren are.

Figure 29.11 Vaynor quarry: a convex subvertical face exhumed
from the burial material. At the base of it a
graded deposit was found in a sheltered hollow.
The hammer gives the scale

The pre-burial karstic landscape of this area can be reconstructed from the paleoforms exhumed by quarrying: it was very
irregular with limestone pinacles and towers several metres high,
the sides of which were subvertical or mamillated. This sort of
karstic landscape is unknown today in Great Britain but it is
quite frequent under hot and wet climates.

It can be deduced from the deepness and apparent floor of
the pockets that this paleokarst was related to a topographic
surface not very different from the present one. The area between Taf Fawr and Taf Fechan belongs to an asymmetrical tilted
block with a very steep west side (the limestone scarp of Daren
Fach) and a gently dipping east side on which is situated the
Vaynor quarry. Eastwards, beyond the Taf Fechan valley, the
paleokarstic surface lies one or two hundred metres higher.
These facts are explained by the result of a complex block tectonics pattern (Battiau-Queney, 1978, 1979).

Everywhere, the quarrying activities below the pocket level
shows that these karstic cavities are true solution landforms
and not the consequence of collapsed cave-roofs. The presently

active solution dolines on the limestone plateau over Cwar yr Ystrad are not related to the pockets below but belong to a newer generation of karstic landforms.

The pocket infilling material

Everywhere it consists of loose unconsolidated material showing no evidence of cementation. The absence of post-depositional diagenetic reactions gives some indications concerning its age. It cannot be very old and a Carboniferous age which could be suggested by the frequent emplacement of pockets at the junction between Carboniferous Limestone and Namurian Basal Grit, is excluded. If they were Carboniferous in age 300 millions years has elapsed and the infilling material should have been lithified, cemented and compacted as observed in the true Carboniferous paleokarsts described by V.P. Wright in the same area (Wright, 1982a). A Cenozoic age is much more probable.

The material is completely unsorted. Sizes vary from clay particles to boulders of several decimetres. Coarse and fine material are usually mixed in the same pocket. Nevertheless, in some cases, masses of pure clayey material can be found with up to 50% of the particles under 2 microns and 85% under 50 microns. Even in these cases the sorting is very poor. At Vaynor and Cwar yr Ystrad, and also at Trefil, a true stratification is never observed, contrary to the Brassington Formation in Derbyshire (Walsh et al., 1980). The lack of sorting and the absence of stratification suggest a transporting agent similar to mud flows with high competence and insignificant attrition for the sand grains are angular or subangular and the cobbles and pebbles are subangular or slightly subrounded.

The mineralogical composition shows a Millstone Grit or Garn Caws Sandstone provenance. These rocks outcrop immediately near the limestone quarries. The short distance of transportation may have also contributed to the absence of sorting and stratification in the deposit. Since this near-by source seems indisputable it is also evident that the source material was more or less deeply weathered. Three main reasons can be advanced in support of this.

Firstly, sandstone fragments can be easily crumbled down into sand when pressed in the hand. The process of decementation can be observed in thin sections; quartz grains are coated with a film of ferric oxide or divided into a microcrystalline mosaic (Figure 29.12). The rare micas are weathered into clay minerals. Weathered quartzitic sandstones have been changed into ferruginous sandy aggregates. A similar process of weathering has been described on quartzose red sandstones in tropical Africa in regions receiving at least 1200 mm of rain (Fauck, 1972): quartz grains are divided into very small particles surrounded by ferric hydroxides. The role of iron seems important in this weathering process. It implies solution of silica directly from quartz. The bulk of dissolved silica is leached out but a minor part of it may recrystallize in the profile and give bipyramidal quartz crystals. Euhedral quartzes are commonly found in the material filling the paleokarst pockets at Vaynor and Cwar yr

562

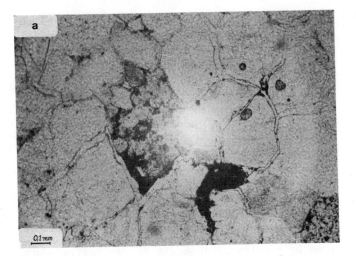

Figure 29.12 Vaynor quarry: thin sections of partially de-
cemented sandstone fragments found in a karstic pocket, mixed
with a sandy clayey material
a.   The fresh rock was an orthoquartzite. Original cementation
by enlargement is still visible but a film of ferric oxides
coats the quartz grains. One of them has been divided into
very small grains set in a ferric oxide matrix (in the middle
of the photograph). The hand specimen looks like a friable
ochrish sandstone. Polarized light
b.   The fresh rock was a quartzarenite. Quartz grains are
coated with a film of ferric oxides. In the middle of the
photograph, a microcrystalline patch is impregnated with iron
oxide. Crossed nicols

Ystrad. Secondly, the burial material is completely or nearly free from carbonates (always less than 1%). Thirdly, the nature of the clay fraction has been determined by X-ray diffraction. Where the clay fraction is very abundant it is mainly composed of kaolinite with a smaller percentage of illite, vermiculite and other clay minerals. Quartz and goethite are also present in the clay fraction. Kaolinite is found in small quantities in the Gilwern Clay Member (Wright, 1982b) but it is not usual in Carboniferous rocks. An abundant kaolinitic composition is more easily explained by a weathering process (hydrolysis of alumino-silicates like micas, present in the parent rocks).

PALEOGEOMORPHOLOGICAL IMPLICATIONS

The textural, chemical and mineralogical properties of the material filling the pockets are very similar to those observed in ferrallitic or tropical ferruginous soils. Truncated paleosols belonging to this group have been effectively recognized *in situ* on Millstone Grit outcrops in South Wales (Battiau-Queney, 1984). In the paleokarstic pockets, a typical soil structure with different horizons cannot be recognized (except for the upper part, as described below). The material could not have been produced *in situ*. The only satisfactory explanation taking into account all the facts observed is a sudden erosion of deep strongly leached soils and the subsequent removal of their constituents by mud flows down into karstic hollows. It must be remembered that ferrallitic and ferruginous tropical soils are often friable and poorly structured. Consequently, they are relatively weak and may be easily stripped off by surface erosional processes when the climax vegetation is destroyed.

At the geological time scale, the destruction of deep soils was a catastrophic event, but it was probably initiated by a slow climatic deterioration and increased erosion with steepening slopes. Beyond a certain threshold the previous morphoclimatic system shifts to an unstable state and the geomorphological response is rapid.

Further studies are needed to appreciate the respective role of diastrophism and climatic deterioration in the initiation of change in this Welsh region. Meanwhile several preliminary remarks can be made.

A similar catastrophic event implying sudden destruction of deep tropical soils is recognized in many other British areas (Vale of Glamorgan, Pembrokeshire, Forest of Dean, Mendip Hills, northwest Wales). It is assumed that a general climatic trend (dryer? cooler?) is necessary to explain a similar event over such a large area. Nevertheless the initiation of the event did not occur necessarily at the same time everywhere because a second cause of instability must be considered, that is diastrophism.

At Vaynor and Cwar yr Ystrad, it is assumed that pinnacles, towers and other subaerial karstic features were formed under a wet and hot climate when the watertable was not as deep as now and when large cave systems were developing under Mynydd Llangattock and Llangynidr. The caves are presently at 200 m or more above the local river system and this hanging position is explained by the subsequent uplift of the plateaux and simultaneous deep incision of the rivers. The rapid subsidence of the water table in that area and a cooling climate set up new conditions less favourable to subaerial karstic landforms. This explains why karstic pinnacles and towers could no longer be formed even where limestones were still outcropping. At Vaynor, the Taf Fechan River flows 100 m below the plateau surface and the localization of the paleokarst at the foot of a slope capped by Millstone Grit helped its rapid burial. The asymmetrical tilting of the Cefn Cil Sanws block preceded the stripping of soils and burial of pinnacles.

THE POST-BURIAL EVOLUTION

Some indications of post-burial processes can be deduced from my field observations. The fact that the pocket sides exhibit more or less strongly degraded channel and groove features implies postburial solution of the limestone. Its effect was limited, however, because of the low permeability of the material.

More interesting indications could come from a superficial formation discovered in July 1983 above the northeastern face of Cwar yr Ystrad quarry (NG: 093145). Here ferruginous concretions lie on top of the material filling large subvertical sided pockets. They range from a few to fifteen centimetres long and their centres are completely or partially hollow. In this case, the original rock (generally limestone or chert) is still recognizable. Their internal structure shows the progressive development of a ferruginous cortex around the initial rock pebble. On their external face, many quartz grains appear to be cemented on to the ferruginous cortex. Their shape is generally subrounded but they are true concretions and not water rounded pebbles. This sort of feature needs a great mobility of iron and a climate with strongly alternating wet and dry seasons. Hot subarid climates as well as cool climates seem favourable. Research is in progress to elucidate this point. In the Vaynor quarry other interesting observations have been made within the upper parts of some pockets which suggest that post-burial, pre-glacial alteration may have occurred. A podzolic-type alteration is normally observed at the top of many pockets at Cwar yr Ystrad and Trefil. The burial material has behaved like a parent rock and a classic podzol profile can be seen. Podzol soils are frequently fossilized under periglacial slope deposits suggesting a relatively old age (perhaps Devensian or pre-Devensian).

CONCLUSIONS

i)   The Vaynor and Cwar yr Ystrad quarries exhibit paleokarstic landforms which were created subaerially under a hot and wet climate.

ii)   Concomitant development of deep ferrallitic or ferruginous tropical soils on non-carbonate rocks occurred during this period.

iii)   The deterioration of the climate coupled with block tectonic movements contributed to the sudden destruction of the soils and to the burial of karstic pinnacles and towers.

iv)   This event cannot be dated exactly but in the present state of reasearch, a post-pocket filling pedogenesis (implying still relatively hot climates) is not excluded.   If this hypothesis is confirmed, a lower Neogene age is suggested. (Battiau-Queney, 1984).

The good preservation of these karstic landforms is consistent with many other field observations which suggest more widespread survival of Tertiary paleoforms in the present British landscape.

Acknowledgements

My thanks are extended to Dr P.V. Wright for commenting on an initial draft of this article and to Dr M.M. Sweeting and Dr K. Paterson for their assistance in connection with the Symposium.   I gratefully acknowledge, too, the help of the Powell Duffryn Quarries Ltd for allowing me to work in the Vaynor quarry (the only one still active) and to visit it with the Anglo-French Symposium in September 1983.

REFERENCES

Battiau-Queney, Y. 1973.   Mise en evidence d'un karst tropical fossile au Pays-de-Galles, *Norois,* **77**, 136-140.

Battiau-Queney, Y. 1978.   *Contribution a l'etude geomorphologique du Massif Gallois,* these Lettres Brest, 797pp, (published at Lille in 1980).

Battiau-Queney, Y. 1979.   Origine tectonique de quelques grands escarpements du Pays-de-Galles, *Revue de Geologie Dynamique et de Geographie Physique,* **21(2)**, 109-126.

Battiau-Queney, Y. 1984.   The pre-Glacial evolution of Wales. *Earth Surf. Proc. & Landforms,* **9**, 229-252.

Fauck, R. 1972.   *Les sols rouges sur sable ou sur gress d'Afrique occidentale,* These Science, ORSTOM, Paris.

Ramsbottom, W.H.C. 1973.   Transgressions and regressions in the Dinantian: a new synthesis of British Dinantian Stratigraphy. *Proceedings of the Yorkshire Geological Society,* **39**, 567-607.

Walsh, P.T., Collins, P., Ijtaba, M., Newton, J.P., Scott, N.H. and Turner, P.R. 1980. Paleocurrent directions and their bearing on the origin of the Brassington Formation (Miocene-Pliocene) of the Southern Pennines, Derbyshire, England. *Mercian Geologist,* **8**(1), 47-62.

Wright, V.P. 1982a. The recognition and interpretation of paleokarsts: two examples from the Lower Carboniferous of South Wales. *Jl. Sedim. Petrology,* **52**(1), 83-94.

Wright, V.P. 1982b. Calcrete palaeosols from the Lower Carboniferous, Llanelly Formation, South Wales, *Sedim. Geol.,* **33**, 1-33.

Wright, V.P. 1983. A rendzina from the Lower Carboniferous of South Wales, *Sedimentology,* **30**, 159-179.

30

The polyphase karstification of the Carboniferous Limestone in South Wales

V.P. Wright

SUMMARY

The Carboniferous Limestone in South Wales has undergone multiple phases of karstification during its long history. The earliest of these phases took place during the Lower Carboniferous and a number of palaeokarstic surfaces occur within the limestone sequence. At the end of Lower Carboniferous times a major phase of erosion and karstification occurred prior to the deposition of the Upper Carboniferous (Namurian) Millstone Grit. In the Triassic and Jurassic the limestones again underwent karstification and contain important faunas and floras preserved in fissures and caves. Karstification also occurred in the Tertiary, possibly under tropical conditions.

RÉSUMÉ

Le Calcaire Carbonifère (Carboniferous Limestone) au sud du Pays de Galles a subi de nombreuses phases de karstification, pendant sa longue histoire. La première de ces phases remonte au Carbonifère inférieur et une série de surfaces palaéokarstiques existe à l'intérieur même de la séquence calcaire. Une phase d'érosion et de karstification importante eut lieu à la fin du Carbonifère inférieur, avant le dépôt du Millstone Grit au Namurien (Carbonifère supérieur). Au Trias et du Jurassique les calcaires ont été karstifiés encore une fois et des flores et des faunes sont préservées dans den fissures et des grottes. Au Tertiaire les calcaires ont été à nouveau karstifiés, peut être sous un régime tropical.

INTRODUCTION

Palaeokarsts have attracted much interest for besides providing evidence of earlier phases of karstification they also provide useful information on palaeoclimates and are associated with a variety of hydrocarbon and mineral deposits (Bardossy, 1982; Kyle, 1983; Quinlan, 1972; Zuffardi, 1976). Palaeokarsts represent phases of subaerial exposure and it is now widely acknowledged that many ancient limestones were lithified and mineralogically stabilized during such exposures to meteoric groundwaters early in their history (Longman, 1982). There has therefore been considerable interest in recognizing such phases of groundwater related diagenesis because during such phases porosity may form and cementation may occur.

In the Carboniferous Limestone of Britain a major effort has been made by many workers to recognize evidence of subaerial exposure. This is a result of the suggestion by Ramsbottom (1973) that the limestones contain many stratigraphic breaks caused by regressions (sea level falls) followed by subaerial exposure.

The Carboniferous Limestone of South Wales has been periodically exposed not only during Lower Carboniferous times but also at several other periods including the Triassic, Jurassic and Tertiary.

PALAEOKARST TERMINOLOGY

Palaeokarst represents karstification in a past landscape, and there are three main types: relict, buried and exhumed palaeokarst (Figure 30.1). Relict palaeokarst represents morphological forms which originated under different climatic conditions from which the karst is now found (Sweeting, 1973 and 1980). In South Wales relict tropical karst features may occur along the northern limestone outcrop (Battiau-Queney, 1980 and this volume).

Buried palaeokarst is overlain by a cover of younger sedimentary rocks and represents karstification prior to the deposition of the overlying cover. Many spectacular examples occur in the geological record, such as the Devonian-Carboniferous mogote karsts of Europe and North America (Bless, et al., 1980; Maslyn, 1977 and Poty, 1980).

Exhumed palaeokarst represents buried palaeokarst which has been reexposed by erosion. Sweeting (1980) has referred to such palaeokarst as fossil karst (fossilis = dug up) and has reviewed several examples.

One problem is recognizing buried palaeokarstic surfaces is to differentiate them from interstratal (or subjacent) karst (Martin, 1965; Quinlan, 1966; Sweeting, 1972). This is karst

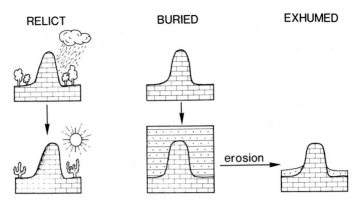

Figure 30.1   Major types of palaeokarst

which was not part of a landscape and is younger than the overlying deposits. This karstification occurred within a sequence
and often occurs at major stratigraphic boundaries where permeable
deposits overly limestones. In South Wales interstratal karst
has developed on the top of the Carboniferous Limestone beneath
a cover of Millstone Grit (Thomas, 1973, 1974).

BURIED PALAEOKARST IN SOUTH WALES

The Lower Carboniferous limestones in South Wales were deposited
on a carbonate shelf, approximately 100 km wide. This shelf was
bordered to the north by a land area (St. George's Land) over
what is now mid-Wales, and to the south by a deep basin. As a
result of sea-level fluctuations, these shelf limestones contain
a number of subaerial exposure surfaces. During the Chadian-
Arundian stages two contrasting palaeokarstic surfaces developed
(Wright, 1982a). On the north east limestone outcrop a prominent
solution piped horizon occurs which passes laterally into a
rubbly horizon resembling kavernossen karren. These solution
effects resemble tropical karsts yet are overlain by palaeosols
bearing petrocalcic horizons which may reflect a climatic shift
to more arid conditions (Wright, 1980). At approximately the
same horizon in the Gower, a palaeokarstic surface occurs which
has been interpreted as a deckenkarren and is associated with
rhizoliths (Wright, 1982a).

The palaeokarst developed in the northeast outcrop will be
described in more detail. This example serves to illustrate how
geomorphology, sedimentology and detailed diagenetic studies are
needed to fully elucidate the nature of these ancient karsts.
The palaeokarst occurs at the top of the early Carboniferous
Oolite Group and is well developed in outcrops from Abergavenny
to Penderyn in South Wales (Figure 30.2). The paleokarst is
overlain by the Llanelly Formation which is a complex unit containing both fluvial and marine deposits. Further details of
the localities and stratigraphy are to be found in Wright, 1982a.

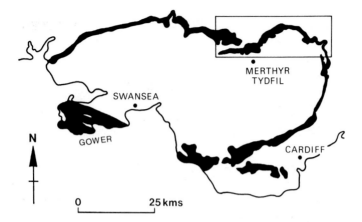

Figure 30.2   The Carboniferous Limestone outcrop in south east
               Wales (in black). The boxed area shows the north
               east outcrop which contains the sub-Llanelly
               Formation palaeokarst

The solution features are exposed in vertical quarry faces giving
only two-dimensional views. This is a common problem in studying
buried palaeokarsts.

     Two types of palaeokarst features can be recognized in the
area. The most common type consists of a rubbly horizon up to
5 m thick which appears on weathered faces rather like a huge
boulder bed. The horizon consists of a dense network of irregular clay-filled fissures and pipes (Figure 30.3). The geometry
of these features has been further complicated by local collapse
resulting in a jumbled mass of fluted blocks of oolitic limestone. The second type of palaeokarstic feature consists of a
less densely piped zone with larger solution pipes (Figure 30.4).
These are up to 40 cm wide and are up to 2 metres long. Locally
beneath this piped horizon there is a sinuous fissure, perpendicular to the pipes, 10 to 20 cm wide. The fissure pinches and
swells and is not related to any bedding planes but occurs within
a structureless oolite.

     All the fissures and pipes, when freshly exposed are filled
with a green clay. The pipes and fissures are truncated by the
basal beds of the overlying Llanelly Formation. These basal
beds contain a variety of sheet flood and stream flood deposits,
and palaeosols with well developed petrocalcic horizons (Wright,
1980, 1982b).

     The densely solution fissured zone is analogous to recent
kavornossen karren and there are striking similarities to some
of the features developed on the Aymamon Limestones of Puerto
Rico described by Ireland (1979). These limestones are riddled
with solution pipes to such an extent that they appear as a mass
of cobbles and small boulders, honeycombed by irregular holes.
A similar process may have occurred at the top of the Oolite
Group but to such an extent that small scale solution collapse

572

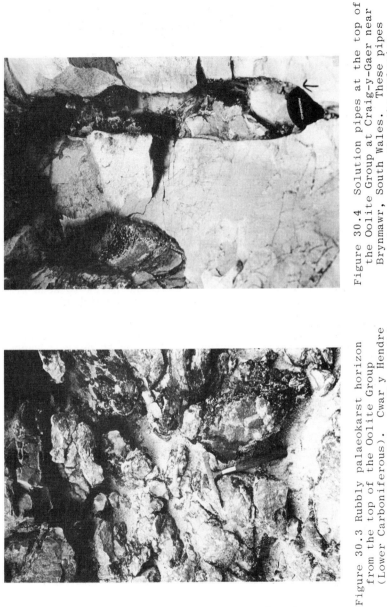

Figure 30.3 Rubbly palaeokarst horizon from the top of the Oolite Group (Lower Carboniferous). Cwar y Hendre near Trefil, South Wales. The oolitic limestones are riddled with narrow solution pipes and fissures filled with clay

Figure 30.4 Solution pipes at the top of the Oolite Group at Craig-y-Gaer near Brynmawr, South Wales. These pipes are less common than the solution rubbling and may have formed in more strongly cemented limestones

resulted. Some of the smaller pipes may be root lapies but clear evidence of root activity such as carbonaceous traces or rhizocretions are absent. The larger pipes are simple solution pipes. The sinuous, horizontal fissure is similar to the 'water-table cave' fissure described by Land (1973) from the karsted Pleistocene of Jamaica. Land found a persistent narrow solution zone developed at the water-table during shallow drilling.

Further details of the karstification can be obtained by a study of the cementation of the oolitic sediments associated with the karst. It is now known that many ancient marine sediments became mineralogically stabilized and cemented during contact with fresh groundwaters. The importance of this groundwater related alteration has led to considerable study of vadose and phreatic diagenetic processes in limestones. The result is that criteria for recognizing the products of these processes are well known (Longman, 1980).

Vadose zone alteration of exposed carbonate sediments results in a variety of cement fabrics affected by capillary and gravitational influences. This results in irregularly distributed cements usually at pore throats where capillary waters become concentrated. Solution is also more intense in this zone and pedogenic processes also occur. In the phreatic zone cementation is more regular in distribution and the cements are much coarser in crystal size than in the vadose zone where rapid precipitation results in smaller crystal sizes. These cements also have different isotopic signatures and some workers have used isotopic analyses in ancient limestones to delimit vadose from phreatic cements.

Much of the top of the Oolite Group was cemented and eroded prior to karstification but locally vadose cementation products do occur (Raven, 1981). Such cements usually are found within the horizon above the sinuous fissure but are absent below it (Raven, 1983). This is evidence that the fissure probably was a water table 'cave' (Figure 30.5). This also indicates that

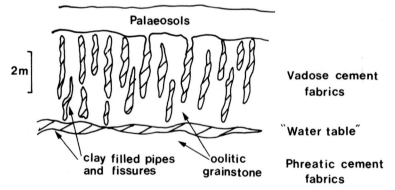

Figure 30.5   Palaeogroundwater zones in the top of the Oolite Group.

574

the palaeokarst was, at least locally, syngenetic - that the solution was concurrent with cementation (Jennings, 1968). The kavornossen karren described by Ireland (1979) also formed in part syngenetically.

Other Intra-Carboniferous Palaeokarst in South Wales

Later in Lower Carboniferous times, during the late Asbian stage several palaeokarstic surfaces developed, one of which exhibits large dolines (Thomas , 1953). In the Gower peninsula during the Asbian - Brigantian, 'mammillated' palaeokarstic surfaces occur identical to those described from similar sequences in Derbyshire (Walkden, 1974). Palaeokarstic surfaces are numerous and widespread in the late Dinantian (Lower Carboniferous times) of Britain, e.g. in northeast Wales (Somerville, 1979 a, b, c) and Anglesey (Walkden and Davies, 1983).

These numerous surfaces provide evidence of widespread phases of subaerial exposure throughout Britain. They occur in areas with varied tectonic histories and their widespread distribution may reflect major eustatic sea-level falls which can be identified on other continents (Walkden, in press). Such surfaces may provide important stratigraphic markers for world wide correlation but the origin of the sea-level falls remains problematic since extensive glacial deposits of this age have yet to be found.

Along the north east part of the Carboniferous Limestone shelf in South Wales tectonic uplift occurred in the late Dinantian which resulted in major erosion of the limestone sequence (Barclay and Jones, 1978). The top of the limestone is highly irregular with slumped masses of Millstone Grit filling depressions in the limestone (Jones and Owen, 1966). These authors considered the solution to be post-Millstone Grit (interstratal) but Thomas (1973, p 74) believed that the contact represented buried palaeokarst. The distribution of the irregularities in the top of the limestone may have influenced lateral interstratal solution (Thomas, 1974, p 150). Kasig (1980) has figured a major palaeokarst between the Carboniferous Limestone and Namurian of Aachen in West Germany, and a considerable palaeokarstic surface also occurs at this level in north Belgium which has been detected in the subsurface using reflection seismics (Vanderberghe et al., 1984). Boreholes have revealed probable convective water movements in this buried karstic zone with high CO_2 contents perhaps suggesting a continuing dissolution of the limestone. This is another example of palaeokarst being affected by subjacent karst.

Mesozoic and Tertiary Palaeokarst in South Wales

During Mesozoic times the Carboniferous Limestone in the southern part of the outcrop, in what is now South and Mid-Glamorgan, again underwent solution. Those limestones in the northern part of the coalfield (on the other limb of the coal field syncline), were still covered by Upper Carboniferous sediments. During the late Triassic period the climate in Britain was arid to semi-arid and in South Wales alluvial fans, ephemeral streams and playas existed south of the present coalfield (Tucker, 1977). Extensive outcrops of Carboniferous Limestone occurred which were karsted with the formation of deep fissures and caves (Thomas, 1952). Some of these fissures and cave deposits are rich in vertebrate remains (Robinson, 1957).

Later in the Triassic (the Rhaetic) and early Jurassic a major transgression led to the drowning of the area creating a number of islands called the Mendip-Glamorgan Archipelago (Anderton et al., 1979). The climate was less arid and there was a plant cover. Some fissures of this age contain plant remains which show evidence that forest fires occurred during this time (Harris, 1957). Other fissures and caves contain vertebrate remains (Robinson, 1971).

Karstification also occurred along the northern outcrop area during the Tertiary, possibly under tropical conditions (Battiau-Queney, this volume). This resulted in tower Karst-like features buried beneath heavily weathered Namurian siliciclastic deposits.

CONCLUSIONS

Limestones are unique in that they produce distinctive erosional features which often have a high preservation potential. Many karstic features develop 'within' the limestones and are already 'fossilized' beneath protective cover. During the 300 million years since the Carboniferous Limestone was deposited it has been subjected to many phases of solution. The limestones were deposited in shallow water settings and were prone to sea-level fluctuations. As a result the sequence contains many intra-Lower Carboniferous palaeokarstic horizons. These are best studied using geomorphological, sedimentological and diagenetic techniques. These palaeokarstic horizons can be used for palaeo-environmental reconstruction providing information on the climates and hydrology of the time as well as being used for correlation. Such early subaerial phases result in groundwater cementation in the limestones as well as porosity development. A major phase of karstification occurred prior to the deposition of the Namurian Millstone Grit and this palaeokarstic surface may have controlled later interstratal solution. A similar palaeokarst can also be traced in Belgium and Germany. During the Mesozoic the Carboniferous Limestone again underwent karstification and many of the fissures acted as dustbins for important vertebrate and plant remains. Karstification also occurred in the Tertiary and up to the present day. The multiple phases of karstification which have affected the limestones of the northern outcrop of the present coalfield are shown in Figure 30.6.

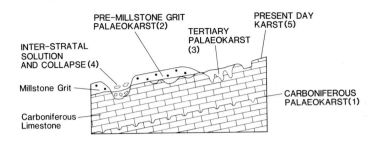

Figure 30.6 Phases of karstification in the Carboniferous Limestone of the northern outcrop of the South Wales coalfield syncline

Acknowledgements

I should like to thank Madeleine Raven (Robertson Research) for many discussions on the diagenesis of the Oolite Group and for permission to discuss some of her unpublished results. I also wish to thank Beryl West and Ian Glennister respectively for typing the manuscript and preparing the diagrams.

REFERENCES

Anderton, R., Bridge, P.H., Leeder, M.R. and Sellwood, D.W. 1979. *A Dynamic Stratigraphy of the British Isles.* (George Allen & Unwin, London).

Barclay, W.J. & Jones, D.G. 1978. Recent boreholes in the attenuated Carboniferous strata of the Blaenavon - Pontypool area, Gwent. *Bull. Geol. Surv. of Great Britain* No. 67, 17pp.

Bardossy, G. 1982. Karst bauxites. Bauxite deposition on carbonate rocks. *Developments in Economic Geology,* (Elsevier, Amsterdam), 441pp.

Battiau-Queney, Y. 1980. *Contribution a l'etude geomorphologique du Massif Gallois.* These de Bretagne Occidentale, Universite de Lille.

Bless, M.J.M., Bouckaert, J. & Paproth, E. 1980. Environmental aspects of some pre-Permian deposits in N.W. Europe. *Meded. Rijks Geol. Dienst.,* 32, 3-13.

Harris, T.M. 1957. A Rhaeto-liassic flora in South Wales. *Proc. Roy. Soc. Lond., B.,* 147, 289-308.

Ireland, P. 1979. Geomorphological variations of 'case hardening' in Puerto Rico. *Z. Geomorph., N.F., Suppl.-Bd.,* 32, 9-20.

Jennings, J.N. 1968. Syngenetic karst in Australia in Williams. In: *Contributions to the Study of Karst,* eds. P.W. & J.N. Jennings, (Nat. Univ. Dept. Geogr. Pub. G/5, Univ. Canberra Press), 41-110.

Jones, D.G. & Owen, T.R. 1966. The Millstone Grit succession between Brynmawr and Blorenge, South Wales. *Proc. Geol. Assoc.*, **77**, 187-198.

Kasig, W. 1980. Dinantian carbonates in the Aachen region, F.R.G. *Meded. Rijks Geol. Dienst.*, **32**, 44-52.

Kyle, J.R. 1983. Economic aspects of subaerial carbonates. In: *Carbonate Depositional Environments*, eds. P.A. Scholle, D.G. Bebout, & C.H. Moore, (Am. Assoc.), 73-92.

Land, L.S. 1973. Holocene meteoric dolomitization of Pleistocene limestone, North Jamaica. *Sedimentology*, **20**, 411-424.

Longman, M.W. 1980. Carbonate diagenetic textures from near-surface diagenetic environments. *Amer. Assoc. Petrol. Geol. Bull.*, **64**, 461-487.

Longman, M.W. 1982. Carbonate diagenesis as a control on stratigraphic traps. *Am. Assoc. Petrol. Geol. Education Course Note Series 21.*

Martin, J. 1965. Quelques types de depressions karstiques du Moyen Atlas central. *Revise Geogr. Maroc.*, **7**, 95-106.

Maslyn, M.R. 1977. Fossil tower karst near Molas Lake, Coloradeo. *The Mountain Geologist*, **14**, 17-25.

Poty, E. 1980. Evolution and drowning of palaeokarst in Frasnian carbonates at Vise, Belgium. *Meded Rijks Geol. Dienst.*, **32**, 53-55.

Quinlan, J.F. 1966. Classification of karst and pseudokarst types: a review and synthesis emphasizing the North American literature. 1941-1966; paper, *123rd Meeting of Am. Assoc. Adv. Sci. Symp.* of 25 years of American Speleology.

Quinlan, J.F. 1972. Karst-related mineral deposits and possible criteria for the recognition of paleokarsts. *24th Int. Geol. Congress,* Montreal, Sec. 6, 156-168.

Ramsbottom, W.H.C. 1973. Transgression and regressions in the Dinantian: a new synthesis of British Dinantian stratigraphy. *Proc. Yorks. Geol. Soc.*, **39**, 567-607.

Raven, M. 1981. The Oolite Group. In: *A Field Guide to the Lower Carboniferous Rocks near Abergavenny*, eds. V.P. Wright, M. Raven & T.P. Burchette, (Dept. Geol., Univ. Coll. Cardiff Pub.), 28-35.

Raven, M. 1983. *The Diagenesis of the Oolite Group between Blaen Onnen and Pwll Du, Lower Carboniferous, South Wales.* Unpubl. Ph.D. thesis, Univ. of Nottingham.

Robinson, P.L. 1957. The Mesozoic fissures of the Bristol Channel area and their vertebrate faunas. *Proc. Linn. Soc. (Zool.)*, **43**, 260-282.

Robinson, P.L. 1971. A problem of faunal replacements on Permo-Triassic continents. *Palaeontology*, **14**, 131-153.

Somerville, I.D. 1979a. A cyclicity in the early Brigantian (DZ) limestones east of the Clwydian Range, North Wales and its use in correlation. *Geol. J.*, **14**, 69-86.

Somerville, I.D. 1979b. Minor sedimentary cyclicity in late Asbian (upper D1) limestones in the Llangollen district of North Wales. *Proc. Yorks. Geol. Soc.*, **42**, 317-341.

Somerville, I.D. 1979c. A sedimentary cyclicity in early Asbian (lower D1) limestones in the Llangollen districts of North Wales. *Proc. Yorks. Geol. Soc.*, **42**, 397-404.

Sweeting, M.M. 1972. *Karst Landforms*. (Macmillan, London).

Sweeting, M.M. 1973. Some problems of relict and fossil karst in England. Proc. of the Frankfurt karst Symposium. *Geogr. Z.*, **32**, 104-107.

Sweeting, M.M. 1980. Karst and climate - a review. *Z. Geomorph. N.F., Suppl. - Bd.*, **36**, 203-216.

Thomas, T.M. 1952. Notes on the structure of some minor out-lying occurrences of littoral Trias in the Vale of Glamorgan. *Geol. Mag.*, **89**, 153-162.

Thomas, T.M. 1953. New evidence of intra-formational piping at two separate horizons in the Carboniferous Limestone (Dibunophyllum Zone) at South Cornelly, Glamorgan, *Geol. Mag.*, **90**, 73-82.

Thomas, T.M. 1973. Solution subsidence mechanisms and end pro-ducts in south-east Breconshire. *Trans. Inst. Brit. Geog.*, **60**, 69-86.

Thomas, T.M. 1974. The South Wales interstratal karst. *Trans. Brit. Cave. Res. Assoc.*, 1, 131-152.

Tucker, M.E. 1977. The marginal Triassic deposits of South Wales: Continental facies and paleogeography. *Geol. J.*, 169-188.

Vandenberghe, N., Dusar, M., Dreesen, R. & Bouchaert, J. 1984. Recent subsurface data on the Dinantian in north Belgium. *Eur. Dinant. Envir. 1st. Mtg. 1984,* Abstr., 85-87. Dept. Earth Sciences, Open Univer.

Walkden, G.M. 1974. Palaeokarstic surfaces in Upper Visean (Carboniferous) limestones of the Derbyshire Block, England. *Journ. Sed. Petrol.*, **44**, 1234-1247.

Walkden, G.M. (in press). Cyclicity in late Dinantian marine carbonates of Britain. *Proc. IXth. Int. Cong. Carb. Geology,* Urbana, U.S.A., 1979.

Walkden, G.M. & Davies, J. 1983. Polyphase erosion of subaerial omission surfaces in the late Dinantian of Anglesey, North Wales. *Sedimentology,* **30**, 861-878.

Wright, V.P. 1980. Climatic fluctuation in the Lower Carboni-ferous. *Naturwissenchaften,* **67**, 252-253.

Wright, V.P. 1982a. The recognition and interpretation of palaeokarsts: two examples from the Lower Carboniferous of South Wales. *Jour. Sed. Petrol.*, **52**, 83-94.

Wright, W.P. 1982b. Calcrete palaeosols from the Lower Carboni-ferous Llanelly Formation, South Wales. *Sedim. Geol.*, **33**, 1-33.

Zuffardi, P. 1976.   Karsts and economic mineral deposits. In: *Handbook of strata-bound and stratiform one deposits.* Volume 3, ed. K.H. Wolf, (Elsevier, Amsterdam), 175-212.

31

La régression messinienne dans la Mediterranée et les conséquences pour les phénomènes karstiques

G. Corra

RÉSUMÉ

La crise de salinité du Messinien, en abaissant de plus de 2000 m le niveau de la mer Méditerranée pendant une période d'un million d'années environ, permit aux fleuves de cette région de creuser d'amples vallées et de profonds canyons sur l'ancienne plate-forme continentale. Pendant cette période, tous les bassins hydrographiques concernés subirent une intense érosion. On lui doit également la formation des côtes très découpées de Dalmatie et de Grèce, ainsi que les escarpements très vigoureux de l'arc intérieur des Alpes. Le remarquable approfondissement des vallées provoqua un abaissement considérable du niveau d'érosion. Le grandiose phénomène de la régression messinienne explique aussi aisément la particulière abondance, dans les bassins de la Méditerranée, de canyons, de ponts naturels, de monolithes karstiques, d'abris sous-roche, de dolines normales et d'éffondrement, de poljés, de pertes, de cavernes, d'abîmes, de réseaux karstiques très développés et profonds, de sources vauclusiennes et de galeries fossilisées.

SUMMARY

The Messinian regression which led to a lowering of the Mediterranean Sea by over 2000 m lasted for about one million years. This lowering enabled local rivers to cut large valleys and impressive gorges into the continental shelf. Drainage basin systems of surrounding Mediterranean countries suffered dissection and erosion. The indented Dalmatian and Greek coastlines and the marked escarpments of the inner Alps can be ascribed to this period. The low sea level meant a considerable lowering of local base levels of erosion. This Messinian entrenchment phase can account for the widespread occurrence in the Mediterranean basin of gorges, natural bridges, karst pinnacles, abris-sous-roche, solutional and collapse dolines, poljes, shafts, deep and well-developed cave systems, fossil galleries and vauclusian springs.

INTRODUCTION

La régression endoréique messinienne qui durant le Miocène supérieur, pendant une période d'à peu près un million d'années, intéressa la Méditerranée, en provoquant un abaissement du niveau de la mer de plus de 2000 m (G. Clauzon, 1975), a donné aux fleuves qui débouchaient dans cette mer, une très grande capacité érosive régressive.

Les nombreux forages effectués dans les dernières dizaines d'années ont permis de connaître que pendant le Messinien, le Nil et le Rhône avaient creusé au-dessous des actuelles embouchures, des gorges sous-marines profondes de plusieurs centaines de mètres (A. Desio, 1975).

Les affluents du Pô, qui sortent des lacs subalpins, présentent déjà au-dessous de la bordure extérieure des amphithéâtres morainiques des canyons de creusement fluvial, profonds presque d'un millier de mètres (Figure 31.1). L'origine remonte progressivement au Messinien. Aussi la 'Gonfolite' (traduction italienne du terme suisse 'Nagelfluh' et connue comme 'Conglomerato di Como'), molasse de delta fluvial à gros cailloux arrondis bien cimentés, déposée pendant la période qui va de l'Oligocène supérieur au Miocène moyen, était érodée en canyon durant le Messinien et submergée par des sédiments marins Pliocènes et par des alluvions Plio-Quaternaires.

SCHÉMA SUR LA COMPLEXE ORIGINE DES LACS SUBALPINS
Les données Altimetriques sont inspirées au lac de Garde   850m

HAUTE PLAINE   MORAINE
DU PÔ   FRONTALE   LANGUE GLACIARE   65m
                NIVEAU DU LAC   0m
                NIVEAU ACTUEL DE LA MER   CRYPTODÉPRESSION
                                                            -281m
ALLUVIONS PLIOQUATERNAIRES
SÉDIMENTS MARINE PLIOCÈNIQUES
PROFIL LONGITUDINAL DU FOND DU CANYON CREUSÉ PAR UN FLEUVE PENDANT LA MESSINIEN
                                          ROCHE EN PLACE

(G. Corrà)   0   4   8   12   16 Km

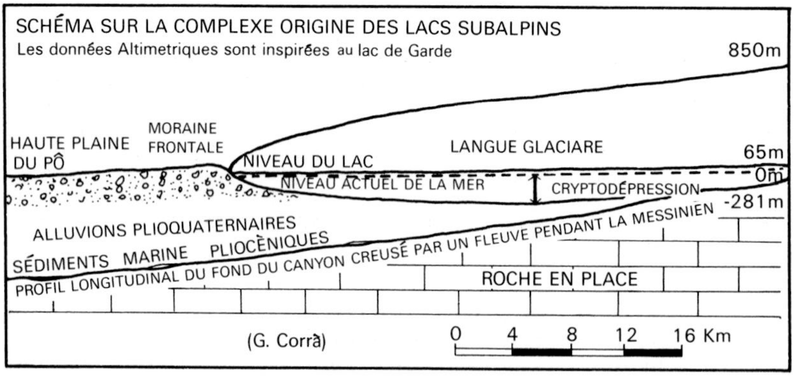

Figure 31.1   Les cryptodépressions des lacs subalpins ne sont pas exclusivement le résultat de l'érosion glaciaire. Dans la régression Messinienne un grand fleuve a creusé un profond canyon. Les étroites vallées gagnées dans le Pliocène par la mer ont donné des formes très semblables aux fiords. Les sédiments marins Pliocèniques et surtout les alluvions Plio-Quaternaires ont couvert le fond des canyons. Les langues glaciaires Quaternaires ont recreusé partiellement les sédiments et les alluvions en donnant aisement des cryptodépressions

Le phénomène est présent dans toute la Haute Plaine du Pô,
à proximité du débouché des vallées subalpines. Toutes ces
vallées sont en effet plates et amples et délimitées par des
interfluves en collines à versants très escarpés. Les reliefs
collinaires sont en outre généralement suivis à brève distance
par un ou deux dos isolés, qui émergent comme des îles des alluvions de la haute plaine (Figure 31.2).

Toutes ces données géomorphologiques démontrent que au-
dessous des alluvions existent des sillons de vallée très profonds. Ils ont été modelés en canyon par une érosion fluviale
active et d'après de nombreuses données fournies par les sondages,
ils datent sans doute du Messinien. En parlant de ces phénomènes
dans la zone de Vérone, R. Albertini (1956), fidèle aux idées
glacio-eustatiques Quaternaires, avança l'absurde hypothèse que
ces vallées, recouvertes d'alluvions, furent très peu profondes
(Figure 31.2). Quelques années plus tard, la découverte de
canyons et de vallées très profonds au-dessous de la Haute Plaine
du Pô et la présence de sédiments marins Pliocènes à grande profondeur dans la Plaine du Pô furent attribuées exclusivement à
des phénomènes de subsidence, que toutefois l'inclinaison des
couches ne pouvait justifier. Il fut nécessaire d'obtenir les
données des forages méditerranéens du navire americain, Glomar
Challenger, relatives aux puissants sédiments évaporatiques au
fond de la mer, pour persuader les géologues qu'il y avait eu
une énorme régression marine au Messinien et de formidables
érosions fluviales dans les bassins de la Méditerranée. Tous
les fleuves circumméditerranéens ont pratiquement creusé au
Messinien de profonds canyons au-dessous de leurs embouchures
actuelles et sur la plate-forme continentale.

Les langues glaciaires qui au Quaternaire ont recreusé
partiellement les alluvions Plio-Quaternaires comblant les canyons messiniens (Bini A, Cita M.B., Gaetani M., 1978), ont pu
former les remarquables cryptodépressions des lacs subalpins
(Lac Majeur -179, Lac de Côme -211, Lac d'Iseo -66, Lac de Garde
-281). Ceux-ci ont été par erreur interprêtés comme le résultat
de l'érosion glaciaire, grâce à leur capacité de surcreusement
de la roche en place qu'il faut aujourd'hui considérer comme
très surestimée (Corrà G., 1983).

LES PRINCIPALES CONSEQUENCES DU PHENOMENE

Les profondes incisions de vallée, creusées par les fleuves dans
tous les bassins tributaires de la Méditerranée, firent reculer
considérablement les lignes de partage des eaux et provoquèrent
beaucoup de captures fluviales, en détruisant systématiquement
les anciennes morphologies karstiques épigées et beaucoup de
celles hypogées et en donnant une remarquable raideur aux versants (Figure 31.2 et 31.3). La raideur de l'arc intérieur des
Alpes n'est pas seulement d'origine structurale, mais aussi le
résultat de la formidable érosion régressive, opérée par les
fleuves en question, pendant le Messinien. Cette raideur est
très évidente déjà dans la bande préalpine (Figure 31.2 et 31.3)
et aussi dans les reliefs de la Dalmatie, de la Grèce et de la
Turquie.

583

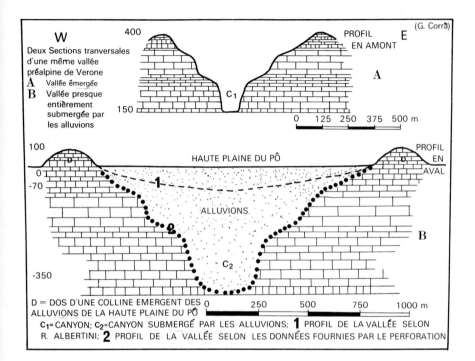

Figure 31.2 Les deux sections transversales d'une même vallée
préalpine de Vérone: une en amont et l'autre en aval.
L'interprétation du profil du fond de la vallée par
R. Albertini (1956) n'est pas géomorphologiquement
proportionée. Elle néglige soit les données carrières de
sables et de graviers de l'Adige dans la zone de piémont
de Villa di Quinzano, à la base du versant occidental de
la valle di Avesa, soit les données des nombreuses perfo-
rations pour la recherche hydrique dans la zone de piémont
des toutes les vallées préalpines

Les bassins hydrographiques tributaires de la Méditerranée, de
nature lithologique en grande partie calcaire, reçurent au
Messinien une nouvelle et remarquable empreinte de karstification qui encore aujourd'hui caractérise clairement cette région
géographique. L'existence d'un karst méditerranéen original fut
comprise intuitivement par J. Nicod, (1970, 1972). La vraie
cause de cette originalité demeurait toutefois encore inconnue
dans la bibliographie.

L'abaissement général et remarquable des niveaux de base
locaux favorisa le développement d'un karst épigé ruiniforme,
particulièrement riche en lapiés géants, monolithes karstiques,
ponts naturels et abris sous-roche (Figure 31.3). L'érosion
rapide et profonde a accentué au maximum les différences litho-

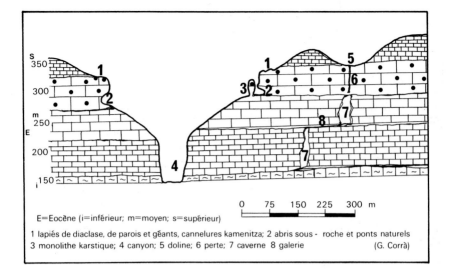

E=Eocène (i=inférieur; m=moyen; s=supérieur)

1 lapiés de diaclase, de parois et géants, cannelures kamenitza; 2 abris sous - roche et ponts naturels
3 monolithe karstique; 4 canyon; 5 doline; 6 perte; 7 caverne 8 galerie   (G. Corrà)

Figure 31.3   Section transversale typique inspirée aux vallées,
      des Monti Lessini, Borago et Galina, dans la zone de Avesa,
      trois kilomètres au nord de la ville de Vérone.   La pré-
      sence d'un grand canyon à basse côte démontre que
      l'érosion torrentueuse fut très forte et seulement dans la
      régression Messinienne il y a eu un niveau de base marine
      suffisamment bas pour justifier une aussi grande capacité
      érosive régressive.   La rapide et remarquable érosion ré-
      gressive, à créer des canyons, a accentué la pente des
      versants en détruisant les précedentes et plus modestes
      morphologies karstiques, en exaltant au maximum les dif-
      férences lithologiques et stratigraphiques et en donnant
      des abris sous-roche, des lapiés géants, de monolithes
      karstiques, des ponts naturels, et en outre de nombreuses
      dolines, pertes, galeries et cavernes.   Le phénomène tend
      à caractérisér toutes les zones à basse côte des bassins
      hydrographiques de la Méditerranée

stratigraphiques des couches sédimentaires et les effets de la
tectonique, en donnant des profils transversaux de vallée très
accidentés (Figure 31.2 et 31.3).   Les réseaux karstiques subirent
un approfondissement et un élargissement particulier.   Cela se
marqua en surface par la disparition fréquente du drainage superficiel, l'apparition de très nombreux poljés, pertes et dolines
normales et d'effondrement, tandis qu'en profondeur cavernes et
abîmes devenaient particulièrement abondants et vastes (Figure
31.3).

      L'intense karstification due à l'abaissement des niveaux
hydriques de base associé aux glacio-eustatismes Quaternaires
fut déjà soulignée par Cavaillé (1970), Gèze (1974) et Nicod
(1982).   Mais ce dernier parlait aussi des conséquences possibles de la régression Messinienne d'une façon hypothétique.

585

Il faut néanmoins se rappeler que dans son article 1967 J. Nicod avait soutenu l'origine Miocène de quelques formes karstiques des Plans du Verdon et dans celui de 1968 (mais publié en 1970) l'origine Miocène de nombreuses morphologies karstiques de Provence.

Le retour à la normale du niveau de la Méditerranée au Pliocène a permis à la mer de submerger des territoires situés très à l'intérieur des terres d'allure décidément très comparbles aux fiords. La sédimentation marine reprit. Les embouchures des fleuves avancèrent rapidement et les alluvions comblèrent une bonne partie des canyons messiniens. Les dépôts alluviaux en bordure des reliefs favorisa la formation de nombreuses et importantes résurgences karstiques vauclusiennes de piémont.

La profondeur et l'élargissement gagnés pendant le Messinien par les réseaux karstiques sont probablement le motif principal de la formation de beaucoup de sources thermales que nous retrouvons très abondantes dans la zone subalpine entre Sirmione et Abano, grâce probablement aussi aux remarquables anomalies géothermiques positives de la région.

Le retour de la mer aux niveaux océaniques et la sédimentation alluviale qui s'en suivit en bordure des reliefs dans la zone de piémont favorisèrent la fossilisation, par des sédiments de type différent, de beaucoup de cavités karstiques; par exemple l'ocre jaune, dérivée de la décantation d'eaux provenant de calcaires riches en pyrite, combla systématiquement et imperméabilisa les galeries karstiques. Les secteurs avals des canyons furent couverts par les alluvions et par conséquent masqués tandis que les côtes marines prirent des formes moins dentelées. Toutefois les côtes de la Yougoslavie, de la Grèce et de la Turquie, dépourvues d'importants fleuves, restèrent remarquablement découpées. Les sources sous-marines sont nombreuses ici (Maire R., 1980), de même que les sources sous-lacustres dans les lacs subalpins, là où les alluvions Plio-Quaternaires furent creusées par les langues glaciaires.

L'enfoncement du drainage qui se produisit sur les reliefs méditerranéens au Messinien ne subit presque pas de changements aux hautes altitudes en créant encore aujourd'hui des conditions d'aridité exagérée. Aux basses altitudes la fossilisation post-Messinienne a conservé intactes beaucoup de morphologies karstiques épigées et hypogées, mais l'évolution très ralentie post-Missinienne, aux altitudes moyennes à permis a un grand nombre de morphologies karstiques de subsister jusqu'à nos jours nonobstant l'appréciable laps de temps de quelques millions d'années.

QUELQUES EXEMPLES SIGNIFICATIFS

En 1971, des considérations stratigraphiques, confirmées aussi par la paléontologie, m'ont permis de comprendre que l'ocre jaune de la colline de Vérone fossilisait un dense réseau karstique hypogé formé pendant une longue phase régressive Miocène et non au Quaternaire, comme tous les auteurs l'avaient affirmé.

Dans les Monti Lessini de Vérone, en 1974 et 1975, en considérant les conditions stratigraphiques, tectoniques et lithologiques, j'ai daté l'origine du profond abîme karstique 'Spluga della Preta' de la fin du Tertiaire et non du Quaternaire, comme quelques auteurs en affrontant le problème, l'avaient supposé.

En 1979, en appliquant aux données pluviométriques moyennes actuelles de cette région, les coefficients de solubilité annuelle, cités par U. Sauro (1979) dans le chapitre de karstologie du volume de Geomorfologia de Gb. Castiglioni (1979), j'ai trouvé que la Dolina della Cola, dans la colline de Vérone, devrait avoir un âge d'environ 4.5 million d'années. Ce résultat, même approximatif, est suffisant pour comprendre que la doline et le voisin et profond canyon de la Val Borago, vers lequel les roches s'inclinent avec une pente moyenne de 10°, doivent leur origine aux très forts phénomènes érosifs fluviaux amorcés par la régression Messinienne. Il est significatif en outre que toutes les nombreuses dolines de la zone et même le poljé de la proche Valle dei Ronchi, soient situés sur la bordure orientale d'un canyon vers lequel les strates s'inclinent (Figure 31.3).

CONCLUSIONS

Les paysages karstiques ruiniformes très répandus, la présence de karsts tropicaux (Chardon M., 1977; Julian M., Martini J., Nicod J., 1978), la très grande abondance de canyons, d'abris sous-roche, de dolines normales et d'effondrement, de poljés, de pertes, de puits d'effondrement, d'amples cavernes et de profonds abîmes, la fréquente fossilisation des réseaux karstiques aux basses altitudes et les grosses sources vauclusiennes ne caractérisent pas par hasard le karst des bassins hydrographiques de la Méditerranée. Une recherche attentive et diversifiée montre que très souvent ces morphologies karstiques sont très anciennes et que leur origine peut être souvent attribuée à la regression marine Messinienne endoréique de la Méditerranée. Pour cela la régression Messinienne représente un point de repère fondamental dans la recherche chronologique des phénomènes karstiques des bassins hydrographiques de la Méditerranée.

Le problème méritait donc d'être officiellement signalé, non seulement par sa grande originalité et par ses énormes conséquences, mais aussi par les nombreux rapports avec d'importants phénomènes géologiques et erosifs et pour cela par les précieuses indications qu'il peut fournir encore a l'étude des phénomènes karstiques et aux différents secteurs de recherche des sciences naturelles.

Le phénomène de la forte régression endoréique Messinienne dans les bassins de la Méditerranée et ses importantes conséquences morphologiques sont restés longtemps inconnus, car le retour de la Méditerranée aux niveaux océaniques normaux a permis à la mer, par ses eaux ou ses sédiments de masquer tous les canyons de la plate-forme continentale, et aux fleuves de les combler progressivement d'alluvions, en faisant disparaître les nombreux paysages de vallée, semblables aux fiords, qui caractérisaient le pourtour des bassins de la Méditerranée au Pliocène.

Une relecture attentive du paysage morphologique des bassins de la Méditerranée, confronté avec celui des régions normales, pourrait mieux souligner son originalité et dans le même temps révéler s'il y a eu d'autres bassins marins interessés par d'importantes régressions endoréiques.

REFERENCES

Albertini, R. 1956. Le alture isolate dell'alta pianura veronese. *Riv. Geogr. It.,* **63(1/2)**, 35-53, 144-165.

Bini, A., Cita, B.M., and Gaetani, M. 1978. Southern Alpine Lakes - Hypothesis of an erosional origin related to the Messinian entrenchment. *Marine Geology,* **27**, 271-288.

Cavaillé, A. 1970. L'évolution des grottes au Quaternaire dans la France méridionale. *Bull. Soc. Hist. Nat.,* 106.

Chardon, M. 1977. Premiers résultats d'une étude des formes karstiques et des dépôts superficiels du Plateau de Serle (Préalpes de Brescia) *Actes de la table Ronde Intern. de Karstologie, St. Trent. Sc. Nat.,* 149-161.

Clauzon, C. 1975. Preuves et implications de la régression endoréique messinienne au niveau des planes abyssales: l'exemple du midi méditerranéen français. *Bull. Ass. Geogr. Franc.,* 429 - 317-333.

Corrà, G. 1971. Le morfologie carsiche nel Veronese. Atti 1° *Conv. Naz. per lo studio, la protezione e la valorizzazione dei fenomeni carsici, Verona,* 15-17 ott., 1971, 41-84.

Corrà, G. 1974. Osservazioni sui problemi speleogenetici della Spluga della Preta. *Relazione spedizione Italo-Polacca,* 1973, alla Spluga della Preta, FIE, Torino.

Corrà, G. 1975. Osservazioni sui problemi speleogenetici della Spluga della Preta. *Natura Alpina,* **26(3)**, 178-212, Museo Trid. Sc. Nat/, Trento.

Corrà, G. 1983. L'origine des lacs subalpins. *Actes du 108e Congrès Nat. des Soc. Savantes,* Grenoble 5-9 avril, 1983.

Desio, A. 1975. L'origine e l'evoluzione del Bacino mediterraneo *Rendiconti Ist. Lombardo, Acc. Sc. e Lett.,* **109**, 18-40.

Gèze, B. 1974. Relations entre les phénomènes karstiques de surface et de profondeur. *Mémoires et Documents n.s., Phén. Karst.,* **15(2)**, 195-207.

Julian, M., Martini, J. et Nicod, J. 1978. Les karsts méditerranéens. *Bull. Méditerranée,* **1(2)**, 115-131.

Maire, R. 1980. Elements de Karstologie physique. *Spelunca,* 1 supplément, spécial, **3**, 1-56.

Nicod, J. 1967. Carte des phénomènes karstiques des Plans du Verdon. *Mém. et Doc. du CNRS, Phén. Karst.,* **4**, 83-100.

Nicod, J. 1970. Sur quelques problèmes des karsts de Provence. *Méditerrannée,* **7**, 109-115.

Nicod, J. 1972. *Pays et paysages du calcaire.* (P.U.F. Paris,) 244p.

Nicod, J. 1982. Niveaux de base régressifs et formes karstiques submergées. *Mémoire de l'Ass. Franç. de Karstologie,* **4**, 67-74.

Sauro, U. 1979. Morfologie carsica (dans le vol. Geomorfologia de Gb. Castiglioni) *UTET,* 208-254, Torino.

32

Karst zonation in China

Chen Zhi Ping

SUMMARY

Karst is widely distributed in China and occurs in well defined
zones. Temperature and precipitation are both important in controlling this zonation but temperature is the key factor involved.
Karst is well developed in eastern and southern China because of
the monsoon climate with high temperatures and heavy Summer and
Autumn precipitation. Most of west China is a dry area having less
than 250 mm of rainfall and has weakly developed karst. The physical and chemical properties of overlying sediments also significantly affect karst development, (e.g. corrosion intensity increases with decreasing soil pH). Three karst zones are recognised
in China: the tropical karst zone (fenglin) of the south; the flat
hill-depression area of Central China; the temperate, semi-humid
zone of north China possessing hilly features and dry valleys.
Palaeoclimatic variations are shown to have had an important influence on the present day pattern of landforms.

RÉSUMÉ

Les paysages karstiques sont très répandus en Chine et se trouvent
dans des zones bien définies. La température et la précipitation
jouent une influence importante dans cette zone mais c'est la température qui est la plus significative. Le karst est bien développé
dans la partie est et sud de la Chine à cause du climat monsoonal
(températures élevées et fortes précipitations en été et en automne).
Une grande partie de l'ouest de la Chine est sèche ayant moins de
250 mm de précipitation. De ce fait elle se caractérise par un karst
peu développe. Les caractéristiques physiques et chimiques des sédiments superficiels influencent également le développement du karst.
(par example, l'intensité de corrosion s'accroit au fur et à mesure
que le pH des sols diminue). Trois zones karstiques sont reconnues
en Chine: la zone tropicale (fenglin) du sud; la région des collines
plates -dépressions de la Chine centrale; et la zone tempérée, semi-
humide du nord de la Chine où on trouve des montagnes karstiques et
des vallées sèches. Finalement on analyse l'importance des variations
paléoclimatiques pour expliquer les phénomènes karstiques actuels.

Temperature and precipitation are important factors controlling the zoning of karst in China. But as far as the detailed influence of temperature and precipitation on landforms are concerned not enough work has been done. The present study examines these problems of climato-genesis from a macro point of view.

Many workers have calculated erosion rates with Corbel's formula by using runoff values which, in China, decrease from south to north (Table 1). The rate of erosion in Duan, Guangxi Province (south) is about twice that in Jinan, Shantong, and about six times higher than that in Su County, Shanxi (mid-China). Generally, it is believed that there is a linear relationship between erosion rate and precipitation. This is shown by the equation $Dc = 0.0079^{1.23}$, which is very similar to the equation $Dc = 0.0043^{1.26}$ given by Engh (1980) and Lang (1977).

Table 32.1   Erosion rates in karst areas in China

Place	Rainfall mm/year	Erosion rates mm/1000 years
Su County, North Shanxi Province	400	10.7
Jin County, Liaoning Province	600	24.1
Jinan, Shantong Province	650	29.91
Saxia, Hubei Province	1200	60.00
West Guiyang, Guizhou Province	1200	44.54
Louping, Yunnan Province	1200	51.53
Duan, Guangxi Province	1700	76.8
Wuming, Guangxi Province	1100	35.0
A place, Guangxi Province		79.0

As the decrease of annual average temperature from south to north is coincident with a decrease of precipitation, there is a good correlation between erosion rate and temperature. In effect both temperature and precipitation are equally important for karst development. However, factors controlling karst development are so complex that it is difficult to explain karst phenomena by any one factor alone. For example, the rainfall in Zhejiang, Jiangxi, and Hunan is about 1500 mm or more, just about the same as that in south China; yet no fenglin has ever been discovered in these provinces, although the precipitation is enough for fenglin development. This fact suggests that the corrosion intensity is much lower than that in south China where fenglin develops perfectly. The precipitation both in the north or Northeast China and in the area between Changjiang and Huaihe is 700-1000 mm per year, but karst is much poorer in the former area than in the latter. Another good example is in Dubrovnik, Yugoslavia, with an annual precipitation of 5000 mm, and a maximum of 8000 mm, but still no fenglin develop there. Therefore, it is suggested that temperature determines the potential solution intensity, while precipitation is only a means of karstification. When rainfall reaches a certain amount, the solutional intensity will also achieve a certain value, depending on the temperature. In some areas, however, the intensity is affected by the amount of precipitation. For instance, it is impossible to develop fenglin in tropical dry and semi-dry areas.

Eastern and southern China belong to the monsoon climate zone with high temperature and precipitation in Summer and Autumn; this is the main reason for karst development. Therefore, fenglin is distributed towards 26°N. But the rainy seasons last differently from south to north, being 7 months in south China, but 3 months only in north China. The precipitation in the north is only half of that in the middle and one-third of that in the south. It can be seen, then, that the rainy season and the precipitation which play an important role in karst processes all decrease from south to north. In addition, there is almost no winter in the south, while winter lasts for half a year in the northeast.

The physical and chemical properties of overlying sediments significantly affect karst development. Chemical weathering predominates in the south where clay weathering crusts are easily washed away by heavy rains, producing bare hills and the opening of fissures. However, mechanical weathering dominates in the region to the north of the Nanlin Mountains. Carbonate rocks in north China are buried by aeolian loess and silty soil and the many corroded fissures are infilled; this limits the rate of seepage. The chemical nature of the soils also plays a marked role in karst development. Soils of different types occur in different regions; for instance, acid soils occur in the areas to the south of Changjiang (Yangtse), neutral soils in the areas between Changjiang and the Qinglin Mountains, and neutral or slightly alkaline soils in north China. 'Stone teeth', for instance, develop chiefly in acid soil areas. The more acid the soil the better the development of the stone teeth, showing that corrosion intensity increases with decreasing pH. On the other hand alkaline soils, with abundant $CaCO_3$ constituents, protect the carbonate rocks beneath from corrosion so that it is rare to find 'stone teeth' in north China. The higher dissolved carbonate hardness of karst waters in the neutral and alkaline soil areas should not be regarded as representative of actual carbonate rock erosion rates. They can be explained by the greater availability of calcium carbonate in these soils. It is worth stressing, too, that the intensity of biochemical action increases with increasing temperature and precipitation. Thus, in China, it is clear that corrosive intensity decreases from south to north, and that this has given rise to distinctive karst zonation.

REGIONAL VARIANTS

Karst geomorpholoy in east China may be divided into 3 zones.

Firstly, the well-known tropical karst of south China typi-
fied by fenglin, depressions and caves. Fenglin is made up of
many limestone hills (hillslopes of 45° or more) in which the
base width is less than the height. Closed depression densities
can be as high as 2.6 depressions per km^2. Distances between
depressions vary from 100-200 m. In other words, the landforms
in this area have been sharply dissected, and the slopes of
positive landforms like the fenglin are steep. The karstification ratio (ratio of total cavern length to total drilling core
length) is over 15%. Complex, well developed subsurface drainage
systems are found and have large catchment areas. For example,
each system in the Guangxi province has a mean area of about
150 km^2. More than 50% of the annual rainfall rapidly penetrates
underground through open fissures, funnels and sinkholes.

Secondly, the positive landforms in mid-China characterized
by gentle hills; their tops are round, their base width is equal
to, or more than their height, and slope angles are in the range
of 25°-35°. In this area, the mean density is less than one
depression per square kilometre, though in some places it may
reach 30 per square kilometre. Numerous funnels occur within
the watersheds. The proportion of dry valleys in the negative
landforms greatly increase in a northward direction. Underground
drainage systems are relatively simple and their catchment areas
are small. The mean catchment area is generally less than 50 km^2,
so that there are many more of these systems than in south China.
The karstification ratio based on borehole results is about 15%.
All these are typical subtropical karst features.

Thirdly, the temperate, semi-humid karst areas in north
China which possess karst landforms that are similar to the
mountainous and hilly features developed on other rocks. Carbonate rocks generally constitute the higher parts of this
region. In areas with high hydraulic gradients, the landscape
is sometimes greatly dissected by the rivers, giving magnificent
valleys; the surface of the rocks is characterized by mechanical
weathering, and few caves occur. A low proportion of rainfall
sinks underground; for the Niangzhiguan Springs, less than 20%
of the annual precipitation sinks into the aquifer and the
groundwater flow velocity is very low. Most rainwater drains
over the surface, and this is why dry valleys predominate here.
The karst ratio is only 2-3%.

Most of west China belongs to the dry climatic zone with
precipitation less than 250 mm. It may be divided into two
parts, north and south. The former includes Xingjiang, Guanshu,
and Inner Mongolia - areas of dry grassland and desert. Here
karst is poorly developed with only small fissures covered by
soil. The southern part of the Xizhang Plateau is with an elevation

of over 4500 m; here the karst consists primarily of frost forms, solutional hills, rocky walls and the occasional depression.

CLIMATIC CHANGE

The present karst landscape is the product of a long period of evolution. As such, it records the imprint of both present and past climatic changes. Two factors account for the climatic fluctuations experienced by China since the Tertiary: global climate changes and the uplifting of the Xizhang Plateau.

At the beginning of the Tertiary, when the land area of China was primarily at a peneplain stage of development, the climate was much warmer than today. The boundary between the warm temperature and temperate zones was 10°-15° further north. The northern limit of the tropical zone was around 25°N. Tropical grassland with few trees and desert lay between 25°-35°N, and the subtropical climate zone, between 34°-45°N (Xingjiang). At that time, it was probably rather more humid than today. In the Neogene the climatic zones shifted southward, the Xizhang Plateau was uplifted and the monsoon climatic pattern in east China changed. This resulted in a zonation similar to that of today. A tropical rain forest belt developed in south China and a subtropical broadleaf forest belt in mid-China; sometimes its northern boundary advanced to mid-north China. Due to the dry climate becoming more humid in this northern region, the rate of karst landform development accelerated, thereby establishing the basis of the present zonation. Since the Quaternary, the climate zones have moved further southward. In south China, the present tropical climate limit has moved south by over 4°N. However, since this southern zone still experiences over 1500 mm of precipitation and a mean annual temperature of 18°C, fenglin still develop. These changes explain why tropical karst appears in the southern subtropical zone. Later the climate changed greatly as a result of two circumstances. First, the climate in mid-China changed from dry to humid, which meant that karstification was more intense in the Neogene than in any other period. Secondly, the climate in north China became temperate and dry and the karst could not continue to develop. The landscape reflects these polygenetic origins. The flat hill-depression landscape, like that in mid-China, has remained on the watersheds of mountains and the flat hill-dry valley landscape, developed in the Neogene, has formed in the lower mountain areas.

Another reason causing climatic change is the uplift of the Xizhang and Yunnan-Guizhou Plateaux; this forced the tropical karst boundary to move eastwards. As the climate became cooler the fenglin geomorphology was greatly transformed and evolved into more gently sloping relief. Under tropical conditions, the depressions among the fenglin absorb surface water, but in the cooler environments, valleys and gullies are the chief conduits for water discharge. A transition zone characterizes the border of the fenglin regions.

The factors influencing the evolution of karsts are very complex. In the regions outside the tropical zone, where marked vertical drainage or lateral undercutting on the valley plain occur, hillslopes may reach 45° - similar to the slopes of the fenglin. It is very important to distinguish the tropical karst fenglin from other comparable karst forms. Some subtropical and temperate karst landforms which appear in the tropical karst areas are a response to lithological variations and the intensity of neotectonic movements. Only in pure lithologies is karst zonation clearly seen. In the less pure carbonates solutional intensity is lower and this results in a lower rate of removal by groundwater drainage systems. Hence many different karst systems may occur in the same climate zone.

To conclude, it is important to stress not only the zonation of Chinese karst but also the many complex factors producing regional variations.

REFERENCES

Engh, L. 1980. Can we determine erosion by a simple formula? *Transaction of the British Cave Research Association,* **7**(1), 30-32.

Lang, S. 1977. Relationship between world-wide karstic denudation, corrosion and precipitation. *Proceedings of the 7th International Speleological Congress,* Sheffield, England, 282-283.

33

The Pinnacle Karst of the Stone Forest, Lunan, Yunnan, China: an example of a sub-jacent karst

Chen Zhi Ping, Song Lin Hua and M.M. Sweeting

SUMMARY

This paper discusses the morphology and evolution of the Lunan Stone Forest, China. Here pinnacle landforms are developed within a valley situation in Mao-Kuo limestones. The pinnacles range from 1 to 35 m in height and 1 to 20 m in width. Each pinnacle, or pinnacle cluster, is separated by corridors (bogaz), 1 - 20 m wide. The local water table plays an important part in limiting the depth of pinnacle development. Their steep slopes are dissected by different generations of runnels, scallops and solution basins. The development of these micro-forms is affected by the presence of chert in the limestone and by dolomitised beds. Most of these weathering features are of relatively recent origin and relate to present climatic conditions. Different viewpoints have been advanced in the Chinese literature concerning the origin of the pinnacles themselves. The present authors argue that evidence from solution and other features suggest that their main development occurred beneath the surrounding cover rocks (Tertiary sands and clays) possibly during the later Tertiary and especially during the Pleistocene. Once the cover rocks are removed, the pinnacles are exposed and the modern weathering forms replace the formerly smooth surfaces.

RÉSUMÉ

Cet article discute de la morphologie et de l'évolution de la Forêt
de Pierre, Lunan, Chine. Les pinacles de cette forêt se trouvent
dans une vallée et se sont développés dans les calcaires Mao Kuo.
Les pinacles varient entre 1 - 35 m de hauteur et 1 - 20 m de largeur.
Le niveau d'eau local joue un rôle important en limitant la profondeur
des pinacles. Les pentes raides des pinacles sont déchiquetées par
des lapiés, des scallops et des bassins de corrosion. Le développement de ces formes est influencé par la présence de silex dans les
calcaires et par les couches dolomitisées. La plupart de ces formes
sont d'origines récentes et se sont développées sous le régime
climatique actuel. Des points de vue différents ont été exprimés
dans la littérature chinoise concernant l'origine des pinacles. Dans
cet article on pense que l'évidence fournie par des formes de dissolution et d'autres phénomènes indique que le développement des
pinacles a eu lieu sous une couverture Tertiaire de grès et d'argiles
peut-être vers la fin de l'époque Tertiaire et surtout dans le
Pleistocène. Dès que ces grès et ces argiles disparaissent les
pinacles apparaissent et l'érosion commence à entailler leurs
surfaces lisses.

INTRODUCTION

The Stone Forest, or Shiling, in the County of Lunan is situated
126 km south-east of Kumming in the Province of Yunnan, (Figure
33.1). It occurs in a preserved natural park of an area of
about 80 hectares, and forms part of a much bigger region covering over 30 000 hectares in which other similar 'stone forests'[1]
can be found. The Stone Forest described in this paper lies at
a mean altitude of 1750 m above sea level; the highest point is
1875 m and the lowest 1625 m. The mean annual temperature is
16.3°C (varying from a minimum of -2°C to a maximum of 39°C);
the mean annual rainfall is 936.5 mm of which 70-90% falls in
the rainy season from June to October.

The Lunan Stone Forest occurs in the Mao Kuo limestones of
lower Permian age (Figure 33.2). The limestones dip gently to
the north-west at about 5°. Overlying the limestones are Tertiary
(Eocene) clays and sandstones of varying thicknesses from 0 m to
30 m and it is from these beds that the limestones are emerging.
Other 'stone forests' can be found over a wide area where the
Tertiary beds have been removed, but this paper will only consider the Lunan Stone Forest.

The pinnacle landforms are developed in pure Mao Kuo limestones, which contain 55-56% CaO and 43% CO_3 - the residual
material being less than 1%. The limestones are a rather evenly
and thickly bedded shelf series and are hard and crystalline;
beds generally 1-2 m thick occur, but they may be considerably
more - Yie Quing Tong (1982) gives examples of beds up to 30 m
thick.

---

[1]*Stone Forest* is the English translation of the Chinese name
given to areas of pinnacle karst of this type.

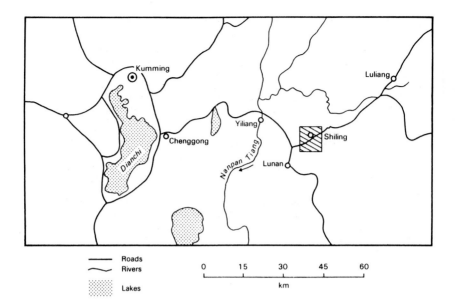

Figure 33.1 Location map of study area, Lunan, Yunnan Province

In certain areas they contain much chert (notably in the Minor
Stone Forest) and some beds are dolomitised. The limestones are
generally without major faults or folds, but are crossed by well
defined joints and fissures which are aligned NW-SE (310°-340°)
and NE-SW (40°-65°); the joints are more or less vertical,
inclining at 80°-90°.

The general relief of the Lunan Stone Forest area is undulating, with relatively shallow surface valleys (about 100 m
deep) cutting through the Tertiary beds and into the Mao Kuo
limestones. The whole region forms part of the Yunnan Plateau.

THE PINNACLE KARST

The Stone Forest consists of separate rock pinnacles of many
sizes, from 1 m in width and height to others of several metres.
The major joints have become widened and may be as narrow as
1 m or as wide as 10-20 metres. Most fissures are about 1.0-
1.5 m wide. The maximum height of the pinnacles is from 30-35 m
with many at about 20 m. In the Lunan area the tallest pinnacles
occur in the centre along the drainage lines. while towards the
ridges the clay cover is greater and the pinnacles are smaller.
But in other 'Stone Forest' outcrops the highest pinnacles often
occur on the watersheds where the clays are being removed, while
the limestones are beneath the clays in the shallow valleys.
The local water table is represented in the Lunan Stone Forest
by the Sword Peak Pond, Lotus Pond and the Stone Forest Lake;
such local watertables appear to be a limiting depth for the

599

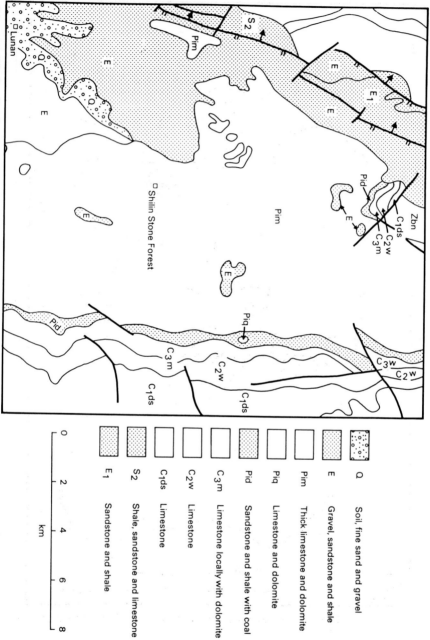

Figure 33.2 Geological map of Lunan area

Q — Soil, fine sand and gravel

E — Gravel, sandstone and shale

Pim — Thick limestone and dolomite

Piq — Limestone and dolomite

Pid — Sandstone and shale with coal

C_3m — Limestone locally with dolomite

C_2w — Limestone

C_1ds — Limestone

S_2 — Shale, sandstone and limestone

E_1 — Sandstone and shale

0   2   4   6   8
km

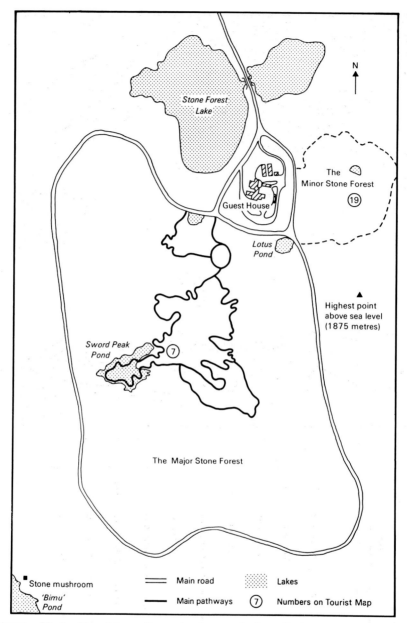

Figure 33.3   The Stone Forest, Lunan (adapted from The Tourist
Map)

601

active development of pinnacles (Figure 33.3). After heavy rain, the water table may rise by as much as 10 m. In 1979 all the tourest paths were under several metres of water. A well defined subsurface stream occurs below the Lotus Pond at a depth of 10 m - indicating water table flow. Water collected from such groundwater contains up to 177 p.p.m. $CaCO_3$ and 30 p.p.m. $MgCO_3$ (Yie Quing Tong, 1982).

The steep slopes of the pinnacles are dissected by several different sizes of runnels (karren), scallops, and solution basins; several generations of these features can be recognized (Figure 33.4). At least two sizes of runnels occur on the pinnacle faces. These are, first, small rillen-karren, similar to rillen-karren described from other environments and equally regularly developed (Osmaston, 1980; Sweeting and Lancaster, 1982). They vary from 1-2 cm wide and several centimetres long on the projecting rock pinnacles, but are wider from 3-4 cm, in troughs in the pinnacles. The rillen-karren have sharp ridges and are interrupted by scallops and rain pits. Secondly, there occur larger and smoother flutes or furrows up to 35 cm wide and 50 cm deep; they are from 1 m to several metres long. These are the most common weathering feature on the upper parts of the pinnacles and are a characteristic feature of the Lunan Stone Forest. At one locality in the centre of the Major Stone Forest (Figure 33.3) historical evidence suggests that some of these furrows (25 cm -20 cm deep) have taken about 1000 years to develop.

Scallops (or cockling) are shallow pits on both vertical and gently sloping surfaces caused by the action of flowing, eddying water; scallops are usually asymmetrical, the steeper side facing in the direction of flow. At least three groups according to size can be recognized. The smallest are 1 cm wide by 1 cm deep and are caused by rills of pulsating rainwater. The medium size scallops are from about 5-15 cm wide and about 5-10 cm deep, and the largest are about 30 cm in width and 15-20 cm deep; they appear also to be the result of solution by eddying water.

Solution basins (kamenitzas) are common on horizontal surfaces and can vary from small basins about 7 cm in diameter and 7 cm deep to much larger features over a metre long and up to 50 cm to 1 metre deep. Many of these solution basins contain algae and soil particles and are being actively deepened today (Figure 33.5).

The development of these weathering features on the pinnacles is affected by the presence of chert in the limestone and by dolomitised beds. Both chert and dolomite appear to inhibit the development of the regular and symmetrical rillen-karren furrows. This is partly due to the occurrence of the nodular chert; in places the nodules have the effect of concentrating rainwater and causing the development of ring-like solution hollows around the nodules - a case of accelerated corrosion (Figure 33.6). It is particularly well seen in the Minor Stone Forest. Other differential weathering of the limestone pinnacles can be observed south-west of the Major Stone Forest in the Stone Mushroom area.

Figure 33.4 General view of Lunan, Stone Forest

Figure 33.5 Solution basin (about 30 cm in diameter)

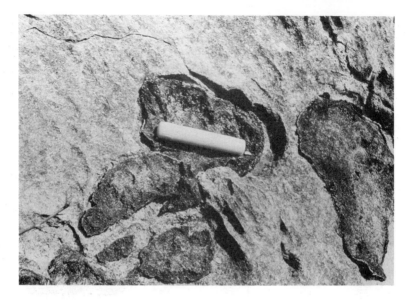

Figure 33.6   Accelerated corrosion surrounding chert nodules.

Figure 33.7   Pinnacles emerging from Eocene sediments.

In this area the rock is much fractured with small criss-cross joints, where weathering takes place more rapidly; the 'stalk' of the Stone Mushroom rock illustrates this phenomenon very well.

It is quite common for the upper 1-3 metres of the pinnacles to be dissected by fresh furrows and rillen-karren: but frequently below this level the pinnacles may be quite differently weathered being pitted and knarled irregularly. In many areas such weathering has been caused by the biological action of the roots of tree creepers and other plants. The weathering resembles that described by Osmaston (1980) on pinnacles on Gunung Api in the Mulu area, Sarawak.

Each pinnacle or pinnacle cluster is separated by corridors (the bogaz of Cvijic) 1-2 m wide and 20-30 m high and which follow the major joint lines. Solution along the major bedding planes is also important and blocks become loosened. As blocks of the limestone collapse and break down, the corridors widen in places and at the intersection of major joints doline-like closed depressions have been formed. These processes break down the pinnacle formation and the relief degenerates into isolated rock masses surrounded by flat fields.

THE SUB-JACENT KARST

The weathering features of the pinnacles which have been described are of relatively recent origin and probably relate to climatic conditions near to those of the present. The main problem is to account for the origin of the separate pinnacles themselves. Clues to this question are given in the area north-east of Sword Peak Pond, and near to point 7 on the Tourist Map. In this section of the Stone Forest, where the limestones are pure and thickly bedded, the sides of the pinnacles are indented by semicircular recesses 2-3 m in diameter and 20-30 m high. These recesses are semicircular potholes formed by the corrosion and erosion of concentrated curtains of water falling probably from cover rocks. They resemble similar features which can be seen in the Mammoth Cave limestones beneath the Big Clifty Sandstone and in the Carboniferous limestones in South Wales beneath the Pennant Grit. These pot-hole-like features have been called 'pohl cells' (Pohl, 1955), and are formed beneath cover rocks. It is probable that such 'pohl cells' were largely demarcated before the cover clays were removed.

The Stone Forest lies in a valley but is surrounded by the cover sands and clays which can be shown to overlap everywhere onto the present relief. In many places, the sands and clays are exposed *in situ*, completely undisturbed, between the pin-nacles; for instance, in the Minor Stone Forest near point 19 on the Tourist Map (Figure 33.3). In other places slumping of the cover rocks has occurred. The sands and shales when first exposed are bluish in colour - but soon oxidise and weather to a red colluvial soil which can be seen to be associated with the limestones over most of their outcrop. In the area of the Lunan Stone Forest there is little sign of fluvial erosive activity except in the areas of the watertable lakes. But in the surrounding countryside, active streams can be seen cutting into the Tertiary clays and sands and revealing underneath a dissected limestone surface, with stone teeth and pinnacles already formed (up to 10 m high). Further removal of the clays could presumably expose more of the pinnacles and other Stone Forests. When first exposed from the clays, the weathering surface of the limestone is smoothed, by pedogenic processes (Figure 33.7).

There are two main points of view in the Chinese literature about the development of the Stone Forest. Yu Jin Piao (1982) states that the main periods for the pinnacles and Stone Forest formation were in the Eocene and early Oligocene; that is the pinnacle karst was more or less formed before the deposition of the Tertiary clays. On the other hand Yie Quing Tong (1982) believes that the Stone Forest has developed since the late Pleistocene and especially in the Holocene; he cites evidence of hydrogeochemical features and the drainage. In this view the stripping of the clays and the formation of the pinnacles would be more or less contemporaneous.

Evidence of the solution and corrosion of limestones under cover rocks was recognized by F. Katzer in 1909 but first dealt with fully in 1924 by A. Penck in his paper 'Das Unterirdische Karst'. It is now known that long caves and large closed depressions can form in limestones beneath cover rocks, for instance, as already mentioned in the Mammoth Cave area in the USA and in South Wales in Britain (Palmer, 1981; Thomas, 1954). Returning, therefore, to the origin of the Stone Forest, perhaps a compromise between the two Chinese viewpoints can be put forward. The Tertiary clays and sands must have been laid down around an eroded, but not necessarily pinnacled limestone surface. However, drainage through these cover rocks may have taken place during both the remaining Tertiary period and the Pleistocene; it is unrealistic to assume that no change and no dissolution of the limestones took place during this long period of time. The development of the main pinnacle relief may have taken place beneath the cover rocks during the later Tertiary and, particularly, the Pleistocene. Solution beneath the cover rocks must also be taking place today. Confirmation of this is provided by measurements of solution at soil level, where the rate of weathering of the limestone is ten times that on bare rock surfaces (Yie Quing Tong, 1982). After removal of the cover rocks, the modern weathering features such as the runnels and solution basins have developed, replacing the formerly smoothed surface of the pinnacles.

The Stone Forests of this part of China thus provide excellent examples of sub-jacent karst - a mode and variety of karst which is probably much more widespread than is generally realized (Sweeting, 1972).

REFERENCES

Katzer, F. 1909. Karst und Karsthydrographie. *Zur Kunde der Balkanhalbinsel,* No. 8 (Sarajevo).

Osmaston, H. 1980. Patterns in trees, rivers and rocks in the Mulu Park, Sarawak. *Geographical Journal,* 146(1), 33-50.

Palmer, A.N. 1981. *A Geological Guide to Mammoth Cave National Park.* (Zephyrus Press, Teaneck, N.J.), 196pp.

Penck, A. 1924. *Das Unterirdische Karst.* Receuil de Travaux offert a J. Cvijic (Belgrade).

Pohl, E.R. 1955. Vertical shafts in Limestone Caves. *National Speleological Society Amer.,* Paper No.2.

Sweeting, M.M. 1972. Karst Landforms, (Macmillan), 297-300.

Sweeting, M.M. and Lancaster, N. 1982. Solutional and Wind Erosion forms on limestone in the Central Namib Desert. *Zeitschrift fur Geomorphologie,* 26(2), 197-207.

Thomas, T.M. 1954. Swallow Holes in the Millstone Grit and Carboniferous Limestone of the South Wales Coalfield. *Geog. Journ.,* 120, 468-75.

Yie Quing Tong, 1982. Karst of the Stone Forest. (unpublished manuscript).

Yu Jin Piao, 1982. The Period of Stone Forest origin and analysis of palaeo-geographical environment in Lunan County, Yunnan Province. In Luizhou Karst, Geomorphology and Speleology Symposium, 1982.

List of participants and authors

Prof. Y. Battiau-Queney	Institut de Géographie, Université de Lille, France.
Dr. H.A. Brown	Formerly School of Geography, University of Oxford, Oxford.
Dr. P. Bull	School of Geography, University of Oxford, Oxford.
Dr. D.M. Carroll	Soil Survey of England and Wales, Harrogate, N. Yorks.
Dr. Chen Zhi Ping	Institute of Geography, Academia Sinica, Peking, China.
Prof. G. Corra	Institut de Géographie, Université de Verona, Verona, Italy.
Miss C. Coxon	Geography Department, Trinity College, Dublin, Ireland.
Dr. J. Crowther	Department of Geography, St. David's University College, Lampeter, Wales.
Dr. M. Day	Department of Geography, University of Wisconsin-Milwaukee, Milwaukee, USA.
Dr. H. Disney	Malham Tarn Field Centre, Settle, Yorkshire.
Dr. D.P. Drew	Geography Department, Trinity College, Dublin, Ireland.
Dr. C.M. Ek	Laboratoire de Géomorphologie et Géologie, Université de Liège, Belgium.
Dr. B.L. Finlayson	Department of Geography, University of Melbourne, Victoria, Australia.
Mrs E. Foxwell	Nature Conservancy Council, Newbury, Berkshire.

Dr. H. Friederich	Department of Geography, University of Bristol, Bristol.
Dr. S.J. Gale	C.C.A.T., Cambridge.
Miss M. Galloway	Formerly Malham Tarn Field Centre, Settle, Yorkshire.
Mr. M. Gewelt	Laboratoire de Géomorphologie et Géologie du Quaternaire, Université de Liège, Belgium.
Dr. H.S. Goldie	Collingwood College, University of Durham, Durham.
Dr. J. Gunn	Department of Environmental and Geographical Studies, Manchester Polytechnic, Manchester.
Dr. R.A. Halliwell	Academic Office, University of Hull, Hull.
Prof. & Mrs J. Hazera	La Farfantello, Villefranche-sur-Mer, France.
Dr. C.O. Hunt	Creswell Crags Visitor Centre, Crags Road, Worksop, Nottinghamshire, S80 3LH
Dr. P. Ireland	26a Wickham Road, Brockley, London.
Dr. G. Jefferson	Department of Zoology, University College, Cardiff.
Dr. Ravinder Kumar	Wadia Institute of Himalayan Geology, Ballupur, Dehra Dun, India.
Mr. T. Lord	Park View, Stainforth, Settle, Yorkshire.
Prof. J. Nicod	Institut de Géographie, Université d'Aix - Marseille II, Aix-en-Provence, France.
Mr. R.L. Otlet	Low Level Measurements Laboratory, A.E.R.E., Harwell, England.
Mr. P. Pappard	Department of Environmental Sciences, University of Lancaster, Lancaster.
Dr. K. Paterson	Geography Department, Christ's and Notre Dame College (L.I.H.E.), Liverpool.
Prof. Dr. Karl-Heinz Pfeffer	Geographisches Institut, Universität zu Köln, W. Germany.
Dr. J.I. Pitman	Geography Department, King's College, University of London, London.
Dr. A.F. Pitty	13, Hungate, Barton-on-Humber, South Humberside.
Mr. L. Rose	Geography Department, University of Lancaster, Lancaster.

Prof. G. Rossi	Institut de Géographie, University of Bénin (Lome).
Prof. J. Salomon	Institut de Géographie, Université d'Aix - Marseille II, Aix-en-Provence, France.
Dr. R. Sjöberg	Vretgatan 7, Umea, Sweden.
Mr. P.L. Smart	Department of Geography, University of Bristol, Bristol.
Dr. Song Lin Hua	Institute of Geography, Academia Sinica, Peking, China.
Dr. T. Spencer	Department of Geography, University of Manchester, Manchester.
Miss G. Sweet	Geography Department, University of Winnipeg, Winnipeg, Manitoba, Canada.
Dr. M.M. Sweeting	St. Hugh's College, Oxford.
Dr. J.L. Ternan	School of Geographical Sciences, Plymouth Polytechnic, Plymouth.
Prof. H. Trimmel	Draschestrasse 77, Wien, Austria.
Dr. S. Trudgill	Department of Geography, The University, Sheffield.
Mr. B. Turnpenny	East Cape Catchment Board, Gisborne, New Zealand.
Miss H. Viles	Department of Geography, University College, London.
Dr. P. Vincent	Geography Department, University of Lancaster, Lancaster.
Dr. R. Walsh	Department of Geography, University College, Swansea.
Dr. A.C. Waltham	Trent Polytechnic, Burton Street, Nottingham.
Dr. J.D. Wilcock	Department of Computing, North Staffordshire Polytechnic, Stafford.
Prof. P. Williams	Geography Department, Auckland University, Auckland, New Zealand.
Mrs V. Winchester	School of Geography, University of Oxford, Oxford.
Dr. V.P. Wright	Department of Geology, University of Bristol, Bristol.

Programme

19-26 SEPTEMBER 1983

Monday 19th September

Evening: Paper session, St. Hugh's College, Oxford.

Tuesday 20th September

Morning: Paper session, School of Geography, Oxford.

Afternoon: Paper session until 5.30 p.m. followed by a University
                     reception in the School of Geography.

Evening: Paper session

Wednesday 21st September

Morning and
early afternoon: Mendip field excursion led by Dr. P.L. Smart.

Late afternoon: Travel to University College, Swansea.

Evening: Lecture 'Cave Fauna in Britain' by Dr. G. Jefferson.

Thursday 22nd September

Morning: S. Wales karst excursion (Dan yr Ogof Cave, collapse
                  dolines) led by Dr. P. Bull.

Afternoon: Palaeokarst excursion, (Llangattock area) led by
                  Prof. Y. Battiau Queney and Dr. P. Wright.

Evening: Reception offered by the Geography Dept., University
                  College, Swansea.

Friday 23rd September

Morning and
Afternoon: Travel to the Malham Tarn Field Centre, Yorkshire.

Evening: Paper session at the M.T.F.C.

Saturday 24th September

Morning and   Malham karst excursion led by Dr. H. Brown, Mr R.L. Otlet,
Afternoon: Dr. A.F. Pitty, Dr. M.M. Sweeting and Dr. A.C. Waltham.

Evening: Paper session

Sunday 25th September

Morning: Morecambe Bay Karst excursion led by Dr. H. Goldie, Mr L. Rose and Dr. P. Vincent.

Afternoon: Gretadale excursion led by Dr. A.C. Waltham.

Evening: Lectures by Mr T. Lord 'Pleistocene animals in the Yorkshire Caves' and by Dr. H. Disney 'Malham Tarn House and Field Centre'.

Monday 26th September

Departure from M.T.F.C.

End of Symposium.